ANIMAL FORM AND FUNCTION

An Introduction to College Zoology

A BLAISDELL BOOK IN THE PURE AND APPLIED SCIENCES

Consulting Editor **PAUL R. GROSS,** Massachusetts Institute of Technology

BLAISDELL PUBLISHING COMPANY

A Division of Ginn and Company

WALTHAM, MASSACHUSETTS · TORONTO · LONDON

THIRD EDITION

Animal
Form
And
Function

AN INTRODUCTION TO COLLEGE ZOOLOGY

W. R. BRENEMAN *Professor of Zoology, Indiana University*

Preface

The decade which has followed the first edition of this text in 1954 has seen the most profound changes in biology that have occurred in the entire history of this science. Studies in the areas of *molecular biology* and *developmental biology* have added luster and even glamour to investigations of living systems. The result has been a revitalization of research, especially at the cellular level. A dilemma has been created by the "new biology"; simply stated, it is the question of how much of the older knowledge of gross morphology and functions should be required of students who are beginning their studies today. Is it sufficient now to investigate biological problems only at the molecular level?

A considerable amount of "soul searching" was exercised during the preparation of this third edition with respect to the balance that should be attained between "traditional" and "modern" biology. It was decided finally that there is actually no fundamental conflict between these two approaches to the life sciences but each supplements and is dependent on the other. The amazing advances made in molecular biology have been, in no small measure, the result of the fact that the new science could build on a solid foundation provided by past discoveries in gross and microscopic morphology. In turn, the new discoveries in the area of cellular and subcellular chemistry are contributing information which is being used for the interpretation of evolutionary processes.

It also was decided that the text should not merely represent the accretion of new material but that a careful integration of newer and older information should be attempted. It will be noted, therefore, that the addition of two new chapters was accompanied by the deletion of considerable amounts of discussion that appeared in the second edition. Some of the elementary chemistry has been relegated to an Appendix because our experience has shown us that students are now entering college with much better training in general chemistry than was true five years ago.

Many aspects of a type-form approach have been retained, however, because we wished to stress the *uniformity* which exists in living systems. Both molecular and developmental biology share this concept with the older studies. This third edition, therefore, continues the strong emphasis present in the first two editions, namely, emphasis on tracing functional and structural complexities through interrelated phyla. It is increasingly apparent that certain organisms are more advantageous for research in microbiology than others. The care with which investigations were made in traditional zoological studies has made it possible to have comparative studies in microbiology as well as in morphology. It is important to know as much general zoology as possible.

The current edition has retained the unifying principle that there is a remarkable uniformity of functions in all organisms. Structural features of the different phyla may be considered as specializations which enable different animals to perform the functions of: *nutrition, respiration, excretion, reproduction,* and *coordination.* This organization of subject matter makes it possible to compare very diverse organisms from protozoans to whales or dinosaurs, and to stress the importance of adaptations. The designation of *body form* has continued to be employed for the description of type forms in each major phylum in order to provide reference points for comparative analyses.

Finally, it is flattering to know that the previous treatment of coelom development and of parasitism as separate topics was well received in the previous editions. This feature has been retained with only slight modification of the subject matter. The chapter on the human organism also has been continued because, although we do not wish to be excessively anthropomorphic, we cannot avoid the fact that current biological research has great impact on human society.

The use of " case histories" to illustrate the scientific method has been continued and expanded. This is especially true in the sections which describe electron-microscopic contributions to the knowledge of cell structure and in the analysis of the roles of DNA and RNA. We have continued to stress the historical importance of the pioneering work of Mendel, Harvey, and Darwin but have added to the discussions of experimental investigations which have been performed in the last decade. We hope that our treatment of modern genetics both factually and as a case history has done justice to this all-pervasive field.

It should be noted that there have been extensive additions to the bibliography. The addition of excellent reference books of "paperback" type has been advantageous in the assignment of supplemental reading for students; a considerable number of these books is listed in the bibliography. Also, numerous references have been included to the very stimulating articles which have appeared in the *Scientific American.*

A third edition of the student laboratory manual, *Laboratory Studies in Animal Biology,* is being prepared to accompany this Third Edition. The manual follows the organization pattern of the text, and new experiments and procedures are being added. The manual also is being modified to make it more adaptable for use in a single three-hour laboratory period.

It is obvious that the author can never acknowledge adequately the assistance of those who directly or indirectly influenced the preparation and content of this edition. Special recognition should be given to Dean Fernandus Payne and

Dr. Theodore W. Torrey, who have been both mentors and consciences for the author. A great debt also is owed to the members of the Zoology Department for suggestions, criticisms, and reviews of manuscript materials. The assistance of Dr. Shelby D. Gerking and Dr. Frank J. Zeller was especially valuable. From time to time, numerous colleagues over the country have made constructive criticisms of illustrative and text material; we are appreciative of this help.

The secretarial assistance of Miss Linda Jefferson and Mrs. Patricia Philpott is gratefully acknowledged. These ladies demonstrated great ingenuity and patience in transcribing scribbles into typewritten manuscript. Also, their devotion in the preparation of references, the reading of galley proof, and the compiling of the index is appreciated.

W. R. B.

Contents

Introduction

Great scientific advances are not now, nor have they ever been, of their own
nature specially difficult of comprehension.—Singer, *A History of Biology*, 1950

Historically, zoological science may be characterized as having progressed
from *natural science* to *comparative anatomy*, thence to *comparative physiology*, and more recently to *molecular biology*. Considered chronologically, the
recording of zoological events is especially impressive because, with very few
exceptions, the major advances have been made in the last 150 years. A predominant feature of the progress has been its dependence on technical improvements, which ranged from the perfection of the light microscope to the
development of the electron microscope, from the discoveries in organic
chemistry to their application in biochemistry, and from gross studies of organisms to morphological and functional investigations at the cellular and subcellular level of organization. Microchemical investigations of vital processes
are enabling biologists and chemists to determine the details of living processes
with amazing precision even though only minute quantities of materials may
be available for characterization. Today, biologists are substituting the electron
microscope for the light microscope, the scintillation counter and radioisotopes
for the test tube, chromatographic procedures for titration analyses, and ultracentrifugation for filtration. It is not surprising, therefore, that a great shift in
research emphasis has presented itself. It is no longer necessary to confine
observations to an entire organism, an organ, a tissue, or even a cell because
structural and functional features now can be successfully investigated at ultramicroscopic levels with great precision.

Probably the most challenging, and certainly the most productive, field of
biology today is that of *molecular biology*. New light has been cast on the
intricacies of the multitude of biochemical reactions which enable organisms

to meet the vicissitudes of life. Insight has been gained into the mechanisms by which the genes regulate intracellular chemistry, and knowledge of gene-enzyme interrelationships is providing a unifying principle, applicable to all living things. *In vitro* experiments in cell-free systems have been remarkably productive in providing data which are applicable for the solution of problems of intracellular chemistry. The use of isotopes, especially those which are radioactive, has added to the exactness of microchemical analyses.

The spectacular successes in molecular biology inevitably have produced some distortion of the relative importance of this field of biology. The distortion occasionally has been enhanced by the excessive enthusiasm of a few investigators who have suggested that this is the only truly significant field in modern biology. Sober reflection has resulted, however, in a healthy blending of the "old" and the "new" and with the realization that the most profitable overview of living things should be based on an analysis in terms of *levels of organization*. Ultramicroscopic structure is intimately correlated with microscopic or cellular organization; cellular interrelationships in turn are integrated with those of tissues and organs; the tissues and organs likewise provide the "warp and woof" of the organism as a whole; and organisms themselves interact in ecological and societal complexes. Thus when Linus Pauling states that *"Life is a relationship among molecules and not the property of any one molecule,"* we can expand this statement to include in biological systems: that an organ is not the property of any one cell, the organism is not the property of any one organ, nor is a society the property of any one organism!

The emphasis on the functional and developmental aspects of biology has had a salutary effect on zoological research. Living, rather than entire preserved animals or parts of, animals are now the center of attention and static zoology has been supplemented by dynamic zoology. The greater opportunities for analysis of organisms, however, have not simplified biological science. Discoveries which have solved many age-old problems have led to the evolution of new and even more challenging questions. An illustration of an unexpected by-product of modern investigations has been the revival of concern with many aspects of morphology. *Experimental morphology* in particular has emerged as a new interest. Such structures as bone and cartilage have attracted renewed attention because of the fact that radioisotope studies have demonstrated them to be plastic and not passive tissues. The possibility that the evolutionary significance of bone lies in its role as a reservoir of potassium rather than primarily as a skeletal feature is a reflection of this new reasearch emphasis. Investigations of neural secretions have similarly redirected attention to the morphology of nerve endings and to aggregations of nerve cell bodies such as the "nuclei" of the hypothalamus. Morphology, therefore, is not a dead subject but has been reincarnated in a new guise.

It is confusing to beginning students in zoology to encounter so many conspicuous variations in both the structures and the functions of organisms. These differences tend to obscure the basic kinship which actually is present among all living things.   It is to the credit of the molecular biologists that they have been able to demonstrate a multitude of similarities from viruses to vicunas. If we remember, however, that the variations which we observe today are primarily a reflection of the ability of organisms to adapt to changing environmental conditions over millions of years, then we will realize that structural and functional differences actually are expressions of the plasticity of living matter.   Furthermore, there is renewed emphasis through biochemistry on the fact that protoplasm is common to all organisms and is, therefore, a common denominator for interrelating all life's variations.

There is not a separate section of this book devoted to the discussion of the scientific method nor to the history of biology.   These fields have not been ignored but illustrations of each have been incorporated where they contribute directly to an understanding of the material which was being discussed.   It has been especially stimulating to utilize this technique in the treatment of Mendelian and modern genetics.

It is hoped that the student who scans the pages which follow will find his imagination stimulated and his interest aroused by the challenge of the tremendous breadth of the field of zoology.   The efforts which have gone into the preparation of the text and illustrations will be rewarded if only a little appreciation of the dynamic aspects of zoology is acquired.

REFERENCES

AMBERCROMBIE, M., C. J. HECKMAN, and M. L. JOHNSON, *A Dictionary of Biology*.   Penguin Book, Baltimore, 1963.

ASIMOV, ISAAC, *A Short History of Biology*.   Natural History Press, Garden City, 1964.

MOMENT, GIARDNER (ed.), *Frontiers of Modern Biology*.   Houghton Mifflin Company, Boston, 1962.

GILSTRAP, MARGUERITE (ed.), *Promise of the Life Sciences*.   United States Department of Agriculture Graduate School, Washington, 1961.

PENNAK, ROBERT WILLIAM, *Collegiate Dictionary of Zoology*.   Ronald Press, New York, 1964.

TATON, RENE, *History of Science: Ancient and Medieval Science*.   Basic Books, New York, 1963.

It is usually easy to detect the difference between animals and plants, between living and nonliving matter. It is easy to distinguish a toad from a toadstool (A), or even a walking stick from a stick (B).

Some molds, however, may change overnight to a large, many-celled plant (A) from a microscopic, rapidly growing, branching stage (B). And viruses (C) giant molecules which can grow and reproduce like living things.

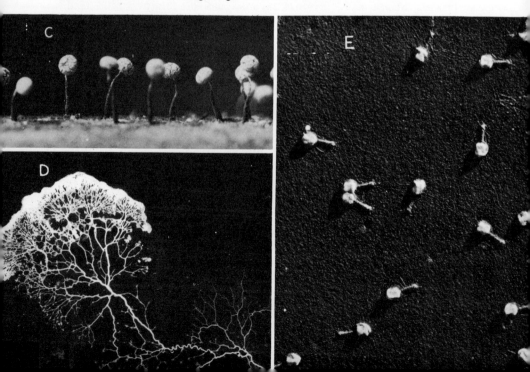

1

This Is Life

The Characteristics of Living Matter

•

Sarcode: I propose to name this what other observers have called living jelly, this glutinous, diaphanous substance, insoluble in water, contracting into spherical masses, sticking to dissecting needles and letting itself be drawn out like slime . . .—Dujardin, 1835

An observant person usually can detect the differences between animals and plants or between living and nonliving matter. Rabbits, birds, worms, insects, or men, which move about actively, grow, reproduce, and respond to stimuli, are recognizable both as living matter and as *animals*. Pine trees, shrubs, or flowers are less obvious in the expression of their activities; movement in these forms may be at a minimum, but careful observation will demonstrate that growth and reproduction occur and that living things characterized by this combination of activities usually are *plants*. There are many forms of life which are intermediate between these two extremes, with the consequence that frequently it is difficult to distinguish between animals and plants. Many plants, especially those of microscopic size, move about rapidly and respond to stimuli as efficiently as many animals. Some animals, on the other hand, are *sessile*—that is, are attached and have no locomotion. The responses of animals of this type to external conditions are slow and often difficult to detect.

Biologists have despaired of devising any list of characteristics that will distinguish between *all* plants and *all* animals; they have been content with the observation that the important distinction between the two groups is the type of *nutrition*. Plants are *autotrophic*; they are self-feeders and have the ability to synthesize their own body substance from simple chemicals such as carbon dioxide, water, and nitrogen compounds. Sunlight provides the energy for this manufacturing process, and the transformation of the simple chemicals into more complex ones is accelerated by *chlorophyll*, a chemical peculiar to plants. Since chlorophyll is green, the presence of this color usually provides

1

a simple means of identifying plants.   Animals, on the other hand, are *hetero-trophic*; they must be fed and, in contrast with plants, do not synthesize their food but are directly or indirectly dependent on the plants for the complex organic substances necessary for existence.   An animal secures its organic food by eating plants or other animals, which in turn may have eaten plants.

Unfortunately, the type of nutrition sometimes is inadequate as a distinguishing characteristic, because some plants contain no chlorophyll and live on small particles of organic matter in suspension.   Other plants may have brown or red pigments which are involved in food synthesis.   There are also living things which in the presence of light will synthesize their food materials but in darkness or subdued light will live on suspended organic materials. These forms may be considered as either plant or animal, depending on whether they are studied by botanists or zoologists.

It is disconcerting to begin the study of zoology with the admission that adequate distinctions cannot be made between plants and animals.   This fact, however, is of great significance because it illustrates the fundamental similarity of all life processes, the adaptability of living things and, as will be discussed later, suggests that there was a common origin for both plants and animals. This similarity of life processes has led to the use of the term *organism* for any living thing, plant or animal, regardless of its size or complexity of structure.

Living matter was first called *protoplasm* by Purkinje in 1840 and *sarcode* by Dujardin in 1835, but the first term has been more widely used.   It is often stated that organisms are composed of protoplasm, but it must be emphasized that protoplasm occurs only as organisms, or organized individuals (plants or animals), and that the protoplasm cannot properly be considered apart from the organism itself.   This has not always been given due consideration in the

Figure 1.1. Bryozoan animals. These colonial animals, which remain fixed, bear a striking superficial resemblance to plants. (Courtesy American Museum of Natural History.)

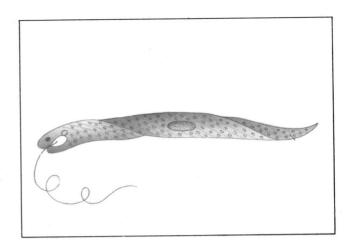

Figure 1.2. Euglena manufactures its own food but moves about like an animal.

study of protoplasm. It should be stressed that although protoplasm can be analyzed chemically, and valuable information as to its physical and chemical nature can be gathered, such an analysis is not that of a living system. Therefore, little information as to the constantly changing chemical and physical constitution of protoplasm can be gained by this method. Fortunately, techniques are available which enable us to study organisms, or parts of organisms, while vital activities are proceeding. Through these techniques, we have organized the properties of protoplasm into three categories: the *biological*, the *physical*, and the *chemical*. These categories are closely interrelated and, while the biological properties cannot be wholly explained now, a promising beginning has been made toward the understanding of complex living processes.

Biological Properties

The *activities* of organisms, mentioned earlier, are fundamental to all life and serve to distinguish living from nonliving matter. Living systems exhibit the phenomena of *growth, reproduction, movement,* and *irritability* while non-living systems are said to lack these biological activities. It has become increasingly evident in recent years that no sharp line of demarcation can be drawn between living and nonliving systems; but the implications of this statement will be understood better if we consider first the general features of the basic activities of these systems. The basic chemical reactions will be considered later (p. 38).

Growth

The *growth* phenomenon is in many respects the most complex of all vital processes. Organisms increase in volume by the formation of new protoplasm, which is synthesized from relatively simple chemical compounds and is peculiar to the organism which synthesizes it. Furthermore, the protoplasm is the structural basis of the organism and furnishes the energy for all activities. The most striking example of this ability to synthesize and grow is the green plants mentioned previously. The general features of the synthesis are known. The reaction for the formation of glucose from carbon dioxide and water can be illustrated by the following simple equation.

$$6 \, CO_2 + 6 \, H_2O + energy + catalyst \rightarrow C_6H_{12}O_6 + 6 \, O_2.$$

carbon dioxide water   sunlight chlorophyll   glucose   oxygen

The reaction by which the glucose is formed in plants is aptly named *photosynthesis*, "manufacturing with light," and it is the most important manufacturing process on earth, because energy from the sun is "stored" in the glucose for subsequent use by plants and animals. The glucose, once produced, becomes the keystone for the formation of other organic compounds. Molecules, or fragments of molecules, of glucose are combined in the protoplasm into more complex compounds: the starches and other *carbohydrates*; the oils and fats, or *lipids*; and, by the addition of nitrogen, the *amino acids* and *proteins*.

Equally important in growth, because of the chemical and physical relationships involved, is the fact that during growth there is also an increase in the amount of water and salts. The proportion of water in protoplasm usually averages from 70 to 80 per cent but can reach the almost fantastic high of 96

Figure 1.3. Some scientists think the dinosaurs became extinct because they failed to reproduce themselves in adequate numbers. Others believe that by overeating they exhausted their food supply. Whatever the reason, the dinosaurs disappeared from the earth because as organisms they could not suit their biological activities to their environment. (Courtesy American Museum of Natural History.)

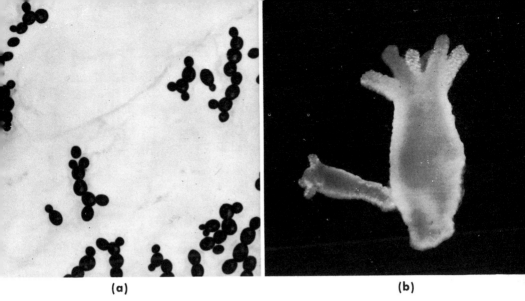

Figure 1.4. Both plants and animals may reproduce rapidly by forming buds which are separated from the parent to become independent organisms. Yeast plants can be seen forming buds in (a), and the hydra in (b) is budding to form a new animal. [(a) Courtesy Adrian J. Iorio; (b) Clarence Flaten.]

per cent. It follows that as the amounts of carbohydrates, lipids, and proteins are increased, so must the amount of water increase, or the protoplasm will become progressively more concentrated.   We shall see later that physical factors such as variations in *viscosity* (changes in the fluid or jellylike consistency of protoplasm) will alter the activities of the organism or its parts.

It should be emphasized again that while animals are able to supply their needs for water and salts, they cannot synthesize carbohydrates, lipids, or proteins from simple chemicals and are entirely dependent on plants for these energy sources and body-building materials. Plants, therefore, are responsible not only for their own growth and maintenance but also for that of the animal kingdom, as well as for those plants such as fungi which do not synthesize protoplasm from simple compounds.

Reproduction

As a result of accident or aging, organisms are destroyed or die. Thus plants and animals, in order to be successful, must not only form new protoplasm but must also create new individuals. If it were not possible to replace old organisms by new individuals at a rate at least as rapid as the average loss of life, plants and animals would disappear from the earth. Such changes in animal populations have occurred in the past, and many species are thought to have disappeared for this reason. The dinosaurs are a classic example of animals that were unable to form new individuals rapidly enough to compensate for their rate of destruction. This phenomenon is not confined to prehistoric times,

Figure 1.5. The sensitive plant is an excellent illustration of the fact that plants as well as animals possess irritability. The leaves fold in a very characteristic manner when part of the plant is touched. (Copyright by General Biological Supply House, Inc., Chicago.)

however, as is evidenced by the fact that in modern times the moa and other birds have become extinct, and many other organisms are on the verge of extinction. It is imperative that organisms reproduce at a rate compensatory with that of destruction.

Two processes are involved in *reproduction*. The *first* concerns the replacement of parts of the organisms which have been lost by accident, worn out, or used up in the activity of the organism. This is commonly designated as *regeneration*. In some instances—as for example, the starfishes—small portions of the original animal may regenerate an entire organism, in which case the process for all practical purposes is identical with the *second* phase of reproduction: the *creation* of a new individual. The manner by which an organism constructs the proper replacement for a lost part and the mechanism which causes the transmission of characteristics from parent to offspring, so that an offspring resembles its parents, are among the most fascinating problems in modern biology.

Movement

Undoubtedly the most vivid characteristic of living matter is *movement*. When we watch the antics of a small boy or a puppy, which can continue hour after hour, we are dumbfounded at the constant *movement* and *locomotion* expressed. Protoplasm is never quiescent; there may be little or no locomotion in many cases, but as long as life continues, protoplasm moves. A frog in the mud on the bottom of a frozen pond or a lungfish in its mud cocoon in the hot African summer may appear to be completely inactive, but a careful examiner will discover slow movement of the protoplasm, occasional heart beats, and slight movement of the blood. Some movement continues as long as protoplasm exists, and there is a corresponding expenditure of energy. A seed or an animal, therefore, could not be dormant indefinitely.

Irritability

The *irritability* of organisms is indicative of the fact that protoplasm possesses an "awareness" of its surroundings and can make "responses" to a variety of stimuli. This characteristic reaches its greatest expression in organisms that may be said to have "consciousness." "Awareness" involves the ability to distinguish in some degree between the stimuli which reach the protoplasm and is often associated with the formation of specialized structures to receive stimuli, such as the *receptors* for light, pressure, and chemical substances. It is not enough, however, merely to be "aware"; the organism must also respond. Response may be *positive* (as for example, movement toward the stimulus) or *negative* (as in movement from the stimulus); and the response may either occur almost instantaneously or be delayed for long periods. Continued stimuli may cause the plant or animal to produce structural *adaptations*, as illustrated by the orientation of plants to light or gravity. Most responses of a given organism can be predicted with surprising accuracy, but varying conditions and the retention of past experiences may, from time to time, alter the response. The kitten which purred in a contented fashion when stroked yesterday may scratch viciously today at the same stimulus.

Chemical Properties

No chemical elements which are found in living matter are unique to protoplasm. As a matter of fact, only 36 of the 92 elements in the traditional periodic table (before atomic scientists added new elements) are common to living matter. The elements themselves are less significant than the compounds they form, but their relative proportion in protoplasm is significant. Six elements constitute nearly 95 per cent of the composition of protoplasm: oxygen (O), hydrogen (H), carbon (C), nitrogen (N), calcium (Ca), and phosphorus (P). Carbon is especially important, not only because each of its atoms has four *valence bonds*, which allow it to attach at four places with the atoms of other elements, but also because carbon atoms have the unique property of combining with themselves.

The remaining 30 elements, which constitute only about 5 per cent of protoplasm, are usually present as traces, or only a fraction of 1 per cent. Of this

Figure 1.6. Irritability. This is a fine example of positive and negative responses. The small frog is reaching for the worm, which is attempting to escape. No highly intelligent reaction is shown, but the responses involve complicated reactions to stimuli. (Courtesy Robert C. Hermes.)

group, the important elements are: sodium (Na), potassium (K), sulfur (S), magnesium (Mg), iron (Fe), iodine (I), and chlorine (Cl). These appear rarely as elemental or independent substances and usually do so only when the reactions in the protoplasm free them from elements with which they form compounds. Carbonates, sulfates, and phosphates are common compounds, and especially significant are the chlorides of sodium and potassium.

Physical Properties

Colloidal nature

Actually it is not possible to separate completely the properties of protoplasm into chemical and physical phases, and the excuse for doing so here is primarily for better organization of information. As we might expect from our knowledge of its high water content, protoplasm is a fluid. It varies considerably, however, in its consistency. Protoplasm becomes very gelatinous at times and can change very rapidly from a watery condition, or *sol*, to a jellylike condition, or *gel*. This enables protoplasm not only to utilize all the advantages which accompany the free movement of fluids but also to retain a stabilized structure which is a result of a semisolid or solid state. Protoplasm is a *colloid*, a physical condition in which relatively large particles, in the form of clumps of molecules or very large molecules, are *suspended* in fluid. The particles in the protoplasm have a great affinity for water, and it is on their surfaces that chemical reactions occur. Since the number of surfaces presented by the colloidal particles is beyond enumeration, and since the particles have tremendous surface area, countless different chemical reactions can go on simultaneously in the protoplasm. Furthermore, specialized structures of relatively large size which can perform specific functions are created by the protoplasm. It will not be surprising, in the light of this brief preview, to observe later that one region of an organism can be constructive, or *anabolic*, while an adjacent region may be destructive, or *catabolic*, in its activity.

Figure 1.7. Emulsion. Left: Oil-and-water mixture; center: emulsifying agent added; right: emulsion which results from the "binding" action of the emulsifying agent.

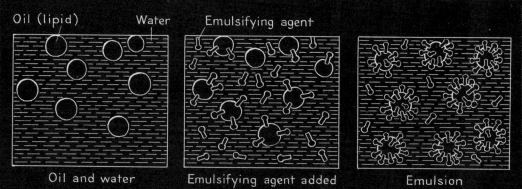

Figure 1.8. A graphic illustration that matter may exist as a solid, a liquid, and a gas. In this case the solid is ice, the liquid is water, and the gas is steam. (Courtesy Clarence Flaten.)

Solvent action of water

Other important features of the physical state of protoplasm are a direct result of the high water content. First of all, water is an almost universal *solvent*. Many diverse chemical substances dissolve in water and thus can be incorporated into the protoplasm. Even such insoluble materials as oils will form *emulsions* with water in the protoplasm. An emulsion is a system in which one liquid is dispersed in another liquid in which it is not soluble. When nearly equal amounts of the two liquids are present, the liquids will separate unless a third substance, an *emulsifier*, is present to bind them together. An emulsifier is a chemical agent in which the ends of the molecule are different; one end is soluble in water and the other in oil. A well-known example of an emulsion is mayonnaise, and the action of soap in helping water remove oil from one's hands is an everyday illustration of the action of an emulsifier. Sodium plays an important role in the formation of emulsifiers; sodium stearate (a soap) will have the sodium end soluble in water and the stearate (lipid) end soluble in oil.

Temperature range

Water has a high *specific heat,* which is merely another way of stating that it changes temperature slowly. The saying, "A watched pot never boils," is indicative of the slowness with which water changes temperature when heated. This slow rate of increase in temperature probably is due to the fact that some of the water molecules are in the form of liquid ice at room temperature, but these details need not concern us, because it is only the end result which is of

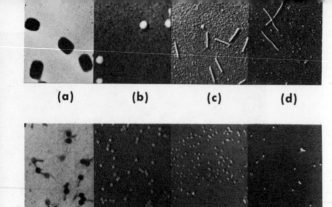

Figure 1.9. Some of the variations to be seen among viruses are shown here: (a) vaccine virus, (b) influenza virus, (c) tobacco mosaic virus, (d) potato X virus, (e) bacteriophage, (f) papilloma virus, (g) bean mosaic virus, (h) tomato bushy stunt virus. (Courtesy C. A. Knight, University of California.)

(a) (b) (c) (d)

(e) (f) (g) (h)

biological importance. Since water, as well as protoplasm because of its high water content, cools slowly and warms slowly, organisms have a decided safety factor when their surroundings become suddenly hotter or cooler. When a frog climbs out of a cool stream onto a sun-heated rock, it has ample time to dive back into the water before its skin is burned. We should note that specific heat also affords a partial explanation for the fact that a man working in a foundry is able to tolerate the very high temperatures from an open furnace for short periods of time.

Finally, water changes its physical state within a very narrow temperature range. At 0° C (32° F) water is a *solid*, ice; between 0° C and 100° C (212° F) it is a *liquid*; above 100° C water becomes a *vapor*, steam. These facts place very definite limits on the existence of protoplasm, which can survive freezing under special conditions for relatively short periods of time but is coagulated and destroyed at high temperatures.

Temperatures in the universe range from −273° C to 3,000,000,000° C. Thus it can be seen that life exists only at relatively low temperatures and has actually been called a "cold, inert, cosmic ash." Some organisms are active at 0° C, or slightly below; and by careful, gradual increases in temperature some animals have adapted themselves and survived heat as high as 70° C (158° F). Some organisms, if cooled slowly, give up some of their water, or *dehydrate*, and can live at temperatures well below 0° C. If cooled suddenly, by submersion in liquid air (temperature −197° C), animals may even *vitrify* (become glasslike); and if warmed quickly they will revive and be little the worse for the experience. Organisms are less adaptable to higher than to lower temperatures, probably because the enzymes are destroyed quickly by heating, and also because the *membrane* surrounding the protoplasm becomes more permeable, allowing materials to pass which ordinarily would not enter or leave.

Human beings might appear, at first glance, to offer exceptions to the above generalizations; but although man may be active and work at temperatures far below 0° C and above 70° C, nevertheless body temperatures (normal: 37° C, or 98.6° F) change only a few degrees, seldom more than ten. Bits of human heart tissue die at temperatures below 16° to 18° C (about 63° F), and the upper limit of survival is about 44° C (111° F).

Organization of Protoplasm

Since we have indicated that protoplasm exists only in the form of organized individuals, or *organisms*, it is important to consider briefly the nature of *protoplasmic organization*. The organism may either be microscopic or gigantic; the protoplasmic mass of an organism may either be a single unit or may be subdivided into numerous small units; and finally, the protoplasm may either be of relatively simple construction or may possess a highly specialized structure. Regardless of these variations, however, each portion of protoplasm has a basic organization comparable with that of all other portions of the protoplasm. There is, first of all, a *visible organization* which can be investigated readily with the microscope, and the development of improved microscopes early in the nineteenth century provided a stimulus for more intensive studies of the fine structure of organisms. These early studies culminated in the development of the cell theory by Schleiden and Schwann in 1838–1839, which stated that "*all organisms are composed of cells.*" This theory, in spite of its importance as a biological concept, actually emphasized the fact that the cell was still an unknown entity with respect to its minuscular structure and its elaborate functions. Fortunately, biologists were assisted in their explorations of microscopic structure by the concurrent advances in chemistry, especially in the field of organic

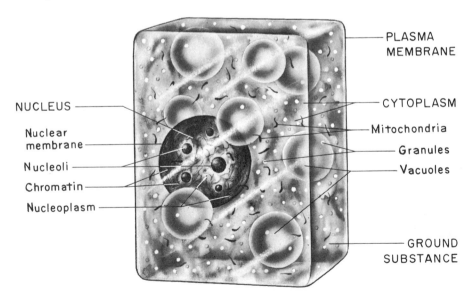

Figure 1.10. Sectional drawing, illustrating the basic structures and organization of protoplasm.

chemistry. Chemists were learning to synthesize dyes, and biologists were intrigued by the discovery that certain dyes would differentially stain various regions of cells. Some dyes stained nuclei, while others were capable of coloring organelles within the cytoplasm. Such organelles as *neurofibrils, myofibrils, granules, vacuoles,* and *intracellular inclusions* could be vividly differentiated. Even more important than the mere coloring was the discovery of significant new cellular features such as the *Golgi bodies, mitochondria,* and the *mitotic apparatus.* Subsequent development of *vital stains,* which colored but did not kill cells, enabled biologists to make limited observations of the interrelationship of organelles to cell functions. The portrait of the typical cell (p. 11) represents a composite picture of the many cell features that were discovered by employing the light microscope in conjunction with staining techniques.

The use of stains continues to be important in the investigation of protoplasmic activities, but the limitations of the staining techniques and of the light microscope for cell study were evident in the early years of the twentieth century. The light microscope, for example, has a resolving power of about 250 mu. This means that two particles in the protoplasm can be distinguished from each other only if they are separated by a distance of approximately 250 mu. Particles closer together than this appear as a single unit. Mitochondria, known to be closely associated with cell activities, differ greatly in size, and the resolving power of the light microscope is inadequate to show the intimate structure of a mitochondrion. The cell membrane, or *plasma membrane,* also is of submicroscopic thickness and its structure, therefore, can not be determined by direct observation with the light microscope. The fact that the plasma membrane selectively regulates the passage of materials into and out of cells also indicated a need for increased knowledge of ultramicroscopic structure.

The gradual improvement of techniques in the twentieth century did much to advance our understanding of both the protoplasmic structure and the microchemical reactions which occur in spectacular fashion in living systems. The

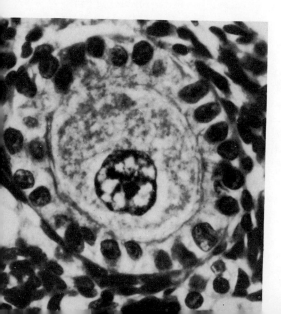

Figure 1.11. Cat ovum. An egg cell, such as the ovum of a cat, illustrates a typical animal cell. The ovum is surrounded by a layer of follicle, or nurse, cells.

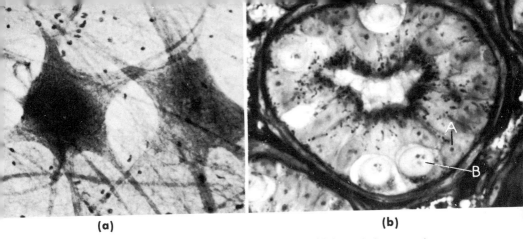

(a)   **(b)**

Figure 1.12. Nerve cells (a) and testis cells (b) illustrate some of the variation present among cells. The shapes of these cells are in marked contrast, for example, with the spherical egg cell of the cat. In (b) you can distinguish a nurse cell (A) and an immature reproductive, or sperm, cell (B). [(a) Copyright by General Biological Supply House, Inc., Chicago; (b) courtesy Clarence Flaten.]

phase microscope enabled biologists to observe living cells, and the creation of microdissection devices permitted *microsurgery* to be performed on cells. The use of *micropipettes* even made it possible to withdraw materials from the protoplasm for *microchemical* analyses. This procedure constitutes a remarkable exercise in miniature biopsy. The use of digestive enzymes and of *ultracentrifugation* enabled biologists to isolate and concentrate nuclei, mitochondria, and other cell structures. The advent of improved methods for *cell* and *tissue culture* expanded the biologist's knowledge of the environmental conditions necessary for cell growth and reproduction. As a significant byproduct of these studies, it was observed that many cell products are released into the culture fluid surrounding the cells, and these often can be analyzed chemically. The methods by which protoplasm performs its vast array of activities ceased to be insoluble puzzles.

In the 1940's, however, biologists were in the unenviable position of having reached the limits of the technical devices at their disposal for observing protoplasmic structure and function. World War II, in spite of its destructiveness, led to the creation of many elaborate analytical instruments for research in chemistry and physics. Infrared and ultraviolet *spectrophotometers* are two representative instruments which biologists quickly found to be applicable for the resolution of some of the difficult problems of cell chemistry. Also, *radioactive isotopes* of many of the common elements in protoplasm were produced in atomic piles, and these isotopes frequently can be substituted for the elements normally used. Many microchemical reactions that occur with fantastic speed within cells now can be analyzed by tracing the behavior of the radioactive elements. The term *molecular biology* began to be used with greater and greater frequency to describe the study of the biochemical events which occur at the molecular level within cells. Seemingly unsurmountable barriers to the understanding of living processes were shattered within a period of a few years.

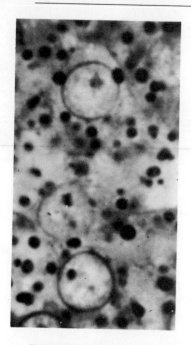
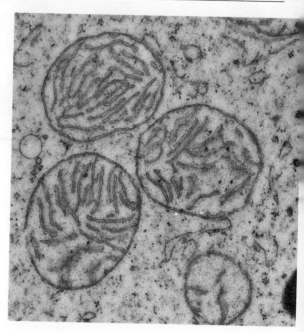

Figure 1.13. Mitochondria. These two photographs illustrate the advantages of the electron microscope. The exceptionally fine picture on the left shows mitochondria (dark dots) as they would appear under the light microscope. The magnification, by taking advantage of photographic enlargement, is 3600X. The photograph on the right was made with the electron microscope, and the fine details of three mitochondria are very evident at a magnification of 20,000X. The structure of mitochondria will be discussed later. (Courtesy Fernandus Payne, Indiana University.)

The *electron microscope* provided an equally spectacular contribution to the understanding of cell and protoplasmic structure. This instrument, which substitutes beams of electrons for beams of light and utilizes magnets instead of lenses for focusing, possesses resolving powers of approximately 2.0 mu. The electron microcope made possible the ascertainment of the fine structure of both the mitochondria and the plasma membrane to a remarkable degree. The light microscope, which gives maximum useful magnifications of approximately 1,200X to 1,500X, is now surpassed by the electron microscope which makes possible routine magnifications of 80,000X and can provide a magnification of 900,000X if special procedures are employed.

A revised portrait of the structure of a typical cell now can be delineated. The living boundary of the cell, the plasma membrane, no longer retains its unknown status. The electron microscope revealed its composition to be of three layers and to have a thickness of approximately 75 Å (Å = angstrom unit, 0.0001 micron). Other surprising features of the membrane were revealed in studies where electron microscopes were used. First of all, the membrane can

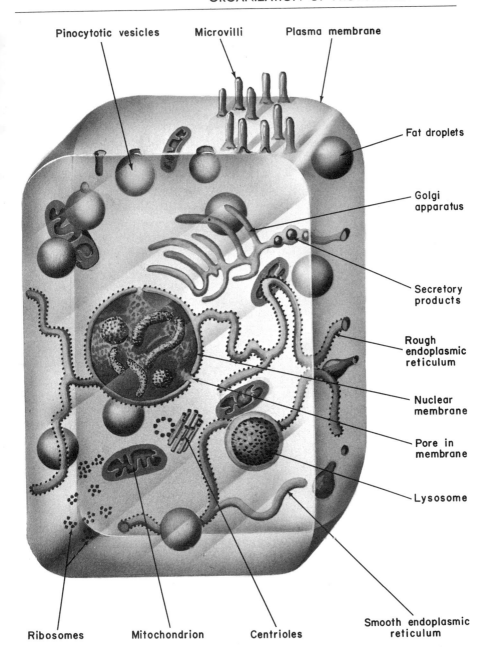

Pinocytotic vesicles   Microvilli   Plasma membrane

Fat droplets

Golgi apparatus

Secretory products

Rough endoplasmic reticulum

Nuclear membrane

Pore in membrane

Lysosome

Ribosomes   Mitochondrion   Centrioles

Smooth endoplasmic reticulum

Figure 1.14.   This composite drawing of a cell as we know it from electron-microscope studies should be compared with the "typical cell" as observed by the light microscope (page 11).   All the features shown here will not be seen in all cells, and other features not shown, like muscle fibrils or neurofibrils, can be seen in specialized cells.

be folded inward or can have projections. The latter are frequently in the form of numerous fingerlike processes called *microvilli*. Second, the folds of the membrane which extend inward (invaginations) can pinch off to form vacuoles. Materials can be transported through the plasma membrane by means of these vacuoles as we will discuss later.   Third, and of great importance with respect to both cell structure and function, was the observation that many of the invaginations of the plasma membrane are continuous with an elaborate network of canals. These canals, or channels, extend throughout the proto-plasm and in some instances may be greatly expanded and appear as vesicles. This network is called the *endoplasmic reticulum,* and close examination reveals that it also is connected internally with the outer membrane of the nucleus. A second connection of the endoplasmic reticulum with the Golgi bodies can be observed clearly in some preparations made with electron microscopes. The Golgi bodies have now been revealed as a series of elongated vesicles compactly arranged in overlapping fashion near the nucleus. Finally, the endoplasmic reticulum is observed to be of two kinds. One type of reticulum has numerous granules on its surface, the *ribosomes*. These bodies give a rough appearance to this type of reticulum and have led to its designation as the *rough endoplasmic reticulum,* or RER. The second type of reticulum lacks ribosomes on its surface and, therefore, it is called the *smooth endoplasmic reticulum,* or SER.

Figure 1.15. Mitochondria in paramecium. The simiarity of mitochondria in different animals can be observed by comparing this electron-microscope photograph with the mitochondrion of the chick shown on page 14. The elaborately developed cristae are a striking feature in this photograph, and the double nature of the mitochondrial membrane can be observed at several places. (Courtesy Ruth Dippell, Indiana University.)

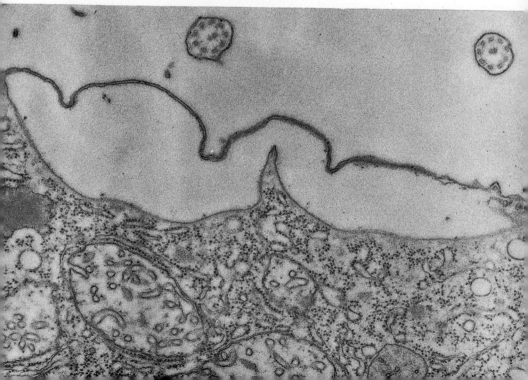

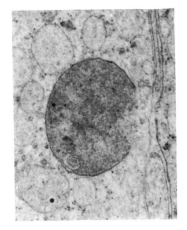

Figure 1.16. Lysosome. This remarkable electron-microscope photograph of a lysosome demonstrates its saclike structure. It appears on the right that the contents of the lysosome may have been discharging at the time the cell was prepared for study. (Courtesy Fernandus Payne, Indiana University.)

Perhaps the most significant contributions to our understanding of the cell have been a result of the electron microscope's capability in resolving the details of fine structure in the mitochondria and other cell organelles. The mitochondria, shown in the accompanying photograph are double-walled structures consisting of an outer membrane and an inner membrane. The latter is folded in a complex manner to provide a great amount of surface area. The folds are called *cristae* and appear to be the site of extensive enzyme activity.

Green plant cells possess special bodies, the *chloroplasts*, which are organelles associated with photosynthesis. These bodies, like the mitochondria, are complicated structures with enzyme systems that participate in the manufacture of carbohydrates. *Lysosomes* are bodies which have been discovered rather recently, and these organelles are known to contain enzymes. It has been suggested that the lysosomes may be sacs which are utilized primarily for the temporary storage of enzymes. This storage could provide a means of protecting the cytoplasm from self-destruction by its own enzymes, which would then be released from the lysosomes only when they are needed.

A remarkable "fibrillar" structure appears in the cytoplasm of cells at the time of cell division. This elaborate device is called the *mitotic spindle* and a prominent feature of the spindle in animal cells is a series of fibrils, called the *astral rays*, at each point of the spindle. These fibrils radiate from a *centriole*. Centrioles can also be observed in the cytoplasm of cells that are not in the process of dividing, and they are composed of two bodies lying at right angles to each other. Even more striking is the fact that the centrioles have fibrillar structure and possess nine fibrils arranged in a circle. Closely related to the centriole in construction are the *cilia* and the *flagella*. These extensions from the surface of the cell are motile and are used either to provide locomotion for the cell or to move substances over the cell surface. Each cilium and flagellum originates from a basal body, a *kinetosome*, and the cilia, flagella, and kinetosomes have a fibrillar structure comparable with that of the centriole, the cilia and flagella also have two central fibrils in addition to the nine marginal ones. This amazing structural similarity can be observed throughout the animal and plant kingdoms wherever cilia and flagella occur.

There has been considerable speculation for many years concerning the *ground substance* of the cell. The electron microscope, unfortunately, is unable to analyze the structural organization of the ground substance. There are various lines of evidence, however, which indicate that the ground substance is not amorphous but is highly organized. The fibrillar nature of the cilia and the centrioles suggest that an ultrafine fibrillar arrangement of molecules also may exist within the ground substance. The presence of neurofibrils in nerve cells and myofibrils in contractile cells adds further support to the idea of fibrillar organization. It is especially noteworthy that the ground substance is not static and that it is not merely a viscous jelly in which organelles are suspended. The ground substance may be fluid, *sol*, or jellylike, *gel*, in its consistency and can change readily from one state to the other. We will have an opportunity to observe this phenomenon later in such organisms as the amoeba, in which changes from the jellylike to the fluid states are associated with locomotion. The ground substance will be discussed further after we have described the macromolecules of cells (p. 34).

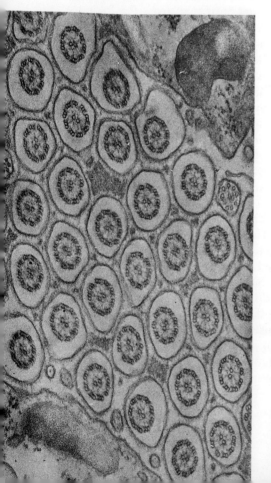

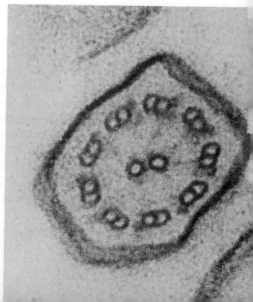

Figure 1.17. Structure of a flagellum and of cilia. Cross section showing the fine structure of cilia and flagella. Cilia are from the gastrovascular cavity of a planarian; flagellum, from the gastrovascular cavity of hydra. Note, especially in the flagellum, the nine marginal fibrils and the central fibrils. (Courtesy Russell Barrnett, Yale University.)

NA to RNA. We will observe later that the impact of these ideas
a revolution in the interpretation of biological events in all organisms.
gical revolution will be considered subsequently in a more significant
e mechanisms of genetics and of cell differentiation.

Versus Non Living Matter

mplexities of protoplasm suggest that it should be simple to distinguish
living and nonliving matter, as indeed it is in many instances. It has
wn for many years, however, that it is possible to simulate many of
ities of protoplasm in models, and these models have often been of
explaining biological phenomena. Lord Kelvin exclaimed, many years
n ye make a model of it? For if ye can, ye can understand it; and if ye
e dinna!" Such problems as the nature of the membrane surrounding
oplasm, the transmission of impulses along nerve fibers, the movement
ials into and out of the protoplasm, the nature of movement, and even
ion of protoplasm have been partially solved by studying models.
tudies of *viruses* during the past twenty years have been even more im-
in demonstrating that no absolute distinction can be made between
nd nonliving matter. The viruses are a kind of giant molecule. They
in a most unexpected way, however, for unlike most molecules, these
of atoms have the ability to form crystals and at the same time manifest
ver of self-duplication! The viruses cause many diseases in both plants
mals; for example, smallpox and influenza in animals, and the tobacco
alfa mosaic diseases in plants. Most of the viruses are very minute, much
than the smallest bacteria, and exist only on living organisms. The
, however, do grow and *reproduce,* and recently it has been demonstrated
ey undergo changes, or *mutations,* which can be transmitted to the next
tion! Should they be considered as very minute forms of parasitic or-
s? The *vaccine virus* is actually larger than some of the smaller bacteria;
out 60 per cent water; it has proteins, carbohydrates, lipids; it has at least
enzymes and has some vitamin B. At the other extreme are the *mosaic*
s: *alfalfa, bean, and tobacco.* The tobacco mosaic virus, which has about
me diameter as the alfalfa virus, is composed of 94 per cent protein and 6
nt nucleic acid. Almost every gradation in size and chemical complexity
ountered in other viruses. We must conclude that the viruses undoubt-
provide a connecting link between ordinary molecules and protoplasm.
act, instead of being disturbing to the biologist, is considered to be for-
s, because it offers hope that in the solution of biological problems of great
rn to the human race, the viruses will be extremely helpful forms for
sis and experimentation.
citing new discoveries in virus research by Fraenkel-Conrat and William
served to stimulate our interest in the relationship between viruses
r organisms. These workers have been able to separate the protein f

During the period when studies with electr
niques of cell study were disclosing more and m
structure, the nucleus was not being neglected.
was recognized early by biologists. The term nu
was not given to this body merely because of its
found in the morphological center of the cell. T
applied because it was evident to nineteenth-c
body was the *functional center* of the cell. The
remarkable behavior of the nucleus at the time of
ization after cell division was additional evidence
teresting to note that our intimate knowledge of t
features was much more advanced in the early p
than was our information about other regions of th

Several factors contributed to our greater un
The nucleus is the largest body within the cell and
remainder of the cell with relative ease. In the 1
prepare for chemical analyses concentrations of nu
of cytoplasm. Later, he utilized salmon sperm as a
realized that sperm cells are composed of only min
surrounding a nuclear sperm "head." The chemic
performed with nuclei established the fact that the
amount of protein as well as a second type of substanc
The novelty of Meischer's chemical experiments and
they were performed justify his designation as the "Fa

A second factor contributing to the understanding
development of fixing and staining techniques that der
ture to a remarkable degree. The appearance of da
chromosomes, that arise in the nucleus at the time of
to be a universal phenomenon. Furthermore, chrom
number for each species of plant or animal, and they
individuality from cell generation to cell generation.
century additional chemical studies established that M
composed of two types of nucleic acids. One of these,
DNA, was found to be associated only with chromosomes
acid, RNA, was observed to be present in both the nucle
Special stains were developed which were specific for
acids. One of these, Schiff's reagent which reacts only
well-known *Feulgen reaction.* This reaction, therefor
method for demonstrating the presence of chromatin ma

The early observations of the nucleus directed attention
as the possible carriers for the units of inheritance, and
in the physical-chemical as well as biochemical analyses
These investigations culminated in the 1950's in the elabor
Crick model for the structure of DNA and of theories conc

ship of D
produced
This biol
setting: t

Living

The co
between
been kn
the activ
value in
ago, "Ca
canna, y
the prot
of mater
the divi

The s
portant
living a
behave
groups
the po
and an
and alf
smaller
viruses
that th
genera
ganisr
it is al
three
viruse
the sa
per c
is en
edly
This
tuito
conc
anal
E
have
high

During the period when studies with electron microscopes and new techniques of cell study were disclosing more and more exact details of cytoplasmic structure, the nucleus was not being neglected. The importance of the nucleus was recognized early by biologists. The term nucleus, indicating the "center," was not given to this body merely because of its position. Actually, it is rarely found in the morphological center of the cell. The designation of nucleus was applied because it was evident to nineteenth-century investigators that this body was the *functional center* of the cell. The subsequent discovery of the remarkable behavior of the nucleus at the time of cell division and its reorganization after cell division was additional evidence of its importance. It is interesting to note that our intimate knowledge of the nucleus and its structural features was much more advanced in the early part of the twentieth century than was our information about other regions of the cell.

Several factors contributed to our greater understanding of the nucleus. The nucleus is the largest body within the cell and can be separated from the remainder of the cell with relative ease. In the 1870's, Meischer was able to prepare for chemical analyses concentrations of nuclei almost completely free of cytoplasm. Later, he utilized salmon sperm as a source of nuclei because he realized that sperm cells are composed of only minute amounts of cytoplasm surrounding a nuclear sperm "head." The chemical studies which Meischer performed with nuclei established the fact that the nucleus contains a large amount of protein as well as a second type of substance which he called *nuclein*. The novelty of Meischer's chemical experiments and the exactness with which they were performed justify his designation as the "Father of Biochemistry."

A second factor contributing to the understanding of the nucleus was the development of fixing and staining techniques that demonstrated nuclear structure to a remarkable degree. The appearance of darkly staining bodies, the *chromosomes*, that arise in the nucleus at the time of cell division was shown to be a universal phenomenon. Furthermore, chromosomes are *constant in number* for each species of plant or animal, and they possess morphological individuality from cell generation to cell generation. Early in the twentieth century additional chemical studies established that Meischer's "nuclein" was composed of two types of nucleic acids. One of these, *deoxyribonucleic acid,* DNA, was found to be associated only with chromosomes; the other, *ribonucleic acid,* RNA, was observed to be present in both the nucleus and the cytoplasm. Special stains were developed which were specific for each of these nucleic acids. One of these, Schiff's reagent which reacts only with DNA, gives the well-known *Feulgen reaction*. This reaction, therefore, became a precise method for demonstrating the presence of chromatin material.

The early observations of the nucleus directed attention to the chromosomes as the possible carriers for the units of inheritance, and interest was aroused in the physical-chemical as well as biochemical analyses of DNA and RNA. These investigations culminated in the 1950's in the elaboration of the Watson-Crick model for the structure of DNA and of theories concerning the relationship of DNA to RNA. We will observe later that the impact of these ideas produced a revolution in the interpretation of biological events in all organisms. This biological revolution will be considered subsequently in a more significant setting: the mechanisms of genetics and of cell differentiation.

Living Versus Nonliving Matter

The complexities of protoplasm suggest that it should be simple to distinguish between living and nonliving matter, as indeed it is in many instances. It has been known for many years, however, that it is possible to simulate many of the activities of protoplasm in models, and these models have often been of value in explaining biological phenomena. Lord Kelvin exclaimed, many years ago, "Can ye make a model of it? For if ye can, ye can understand it; and if ye canna, ye dinna!" Such problems as the nature of the membrane surrounding the protoplasm, the transmission of impulses along nerve fibers, the movement of materials into and out of the protoplasm, the nature of movement, and even the division of protoplasm have been partially solved by studying models.

The studies of *viruses* during the past twenty years have been even more important in demonstrating that no absolute distinction can be made between living and nonliving matter. The viruses are a kind of giant molecule. They behave in a most unexpected way, however, for unlike most molecules, these groups of atoms have the ability to form crystals and at the same time manifest the power of self-duplication! The viruses cause many diseases in both plants and animals; for example, smallpox and influenza in animals, and the tobacco and alfalfa mosaic diseases in plants. Most of the viruses are very minute, much smaller than the smallest bacteria, and exist only on living organisms. The viruses, however, do *grow* and *reproduce,* and recently it has been demonstrated that they undergo changes, or *mutations,* which can be transmitted to the next generation! Should they be considered as very minute forms of parasitic organisms? The *vaccine virus* is actually larger than some of the smaller bacteria; it is about 60 per cent water; it has proteins, carbohydrates, lipids; it has at least three enzymes and has some vitamin B. At the other extreme are the *mosaic viruses: alfalfa, bean,* and *tobacco.* The tobacco mosaic virus, which has about the same diameter as the alfalfa virus, is composed of 94 per cent protein and 6 per cent nucleic acid. Almost every gradation in size and chemical complexity is encountered in other viruses. We must conclude that the viruses undoubtedly provide a connecting link between ordinary molecules and protoplasm. This fact, instead of being disturbing to the biologist, is considered to be fortuitous, because it offers hope that in the solution of biological problems of great concern to the human race, the viruses will be extremely helpful forms for analysis and experimentation.

Exciting new discoveries in virus research by Fraenkel-Conrat and Williams have served to stimulate our interest in the relationship between viruses and higher organisms. These workers have been able to separate the protein from the nucleic acid of tobacco mosaic virus.   Neither of the separated fractions is able to infect tobacco nor to grow and reproduce.   It was possible to recombine the protein and nucleic acid, however, and the reconstructed material was once more an active virus.   Even more astounding was the fact that the nucleic acid of one strain of tobacco mosaic virus could be combined with the protein of a second slightly different strain to produce a hybrid virus.

REFERENCES

ALLEN, R. D., and N. KAMYIA, *Primitive Motile Systems in Cell Biology.*   Academic Press, New York, 1964.

BURNET, F. M., *Virus as Organism.*   Harvard University Press, Cambridge, Mass., 1946.

DE DUVE, CHRISTIAN, "The Lysosome," *Scientific American, 28,* May 1963, pp. 64–72.

DE ROBERTIS, E. D. P., W. W. NOWINSKI, and F. A. SAEZ, *General Cytology.*   W. B. Saunders Company, Philadelphia, 1948.

FLORKIN, MARCEL, *Comparative Biochemistry; a Comprehensive Treatise.*   Academic Press, New York, 1962.

FRAENKEL-CONRAT, HEINZ, and ROBLEY C. WILLIAMS, "Reconstitution of Active Tobacco Mosaic Virus and Nucleic Acid Components," *Proceedings National Academy of Sciences, 41,* October 1955, pp. 690–698.

FRAENKEL-CONRAT, HEINZ, "Rebuilding a Virus," *Scientific American, 194,* June 1956, pp. 42–47.

GERARD, R. W., *Unresting Cells.*   Harper and Brothers, New York, 1949.

GREEN, DAVID E., "The Mitochondrion," *Scientific American, 210,* January 1964, pp. 63–78.

LEHNINGER, ALBERT L., *The Mitochondrion: Molecular Basis of Structure and Function.*   W. A. Benjamin, New York, 1964.

LOWEY, ARIEL G., and PHILIP SIEKEVITZ, *Cell Structure and Function.*   Hope, Rinehart, and Winston, New York, 1963.

PRESCOTT, DAVID M. (ed.)., *Methods in Cell Physiology.*   Academic Press, New York, 1964.

RICH, ALEXANDER, "Polyribosomes," *Scientific American, 209,* April 1963, pp. 44–53.

SCHMIDT-NIELSON, KNUT. *Animal Physiology.*   Prentice-Hall, Englewood Cliffs, 1960.

SIRI, W. E. (ed.), *Isotope Tracers and Nuclear Radiations.*   McGraw-Hill Book Company, Inc., New York, 1949.

2

Giant Molecules

of the Cell

Organic

Molecules

●

Alice laughed. "There's no use trying," she said. "One can't believe impossible things." "I daresay you haven't had much practice" said the Queen. "When I was your age, I always did it for half-an-hour a day. Why sometimes I've believed as many as six impossible things before breakfast . . ."—Lewis Carroll, 1869

Fortunately for the science of biology, scientists have been inclined to accept the attitude of the Queen rather than the conservatism of Alice. Biologists have been challenged to imagine how protoplasm might be organized at the submicroscopic level. The very rudimentary biochemical experiments that could be performed in the past were not precise and, almost without exception, they involved killing the protoplasm. It was always questionable, therefore, whether living material actually was being analyzed. Biologists could only "imagine" the nature of the protoplasm until the modern advances in instrumentation and biochemical procedures emancipated them from the bondage of crude analyses. For example, our discussion of the properties of living matter in Chapter 1 was elementary in respect to the chemical composition of protoplasm. We indicated that vital processes depend on the high water content of protoplasm and that salts, minerals, carbohydrates, fats, and proteins are essential to life. Now it is possible to examine in detail the importance of the organic molecules represented by the carbohydrates, fats, and proteins. First of all, we should emphasize that these molecules may be present as relatively small, single chemical units, the *monomers*, for example, glucose, glycerol, and amino acids. They also may exist as immense branched or unbranched *polymers*, the *macromolecules*, which are combinations of many *monomers* linked by ordinary or *covalent* chemical bonds. To emphasize the most significant features of the carbohydrates, fats, and proteins, it is best to consider them separately with respect to their biological significance and to their chemical composition.

Carbohydrates

Carbohydrate molecules are excellent *energy* sources for organisms. Because certain of the carbohydrates are readily soluble, they are also excellent transport forms. Glucose, for example, is carried in the blood to all parts of the human body for the use of the individual cells. *Sucrose*, likewise, is a soluble sugar that is transported in plants from one region to another. A second important feature of carbohydrates is their ability to be stored as food reserves in the form of starches (*polymers*). We are well acquainted with potato starch but perhaps not aware that animals also store *glycogen*, often called "animal starch," for an energy reserve. The fact that oysters deposit large quantities of glycogen in their tissues accounts for their popularity as a food delicacy. Finally, a carbohydrate macromolecule, *cellulose*, is an important *structural molecule*. A *cell wall* of cellulose is deposited as a nonliving framework outside the plasma membrane of most plants. It is rare, however, to find cellulose as a structural component in animals. Proteins usually perform this function in the animal kingdom.

The most important sugar for all organisms is glucose. This is a six carbon sugar with the following structure. We have noted that it is readily transported

The glucose molecule. Two methods of indicating the glucose molecule are shown above. We find it most convenient in discussion to employ the simplest designation, namely $C_6H_{12}O_6$.

and also is easily utilized. Glucose must be *phosphorylated* before it can be used by cells. As soon as phosphorylation has been accomplished, glucose molecules can be converted to glycogen and stored or they can be broken down to supply energy needed for living processes. Glucose actually is the key organic compound for the synthesis of starch as well as of complex sugars, cellulose, and fats. The first step in the manufacture of the more complex carbohydrates involves the coupling of glucose molecules. This can be illustrated by two glucose

Glucose + glucose ⟶ maltose + water

The formation of maltose. Maltose is a disaccharide or "double sugar." It is formed, as the diagram indicates, by the linking together of two glucose molecules and the elimination of a molecule of water. Conversely, the enzyme maltase can hydrolyze maltose ("split with water") into two glucose molecules.

molecules that combine to form a molecule of *maltose* with the simultaneous release of a molecule of water. Since maltose is composed of two glucose units, it is called a *disaccharide.* Sucrose also is a disaccharide but it is a combination of a molecule of glucose with its isomer* fructose. Plant and animal starch, on the other hand, may be composed of thousands of individual glucose units (monomers). Hence, the starches are examples of *polymers* and are specifically designated as *polysaccharides.*

The fact that special catalysts, or *enzymes,* make it possible to combine water with disaccharides or polysaccharides to free glucose or other monomer molecules is of special biological significance. This process is appropriately called *hydrolysis. Amylase* is the enzyme that hydrolyzes the starch *amylose; maltase,* the enzyme that hydrolyzes *maltose;* and *cellulase, cellulose.* It is in-

Polysaccharide polymer diagram. Chains of molecules can form polymers. In the example, chains of glucose molecules are coupled and oriented in the same way to form *starches.* The glucose chains may be straight or branched in different starches. Cellulose also is formed by chains of glucose molecules but the molecules alternate in their orientation. Cellulose is composed of extremely long and branched chains of molecules. Since both starch and cellulose are composed of many sugar monomers, they are representative of the *polysaccharide* carbohydrates.

* An isomer is one molecule with the same molecular formula as another but with a spatial rearrangement of the atoms within the molecule.

teresting that higher animals do not possess the enzyme cellulase and, therefore, cannot digest cellulose. Many animals, notably termites and ruminants, have unicellular "guests" living in their digestive systems, who can secrete cellulase. The host animal, therefore, is able to secure glucose from the cellulose as a result of this cooperative arrangement.

Fats or lipids

There are many similarities between fats and carbohydrates in their role in biological systems. Fats also are excellent energy sources and their energy value is more than twice that of the carbohydrates per unit of weight. Stored fat, often in the form of adipose tissue, is the predominant energy reserve for many organisms and in this respect is much more important than glycogen. Fat also provides protective shock-pads about the vital organs in most animals, for example, in surrounding the human kidneys. A thick layer of fat may be deposited beneath the outer layers of the skin and in such cases will function as an insulating blanket. The thick blubber of whales and other aquatic warm-blooded animals vividly illustrate this statement. Finally, because of the ratio of hydrogen to oxygen in fat molecules, oxidation of fats can result in the formation of water molecules. Many animals, notably desert-dwelling ones, are able to use this "metabolic" water and may need very little or no water from external sources in order to maintain themselves.

The fat molecule is formed by the combination of glycerol molecules and fatty acid molecules with the liberation of water. The accompanying diagram illustrates how the fat *tripalmitin* is formed by the union of three molecules of palmitic acid with one molecule of glycerol. This reaction is readily reversible, of course, and when fats are digested the enzyme *lipase* acts in conjunction with water to hydrolyze fats. This hydrolysis is comparable with that of sucrose by sucrase.

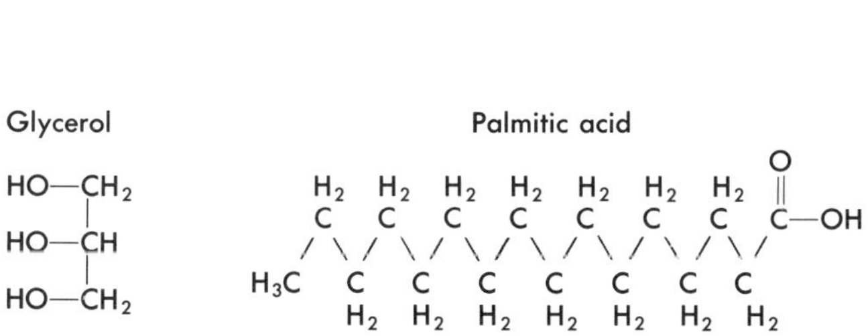

Glycerol   Palmitic acid

$$HO-CH_2$$
$$HO-CH$$
$$HO-CH_2$$

Schematic formula

Glycerol and palmitic acid. Fats are composed of glycerol and fatty acids. The structure of *glycerol* and the fatty acid *palmitic acid* are shown above. Because of the repetitive nature of the fatty acid molecule, it often is convenient to use a very diagrammatic "schematic formula" to represent a fatty acid.

$$\text{3 palmitic acid molecules} \qquad \text{Gylcerol}$$

Tripalmitin.   Tripalmitin is a *fat* formed by the coupling of three molecules of palmitic acid with a molecule of glycerol and the simultaneous release of three molecules of water.   Fats can be formed by the joining of three like or unlike fatty acids with glycerol.

Phospholipids and steroids

Two other kinds of lipids are of great biological significance.   These are the *phospholipids* and *steroids*.   The phospholipids are fats which incorporate phosphorous and nitrogen into the molecule.   They, like the proteins, can serve as *structural molecules* especially in the nervous tissues, the plasma membrane, and the mitochondria.   The fats are not water soluble but the phospholipids are and, therefore, can serve as transport forms.   This is a situation comparable to the phosphorylation of glucose and is another illustration of the fact that the phosphorylation of a molecule enhances its utilization in living systems.

Steroids are complexes of four interlocking rings.   One of these rings contains

Figure 2.1.   Carbon chain.   Carbon atoms, because of their ability to share electrons, can form long chains, as this fat molecule demonstrates.   Carbon atoms are shown in black.   (After *Essentials of Chemistry,* by Garrett, Haskins, and Sisler, courtesy Ginn and Co.)

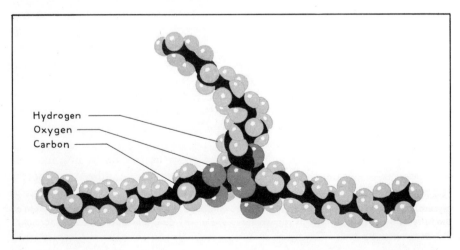

Hydrogen

Oxygen

Carbon

five carbon atoms whereas the other three rings are composed of six carbons. Some major steroids are: *cholesterol, testosterone* (male hormone), *estradiol* (female hormone), and *vitamin D*. In addition to their regulatory functions as hormones and vitamins, we find that steroids are abundant in nervous tissues.

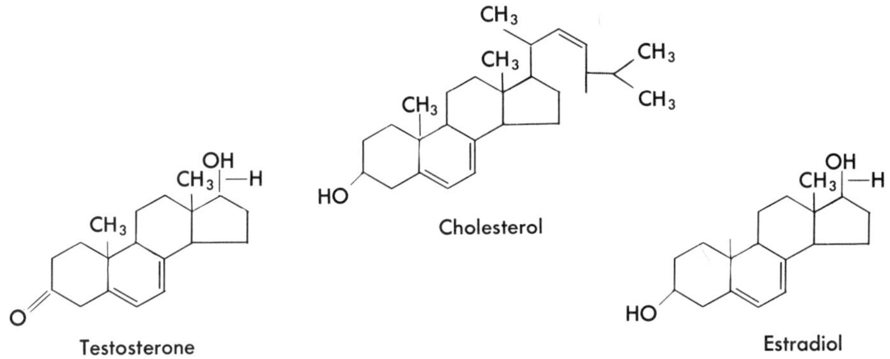

Representative steroids. The steroids are an important class of biological compounds and three very characteristic ones are shown above. Testosterone is the *male sex hormone* and estradiol is one of the *female sex hormones*.

Proteins

Many volumes have been written about the proteins. The information about their varied biological functions and their complex chemical compositions is so encyclopedic that we can present only an abbreviated account of their significance. The biological roles of the proteins are much more varied than those of either the carbohydrates or the fats. The proteins are among the very largest of the macromolecules and as we observed previously, they are of great *structural* importance. The cell wall of animals, often called the *pellicle*, usually is composed of protein in contrast to the cellulose cell wall of most plants. The long-chain polymeric structure of proteins also lends itself readily to fiber formation, and the *collagen fibers* of connective tissues or the *contractile fibrils* of muscle cells are good examples of such polymers. *Enzymes* are proteins, and life could not exist without these organic catalysts. Many *hormones*, notably insulin, are proteins. Proteins also conjugate with other chemicals to form other biologically important compounds, for example, the *hemoglobin* and *hemocyanin* molecules which are the oxygen-carrying chemicals of animals that possess circulatory systems. Finally, we should record that proteins also can contribute to the *food reserve* of the organism. This is, however, an emergency reserve in most animals. The proteins can be hydrolyzed, the nitrogen removed, and the remains of the molecule can be utilized for energy. They are "expensive" foods for any organism and, if any extensive demand is placed on proteins as energy sources, the structural organization and enzyme reserve is rapidly depleted. Death usually will follow quickly.

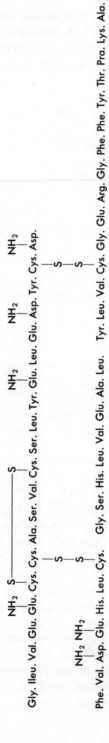

Gly. Ileu. Val. Glu. Glu. Cys. Cys. Ala. Ser. Val. Cys. Ser. Leu. Tyr. Glu. Leu. Glu. Asp. Tyr. Cys. Asp.

Phe. Val. Asp. Glu. His. Leu. Cys.   Gly. Ser. His. Leu. Val. Glu. Ala. Leu.   Tyr. Leu. Val. Cys. Gly. Glu. Arg. Gly. Phe. Phe. Tyr. Thr. Pra. Lys. Ala.

Insulin molecule. The amino acid composition of insulin is shown for the two chains of the protein hormone insulin. The upper sequence is the "A-chain" and the lower sequence, the "B-chain." Note the internal S-S linkage in the A-chain and the S-S cross linkage between the cystine molecules of the A- and B-chains.

The chemical structure of the proteins is imposing with respect both to the size of the protein molecules and to their complexity. One of the smallest proteins, the hormone insulin, has a molecular weight of 6,000. At the other extreme, if certain viruses are excluded, we find respiratory pigments with molecular weights of several million. Hemoglobin is a representative medium-sized protein molecule. This respiratory pigment in man has a molecular weight of 68,000 and its composition is as follows: $C_{3032}H_{4016}O_{872}N_{780}S_8Fe_{74}$. The presence of sulfur is common in most proteins, and iron is especially significant in the hemoglobin molecule because of its role in oxygen transport. Large complex molecules like the proteins are obviously resistant to chemical analysis. Indeed, chemists dispaired for many years of ever being able to analyze even the composition of the insulin molecule. The proteins, however, have yielded some of the secrets of their elaborate construction during the last few decades and even hemoglobin has been "fingerprinted" with remarkable accuracy.

Amino acids

The basic units of the proteins, the monomers, have been known for many years. These are the *amino acids* of which only 20 are commonly found in proteins. The manner in which the amino acids can be coupled to form chains also was understood, and a few simple facts about amino acids will now serve to establish the basic chemical factors involved in protein synthesis. First of all, amino acids contain an *amino group*, NH_2, and a *carboxyl group*, COOH. The general formula for an amino acid and the specific formulas for two amino acids, *glycine* and *alanine*, appear in the accompanying diagram. The letter

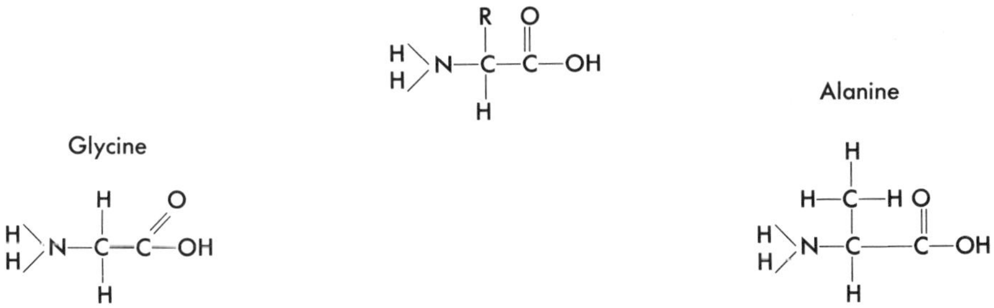

Amino acids, general formula. The structure of all amino acids follows a basic plan which is shown in the generalized formula. There is an amino group $\left(\begin{array}{c} H \\ \diagdown \\ \diagup \\ H \end{array} N \right)$ and a carboxyl group $(-\overset{O}{\overset{\|}{C}}-OH)$. In addition a *radical* represented by R in the diagram is present. Glycine has H as the radical whereas alanine has $H-\overset{H}{\underset{}{C}}-H$ as its radical.

R in the general formula for an amino acid signifies a "radical." In the case of glycine, R is equivalent to H, while in alanine, R is equivalent to CH_3. Other, more complex, radicals are common in amino acids. It should be noted that in each of the formulas the amino groups are shown at the left of the diagram and the carboxyl groups at the right. One unique feature of the amino acids should be emphasized at this point in our discussion. This concerns their ionic forms. The diagram illustrates the changes in the ionic states of a generalized amino acid following a gain or loss of H+.

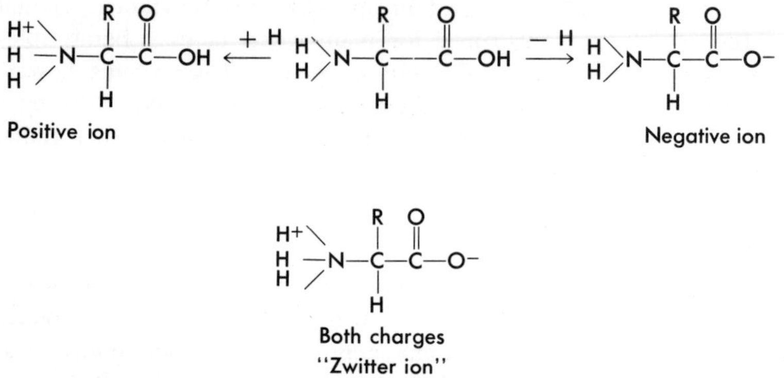

Positive ion   Negative ion

Both charges
"Zwitter ion"

Ionic forms of amino acids. The presence of both basic and acidic groups (NH_2 and COOH) in an amino acid can lead to the formation of positive or negative ions if a hydrogen is gained or lost. It also is possible for the simultaneous gain and loss of a hydrogen to occur, in which case one "end" of the amino acid has a positive charge and the other "end" a negative charge. The significance of this type of ion in the regulation of movement of materials through a cell membrance is very great (p. 56).

The German term applied to the ionic states of amino acids is *Zwitterions*, meaning that "both kinds" of ions can be present. This characteristic of amino acids is very significant in many of the chemical reactions in the cell and especially in those of the plasma membrane.

We have indicated that amino acids are the monomers of the polymeric proteins. The coupling of amino acids can be demonstrated very simply by utilizing the two amino acids, glycine and alanine, which were shown in the earlier diagram.

We can observe that the reaction produces a "dipeptide," *glycylalanine,* with the liberation of a molecule of water. This reaction is employed by organisms to couple amino acids into *polypeptide* chains. The 20 amino acids common to proteins may be arranged in an almost infinite variety of sequences and in varying numbers. The diagram of the insulin molecule illustrates this feature. Amino acids often have been called the "alphabet" of the proteins, and the protein "words" they spell are determined by the genetic makeup of each living thing. It is not surprising, in view of the immense variety of "words"

Glycine + alanine ⟶ glycylalanine + water

Dipeptide formation. Individual amino acids, like sugars, may be coupled to form larger molecules. Thus glycine and alanine join to create *glycylalanine* with the elimination of a molecule of water. It is the coupling of amino acids in this fashion that can result in polypeptide and protein synthesis.

which can be "spelled," that each organism can have its own peculiar types of proteins.

Finally, it should be noted that there is no sharp line of separation between long polypeptide chains and the proteins. Arbitarily, a molecular weight of 10,000 is usually considered to be the point of demarcation. Insulin is one of the notable exceptions because it has a molecular weight of only 6,000 but is considered to be a protein. Obviously, other factors such as cross-linkages within, or between, polypeptide chains play an important role in determining the protein molecules. Proteins also have different configurations. They may be long chains, folded chains, spirals (called helices), or globular.

We mentioned earlier that proteins can be used for "fuel" by organisms. The union of amino acids to form dipeptides is a reversible reaction, and the process demonstrates what happens when proteins are broken down into their constituent amino-acid elements. The action of various protein-splitting enzymes, such as *trypsin* from the pancreas, results in the hydrolyzing of the polypeptide or dipeptide chains to their amino acids monomers. The amino acids subsequently have the nitrogen split from them, a process called *deamination*, and the residues enter into the metabolic pool of small molecules.

Nucleic acids

A discussion of the polymers that are of biological significance would not be complete without a brief introduction to the chemistry of the nucleic acids. We recall that Meischer in the 1870's was the first to demonstrate the presence of the nucleic acids. These are the largest polymers in living systems and are composed of monomers in the form of nucleotides. Before we define a nucleotide, it will be advantageous to describe the chemical units which comprise these monomers. There are two nucleic acids: *deoxyribonucleic acid* (DNA) and *ribonucleic acid* (RNA). Both DNA and RNA possess *phosphate* and a *sugar*, as well as a *purine* or *pyrimidine base*. Since DNA contains the sugar deoxyribose and RNA the sugar ribose, it is obvious that their names reflect the sugar which is present in them.   The phosphate and sugar molecules are shown in the accompanying diagram.

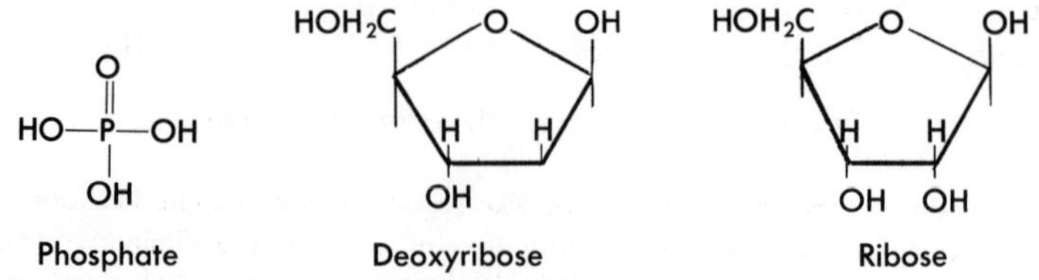

| Phosphate | Deoxyribose | Ribose |

Key molecules of DNA and RNA.   A *phosphate* is coupled with a *sugar* in both DNA and RNA. The coupling is between the phosphate and *deoxyribose* in deoxyribonucleic acid (DNA) and between the phosphate and *ribose* in ribonucleic acid (RNA).

There are two purine bases, *adenine* and *guanine,* and three pyrimidine bases, *cytosine, thymine,* and *uracil.*   Three of the five bases are found in both nucleic acids.   Uracil is present   only in RNA; thymine is found only in DNA.

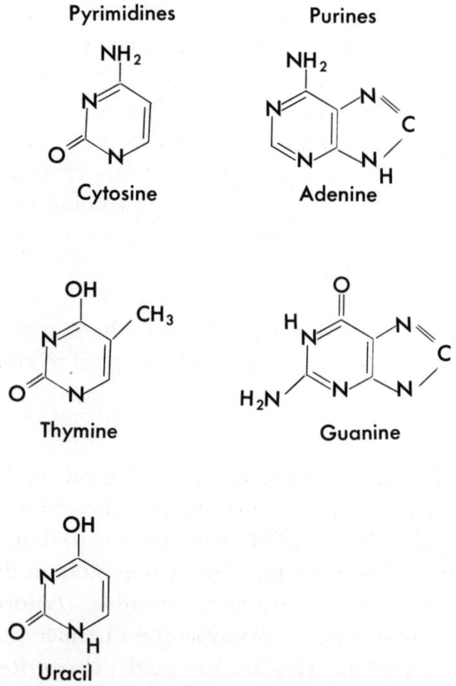

Pyrimidines   Purines

Cytosine   Adenine

Thymine   Guanine

Uracil

Bases of DNA and RNA.   Three of the five bases found in DNA and RNA are the smaller *pyrimidines:* cytosine, thymine, and uracil.   Two of the bases are the larger *purines:* adenine and guanine.   Thymine is restricted to DNA and uracil to RNA.

It is possible now to define and illustrate what is meant by a nucleotide monomer. The combination of a phosphate molecule plus a deoxyribose molecule plus a thymine molecule would produce a *thymidine monophosphate nucleotide*. Similar combinations of each of the remaining four bases with either of the sugars and the phosphate would form the remaining nucleotides.

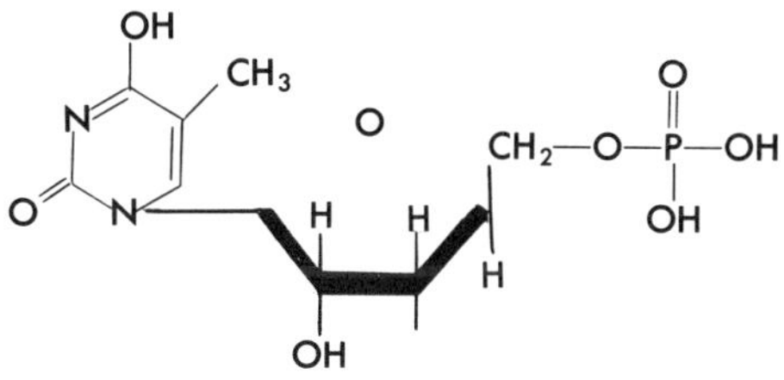

Base + Sugar + Phosphate
Thymidine monophosphate

Nucleotide.   The nucleotide illustrated here is composed of the pyrimidine base *thymine*, the sugar *deoxyribose*, and a *phosphate* molecule.   A nucleotide of this type can be coupled with the purine nucleotide, *adenosine monophosphate* to form a nucleotide pair in DNA.

Recent studies have demonstrated that deoxyribonucleic acid is confined to the nucleus except for very small amounts in certain cytoplasmic structures, such as mitochrondia and chloroplasts. Ribonucleic acid however, can be found in both the nucleus and the cytoplasm. These observations show the chemical nature of the nucleic acids and their distribution in cells to be of tremendous importance in the regulation of cellular activity and heredity. We will delay the detailed discussion of the significance of the nucleic acids until we consider the subject of genetics.

We find it advantageous to summarize our discussion of the protoplasm since modern biochemical studies have enabled us to analyze its most intimate details. The complex colloidal system with a high water content which initially challenged the imagination of biologists has now been revealed to be a composition of carbohydrates, fats, and proteins that can exist either as monomers or polymers. The synthesis of the complex polymeric substances from the various monomers enables protoplasm to store high-energy fuels for the future energy requirements of the cell. Equally significant is the fact that the polymeric molecules are used by cells for an architectural function: for example, cellulose serves for the cell walls of plants and proteins for the cell walls (pellicles) of animals. Fibrillar organelles such as centrioles, cilia, and myofibrils or neurofibrils are other examples of assemblies of architectural polymers.

Pairing of bases. When the bases of nucleotides pair, they can do so only in a restricted fashion. Thus only those with two valences or those with three valences can join. An example of each is shown: *thymine with adenine* or *cytosine with guanine*. It will be noted in the text that the second restriction also involves a larger molecule pairing with a smaller molecule in each instance.

We can now develop a reasonable concept of the nature of the ground substance of the cell even though we recall that the fine details are invisible to the electron microscope. This ubiquitous material must be composed of a mixture of the various polymers, monomers, and ions of simpler molecules. The fact that the ground substance can transform readily from a viscous to a fluid state is understandable. We only need to recall that the immense chain molecules of the polymers can be hydrolyzed to their respective soluble monomers and that the reverse transformation occurs readily. The rapid change from the gel to the sol state and the reverse is probably a result of reversible reactions among the macromolecules. This will be discussed in genetics.

REFERENCES

BRACHET, JEAN, and ALFRED E. MIRSKY, *The Cell*, Vol. 1. Academic Press, New York, 1959.

BRACHET, JEAN, and ALFRED E. MIRSKY, *The Cell*, Vol. 2. Academic Press, New York, 1961.

BASERGA, RENATO, and W. E. KISIELESKI, "Autobiographies of Cells." *Scientific American, 209*, August 1963, pp. 103–119.

DEROBERTIS, E. D. P., W. W. NOWINSKI, and F. A. SAEZ, *General Cytology*. W. B. Saunders Company, Philadelphia, 1948.

EHRET, C. F., "Organelle Systems and Biological Organization." *Science, 132*, July 15, 1960, pp. 115–123.

FRAENKEL-CONRAT, HEINZ, *Design and Function at the Threshold of Life—The Viruses*. Academic Press, New York, 1962.

FRAENKEL-CONRAT, HEINZ, and ROBLEY C. WILLIAMS, "Reconstitution of Active Tobacco Mosaic Virus and Nucleic Acid Components," *Proceedings National Academy of Sciences, 41*, October 1955, pp. 690–698.

LEHNINGER, ALBERT L., *The Mitochondrion*. W. A. Benjamin, New York, 1964.

Lowey, Ariel G., and Philip Siekevitz, *Cell Structure and Function.* Hope, Rinehart, and Winston, New York, 1963.

Maddox, John, *Revolution in Biology.* The Macmillan Company, New York, 1964.

Mazia, Daniel, "The Life History of the Cell," *American Scientist, 44,* January 1956, pp. 1-32.

Morowitz, H. J., and M. E. Tourtellottee, "The Smallest Cells," *Scientific American, 206,* March 1962, pp. 117–127.

Parsons, Donald F., "Mitochondrial Structure." *Science, 140,* May 1963, pp. 985–987.

Schmidt-Nielson, Knut, *Animal Physiology.* Prentice-Hall Inc., New Jersey, 1960.

Sussman, M., *Growth and Development,* 2nd ed. Prentice-Hall, Inc., New Jersey, 1964.

Swanson, Carl P., *The Cell.* Prentice-Hall Inc., New Jersey, 1960.

3

How Work

Is Done

The

Functions

of Organisms

●

Morphology, therefore, must be intimate with function, since it must see forms as plastic physical adaptations to the work to be performed.—Snodgrass, Principles of Insect Morphology, 1935

The four *activities* of living matter—growth, reproduction, movement, and irritability—are possible as a result of a series of functional adaptations of organisms. Regardless of the complexity of structure or the size of the animals, certain *functions* are common to all. The total of these functional activities is the *metabolism*, or metabolic activity, of the organism. It is important to note that metabolism consists of two phases: *first*, a constructive phase, *anabolism*, in which there is an increase in the protoplasm, with a storage of energy materials; and *second*, a destructive phase, *catabolism*, in which there is an expenditure of energy with slight or extensive utilization of protoplasm. It is convenient for a comparative study of the various groups of animals to recognize five major functions as making up the sum total of life activities: (1) *nutrition*, (2) *respiration*, (3) *excretion*, (4) *reproduction*, and (5) *coordination*. Nutrition and reproduction may be considered to be primarily constructive, or *anabolic*; the remaining three—respiration, excretion, and coordination—involve primarily the expenditure of energy and are considered to be destructive, or *catabolic*. The most important biological feature of metabolic activity, however, is that even in the formation of new protoplasm by synthesis, or of new individuals by reproduction, there is some expenditure of energy. Since even constructive metabolism requires energy and is always accompanied by destructive metabolism, it should be clear that whenever the energy expenditure of catabolism exceeds the energy build-up of anabolism, death and disintegration of the organism will follow.

Nutrition

The term *nutrition*, as used in this text, includes a variety of conditions and processes. We noted previously that organisms secure food either by synthesis, as in plants, or by the consumption of other organisms, as in animals. In a broad sense, food is any substance used for energy, to build protoplasm, or to maintain the proper physical–chemical relationships in the protoplasm. Inorganic substances—such as water, minerals, and salts—are as important, therefore, as the organic foods in the form of carbohydrates, fats, proteins, and vitamins. The carbohydrates, fats, and proteins eaten by an animal must be broken down into simpler chemical substances and resynthesized within the protoplasm. This process involves the well-known steps of *digestion, absorption,* and *resynthesis*. Finally, each group of organisms has developed a series of structures associated with nutrition. These range from simple *vacuoles*, fluid-filled spaces in the protoplasm, to complicated *alimentary canals*, with highly specialized regions for digestion and absorption. Organisms that have adopted a parasitic mode of life have evolved bizarre features which enable them to secure food from the host in or upon which they live.

Types of nutrition

A word should be said here about the classification of the types of nutrition. An autotrophic organism, one which manufactures its own organic food, as in the case of green plants, is said to have *holophytic* (completely plantlike) *nutrition*. A heterotrophic organism, one entirely dependent on other organisms for food, is said to have *holozoic* (completely animal-like) *nutrition*. An animal living on organic matter in solution is said to have *saprozoic* (animal living on dead matter) *nutrition*. Parasites would be considered in the last category, because their food is secured from organic solutions in the body of the host. A plant living on organic matter in solution, however, is said to have *saprophytic* (plant living on dead matter) *nutrition*. But no matter how organisms *obtain* their food, the utilization of food is basically the same for all organisms.

Energy release

The energy for metabolism must be derived from the food eaten or synthesized by the organism. The energy, however, must be "released" from the food by oxidation. The relation of oxidation to energy release can be shown by the equation for the burning of glucose, either within the protoplasm or in a test tube, which follows.

$$C_6H_{12}O_6 + 6\,O_2 \rightarrow 6\,CO_2 + 6\,H_2O + \text{energy}.$$
glucose   oxygen carbon dioxide water

The energy may be in the form of motion, heat, electric energy, or work of secretion or excretion; the kind of energy released is determined by the protoplasm. Scrutinizing the equation closely we can see that, if the direction of

(a) Holophytic

(b) Intermediate Carnivore

Figure 3.1. These organisms typify the important types of nutrition defined in the text. The sunflowers (a) have holophytic nutrition. Venus' flytrap (b) is an intermediate carnivore, for it actually lives on insects and other animals it traps in its jawlike leaves, so that it almost has holozoic nutrition. (Courtesy Rutherford Platt.)

the arrow is reversed, the reaction is the same as previously observed in photosynthesis. Reference to the simplified equation for the synthesis of glucose by green plants will show that the energy source was sunlight.

Energy such as that "stored" in glucose is usually spoken of as *potential energy,* and energy such as light or heat is called *kinetic energy.* The two equations for glucose synthesis and oxidation can be rewritten with the above observations in mind as follows:

Photosynthesis

$$6\,CO_2 + 6\,H_2O + \underset{\text{kinetic energy}}{\text{sunlight}} + \text{chlorophyll} \rightarrow \underset{\text{potential energy}}{C_6H_{12}O_6 + 6\,O_2};$$

Oxidation

$$C_6H_{12}O_6 + 6\,O_2 \rightarrow 6\,CO_2 + 6\,H_2O + \text{kinetic energy}.$$

Respiration

Without exception, the most effective release of energy in animals results from the eventual combination of oxygen with the energy foods, a process known as *oxybiotic respiration.* It is possible for most animals, even man, to release energy for short periods of time by another destructive process, *anoxybiotic respiration,* but in most such cases the byproducts eventually combine with oxygen. Some animals may practice anoxybiotic respiration for long periods of time, but the amount of energy released from glucose by this method is only about five per cent of that released by oxidation. The function of respiration in animals is to make it possible for the protoplasm to secure ample supplies of oxygen for energy needs and to remove carbon dioxide, which is a byproduct

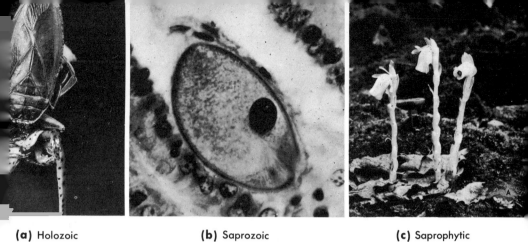

(a) Holozoic   **(b)** Saprozoic   **(c)** Saprophytic

Figure 3.2. More typical of holozoic nutrition is the giant water bug (a) shown devouring a salamander originally larger than itself. The protozoan of dysentery (b) shows parasitic, or saprozoic, nutrition. The Indian pipe plants (c) show saprophytic nutrition. Of the five, (including the two in Figure 3.1) only the sunflowers are true autotrophs. [(a) courtesy Lynwood M. Chace; (b) Armed Forces Institute of Pathology; (c) Rutherford Platt.]

of the oxidation reaction. As we shall see, the removal of carbon dioxide overlaps the function of excretion. It is generally recognized that respiration actually involves two steps: *external respiration* and *internal respiration*. The former is confined to the animals of relatively large size, which we shall subsequently call the *metazoa*, in which much of the protoplasm is remote from the source of oxygen. External respiration is the exchange of oxygen and carbon dioxide between the air or water in which the animal lives and the body fluids of the animal. (See Figure 19.11.) Internal respiration, on the other hand, is the exchange of oxygen and carbon dioxide between the body fluids and the protoplasm. No distinction can be made between internal and external respiration in the case of most microscopic animals—for example, the Protozoa—since the small size of the animal makes it possible to have direct exchange between the protoplasm and the fluid in which the animal lives.

Excretion

An analogy is sometimes drawn between the energy transformations in protoplasm and those in a gasoline or steam engine. There are many objections to this analogy, but one of the valid comparisons is that in both instances utilization of fuel gives rise to waste products which must be eliminated. Neither the protoplasm nor the engine, therefore, is 100 per cent efficient. An important distinction must be made between *excretion* and *egestion*. The waste products formed during energy release are a result of the utilization of foods within the protoplasm, a process we have previously called *catabolism*. Excretion, therefore, is limited to the processes involved in the elimination of these substances. Not all material taken in by organisms is digested or utilized,

(a)

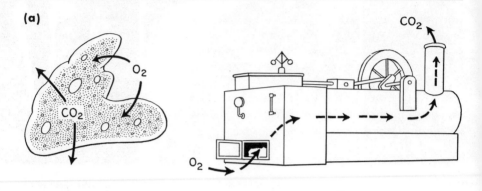

(b)

Sunlight

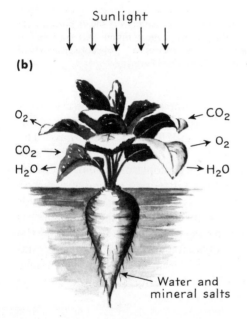

Water and
mineral salts

Figure 3.3 (a). The animal and the ma-
chine. Organisms, like machines, "burn"
fuel (for example, carbohydrates) to release
energy, with the liberation of carbon dioxide
as a waste product. (b). Photosynthesis is
the most important manufacturing process
on earth. Water and carbon dioxide are
combined to form carbohydrates with
"stored energy." These carbohydrates are
the building materials for other basic organic
substances needed by all living things.

that is, actually becomes part of the protoplasm, and these undigested materials
are *egested*, not excreted. The problem of excretion can be illustrated by the
oxidation of glucose, which was mentioned previously in our discussion of the
transformation of potential and kinetic energy, as follows:

$$C_6H_{12}O_6 + 6\,O_2 \xrightarrow{\text{enzyme}} 6\,H_2O + 6\,CO_2 + \text{kinetic energy.}$$

potential energy

Water and carbon dioxide are the waste products in this reaction and must
be eliminated in varying amounts. It should be emphasized that some water
and some carbon dioxide will be utilized by the protoplasm, but excess amounts
must be excreted. We shall observe among the animals many different struc-

tures which are used for water excretion. As we previously noted, carbon dioxide is excreted during the exchange of gases in respiration. The most important toxic waste products to be excreted by organisms are formed as by-products of the oxidation of another class of energy foods, the proteins. We have seen that the proteins are composed primarily of carbon (C), hydrogen (H), and oxygen (O), and also of nitrogen (N). Sulfur (S) and phosphorus (P) are also commonly found in proteins. We will limit the remarks in our discussion to the first four elements.

Types of waste products

The protein molecule is so large and complex that it is convenient to designate it simply as a CHON compound, with the understanding that hundreds or thousands of each of the individual atoms may be present in the protein molecule. A further liberty will be taken when writing an equation to represent the oxidation of a protein: no attempt will be made to "balance" the equation. When we write the reaction for the oxidation of a protein, it can be represented as follows:

$$\underset{\text{potential energy}}{CHON} + O_2 \xrightarrow{\text{enzyme}} H_2O + CO_2 + \text{nitrogen compounds} + \text{kinetic energy}.$$

It is obvious immediately that as in glucose oxidation, water and carbon dioxide are present; but now, in addition, nitrogen compounds also are waste products. These compounds present an additional problem to the organism, because they are highly toxic.

Four major nitrogen compounds are excreted by animals, and in addition there are several others of minor importance. The four compounds with which animals are primarily concerned are: *ammonia, urea, uric acid*, and *amino acids*; and they decrease in toxicity to the protoplasm in the order named. Some microscopic animals may have as much as 90 per cent of the nitrogen excreted

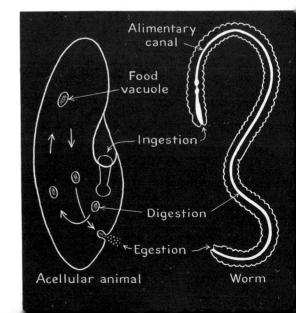

Figure 3.4. Digestive systems. The process of ingestion, digestion, and egestion takes place in animals regardless of size or complexity. The food vacuoles perform the same functions in acellular (microscopic) organisms as those performed by the alimentary canal of the larger many-celled animals.

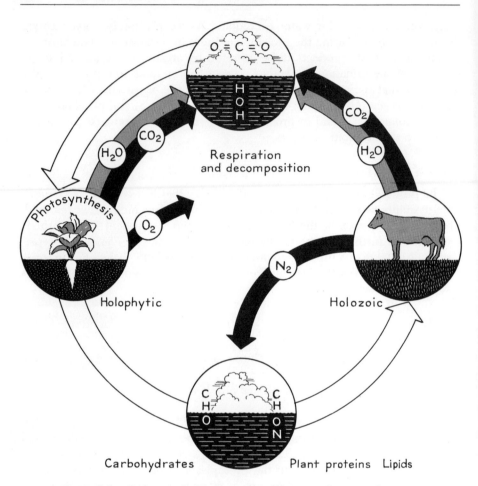

Figure 3.5. Carbon and nitrogen cycle. Waste products are shown as shaded arrows.

as ammonia, but in man the amount may be as low as four per cent.   Urea is found only in traces in the microscopic animals, but is the chief nitrogenous excretory product in man.   Uric acid excretion is confined chiefly to the reptiles (snakes, turtles, and lizards) and to the birds and is especially important in some arthropods.   Amino acids, which serve as excellent food materials, strangely enough are excreted by several animal groups.   This obviously is a very wasteful procedure and is only one of many examples of the fact that nature is not always right.   The octopus and some related forms, the starfish and some of its close relatives, as well as some fishes excrete amino acids.

We can see from the foregoing that three types of materials must be excreted: (1) a *gas* (carbon dioxide); (2) a *liquid* (water); and (3) *solids* (some nitrogenous compounds).   The different groups of animals have developed various structures to accomplish their excretion. Carbon dioxide is taken care of in conjunction with the respiratory function; water is often eliminated by direct diffusion through the surface of the organism, or in conjunction with the excretion of the nitrogenous wastes; the latter are excreted in most animal groups by the development of filtration devices—for example, the kidneys in man.

Reproduction

When we commented upon the problem of reproduction in the chapter dealing with the activities of living matter, attention was directed toward the fact that reproduction can be a dual process: either a part of an individual or a new individual may be produced. Animals which have the body subdivided into those structural units called cells will replace parts, grow, or enlarge regions of the body by the formation of new cells. This process of cell division is called *mitosis* and will be discussed at length in the chapter which describes the transition of organisms from an acellular to a many-celled condition. The second phase of the reproductive process, the formation of new individuals, is accomplished by several processes. This phase of reproduction embraces the problem of the transmission of like characteristics from parent to offspring. The importance of this feature of reproduction will be considered in the chapter on inheritance, as well as in those portions of the text which describe the major animal groups.

Types of reproduction

The methods of formation of new organisms fall into two categories: (1) *asexual reproduction*; and (2) *sexual reproduction*. Asexual reproduction involves the splitting of the body into two or more parts, which then are separated to become new individuals. This type of phenomenon, called *binary fission*, may be either transverse or longitudinal. A body, or *bud*, also may form on the parent animal and become a new individual. These buds do not always separate but may remain attached to form a *colony* of individuals. Sexual reproduction, on the other hand, is characterized by the formation of specialized reproductive units, or *gametes*. These are the *sperm*, or male reproductive cells, and the *ova*, or female reproductive cells. Certain of the microscopic animals may have the entire individual transformed into a male or a female gamete. New animals commonly arise as a result of the union of an ovum and a sperm, but many organisms regularly, or at certain seasons, will develop from

Figure 3.6. Sexual reproduction. The hereditary significance of this process is that the new individual is a blend of characteristics transmitted from the mother's ovum and from the father's sperm.

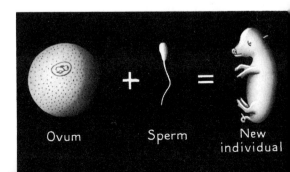

Ovum   Sperm   New individual

eggs which have not united with sperm—that is, have not been fertilized. The development of an ovum without fertilization is a special type of sexual reproduction, called *parthenogenesis*, or "virgin birth."

Coordination

The complex physical and chemical changes which constantly occur within the protoplasm require delicate adjustments between parts of the organism and between the organism and its external surroundings, or *external environment*. As organisms increase in size, much of the protoplasm is isolated from the external environment and is remote from other parts of the animal. This situation results in the creation of an extensive *internal environment* and the development of elaborate integrating mechanisms. Animals have developed two systems of coordination, which supplement each other in the adjustments of the organisms to fluctuations in the external and internal environments.

Types of coordination

The better known of the two methods of coordination may be referred to as *nervous coordination*. Certain parts of the animal are especially adapted for *receiving* stimuli and *conducting* messages, or *impulses*, to other areas of the animal, which can then *respond*. Many of the microscopic animals composed of undivided masses of protoplasm have special fibers, or *fibrils*, which carry impulses; and those animals which have the protoplasm subdivided into cells have certain of these cells specialized for the transmission of impulses. The organization of the brain, spinal cord, and all the peripheral nerves of man is a good example of this type of coordinating system. The transmission and response in nervous coordination are *rapid*, of *short duration*, and in most animals *centralized*, with special pathways for transmission being selected by the brain or a corresponding structure.

The second type of coordination, *chemical coordination*, is equally important and in certain animals is almost as complex as nervous coordination. The simplest expression of chemical coordination is related to the local production in the protoplasm of carbon dioxide and other *chemical substances* which are byproducts of catabolism. These react to modify the acidity of the protoplasm, to speed up or slow down chemical reactions, to change the fluid condition, and to influence the movement of *materials* into and out of the protoplasm. Such chemical substances in larger animals may be carried by the blood or body fluids to areas remote from their origin and thus modify the activity of distant areas of the body. An excellent illustration of this phenomenon is the increase in carbon dioxide in man while exercising. This carbon dioxide is carried to all parts of the body and will increase the rate of breathing, with the result that more oxygen will be taken in and more carbon dioxide eliminated. Many animals, in addition to the chemical effects produced as a result of the byproducts of catabolism, have special tissues or glands which secrete chemical substances directly into the blood or body fluids. These substances are called *hormones* and are extremely important in many groups of animals. Hormones control such varied functions as growth, development of the reproductive system, utilization of carbohydrates, the water-and-salt balance, and general body responses in emergencies or stress.

Chemical coordination is very different from nervous coordination in several important respects. Action is relatively *slow, long lasting*, and of necessity, *diffuse*. Some of the end results of the action of chemical coordinators may not be apparent until days, weeks, or even months have elapsed. Even the rapid responses to the hormones usually require the lapse of seconds, whereas nerve impulses are transmitted in hundredths or thousandths of a second.

Energy Relationships

We shall now direct our attention to the carbohydrates, fats, and proteins as energy reserves for the metabolic activities of the cell. We observed in the previous chapter that the macromolecules of each of these can be hydrolyzed to their respective monomers by the action of appropriate enzymes. We also noted that the small chemical units, namely glucose, the fatty acids, and the amino acids, can be "burned" to release energy in several forms. It is advantageous to confine our attention primarily to glucose utilization, since this simple sugar is the major energy source for most organisms, and its fate is illustrative of the chemical events which occur when other molecules are used.

Glucose oxidation

Let us begin our analysis of the role of glucose by oxidizing ("burning") glucose in a closed container in the laboratory. First, some form of ignition, an electric spark for example, will have to be applied, and when this is done, the glucose molecules can be completely oxidized to carbon dioxide and water with the liberation of heat. The reaction is illustrated as follows:

$$C_6H_{12}O_6 + 6\,O_2 \xrightarrow{\text{spark}} 6\,CO_2 + 6\,H_2O + \text{heat.}$$

The kinetic energy (p. 38) of this reaction is heat which was derived from the potential energy present in the glucose molecule. The breakdown of the complex glucose molecule to the smaller carbon-dioxide and oxygen molecules in the reaction results in the sudden release of heat energy. A similar response would occur, of course, if a handfull of glucose were tossed into an open flame. There are several obvious reasons why such a rigorous reaction is impractical in living systems. Two examples of the inadequacy of this reaction for the cell's purpose are that the release of any large amounts of heat would cook the protoplasm and that heat is lost rapidly from cells to their surroundings and would not be available for vital processes.

High-energy phosphate

Living systems, however, have the ability to "oxidize" glucose in a stepwise fashion with the liberation of small "packets" of energy. An analogy might be that instead of lighting a cigarette with a burning log, one could cut the log into thousands of matches and then use only a small match as a light. Actually, although we are using glucose as our illustration, all carbohydrates, fats, and proteins, when they are utilized for energy, produce *intermediate* products which enter into a common combustion pathway in the cell. This metabolic system has been determined with great exactness and is named the *Krebs cycle*, after Hans A. Krebs who was primarily responsible for its characterization. A more exact chemical designation for this cycle is the *tricarboxylic acid* cycle. In the Krebs cycle, a series of enzymes transforms the intermediate products stepwise and, during the process, "packets" of energy in the form of a high-energy phosphate molecule—*adenosinetriphosphate* or ATP—are produced. It is important to note that the production of ATP by way of the Krebs cycle is a universal phenomenon occurring in both plant and animal cells. It is present in the cells of both microscopic animals and plants and large animals and plants. The molecule of ATP is composed, in part, of two previous acquaintances of ours: the purine *adenine* and the sugar *ribose*. In addition it contains a chain of three phosphates. The third phosphate in the chain has a "high-energy" bond and is written symbolically as $\sim$ P. The freeing of this $\sim$ P from ATP to supply energy results in the formation of *adenosinediphosphate*, ADP. This latter substance is called an acceptor because it is available in the cell to accept additional $\sim$ P to produce a new supply of ATP. Thus we have

$$\text{ATP} \underset{-\sim P}{\overset{+\sim P}{\rightleftharpoons}} \text{ADP.}$$

Two highly significant facts can be ascertained about the energy release which results in the utilization of glucose in the cell. The first fact involves a comparison of the burning of glucose in the laboratory with the utilization of glucose in the cell. When a mole° of glucose is completely burned (oxybiotically) in the laboratory, 690,000 calories† of energy are released. The formation of $\sim$ P packets in the Krebs cycle produces 380,000 calories. Protoplasm, therefore, can be said to be about 55 per cent efficient [(380,000/690,000) $\times$ 100] in its energy utilization. This is excellent efficiency! A second interesting comparison can be made for oxybiotic *vs.* anoxybiotic respiration. We observed that the oxidative utilization of a mole of glucose results in the production

° The weight of a substance in grams, equal numerically to its molecular weight.
† The amount of heat necessary to raise one gram of water through 1° C, from 14.5 to 15.5° C.

of 380,000 calories of energy, but, in contrast, the utilization of a mole of glucose anoxybiotically produces only 20,000 calories. Anoxybiotic respiration, therefore, is only approximately five per cent as efficient [(20,000/380,000) × 100] for energy utilization as is oxybiotic respiration.

The work of the cell

We suggested earlier that the energy requirements of organisms are extremely varied. Work must be done when macromolecules are synthesized or are fragmented into their respective monomers. This can be designated as *chemical work*. The movement of materials through the plasma membrane into or out of cells rarely is passive and usually requires active transport. Such energy expenditures can be called *osmotic work*. The movement of cilia and flagella, as well as the contraction of muscle fibrils, represents the utilization of energy for *mechanical work*. The transmission of impulses by neurofibrils is an electrical phenomenon. Finally, there are even rather unique energy expenditures such as *bioluminescence,* or "living light," in some bacteria, protozoans, and the well-known fireflies. The *electrical shock* produced by the electric eel is another unusual energy expression. The very diversity of these energy expenditures is an indication of the versatility of the biochemical reactions which occur constantly. It seems incredible that a microscopic chemical laboratory as tiny as a cell can perform such elaborate tasks and usually at speeds measured in thousandths of a second. One only needs to recall the time spent and the equipment needed to complete a simple chemical experiment in a chemistry laboratory to appreciate the magnitude of the work in the protoplasmic laboratory.

Site of Energy Transformations

The mitochondria

It was apparent when the cell theory was formulated that it would be advantageous if chemical events could be associated with specific cell organelles. Such associations, however, have been difficult to discover. The plasma membrane obviously is involved in osmotic work, but it is not readily apparent what organelle, or organelles, make available the energy needed for chemical, electrical, and mechanical work. There were strong suspicions that among the most important structures in the cytoplasm concerned with cell activities are the mitochondria, but the evidence was entirely circumstantial. We can observe mitochondria in aggregations in regions of high activity in the cell. Sometimes the mitochondria appear in clumps adjacent to the nucleus and at other times, or in other cells, they are in the region where secretory products are being manufactured. Muscle cells have high energy requirements, and mitochondria are very numerous and often greatly enlarged in muscle cells

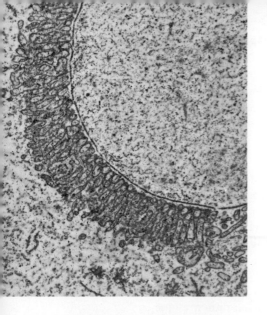

Figure 3.7. Clumping of mitochondria. This unusual electron microscope photograph shows the "clumping" of mitochondria at one side of the nucleus. The mitochondria are elongated and appear to be "standing on end." A small area of cytoplasm between the mitochondria and the nucleus can be clearly seen. This is a picture of a developing sperm cell of a Toadbug. (Courtesy Fernandus Payne.)

where they are interspersed among the muscle fibrils. Finally, in cells which possess cilia or flagella, the mitochondria are seen to be concentrated near the basal body. The circumstantial evidence is very indicative, and many biologists were willing to accept the idea that mitochondria are involved in the energy transformations in cells. The difficulty was that until recently there has been no satisfactory method for direct measurements of mitochondrial function, and equally disturbing was the fact that mitochondria usually appear under the light microscope to be amorphous dots or rods.

Once again new and improved techniques and the development of electron microscopy provided the assists which were needed to verify the ideas derived from circumstantial evidence. It was discovered that an ordinary kitchen utensil, a Waring blender or Osterizer, will chop up cells without destroying the functional activity of the mitochondria. The cell fragments can be placed in an

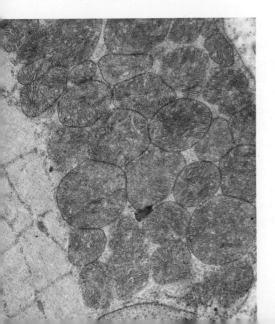

Figure 3.8. Mitochondria in muscle. The large size and great number of mitochondria in muscle are shown in this striking electron micrograph. (Courtesy Russell Barrnett, Yale University.)

ultracentrifuge and subjected to centrifugal forces many thousand times the force of gravity. The cell structures with the greatest mass will separate first and can be removed. Gradual increases in the speed of the centrifuge will remove successively the lighter cell components. This procedure leads to the isolation of nuclei, large and small mitochondria, lysosomes, fragments of the endoplasmic reticulum, and cytoplasmic granules. Our interest, at the moment, is centered on the mitochondria. These organelles, after separation from the cell, can be placed in a nutritive medium to which oxygen and any substance which we wish to study can be supplied. The mitochondria continue to function for long periods of time in a culture medium, and results of the experiments have been most gratifying.

Mitochondria definitely are the organelles in which the energy-transport system is operating. The energy transformations can be followed step by step, the predicted byproducts can be observed, and the function of the mitochondria can be interfered with in many ways, often with predictable results. The observations made with light microscopes gave us no insight into the fine structure of the mitochondria, but the electron microscope shows a mitochondrion as a double-walled sac with a smooth outer membrane and an extensively folded inner membrane. The folds of the inner membrane are named *cristae* (singular: crista). Furthermore, it has been demonstrated that the mitochondria can swell or contract which indicates that a rapid exchange of materials occurs between the cytoplasm and the mitochondria. It also has been observed that mitochondria can be shattered by ultrasonics (sound waves inaudible to the human ear). This rending of the mitochondria separates the external membrane from

Figure 3.9.   Mitochondrion showing cristae.   This electron microscope picture of a mitochondrion demonstrates clearly the relationship of the cristae.   A close examination will also disclose the double nature of the membrane of the mitochondrion.   This is a picture of a region of chick testis.

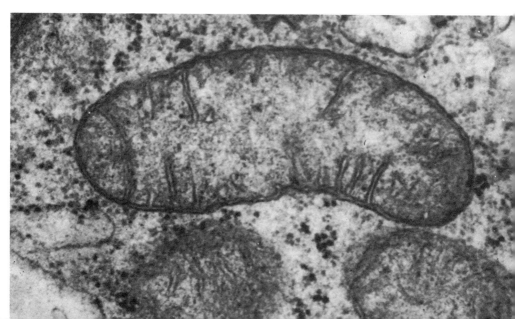

the folded internal membrane and demonstrates that the energy-transport system for the production of ATP is associated with the cristae.   If the ultrasonic treatment is so severe that the cristae are fragmented as well, the energy-transport system is interrupted and reactions do not go to completion.   The hypothesis has been developed, and it appears to be valid, that the stepwise chemical reactions are accomplished by the transport of the energy-producing molecules in a linear fashion along the cristae.   Impressive experiments have also established that a chain of six enzymes exists in each energy transfer sequence, and that each mitochondrion has thousands of these six-enzyme functional units.   These remarkable observations have led biologists and biochemists to speak with great respect of the mitochondria as the "powerhouses of the cell."

REFERENCES

DIXON, MALCOLM, *Enzymes*. Academic Press, New York, 1964.

EPSTEIN, H. T., *Elementary Biophysics*. Addison-Wesley Publishing Co., Reading, 1963.

FLORKIN, MARCEL, *Comparative Biochemistry*. Academic Press, New York, 1962.

GREEN, DAVID E., "The Mitochondrion," *Scientific American, 210*, January 1964, pp. 63–78.

HARRISON, KENNETH, *A Guide-Book to Biochemistry*. University Press, Cambridge, 1960.

HORNE, R. W., "The Structure of Viruses," *Scientific American, 208*, January 1963, pp. 48–69.

KARLSON, P., *Introduction to Modern Biochemistry*. Academic Press, New York, 1963.

LOCKE, MICHAEL (ed.), *Cytodifferentiation and Macromolecular Synthesis*. Academic Press, New York, 1963.

McELROY, W. D., and H. H. SELINGER, "Biological Luminescence," *Scientific American, 206*, December 1962, pp. 76–91.

PRESCOTT, DAVID M., *Methods in Cell Physiology*. Academic Press, New York, 1964.

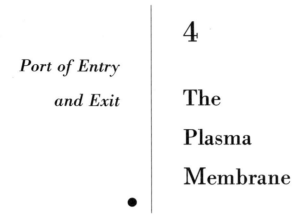

4

Port of Entry

and Exit

The

Plasma

Membrane

•

One problem of animal life is to maintain inside the organism just the proper amount of water—not too much, not too little.—Prosser, 1950

The continued existence of protoplasm depends on its ability to maintain the proper physical and chemical relationships between its own composition and the alterations which are continuously taking place in the medium in which it lives. The surface of the protoplasm is constantly bombarded from without by excess water and salt molecules, by nutritive materials, by oxygen, carbon dioxide, and other gases, and by toxic substances. Hundreds of substances are denied admission into the protoplasm, and other hundreds are admitted readily. The protection provided the protoplasm depends almost entirely on the nature of its limiting surface, the ultramicroscopically thin, gelatinous, and very selective *plasma membrane*. The ability of this membrane to control selectively the entrance or exit of materials is an amazing phenomenon. The plasma membrane has been subjected to exhaustive study, by use of techniques ranging from simple, direct observations and the use of models to more elaborate physical and chemical methods. It would be well, however, before we enter into a discussion of the nature of the plasma membrane, to consider some simple facts about the movement of molecules and especially their behavior when confronted by a membrane.

Movement of molecules

Molecules in a group, whether in gas, liquid, or solid state, are in continuous motion. This movement is not obvious in a solid, but it can be demonstrated. It is relatively simple, however, to illustrate molecular movement indirectly in a fluid by observing, under an ordinary microscope, water containing a fine suspension of oil droplets. The water molecules are not visible, of course, but in

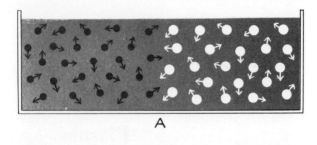

A

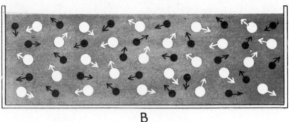

B

Figure 4.1. Diffusion. Molecules are in constant but random motion. When two different types of molecules (a) come in contact, they will slowly become mixed (b) and tend to become distributed evenly. The white and black dots represent two types of molecules; the arrows, direction of movement.

their movement they constantly bump and push both each other and the oil droplets, which are large enough to be seen with ordinary magnification. The visible bits of oil are made to dance about in what is designated as *Brownian movement,* never resting in one place but always being kicked hither and yon as the water molecules bump about continuously. The situation is analogous to the behavior of a group of boys engaged in a volleyball game: the ball is never at rest but is constantly batted from place to place. The movement of molecules also can be illustrated in a different way by carefully placing in contact two groups of molecules of different kinds. For this purpose, the use of two dye solutions of different colors is very effective. The two colors are completely separate at first, but gradually the area in which they are in contact becomes a blend of the colors—that is, a mixture of molecules of both dyes—and this area of mixture gradually spreads as the molecules invade each other's territory, until eventually a complete blending of the colors, or a mixture of molecules, results. This phenomenon, called *diffusion,* will occur even though a membrane separates the two groups of molecules, provided that the membrane is *fully permeable* and allows both types of molecules to pass. Should the membrane allow only one type of molecule to pass—that is, be only *semipermeable*—then a very different situation will result.

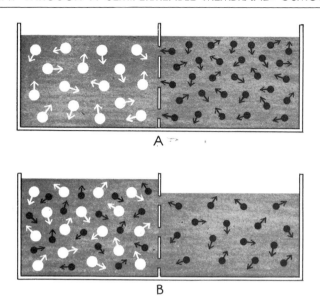

Figure 4.2. Effect of a semipermeable membrane. When molecules of different types are separated by a membrane which will permit the passage of only one type (a), an unequal distribution of molecules follows (b). A greater number of molecules, therefore, will accumulate on one side of the membrane.

Movement through a semipermeable membrane: osmosis

The behavior of a *semipermeable membrane* is much like that of a head waiter in a swank club who opens the door to selected persons but bars the entrance of others. One type of molecule in its random movement strikes the semipermeable membrane and is rebuffed, whereas a second type of molecule is able to pass readily *in either direction*. In the latter case, equal numbers of the favored molecules will be found on each side of the membrane after a period of time, but all the rebuffed molecules will be on the original side. The steps in the entire process can be shown diagrammatically, and we note that a very significant thing will happen: more material will be found on one side of the membrane than on the other.

If we separate the two groups of molecules by a semipermeable membrane but place them in a container which is open at the top, the height of the column of molecules will be different on the two sides of the membrane. If, in addition, we insert a piston above the column that contains the molecules that do not diffuse through the membrane, we observe that the molecules entering from the opposite column accumulate, and the piston is raised gradually. There is, therefore, a definite pressure exerted against the piston, and this can be measured in a

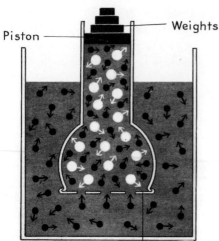

Figure 4.3. Osmotic pressure. The accumulation of molecules on one side of a semipermeable membrane as a result of selective action will create a pressure (osmotic pressure).

crude fashion merely by placing weights on the piston until its rise is prevented (Figure 4.3). The movement of materials through a semipermeable membrane is called *osmosis,* and the pressure necessary to prevent this movement—for example, the weight which will prevent the rise of the piston—is spoken of as the *osmotic pressure.*

Finally, an additional fact should be emphasized, which is readily illustrated by the diagrams: the movement of the molecules in diffusion and osmosis is from *greater to lesser concentration.* When the concentration of the molecules is uniform throughout a mixture, or is equal on the two sides of the semipermeable membrane, movement does *not* cease, but the number of molecules going in opposite directions is equalized, and an apparently static condition exists. When this condition has developed, the system is said to be in *osmotic balance.* A complete definition of osmosis, therefore, should be: *the movement of molecules from greater to lesser concentrations through a semipermeable membrane.*

Let us now imagine that the molecules which do not penetrate the semipermeable membrane are completely surrounded by the membrane, but that diffusible water molecules are outside this sac. The water molecules will enter the closed sac, which will slowly increase in volume. If the membrane is strong enough it will stretch and not tear; but a very strong membrane is required to withstand the pressure which develops if many diffusible molecules are present. A sac with a weak wall will rupture under these conditions. Plant cells, for example, normally may withstand osmotic pressures as high as 10 atmospheres, the equivalent of nearly 150 pounds of pressure per square inch at sea level. This intracellular pressure is called *turgor pressure.* A simple illustration which can demonstrate that the plasma membrane is semipermeable is based on the model described above. A microscopic animal, such as a paramecium, when placed in distilled water for a considerable period of time may swell and explode; the human red blood cell will behave in a similar fashion (Figure 4.4).   The same technique can also be used to illustrate that molecules are moving out of the protoplasm.   A paramecium or a blood cell placed in a concentrated salt solution will have relatively more water molecules diffusing out of the protoplasm than are entering, and the animal or the blood cell will gradually shrivel.

The plasma membrane as a semipermeable barrier

Biologists realized many years ago that the selectively permeable nature of the plasma membrane could not be explained merely by the movement of materials by diffusion from greater to lesser concentration.   There are some molecules, for example, which will enter the cell readily even though they are larger than the estimated sizes of the "pores" in the plasma membrane.   Conversely, ions or even molecules of approximately the same size will be transferred at different rates.   Sodium ions usually pass slowly through the plasma membrane whereas potassium ions enter the cell with ease.   The potassium ions actually can enter cells *against* a concentration gradient—that is, the ions will move from a region of low concentration to one of high concentration.   Some molecules may enter the cell on one side while the same type of molecules are being eliminated on the opposite side of the cell.   This phenomenon is common in gland cells.   The conclusion was reached from these and other observations that the plasma membrane is not a passive structure but an active one, and the term

Figure 4.4.   Cells and osmosis.   Normal red blood cells (A) placed in distilled water will swell and burst (B); placed in strong salt solution, the cells will lose water and will shrivel (C).

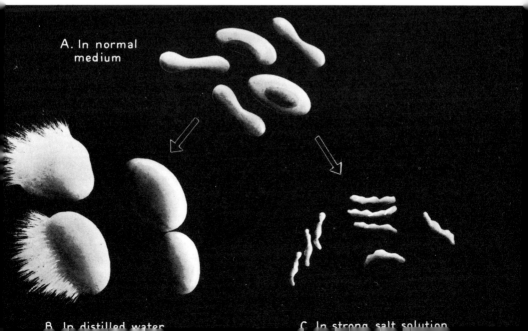

A. In normal medium

B. In distilled water   C. In strong salt solution

active transport was thus applied to the selective action of the plasma membrane for those cases which can not be explained by diffusion. Active transport requires the expenditure of energy and presents another aspect of the functional complexity of the plasma membrane.

Using the excellent resolving power of the electron microscope, cytologists have been able to observe directly many features of the plasma membrane. Our knowledge of the selective action has also been augmented because there is good, although indirect, chemical evidence to indicate that the plasma membrane is composed of proteins and phospholipids. Although the exact arrangement of these molecules is unknown, observations made with electron microscopes show that the plasma membrane has an amazingly uniform appearance in a diverse assortment of cells. It is so uniform that it is frequently designated as a *unit membrane*. The thickness of the membrane is usually about 75Å°, and there is excellent support for the idea that the unit membrane has a 35-Å thick layer of phospholipids which is sandwiched between inner and outer layers of proteins each of which is roughly 20 Å in thickness.

The fact that protein layers can have either positive or negative charges (p. 30) certainly is an important factor in regulating the passage of ions through the unit membrane. The phospholipid layer must also contribute to the solubility of lipid molecules in the unit membrane and to their subsequent entrance into or out of the cell. Studies made with the electron microscope have contributed other information concerning the structure of the plasma membrane because we can observe that typically the membrane is not stretched smoothly over the cell but often is very irregular in its configuration. The formation of *vesicles* and the presence of minute extensions of the membrane, the *microvilli*,

°Å = angstrom unit, 0.0001 μ.

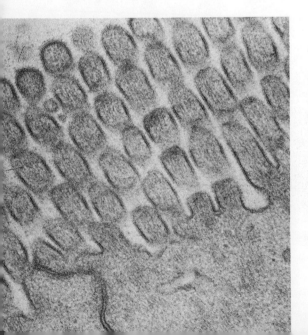

Figure 4.5. Striated border of plasma membrane and its "unit membrane" character. This photograph of a cell from the small intestine of the rat shows two features of the plasma membrane. The cell membrane obviously does not have the smooth surface it has when viewed by the light microscope. The fingerlike projections are so numerous, they are called a *striated border*. At many of the projections' edges and at the lower left of the figure, the unit nature of the plasma membrane is clearly visible. (Courtesy Russell Barrnett, Yale University.)

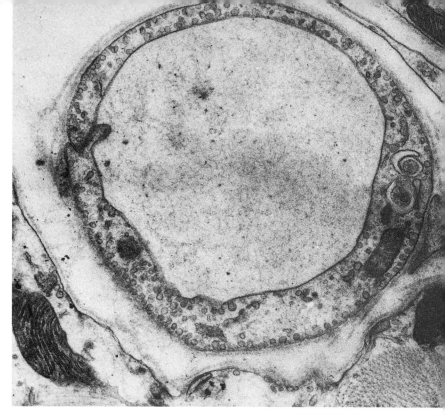

Figure 4.6. Pinocytotic vesicles show beautifully in these cells which comprise the walls of a capillary in a skeletal muscle. Their presence in these cells suggest their role in fluid transport. (Courtesy Russell Barrnett, Yale University.)

were discussed earlier. These structures obviously are instrumental in the more efficient acquisition or elimination of molecules by cells. The process of *pinocytosis* involves the formation of very small invaginations (vesicles) at the surface which engulf water and even organic molecules. It appears that glucose can be taken into the cell readily by pinocytosis, especially if small amounts of proteins also are present. The process can also work in the reverse direction. Small vesicles containing secretory products may open through the surface of the unit membrane to discharge their contents from the cell. The microvilli increase the surface area of the plasma membrane immensely, thereby enhancing the exchange of molecules.

The *endoplasmic reticulum* plays a very critical role in exchange processes and in the movement of materials through the cytoplasm. We noted in the discussion of the ultrastructure of cells that this network has external openings through the plasma membrane and that internally it also penetrates the outer of the two nuclear membranes. The endoplasmic reticulum, therefore, provides a route for the delivery of materials to both the cytoplasm and the nucleus. The endoplasmic reticulum also is available for reverse passage. Materials can be transferred from the interior of the cell to the outside. Since the endoplasmic

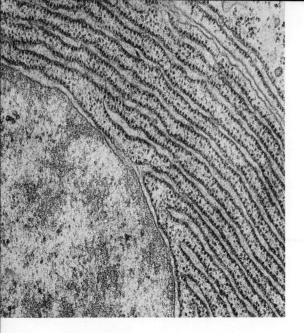

Figure 4.7. Endoplasmic reticulum and its connection with nuclear envelope. This electron micrograph illustrates the nature of the rough endoplasmic reticulum (RER). It also demonstrates beautifully, in the center of the photograph, a connection of the endoplasmic reticulum with the membrane of the nucleus. This is a cell of a planarian. (Courtesy Russell Barrnett, Yale University.)

reticulum traverses the entire cell, it is possible for molecules to enter on one side of the cell, follow the tortuous channels of the reticulum to the opposite pole of the cell, and be discharged. It has been suggested that the endoplasmic reticulum of some cells is not a static system of channels similar to the plumbing in a house but actually may be changing constantly. An infolding of the plasma membrane may occur on one side of the cell to form the endoplasmic reticulum while simultaneously the endoplasmic reticulum is becoming part of the unit membrane on the opposite side. The reticulum would seem to "flow" through the cytoplasm. Materials which had been engulfed at the surface of the plasma membrane might be carried across the cell as though they were on a conveyor belt. This process has been designated *membrane flow*.

Figure 4.8. Sol–gel state of the plasma membrane. The formation of a normal plasma membrane (a) is dependent on the presence of calcium. When calcium is absent or deficient, a membrane will not form (b).

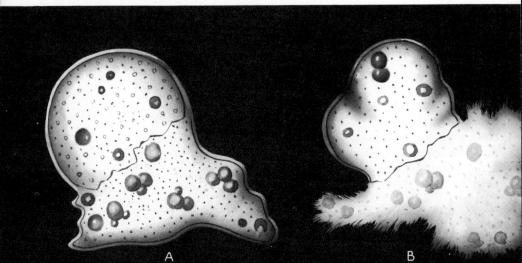

A   B

REFERENCES

BARNES, T. C., *Textbook of General Physiology*. P. Blakiston's Son and Company, Philadelphia, 1937.

BONNER, JAMES, and ARTHUR W. GALSTON, *Principles of Plant Physiology*. W. H. Freeman and Company, San Francisco, 1952.

GERARD, R. W., *Unresting Cells*. Harper and Brothers, New York, 1949.

HEILBRUNN, L. V., *An Outline of General Physiology*. W. B. Saunders Company, Philadelphia, 1950.

KROGH, AUGUST, *Osmotic Regulation in Aquatic Animals*. Cambridge University Press, London, 1939.

LOCKE, MICHAEL (ed.), *Cellular Membranes in Development*. Academic Press, New York, 1964.

MITCHELL, P. H., *A Textbook of General Physiology*. McGraw-Hill Book Company, New York, 1948.

PROSSER, C. LADD (ed.), *Comparative Animal Physiology*. W. B. Saunders Company, Philadelphia, 1950.

ROBERTSON, J. DAVID, "Membrane of the Living Cell," *Scientific American*, 206, April 1962, pp. 64–83.

SCHMIDT-NIELSON, KNUT, *Animal Physiology*. Prentice-Hall, Englewood Cliffs, 1960.

The Ulta-Structure of Mammalian Cell Membranes. A Symposium on the Cell Membrane. Michigan Academy of Science, University of Michigan Press, Medical Bulletin 25, Ann Arbor, 1959.

5

Acellular

Organisms

Phylum

Protozoa

●

When Alice stepped through the looking glass she encountered nothing more marvelous than the universe of protozoa that is revealed to us when we view through the microscope a bit of scum from the surface of a pond.—Hegner, Big Fleas Have Little Fleas, 1938

We remarked previously that the protoplasmic mass of an organism may be partitioned into structural and functional units called *cells*. The term *cell* was coined for these units in 1665 by the Englishman, Robert Hooke, who observed the partitions, *cell walls*, in slices of cork. The primordial life which first appeared on earth was unquestionably a blob of protoplasm without subdividing walls. The cellular forms of life appeared at a later date. The animals in existence today which probably are most like the primordial forms are the Protozoa, meaning "first animals." The majority of these organisms are microscopic, although some may form shells which are several inches in diameter. Frequently these organisms are spoken of as "simple one-celled animals." We shall observe that they definitely are not simple, and today many zoologists prefer to consider them as organisms which do not have the body subdivided into cells—therefore, that they are noncellular, or *acellular*. There are several reasons for this conclusion: *first*, they are complete organisms; *second*, they are structurally complex since many of them possess structures for contraction, for locomotion, for nervous conduction, or for attack and defense, and some even have elaborate sensory devices; *third*, reproductive nuclei, comparable with those in manycelled organisms, are formed in most protozoa; and *fourth*, immature stages and embryonic development occur in several members of the Protozoa. These special structures which are present in protozoans are frequently spoken of as *organelles*, "little organs."

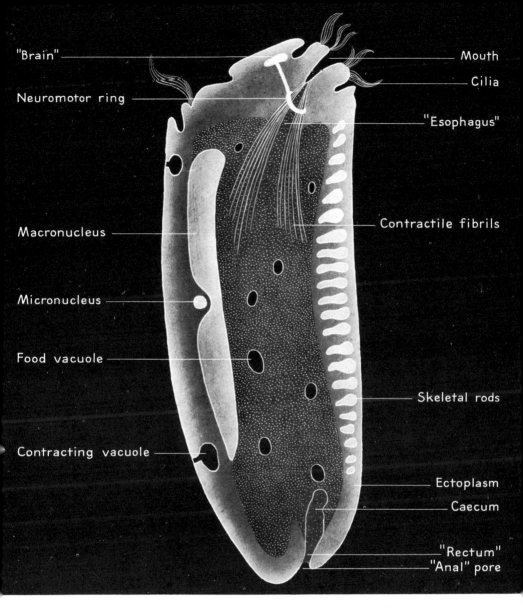

Figure 5.1. The fact that protozoans are not simple animals is well illustrated by Diplodinium. The complexity of its structure exceeds that found in many animals composed of thousands of cells.

The Protozoa

The biologists first had their attention directed to the Protozoa in the middle of the seventeenth century by a crusty, self-educated Dutchman, Antony van Leeuwenhoek. An account of Leeuwenhoek's discoveries reads like the story of an exploration into a new-found universe. He had an obsession for examining objects of strangely diverse nature under his homemade microscopes, of which he possessed nearly 300.   Leeuwenhoek examined pepper with the hope that he could determine what made it hot, gunpowder to discover what caused it to explode, the scum, or "bloom," on ponds to see of what it was composed, and scrapings from his own teeth, as well as those of his daughter and his friends, to study the nature of the film which was present.   At one time or another, he examined human, frog, and fish blood, male reproductive cells, fecal material, fleas, and the contents of the intestines of frogs.   Although he was unable to analyze either the hotness of pepper or the explosive character of gunpower, he made the amazing discovery that if he allowed rain water to stand on pepper grains for a short times this "pepper water" would contain millions of what he called "little animals."

Equally intriguing to Leeuwenhoek was the fact that similar little animals were present in teeth scrapings, fecal matter, pond scum, and in the intestines of the animals he examined.   Their numbers, small size, and constant activity amazed him.   He devised methods for calculating their number in a drop of water and discovered that thousands could live in such a miniature universe. Leeuwenhoek also invented a method for estimating the size of these organisms which, when compared with modern techniques, seems extremely crude, but which in his hands gave remarkably accurate measurements.   He was misled by the activity of the organisms and referred to all of them as "little animals." We know now that many of the forms he saw were bacteria or other plants. His observations were diverse and haphazard, but he wrote accurate descriptions, and because of this fact he is credited with being the first to discover the bacteria and many of the Protozoa.

Leeuwenhoek reported his observations only in personal communications and letters.   Many of the letters were sent to the Royal Society in England,

Figure 5.2.   A model of the simple magnifying lens used by Leeuwenhoek is shown in (b).   This was often called a "flea glass."   The picture in (a) is of a flea taken through a lens with the same magnification (270X) as Leeuwenhoek's instrument and illustrates its excellence.   (Courtesy Bosch and Lomb Optical Company.)

(a)   **(b)**

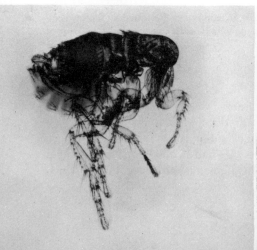
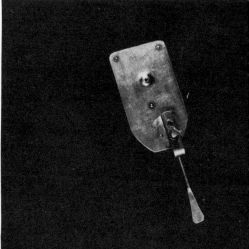

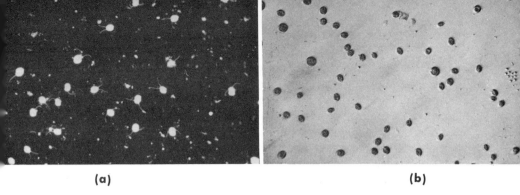

(a)   (b)

Figure 5.3. Dark field and oblique lighting. It is often possible to see detail in microscopic animals by use of different lighting techniques. For example, dark field illumination (a) can be used advantageously even by beginning students. In (b) we have the usual appearance in transmitted light. (Copyright by General Biological Supply House, Inc., Chicago.)

where his astounding discoveries aroused tremendous interest. There were, however, very few microscopes in existence, and those had low magnifying power. Partially as a result of this fact, the initial interest was not sustained, and more than a century elapsed before the combination of better microscopes and renewed interest led to significant studies of protozoans. One of the first workers to advance our knowledge of the acellular organisms was the German investigator, Christian Ehrenberg.

Protozoa are complex

In 1838 Ehrenberg published the results of his investigations of hay and grass infusions in a treatise entitled *The Infusorian Animals as Complete Organisms*. The idea that these tiny specks of living matter were as complex and complete in their functions as man or any other animal was a startling concept. Ehrenberg imagined that he could see many "stomachs," which he thought were part of a complicated alimentary canal in the animals. Some naturalists of his time thought that the Infusoria were embryonic stages of worms and, as a result, the rightful place of Leeuwenhoek's little animals in the animal kingdom was uncertain. Ehrenberg's work was beautifully illustrated, and other investigators were stimulated to attempt to verify or disprove his observations, which led to a controversy that continued for years. Such a controversy can be resolved easily today in beginning laboratory exercises, because of the simple fact that the present-day microscopes available to most students are far better than those used by the investigators of Ehrenberg's time.

Ehrenberg had been so impressed with the nutrition of the Infusoria that he concluded the animals possessed complex permanent structures which enabled them to carry on their vital functions. Others did not believe that the structures were either complex or permanent, and the leader among the dissenters was the Frenchman, Félix Dujardin. In 1835 and in 1841, he published accounts of his observations on protozoans other than those studied by Ehrenberg, and on which Dujardin himself had made his careful studies of the living material, to which he applied the term *sarcode*.   Dujardin was convinced that the protozoans had only transitory structures, which appeared and subsequently disappeared and indicated the great adaptability of the sarcode.   We now know that some of Ehrenberg's observations and conclusions were erroneous, and that the broad concepts of Dujardin were more nearly correct.   An important difficulty in the way of clarifying the controversy was the fact that although both men were studying protozoans, they were examining different organisms included in that group.   Ehrenberg examined the Infusoria, which have certain permanent structures, while Dujardin investigated a group, later called the Sarcodina, which have few permanent structures.   The knowledge of the actual structure of these tiny units of living matter now contributes significantly to an understanding of important biological principles and problems.

The numbers of protozoans

The Protozoa are one of the most adaptable groups in the animal kingdom. Only one other major division—that represented by the insects, spiders, and their relatives—approaches them in variety of habitat, modification of basic structures, or functional adaptation.   Truly astronomical numbers of protozoans live in the sea and in fresh water, they are numerous in the soil, and they live as guests or parasites in other animals and plants.   It has been estimated that a column of water four inches in diameter and reaching to the average depth of the Atlantic ocean would contain 576,000,000,000 protozoa, that the waters of the Mediterranean average 4,000,000 protozoa per quart, and that even one pound of some soils may contain over 4,000,000 protozoans.   The snow on mountain peaks and the waters of oceans sometimes become blood-red from the growth of protozoans that contain red pigment.   Other protozoans cause such serious diseases as dysentery, malaria, and African sleeping sickness, and many of them also live as guests or associates in man and other organisms.   Termites would starve were it not for the friendly protozoans which swarm in their intestines and break down, or digest, the cellulose upon which the termites exist.

Figure 5.4.   The development of shells is characteristic of many protozoans, as these animals illustrate.   (a) Globigerina; (b) Nummulites; (c) Radiolaria.   [(a), (c) courtesy American Museum of Natural History; (b) Courtesy Yale University, Peabody Museum of Natural History.]

(a)   **(b)**   **(c)**

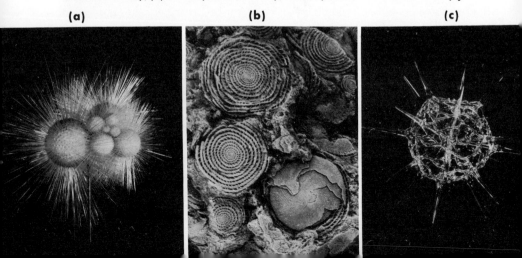

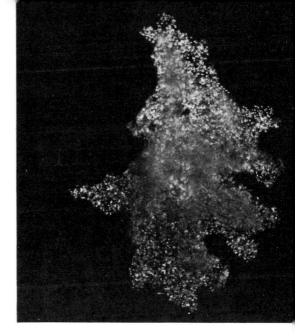

Figure 5.5. Amoeba proteus is used to illustrate features common to all acellular organisms. (Courtesy American Museum of Natural History.)

Protozoa also may be a minor annoyance to mankind. *Uroglena* imparts a fishy taste to water, as does also *Dinobryon*. Do not accuse your water commissioner of killing the fish in the city reservoir when the water in late summer becomes obnoxious; blame *Uroglena* for the bad taste. Still another protozoan, *Synura*, imparts a bitter taste to water and is so potent that it can be detected in dilutions of one part in 25,000,000 parts of water.

Some Protozoa are responsible for the formation of large parts of the earth's crust; compressed shells of globigerinans and related forms in prehistoric times became the chalk cliffs of Dover, the Indiana limestones, and certain flints. The work these tiny animals do to produce shell to make the flint is prodigious; one ton of sea water must be filtered to secure silicon for one ounce of shell.

The development of better techniques for the microscopic study of protozoans has made it possible for us to study their digestion, calculate their oxygen consumption, analyze their excretory products, observe the interactions between them and their environment, and investigate important problems of inheritance. Even aging and death are being scrutinized in the protozoa, and the findings are being applied to other animals.

Representative protozoans

If we attempted to investigate even a small fraction of the different kinds of protozoans in the world, we should soon find ourselves submerged in a multitude of major and minor differences in both structural and functional adaptations. Fortunately, we can select a few representative types for study and from them derive certain generalizations which are applicable to all. We can, as a matter of fact, apply this technique of the study of *type forms* to other major groups of animals with the same success. There is actually no better place to begin our study than with the very organisms which attracted the attention of

Dujardin and Ehrenberg. *Amoeba proteus* is an excellent example of the group with which the former worked, and *Paramecium caudatum* is representative of Ehrenberg's infusorians.

Amoeba Proteus—Class Sarcodina*

Larger specimens of *Amoeba proteus*, when extended, may reach as much as 1000 microns (1 millimeter) in length.† Since these animals are relatively sluggish, seldom moving at a speed in excess of two or three microns per second, they are especially favorable for study by those who are beginning to use a microscope.

Body form

Amoebae do not have a definite body form. The protoplasm is often described as being "naked" because no stiff external covering, or pellicle, is secreted about the organism. The outermost boundary is the *plasma membrane*, which is continuous with a definite nongranular, jellylike region, the *ectoplasm* ("outer fluid"). The bulk of the organism is composed of the *endoplasm* ("inner fluid"), within which many structures, most importantly the *nucleus*, are to be found. The endoplasm, in addition to the nucleus, contains *food vacuoles*, a *contracting vacuole*, various *granules*, and *crystals*.

The absence of a definite body form in *Amoeba proteus* is not only a reflection of the lack of an outer pellicle but is a result also of the method of locomotion used by these animals. When an amoeba moves, it may extend a projection, a *pseudopodium* ("false foot"), at any point on the body, and the endoplasm from other parts of the body flows into this extended pseudopodium. The most reasonable explanation of the formation of these projections is based on variations in the sol and gel state of the protoplasm. The gelatinated ectoplasm liquefies as a result of local chemical action to a sol state at the point of formation of the pseudopodium; the endoplasm flows through this weakened surface, and as it does so, the surface gelatinizes to form a growing tube of ectoplasm. Elsewhere in the body, ectoplasm is converted into endoplasm, and the animal literally flows into its foot. Pseudopodia may be blunt, pointed, or branched; the type of pseudopodium so formed is typical and can be used to classify different amoebae.

Nutrition

Amoebae do not manufacture their food but feed entirely on other organisms, a type of nutrition which we have designated as *holozoic*. They eat other proto-

---

* The proper naming of animals will be discussed in Chapter 6, Cataloguing Animals: Classification.
† Scientists use the metric system of measurement. It is convenient because all units are divisible by ten. A millimeter is about 1/25 of an inch in length; a micron is 1/1000 of a millimeter, and therefore, roughly 1/25000 of an inch.

zoans, tiny green plants, bacteria, and even small many-celled animals. Although sluggish and slow-moving, amoebae are nevertheless able to capture fast-moving protozoans or bacteria. The capture and engulfing of food is made possible by the pseudopodia. A pseudopodium immobilizes the object to be eaten by simultaneously flowing over and around it to form a *food cup*. Careful observation shows that the walls of the food cup are formed in the ectoplasm from plasma membrane. The food cup is freed from the ectoplasm and "circulates" in the endoplasm as a *food vacuole*. The process of taking food material into the protoplasm via the food vacuole is known as *ingestion*.

Food within a food vacuole cannot be used until it is *digested*, because the particles are too large and complex to penetrate the wall of the food vacuole. The particles must be split into simpler compounds by digestion. Digestion is accomplished by special organic catalysts, the *digestive enzymes*. These enzymes speed up the process of breaking down complex food materials into the simpler molecules which can pass through the wall of the food vacuole into protoplasm. The simpler molecules will be recombined in the protoplasm, with the aid of other enzymes, into complex foods. Carbohydrates are converted by digestion into *simple sugars*, such as glucose; fats into *fatty acids* and *glycerol*; and proteins into *amino acids*. Although the complete story of digestion in *Amoeba proteus* is not known, it is clear that proteins and fats are digested. Protozoans other than amoebae have been shown to digest carbohydrates, and it is probable that amoebae also do so. Undigested food material is *egested* at any point on the surface of the amoeba, the food vacuole simply breaking through the body surface. The wall of the vacuole once again becomes part of the surface ectoplasm.

Respiration

Amoeba proteus is *oxybiotic*—that is, uses oxygen for metabolic activities. Amoebae may survive, however, for a considerable period of time without

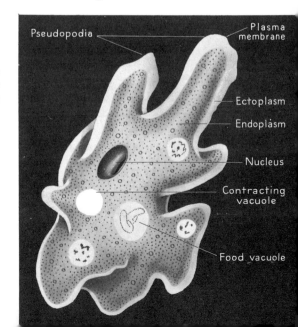

Figure 5.6. Amoeba proteus. This drawing illustrates that even the supposedly "simple amoeba" is a structurally complex animal.

Pseudopodia

Plasma membrane

Ectoplasm

Endoplasm

Nucleus

Contracting vacuole

Food vacuole

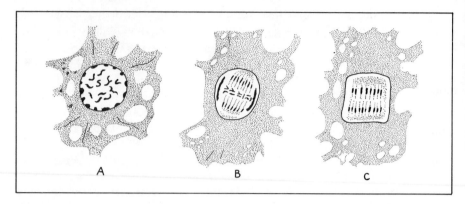

Figure 5.7. Mitosis in a heliozoan.   Successive stages in the mitosis of a close relative of Amoeba.   Although the nuclear membrane remains intact, as in Amoeba, chromosomes appear and are distributed equally to the new individuals.

oxygen.   Oxygen, dissolved in the water in which the amoeba moves, enters the protoplasm by diffusion through the plasma membrane.   It is known that in other animals ample supplies of oxygen can be supplied by diffusion if the area of the protoplasm concerned is not more than one millimeter distant from the surface.   Amoebae obviously have a considerable margin of safety as long as oxygen is present in the external environment.   If the supply of oxygen is depleted, the amoeba must move to another region where ample oxygen is present, but if it cannot do so, death will result after a short lapse of time.   When oxygen enters the protoplasm, it combines with carbohydrates, fats, and proteins, and probably no free oxygen is allowed to remain.   Carbon dioxide is eliminated from the protoplasm by diffusion, provided the concentration in the external environment is lower than that in the protoplasm.   This will be considered in detail later.

Excretion

We noted previously that all organisms must excrete carbon dioxide, water, and various nitrogenous compounds.   These substances, therefore, must be excreted by *Amoeba proteus.*   Carbon dioxide is eliminated from the protoplasm by diffusion as part of the respiratory process, but the other two excretory products present special problems.   The regulation of the water content of an amoeba is important for the maintenance of the proper physical state of the protoplasm.   Water accumulates in amoebae in three ways: *first* as a result of the oxidation of foods, *second,* as a result of water taken in with the food cup, and *third,* by diffusion of water through the plasma membrane from the external environment.   The structure primarily responsible for the elimination of the excess water is the *contractile vacuole.*   This structure is one of the most obvious features of the living amoeba because it can be observed to increase slowly in size and suddenly collapse in a manner which, as the action is repeated, simulates pulsation. The increase in size is due to the accumulation of water; the collapse is associated with the discharge of water to the exterior. Many marine protozoans lack a contractile vacuole, and even fresh-water amoebae, when placed in sea water, can be observed to have a much slower pulsation rate of the contractile vacuole. This is due in part to the fact that the relative number of water molecules is less in sea water than in fresh water. A more favorable differential is present between the water molecules in the protoplasm and the water molecules in the sea, and a marine amoeba, therefore, is able to excrete water by diffusion through the plasma membrane. The pumping action of the contractile vacuole is not needed.

Undoubtedly, small amounts of nitrogenous waste compounds are excreted *in solution* in the water expelled by the contractile vacuole. This has not been shown, however, to be of any great significance for amoebae. Little is known concerning the actual form of the nitrogen compound or compounds excreted. It is probably safe to assume that the chief substance excreted is ammonia, because this is the most common nitrogenous compound excreted by other protozoans. Excretion probably is mostly by *diffusion* through the plasma membrane.

Reproduction

The amoeba regularly reproduces by a process of splitting into approximately two equal parts, a process called *binary fission*. This is *asexual* reproduction, because no special reproductive structures are formed, but it is not a simple

Figure 5.8. Paramecium aurelia. Although less well known to beginning students than P. caudatum, this species has become a valuable animal in laboratory research.

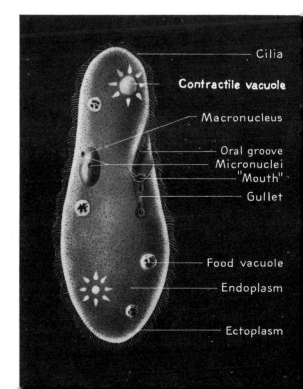

Cilia

Contractile vacuole

Macronucleus

Oral groove
Micronuclei
"Mouth"
Gullet

Food vacuole

Endoplasm

Ectoplasm

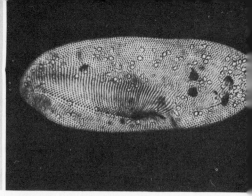

Figure 5.9. Structure of pellicle. These animals, members of the genus Euplotes and of the genus Paramecium, were stained in a special manner to show structure of pellicle and arrangement of cilia. Note especially the concentration of cilia about the oral groove of Euplotes. (Copyright by General Biological Supply House, Inc., Chicago.)

process. The most important feature of this type of reproduction is the series of changes which take place in the *nucleus*. These changes are not as evident in amoebae as in certain other protozoans, but the type of division is spoken of as *mitotic*, and the process as *mitosis*. There is a nuclear reorganization (Figure 5.7), and a definite number of bodies, the *chromosomes*, appear. These chromosomes duplicate themselves, so that the number is doubled, then line up in the middle of the organism and separate, exactly half of the double number going to each end of the animal. The protoplasm and the nucleus constrict and two new individuals are formed. Each animal will have exactly the same number of chromosomes due to this behavior of the chromosomes during mitosis, and the number will be equal to that of the parent amoeba. The new animals, therefore, have similar nuclei. We will give a detailed discussion of mitosis later, because it is a significant process in all organisms. Although nothing has been said thus far concerning the function of the nucleus, you may expect to find that it has an important part to play in heredity because of its complicated changes during reproduction. We should note that if microsurgery is performed on an amoeba and it is cut into two parts, one part containing the nucleus and the other part being without a nucleus, the *non*nucleated part dies in a short time, whereas the nucleated portion will continue to live, grow, and reproduce.

Coordination

The reactions of amoebae are many and varied. Touch, temperature fluctuations, light, vibration, chemicals, and electrical current will stimulate the animals, and the responses may be *positive* or *negative*. Thus, an amoeba will extend pseudopodia toward food particles and will even begin the formation of food cups in the direction of dissolved foods in the water in which it is moving. Most chemicals, bright light, and other strong stimuli will usually elicit an avoiding, or negative, reaction; the amoeba stops, projects a pseudopodium in another direction, and slowly moves away.   Under the conditions of a relatively normal environment, the amoeba will move to a position which is most advantageous.   It reaches the advantageous location, however, as a result of a series of *trial-and-error* adjustments involving both positive and negative responses.   It is noteworthy that when one of these animals is stimulated by a gentle touch, the body may respond at a point distant from the stimulus, showing that transmission of a message occurs.   The ectoplasm apparently is responsible for reception and transmission, since animals in which most of the endoplasm has been removed still respond to stimuli.

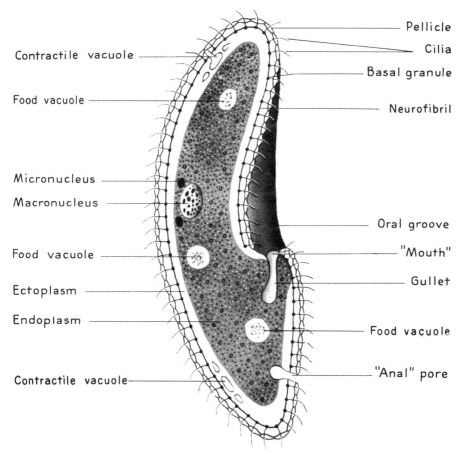

Figure 5.10.   Longitudinal section of a typical paramecium.   The proportions are altered slightly to show the relationship between the cilia and neurofibrils.   Ehrenberg was understandably impressed by the complexity of this animal.

Paramecium Caudatum—Class Ciliata

Body form

The contrast in the appearance of *Paramecium caudatum* and *Amoeba proteus* is apparent immediately. *Paramecium* has a definite shape and is structually among the most complex of the protozoans. There is a definite front, or anterior end. The outermost portion of the ectoplasm forms a tough, flexible layer, the *pellicle*. Two types of nuclei are present: a large *macronucleus* and a small *micronucleus*. One or several of each type of nucleus may be present in different protozoans. Metabolism appears to be controlled by the macronucleus; and the reproductive functions, by the micronucleus. Two contracting vacuoles are present. The surface of the body is covered with tiny protoplasmic processes or outgrowths, the *cilia*, which are used both for locomotion and for feeding. These cilia give the class its name, *Ciliata*. The cilia protrude through slight depressions in the pellicle, and at the base of each cilium there is a *basal granule*. The basal granules are interconnected by fibrils which are often called *neurofibrils*, because messages (*impulses*) are carried from one region of the paramecium to another by these fibrils. Because of this connecting network, the beating of the cilia can be coordinated. A groove, the *oral groove*, runs diagonally across the anterior part of the animal and terminates at its posterior end in a *mouth*. The mouth opens through the pellicle into a *gullet*, at the base of which the *food vacuoles* are formed. Some of the cilia along the oral groove are longer than elsewhere on the body and create a current to sweep food along the groove into the mouth. Very small bodies, the *trichocysts*, are located between the basal granules and may be discharged in the form of "spiked" threads.

Figure 5.11. These are two common protozoans which are often encountered in mixed cultures. The presence of cilia indicates their relationship to Paramecium. (a) Didinium. (b) Stentor. (Copyright by General Biological Supply House, Inc., Chicago.)

(a)   **(b)**

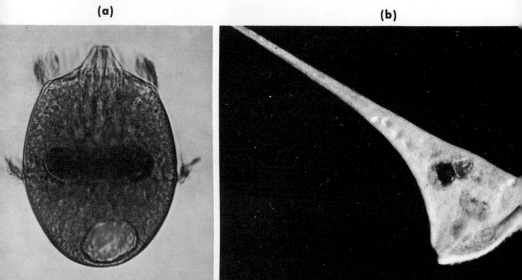

(a)

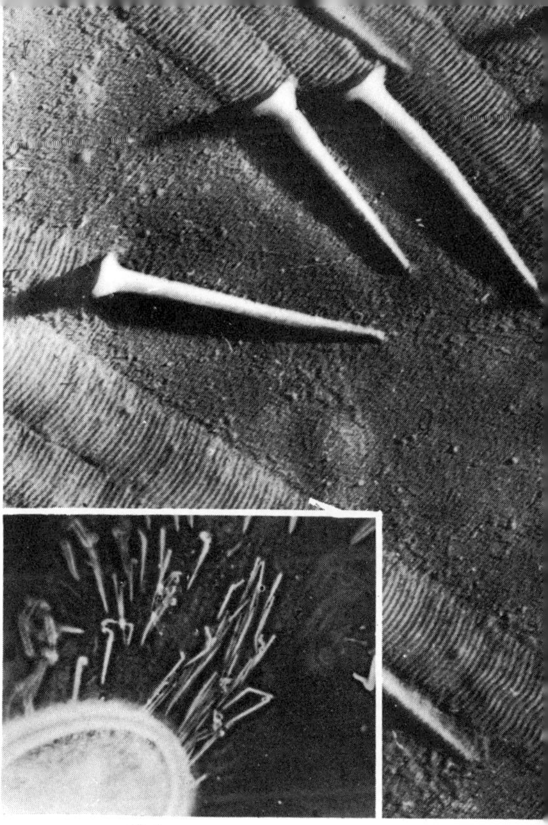

Figure 5.12. The dartlike trichocysts shown in (a) were made by an electron microscope at a magnification of 16,000X. Trichocysts being discharged from the surface of the paramecium are shown in (b). (Courtesy C. E. Hall and M. A. Jackus, Massachusetts Institute of Technology (a); Arthur W. Jones and Will John Cloyd, University of Tennessee (b).)

(b)

Nutrition

Paramecia are primarily holozoic in their food habits, although some food may be taken in the form of organic matter in solution. Bacteria are a primary food source. Ingestion is accomplished by the action of the cilia and the gullet. The food particles are swept along the oral groove by the action of the cilia and —especially in the case of the bacteria—may be rolled into a tight ball by the time they enter the mouth opening. The food vacuoles are released into the endoplasm at the base of the gullet. Protoplasmic streaming carries the food vacuoles in a circuitous route through the endoplasm, during which time digestion occurs. Undigested particles are egested at a definite spot in the surface of the paramecium, and this opening often is referred to as the *anal pore*. Other ciliate protozoans may be carnivorous, even cannibalistic, as is illustrated by the barrel-shaped *Didinium*, which is commonly found in laboratory cultures. The mouth in this animal is terminal and can be greatly distended, so that a didinium can attack, capture, and eventually eat a paramecium originally much larger than itself.

There has been extensive study of the digestive process in *Paramecium* and the details of most of the steps are known. The food vacuole receives some water with the food when it is formed, and additional water is added to the vacuole as it moves through the endoplasm. The food vacuoles in the paramecium follow a rather definite path as they circulate, a fact that led Ehrenberg astray in his observations and caused the logical but mistaken belief that a digestive tract was present. When the food vacuole first forms, the contents are acid because of the presence of hydrochloric acid. The acid undoubtedly aids in killing the organisms which have just been eaten. The contents gradually become alkaline, however, as the vacuole circulates, and it is in this alkaline medium that the digestive enzymes secreted by the endoplasm do most of their work. The acidity or alkalinity of the vacuole can be demonstrated easily in the laboratory by feeding dye materials which change their color when in an acid or an alkaline medium. Enzymes which digest proteins and those which digest carbohydrates have been shown to be present in *Paramecium*, but enzymes for the digestion of fats have not been demonstrated. The fact that oils are present in the protoplasm, and apparently are used, has led to the conclusion, however, that enzymes for fat digestion also must be present.

The function of the trichocysts in the ciliates has been debated. It seems apparent that in the case of aggressive feeders, the trichocysts aid in the capture of food and may even contain a toxic substance which poisons the prey. Paramecia, however, appear to use the trichocysts for *defense:* when attacked by a small didinium, the paramecium may be able to force it away by ejecting a cloud of trichocysts. The paramecia, in addition, use the trichocysts as a means of attachment when feeding, and some authorities think this to be the primary function. The trichocysts undoubtedly should be included when listing accessory nutritive structures.

Respiration

Paramecium, like *Amoeba proteus*, is oxybiotic. Many measurements have been made of the amount of oxygen consumed by paramecia, but there is great variation in the data. This variation will serve to indicate the complexity of an apparently simple biological problem, because some of the factors which influence oxygen consumption are known. First of all, paramecia are very active and may move at a speed 1000 times faster than amoebae—a fact which becomes significant when we stop to consider that the greater the activity, the greater will be the need for oxygen. Secondly, when food has just been eaten, the oxygen consumption will be double or triple that in an unfed animal; conversely, starvation will lower the consumption below normal. In the third place, the age of the paramecia is important. The older animals have slower metabolic processes, and oxygen consumption is less. Finally, the presence of bacteria in a culture medium makes the determination of oxygen difficult because the metabolic activities of the bacteria affect the amount of oxygen in the fluid. Measurements, therefore, should be taken in bacteria-free, carefully balanced culture media, with animals of known age, and with a constant number of animals present. These precautions have been employed in but few experiments. Figures reported for oxygen consumpttion range from

0.00011 to 0.00385 cubic millimeter per hour per animal; the lower figures probably are more nearly correct.

The movement of oxygen into the animals and of carbon dioxide out of the animals is by *diffusion* through the pellicle and the plasma membrane. Although the pellicle probably slows the movement of the gases slightly, it is readily permeable to the gases and does not act as a barrier in any way. The use of oxygen and the formation of carbon dioxide by the protoplasm follow the same rules as those previously discussed under the function of respiration, and undoubtedly is comparable with the situation in *Amoeba proteus*.

Excretion

In *Paramecium caudatum* and the other ciliates, carbon dioxide, water, and nitrogenous compounds must be excreted. The carbon dioxide is eliminated by diffusion through the plasma membrane and pellicle, both of which, as noted, are readily permeable. The bulk of the nitrogenous waste in *Paramecium* is ammonia, which is excreted in the same manner as carbon dioxide, although small amounts may be in solution in the water in the contractile vacuoles. The contractile vacuoles of *Paramecium caudatum* differ from those of *Amoeba proteus* in several respects. There are two vacuoles present in *Paramecium;* these are in the ectoplasm and open to the outside through what appear to be permanent *pores*, which are open only at the time of discharge. Each contracting vacuole has a series of very fine radiating *canals*, which run primarily in the ectoplasm and thus parallel to the surface, but which also project slightly into the endoplasm. These canals drain fluid from the protoplasm into the *vacuolar area*, and it now seems probable that the vacuole is not a permanent structure.

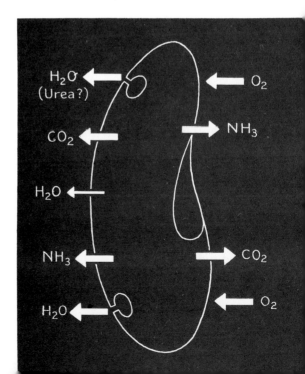

Figure 5.13. Respiration and excretion. The complexity of the functional problems which confront acellular organisms is evident. The chief port of entry and exit for diverse materials is the plasma membrane.

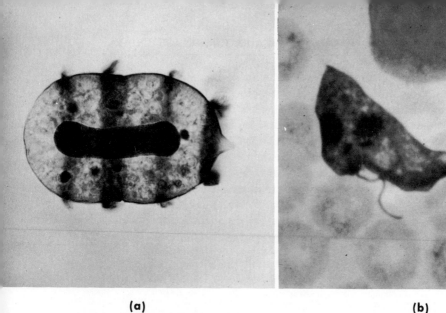

(a)   (b)

Figure 5.14. Division by fission can often be observed in protozoans. (a) The ciliate Didinium has already duplicated its ciliary bands and the macronucleus is already elongated, preparatory to division. (b) The duplication of the nuclei and flagellae can be observed in the flagellate Trypanosoma. (Copyright by General Biological Supply House, Inc., Chicago.)

There is considerable fluctuation in the rate of discharge of the contracting vacuoles. The rate of discharge is increased after feeding, when the water content of the animal has been increased by the fluid taken in by the food vacuole. Paramecia placed in distilled water also will have an increased rate of discharge, but those placed in salt water will have a decreased rate. These observations confirm the conclusions reached with respect to the function of the contracting vacuole of *Amoeba proteus:* that the important action of the contracting vacuoles is to maintain the proper water balance in the body of a protozoan.

Reproduction

Many of the features of reproduction in *Paramecium* can be mentioned only briefly at this time—their true significance will be discussed later, when a better understanding of the biological problems involved will be possible. Reproduction in *Paramecium caudatum* is both *asexual,* by a process of binary fission comparable with that of *Amoeba proteus,* and *sexual.* In sexual reproduction there is either an exchange of nuclear material between two individuals (*conjugation* and *cross-fertilization*) or a fusion of special nuclei within a single animal (*autogamy* or *self-fertilization*). The processes of asexual and sexual reproduction in *Paramecium* are associated closely with aging and inheritance, and today some of the most important research on these two biological phenomena is being done with the ubiquitous paramecia.

ASEXUAL REPRODUCTION • *Paramecium caudatum* has one macronucleus and one micronucleus. Binary fission, sometimes called *vegetative reproduction*, is accompanied by a constriction which separates the protoplasm into two approximately equal parts and by a division of both the large and the small nucleus. Superficially this appears to be a very simple act of constriction, but actually it is not. The macronucleus does divide by constriction, but the micronucleus undergoes a series of changes comparable with those we described for *Amoeba proteus* in *mitosis*. The formed bodies, *chromosomes*, appear, duplicate themselves, and are equally distributed to the two micronuclei that are formed. The nuclear membrane, however, does not break down in *Paramecium*. (This is unusual in mitotic division.) Just as important are some of the changes in the rest of the body. The gullet forms a bud, which migrates to the rear (posteriorly) and takes a position adjacent to the ectoplasm, where it stimulates the formation of a new oral groove and gullet in the posterior half of the paramecium. It is possible, with patience and skill, to perform microsurgery on a paramecium and remove the gullet. When fission occurs after such an operation, a bud cannot be formed, and thus the new animal will not possess a mouth or a gullet. The basal granules of the cilia also divide and give rise to the new cilia necessary for the new surface areas of the animal.

Fission is an extremely rapid method of reproduction for *Paramecium:* indeed, it has been estimated that—with ample food conditions, crowding prevented, and enemies excluded—a single paramecium has the reproductive potential of developing into more than 200,000,000,000 new animals in one month. The group of animals which are produced from a single individual by fission is called a *clone*. Each clone is composed of paramecia which are hereditarily alike, and if reproduction only occurs by fission among these, a

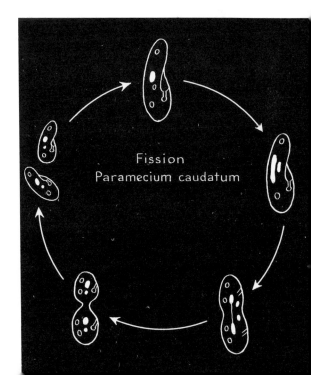

Figure 5.15. Fission. The nuclear reorganization during fission involves nuclear reorganization. The macronucleus divides amitotically but the micronuclei divide by mitosis. When the cystoplasm is constricted, each new animal receives the normal nuclear components. New gullets and contracting vacuoles also are formed.

Fission
Paramecium caudatum

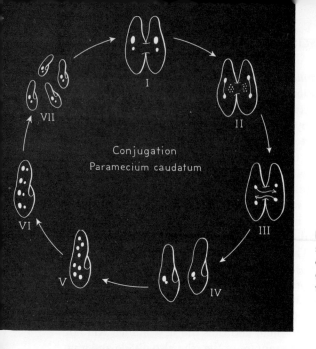

I II III IV V VI VII

Conjugation
Paramecium caudatum

Figure 5.16. Conjugation is a type of sexual reproduction which involves the exchange of nuclear material. The diagram has been simplified by the elimination of several intermediate stages.

clone will age and eventually die. This was demonstrated many years ago by Maupas, a French librarian of Algiers, and raised a storm of protest among biologists who had contended that paramecia (and most other protozoans) are immortal. It was shown later, however, that if *sexual* reproduction occurs, paramecia are "rejuvenated" and death is postponed.

SEXUAL REPRODUCTION • Sexual reproduction is accompanied by a number of complex changes in the paramecia. Two paramecia attach temporarily, or *conjugate*, with their oral surfaces in contact, and a narrow protoplasmic bridge is formed between them. The macronucleus in each paramecium completely disintegrates and disappears, and the micronucleus in each animal undergoes two divisions to form *four* micronuclei. Three of the four micronuclei disintegrate, and the *one* micronucleus divides again to form *two*. These divisions are comparable to those previously described as mitotic, except for the very important difference that during these divisions the chromosome number is *reduced* to *one half* the original number, so that at the termination of the division each of the two micronuclei has only half the normal number of chromosomes. Another significant event now occurs: one micronucleus from each animal, usually called the *male micronucleus*, migrates across the protoplasmic bridge to the other animal and fuses with the micronucleus which stayed in place, usually spoken of as the *female micronucleus*. This *fusion nucleus* will now have the *full number* of chromosomes, one half from the male micronucleus and one half from the female micronucleus. The paramecia now separate, and the fusion nucleus in each animal undergoes a series of successive divisions —into two, four, and finally, eight micronuclei. Some of the new nuclei eventually become macronuclei, while others remain micronuclei. Each paramecium now divides, becoming two individuals; and each of these two paramecia again divides. Thus, each of the original conjugating paramecia has divided into four individuals, giving a total of eight individuals which have resulted from the two original paramecia.

These steps in conjugation can be understood best by studying the diagram of the process. We shall see later that the reduction of the chromosome number to one half in the nuclei and the fusion of such nuclei to form the nucleus of new animals is typical of sexual reproduction in other animals, including man. The process is of great significance in heredity because it means that each new individual receives one half of its chromosomes from each parent.

SELF-FERTILIZATION • Approximately forty years ago Woodruff and Erdmann began to work with clones of *Paramecium aurelia*, a paramecium which is similar to *Paramecium caudatum*, but which has *two micronuclei*. They reported that aging and death could be postponed indefinitely in the absence of conjugation if the old macronucleus degenerated and was replaced by a new macronucleus. They called this process *endomixis*, and it was briefly described as a division of the micronuclei together with the formation of a *new macronucleus* from a micronucleus without fertilization. Most textbooks still record this process in considerable detail, but about twenty years ago W. F. Diller, and later Sonneborn, showed that important facts had been overlooked by Woodruff and Erdmann. Briefly stated, endomixis, as described, does *not* occur; instead, a series of micronuclear divisions occurs in the paramecium, the macronucleus degenerates, and two micronuclei (each with one half the normal chromosome number) fuse. This is comparable with the nuclear fusion that occurs during conjugation, but, in contrast to conjugation, only *one* animal is involved; therefore, the process is self-fertilization, or *autogamy*. This has been proved not only by direct observation but also by genetic studies.

In light of the complex behavior during conjugation, the question may be asked whether or not paramecia are male and female. The answer is a startling one, because Sonneborn discovered in 1937 that paramecia cannot conjugate at random, but only certain ones can join and exchange nuclei. These have been called *mating types* and are designated by Roman numerals. Thus, an animal of mating-type I will conjugate with animals of mating-type II but not with others of mating-type I. It might suggest that one mating type corresponds to a male and the other to a female, except for the fact that more than two mating types exist. Jennings described eight mating types in *Paramecium bursaria* and five in *Paramecium caudatum*. Members of a clone reproducing by fission only will be of a single mating type and must be mixed with animals from another clone of a different mating type before conjugation will occur. This fact has made it possible to study inheritance with paramecia as easily as with cattle or guinea pigs. If, however, members of a clone undergo autogamy, some animals of a different mating type will appear. It was this important observation, plus the fact that mating types are inherited, that made it possible for Sonneborn to secure the genetic evidence to disprove endomixis in *Paramecium*.

Coordination

The fast-swimming, fast-reacting paramecia have been favorite animals for the study of behavior and of adjustment to the environment. We observed that a system of *neurofibrils* is present which makes possible a coordinated beat of the cilia. Paramecia react to heat, light, gravity, chemicals, and contact. Even some "learning" seems to be possible in very limited degree among *Paramecium* and other ciliates. The responses are much more clearly of the type referred to as trial and error than was the case with *Amoeba proteus*, and many clever experiments have amply demonstrated this behavior. If a drop of very weak acetic acid is placed on a slide with the paramecia, the animals can be observed to "wander" into the drop and to swim in a random manner within it. When the paramecia chance to reach the boundary, they turn back; thus animals which reach the acid drop appear "trapped," and gradually the area becomes more and more crowded as additional animals enter. The chemical "sense" of the animals is well developed. A paramecium placed in a mixture of different kinds of bacteria and inert substances such as carbon particles will ingest the bacteria and reject the carbon. Furthermore, the paramecium will

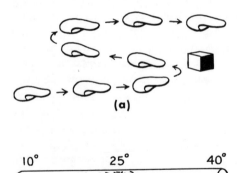

(a)

(b)

Figure 5.17. Reaction to stimuli. When a paramecium (a) approaches a solid object, it backs away, changes direction, and swims around the object. The response to temperature (b) is such that the animals avoid extremes of temperature, and aggregate in a region 24° to 25° centigrade. The response to chemicals (c) is illustrated by the addition of CO_2 and acetic acid to a slide containing paramecia. The animals do not enter the CO_2 but collect around the edge; on the other hand, the animals concentrate within the drop of acetic acid.

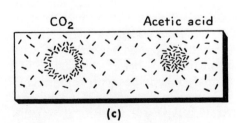

(c)

even select certain of the bacteria and reject others. The response to gravity is easily demonstrated in the laboratory and may be used in a practical way to ensure that students get ample numbers of paramecia for their observations. A culture fluid containing paramecia is placed in a test tube and allowed to stand undisturbed for a period of time. Paramecia respond negatively to gravity, and therefore concentrate in a shallow ring at the surface of the culture fluid. The great number of animals in this ring produces an opaqueness which is easily seen with the naked eye, and a drop of fluid taken from this area will be teeming with paramecia. Temperature reactions of paramecia are not only striking but also important for their survival. If a miniature trough is made with one end cooled at about 15° C and the other end heated to about 42° C, it will be observed that the paramecia gradually aggregate in the region which has a temperature of approximately 25° C. This is a trial-and-error response comparable to that described for the acetic acid experiment. Paramecia are less sensitive to light variations than to other stimuli, although experiments have shown that they are able to distinguish light from darkness.

Many experiments have been performed in an attempt to determine if paramecia can learn. The animals that have been fed carmine for a period of time will "learn" to reject the particles quickly, and this reaction is retained for a few days. This behavior, however, is not transmitted to the next generation when fission occurs but must be learned over again. More complex experiments have been performed in which paramecia are required to *associate* two stimuli—such as light and high temperature, or light and electric shock. If an observation slide is arranged so there is a light and a dark half, the paramecia will be seen to aggregate at the light end. But if this light end is also made unpleasantly hot, then the paramecia will "learn" to associate the light and the heat, and they will avoid the light end of the slide, taking up a compromise position between the light and heat on one side and the darkness and coldness on the other. Furthermore, the paramecia will continue to avoid the light end of the slide even after the temperature difference between the two halves has been eliminated and a uniform, moderate temperature prevails in both halves. In another experiment, the animals are given an electric shock when they swim into the lighted half and "learn" to avoid the lighted half in order to avoid the electric shock. These "learned" responses, however, usually last for only about 15 minutes or so.

It should be apparent from this brief discussion of the behavior of paramecia that in a normal environment animals are capable of making a very complicated series of trial-and-error adjustments. The animals are influenced by temperature variations, chemicals in the water, gravity, contact, and even light. The area that the animal occupies is a result, therefore, of a compromise between all the various stimuli acting upon it. Usually a paramecium will assume a place which is advantageous to it, and to a noncritical observer this might appear to be an intelligent choice. It is, however, only trial-and-error adjustment. Occasionally, one particular stimulus may be so strong that an animal

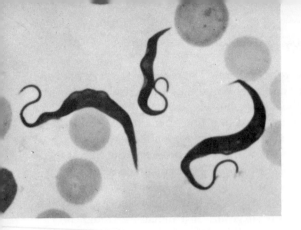

Figure 5.18. Trypanosoma gambiense, the animal which causes African sleeping sickness, is a typical flagellate. The elongated body and the long flagellum are characteristic of these active animals. (Copyright by General Biological Supply House, Inc., Chicago.)

must migrate into an area which could produce its destruction. The avoidance of high temperatures, for example, might cause the animal to occupy an area where toxic chemicals could cause its death.

The Class Flagellata and Other Protozoa

No discussion of protozoans can be complete without extensive reference to the members of the class Flagellata. These "animals" constitute a heterogeneous group which has resemblances to the other classes of the Protozoa as well as to plants. Many members of the class contain chlorophyll and have holophytic nutrition; and we should mention the fact that it is not possible to segregate such flagellates from close relatives which are both holophytic and saprozoic, or other relatives which are both saprozoic and holozoic. The green, plantlike flagellates are well represented by the interesting *Euglena*, which is classified as an animal by zoologists and as a plant by botanists (Figure 1.2). The important point is not that a difference of opinion exists concerning the

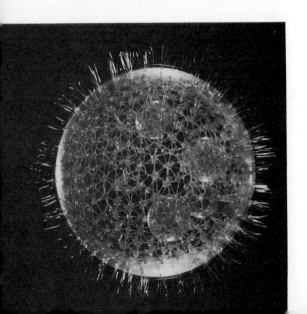

Figure 5.19. Volvox. The class Flagellata contains many colonial forms, of which Volvox is the best known. This animal will be considered in detail later. (Courtesy American Museum of Natural History.)

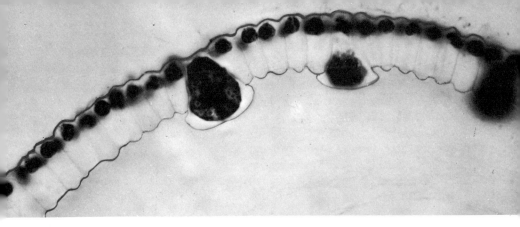

Figure 5.20. Volvox section. An edge view of a Volvox colony shows the arrangement of the individual cells. Protoplasmic strands connect the cells but do not show in this illustration. (Copyright by General Biological Supply House, Inc., Chicago.)

place of this organism, but rather that here is a living thing which possesses features common to both plants and animals. The fact, commented upon earlier, that it is often difficult to distinguish between plants and animals is emphasized by the existence of *Euglena* and its relatives. Although it is somewhat premature to consider problems of interrelationship at this time, it is important to understand the place of the Flagellata as a connecting link between plants and animals, between the various classes of Protozoa, and between the protozoans and the many-celled animals.

Figure 5.21. A fresh-water animal of the class Suctoria, which feeds by capturing other animals with protoplasmic processes which serve as tentacles to "suck" in the protoplasm of the prey.

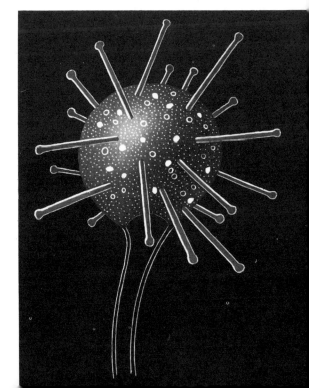

The Flagellata, as the name implies, possess a long, whiplike *flagellum* (plural, *flagella*) with which they swim. Not all flagellates contain chlorophyll, but many are typical animals in their nutritive relationships; even some of those with chlorophyll may feed as animals when grown in the dark or in subdued light. A few of the flagellates lose their flagella, develop pseudopodia, become amoeboid in their movements, and closely resemble the class Sarcodina. Parasitic flagellates reproduce asexually by the formation of resistant "spores," and therefore resemble the members of the class Sporozoa, to be considered later. Some sporozoans, in addition, have flagellated reproductive bodies similar in appearance to flagellates.

Finally, the relationship of the flagellates to the many-celled animals has been the subject of much study. Many flagellates exist in groups, or *colonies*, in which the individuals live together but remain relatively independent. The individuals in some colonies, however, become specialized, and significant differences develop between members of a colony, with a consequent loss of independence of the individual organisms. It is very difficult to separate such flagellate colonies from the simpler many-celled animals, and we will consider this particular problem later in the discussion of the transformation from the acellular to the many-celled organization of animals.

The class Ciliata is so different from other protozoans and so highly specialized that its relationship is obscure. In fact, the only group having features in common with ciliates is the class Suctoria. These remarkable little animals, the suctorians, feed on other protozoans by means of protoplasmic processes which serve as tentacles which "suck" the protoplasm from the prey. The suctorians go through a period of "embryonic" development during which cilia are present; these cilia, however, are lost in the adults. The close resemblance of the young suctorians to the ciliates has caused some zoologists to view the Suctoria merely as a subdivision of the class Ciliata.

The adaptations of protozoa for parasitic existence are considerable and will be discussed later as part of the problem of parasitism. One class of protozoans, the Sporozoa, is entirely parastic and of great importance to man because the members attack man and domestic animals. The malarial organism, *Plasmodium*, is the best-known example of this class.

It is noteworthy, by way of summary, that vitally important studies can be made on the Protozoa concerning the most seemingly advanced subjects—the development of sexuality, embryonic development, inheritance, the relation of an organism to its environment, behavior and nervous conduction, movement, and the development of specialized organelles. This further emphasizes that acellular animals are important in biological research and are not "simple" animals.

Figure 5.22. These drawings of members of Phylum Protozoa show the many structural variations and also indicate the complexity of these minute acellular organisms.

Difflugia

Arcella

SARCODINA

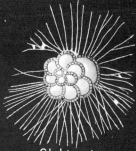

Globigerina

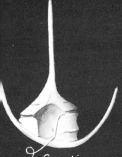

Ceratium

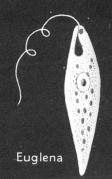

Euglena

FLAGELLATA

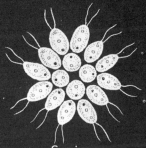

Gonium

Vorticella

Spirostomum

CILIATA

Stentor

Gregarina

SPOROZOA

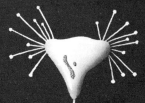

Acineta

SUCTORIA

Classification of Protozoa

Phylum Protozoa   Acellular, often considered one-celled, animals existing either as single individuals or as colonies. Such colonies are not considered many-celled animals because the individuals composing the colony are usually alike except for some specialization for reproductive purposes. The Protozoa do not have tissues or organs but do have specialized structures, the organelles.

CLASS I. FLAGELLATA (Mastigophora). Locomotion by one or several long protoplasmic processes, the *flagella*. Usually elongated, with a definite anterior end. Many have chlorophyll, and these are primarily *holophytic*, hence difficult to separate from plants such as algae. Usually a single nucleus. Examples: *Euglena, Synura, Volvox*, the parasitic *Trypanosoma*.

CLASS II. SARCODINA (Rhizopoda). Locomotion and food capture by means of *pseudopodia*. Less highly specialized than the Flagellata, but many possess a complex shell or a cuticle. Nutrition is *holozoic*. One or several nuclei may be present. Examples: *Amoeba, Difflugia, Globigerina, Actinophrys*.

CLASS III. CILIATA (Infusoria). Locomotion and food capture by means of many small protoplasmic processes, the *cilia*. The most highly specialized of the Protozoa, with definite body form as a result of a tough *pellicle*. Nutrition is *holozoic*. Two types of nuclei usually present: a metabolic *macronucleus* and a reproductive *micronucleus*. Examples: *Paramecium, Stentor, Balantidium, Diplodinium*.

CLASS IV. SUCTORIA. Absence of cilia or other locomotor organelles in adult. Cilia present in young animals, hence they are sometimes classified with the Ciliata. *Tentacles* for capture of food in adult stage. *Macronucleus*, and one to several *micronuclei*. Nutrition is *holozoic* (carnivorous). Examples: *Podophrya, Acineta*.

CLASS V. SPOROZOA. No locomotor organelles present. Form reproductive bodies, *spores*, with protective wall. Nutrition is *saprozoic* and entire class is composed of internal parasites. Examples: *Plasmodium, Gregarina*.

REFERENCES

BOYDEN, A., "Are There Any 'Acellular Animals'?" *Science, 125*, No. 3239, 1957.

BRANDT, P. W., "A study of the Mechanism of Pinocytosis," *Experimental Cell Research, 15*, 1958, pp. 300–313.

BROWN, F. A. (ed.), *Selected Invertebrate Types*. John Wiley and Sons, New York, 1945, pp. 1–69.

CALKINS, G. N., and F. M. SUMMERS, *Protozoa in Biological Research*. Columbia University Press, New York, 1941.

DILLER, W. F., "Nuclear Reorganization Processes in Paramecium Aurelia," *Journal of Morphology, 59*, 1936.

DOBELL, C., *Antony van Leeuwenhoek and His Little Animals.* Harcourt, Brace and Company, New York, 1932.

HALL, RICHARD P., *Protozoan Nutrition.* Blaisdell Publishing Company, New York, 1965.

HYMAN, L., *The Invertebrates: Protozoa through Ctenophora*, Vol. I, Chapters III-IX. McGraw-Hill Book Company, New York, 1940.

JAHN, T. L., and F. L. JAHN, *How to Know the Protoza.* William C. Brown Company, Dubuque, Iowa, 1949.

LANKESTER, RAY (ed.), *Treatise on Zoology*, Part I. Adam and Charles Black, London, 1909.

LWOFF, A. (ed.), *Biochemistry and Physiology of the Protozoa.* Vol. I. Academic Press, New York, 1951.

SONNEBORN, T. M., "Paramecium in Modern Biology." *Bios, XXI*, 1950.

WARD, H. B., and G. C. WHIPPLE, *Freshwater Biology.* John Wiley and Sons, New York, 1945.

6

Cataloging

Animals

Classification

●

There are more things in heaven and earth, Horatio,
Than are dreamt of in your philosophy.—Hamlet

The problem of classifying animals causes more annoyance to students of zoology than any other phase of the subject. It is difficult to understand why a lion should be *Felis leo*, or a dog *Canis familiaris*. The divisions of the animal kingdom are associated with names foreign to the student's experience. They appear to be insignificant except as a memory exercise. There is, to the contrary, a well-organized but simple plan for naming animals, and the divisions within this plan actually indicate the degrees of relationship which exist in the animal kingdom. Approximately one million different animals have been named and described, and probably two million more are as yet undescribed. Obviously it would be impossible for anyone to encompass or use such a body of information without some method for cataloging known facts and for adding new observations. Modern classification, or *taxonomy,* is a very practical method for bringing order to a chaotic situation, and the problems involved can best be illustrated by explaining how the modern system evolved from the disorder, confusion, and dismay of former times.

The first significant classification of animals was made by Aristotle about 330 B.C. and included what we recognize today as about 520 species. During the Middle Ages, many new animals were discovered which did not fit any of Aristotle's descriptions, but which the naturalists of the time quite understandably wished to describe and name. No international system for comparing these observations existed, however, and the situation gradually became worse, until finally complete chaos was produced as a result of the series of explorations which began with the famous thirty years of exploration. These started with the voyage of Columbus in 1492 and continued with the explorations of Vasco da Gama and Magellan until 1522. Many of the plants and animals introduced into Europe from the newly discovered areas of the world were so very different from any seen previously that no method existed which was adequate for their classification. Still another and very irritating complication was the fact that the same animal or plant might be given several different names in several languages, depending on whether it was collected by a Swede, a Spaniard, a Frenchman, a Russian, or an Englishman.

A highly significant attempt to devise a classification system was made by Conrad von Gesner. In the sixteenth century he published *Historia Animalium*, an encyclopedia of some 3500 pages, beautifully illustrated with woodcuts. He listed the animals alphabetically, according to habitat, natural functions, medicinal uses, uses to man, philosophical and poetical references, and quality of soul! The work, although exhaustive, also was inadequate for the purpose of bringing about an orderly arrangement of the animal kingdom. Except for a few minor improvements, the situation remained unchanged for nearly two hundred years, until the publication of Carolus Linnaeus's work, the *Systema Naturae,* in 1758.

Linnaeus, while still a young man, had skyrocketed to fame at the University of Upsala in Sweden as a result of his brilliant lectures, his ability to attract students, and his knowledge of plants and animals. He was able to secure financial aid for himself and his students, which enabled him to take collecting trips, and he and his helpers covered most of Europe on such journeys. The actual classification which he made of animals was incorrect in some instances, but such errors are unimportant because his significant contribution was the creation of a *system of classification*—a system which, with only minor modifications, is the basis for our modern science of taxonomy.

There were three important phases of Linnaeus' classification. *First,* all descriptions were in Latin, the universal language of the educated persons of

Figure 6.1. Carolus Linnaeus, the systematist. (Courtesy Scientific Monthly.)

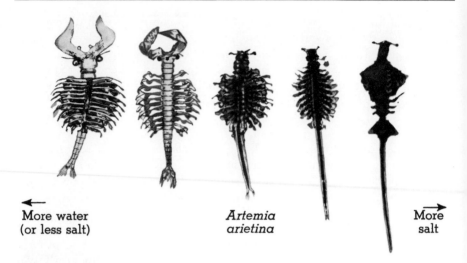

← More water (or less salt)   *Artemia arietina*   More salt →

Figure 6.2. Individual variation-brine shrimp. The difficulty of classifying an organism is often magnified by the effect of environment. The brine shrimp, for example, which normally lives in salt water, changes its form radically when grown in solutions containing more salt or less salt. Animals which develop in low salt concentrations are so different from those which develop in high salt concentrations that they could be considered different species if the intermediate forms were not known. [From Biology and Man, by Greenberg and Bingham, Ginn and Co., (after Abonyi).]

his day. *Second,* each animal was given two names. This *binomial nomenclature* gave a *genus* and a *species* name to each animal, the names being in Latin or having Latin endings, and the species name was written with a small letter. For example, the genus and species name for man is *Homo sapiens. Third,* a system of *paired characteristics* was used to distinguish between organisms which were being classified. Animals, for example, may or may not have a vertebral column, may or may not have lungs, may or may not have hair, and so on. Each set of paired characters may be used to subdivide the animals progressively into groups of smaller size that are more nearly alike, until the basic unit in the classification scheme, the *species,* is reached. For convenience a species may sometimes be subdivided into smaller units. It may not have occurred to you in this light before, but such paired characteristics are used every day in an effective but unconscious manner. For example, when a reference is made to "the red-headed girl next door," we immediately exclude blondes and brunettes, and decrease the number of possible ladies who might be involved. "Next door" leaves only two possible places where she might be found, and eliminates the pretty redhead across the street. Should there be two redheads "next door" we easily handle that problem by saying the "older redhead" or the "younger redhead," as the case might be.

The early naturalists depended almost entirely on the *external structures* of an animal for features to be used in classification. Actual relationships between different organisms are often obscured in adult forms because of superficial adaptations of the organisms to its environment. Some external structures suggest a close relationship when no real relationship exists, while other animals that give little external indication of being closely related sometimes turn out to be on the most intimate family terms. The centipede and the clamworm, for example, look very much alike at first glance, yet the clamworm is a worm, while the centipede is not, being more closely related to the lobster and the crab. Again, who would suspect that the apple tree and the rose are related?

As a result of such facts, taxonomists began to study *embryonic stages* and *internal structures* as well as adult external features. The importance of *homologous structures* became apparent at once. Homologous structures, or *homologs*, are structures which have a similar origin, even though they may have very different functions in the adult. Indeed, homologs may differ considerably in superficial appearance. The fin of a whale, the wing of a bat, the foreleg of a horse, and the arm of a man have similar origins and hence are homologous, but obviously these structures are radically different in appearance and function. The recognition of the homology of structures cleared up many difficulties in classification, and we will use homologies later to illustrate relationships which are important in evolution. In a similar manner it became possible to assign to their proper place structures which were similar in function but different in origin, such as the wing of an insect and the wing of a bat. These are called *analogous structures*, or *analogs*, and they demonstrate that organisms may modify very different structures to perform a common function, for example, flight; but this similarity of function does not indicate a close relationship. Embryological investigations have also been valuable in the study of parasites, many of which are so modified in their adult stages that it is difficult or impossible to place them in their proper category in the animal kingdom except by referring to their embryogeny. Early development is the *only* basis for classifying some animals.

Modern taxonomists also draw heavily on more modern techniques for information to supplement the older methods of study. An increasing number of investigations are being based on *serological tests* (comparable to the blood tests given to blood donors), in which the reaction between tissue extracts of one animal and those of another are tested. These are discussed in Chapter 22. The *distribution* of animals, their type of *habitat*, and the *association* with other animals or plants all contribute information valuable for working out relationships and for classification. Perhaps among the most exciting studies are those which are made of the number and arrangement of the chromosomes. Such investigations have added much to the clarification of groupings in which the species were difficult to delimit by other means. A modern investigator in taxonomy, therefore, may secure information from a dozen sources before he is satisfied that he has determined the proper place and relationship of the species with which he is working. The mere collecting of animals or exhibiting of them in display cases is but a minor phase of taxonomic science.

Since the species is the basic unit of classification, it should be possible, at

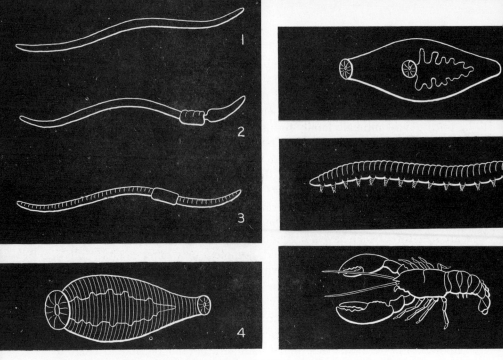

Figure 6.3.   Incorrect grouping.   It is not usually possible to classify animals by any similarity of outward appearance.   The animals here are arranged in similar and dissimilar groups according to appearance.   In Figure 6.4 you see the same animals correctly arranged according to standard classification (note phylum and class numbers).

Figure 6.4.   Correct grouping.   There is no close relationship between Ascaris (1), the acorn worm (2), and the earthworm (3).   The acorn worm is a primitive chordate.   Nor are the leech (4) and fluke (5) related.   However, Peripatus (6) is related to the lobster (7), the spider, and the moth, and is distantly related to the annelid worms (earthworms).

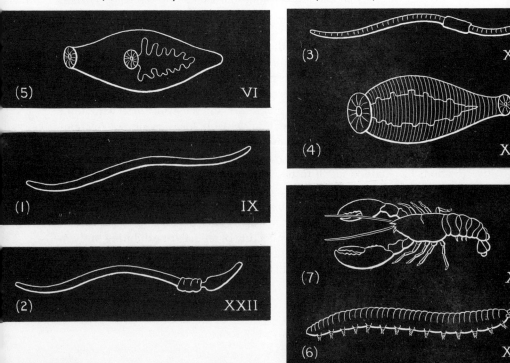

least theoretically, to define this unit with exactness. This definition, however, has plagued biologists for centuries, and although species are often easy to recognize, it is usually impossible to limit them precisely. Species which range over wide areas may be very different at the extreme ends of their geographical range, even though all intergradations will be found between them. They may interbreed at the limits of their ranges with other species to form *hybrids*, which further complicate the picture with unusual variations.

A specialist who works with a small division of the animal kingdom and who has a sufficiently large number of specimens to enable him to know the variations which exist can usually identify animals as to species with a fair degree of certainty. The most familiar definition of species is that of "a group of organisms which will interbreed and have fertile offspring." There are, unfortunately, many exceptions to this definition: sometimes two species will cross and fertile offspring appear; the same is sometimes true between crosses of different genera.

The passage of years has brought about refinements in actual classification as well as in the techniques for classifying animals. The major subdivisions of the animal kingdom have become well established, and the subdivisions are comparable for both plants and animals. We will, however, concern ourselves only with the animal kingdom. Organisms are usually placed in two major groups or kingdoms: the *plant kingdom* and the *animal kingdom*. The animal kingdom is organized from smaller groups, the *phyla* (singular, *phylum*), with one of which we have already become acquainted, the phylum Protozoa. A phylum is further subdivided into *classes* (singular, *class*), and a class is composed of *orders* (singular, *order*). An order is made up of *families* (singular, *family*). A family is organized from a group of *genera* (singular, *genus*), and finally the genus is composed of *species* (singular, *species*). Thus, the species is the smallest unit in the formal classification plan. It is often advantageous, however, to have subgroups such as a *subphylum*, a *subclass*, a *superfamily*, and especially with domestic forms or animals that occupy a limited geographical area, species may be broken up into *varieties, subspecies*, or *races*. The classification of the fox will serve to illustrate the principles of taxonomy applied to a specific animal.

RED FOX—Classification

Kingdom	Animal. Includes all animals.
Phylum	Chordata. Only those animals with a dorsal tubular nervous system and supporting notochord.
Subphylum	Vertebrata. Only those chordates with a backbone.
Class	Mammalia. Only those vertebrates with mammary glands and hair.
Order	Carnivora. Only those mammals with canine teeth and molars for tearing and ripping.
Family	Canidae. Foxes, wolves, wild dogs, domestic dogs.
Genus	*Vulpes*. Some foxes.
Species	*fulva*. Red foxes.

Common sense should be used in taxonomy by both the professional zoologist and the beginning student. The prime function of classification is to convey information. If you state to a friend that you saw a pretty red fox in the field he will understand very well, but to say that you saw a pretty *Vulpes fulva* might cause him to wonder why you didn't dig it up and plant it in your garden. The type of dilemma to which slavish adherence to terminology can lead has been delightfully recounted by Ogden Nash in one of his intriguing jingles entitled "The Purist."[*]

> I give you now Professor Twist,
> A conscientious scientist.
> Trustees exclaimed, "He never bungles!"
> And sent him off to distant jungles.
> Camped on a tropic riverside,
> One day he missed his loving bride.
> She had, the guide informed him later,
> Been eaten by an alligator.
> Professor Twist could not but smile,
> "You mean," he said, "a crocodile."

Excellent reference books are available that can be used to solve the more complicated taxonomic problems, but unless it is necessary to use scientific names for purposes of accuracy when making comparisons between organisms, it is better to use common names.

The classification of organisms, even when most carefully devised, is somewhat arbitrary, and competent taxonomists will frequently disagree concerning the actual place to be occupied by a particular group of animals. Part of the difficulty is a direct result of the fact that intermediate forms exist which may have characteristics of two or more major groups. We have noted such an example in the case of the Flagellata. These intermediate forms may be placed in a special phylum, class, or other subdivision especially tailored to fit them, or they may be assigned an insignificant place in one of the already existing subdivisions. This type of procedure, of course, is exasperating to any scientist who wishes to be exact. Unfortunately, our knowledge of animals is incomplete, and many difficulties will continue to annoy those who are interested in taxonomy. A beginner in zoology cannot be expected to grasp the significance of all the peculiar variations in classifications, and we shall confine our survey to those groups of animals which illustrate especially well the interrelationships between animals. The fact that intermediate forms are present is not a curse but a blessing in disguise, because these afford us an opportunity to speculate on the manner by which one group of animals may have been gradually transformed by evolution into another type during the lapse of millions of years. (See Chapter 22.)

[*] "The Purist"—Copyright 1935 by the Curtis Publishing Company.

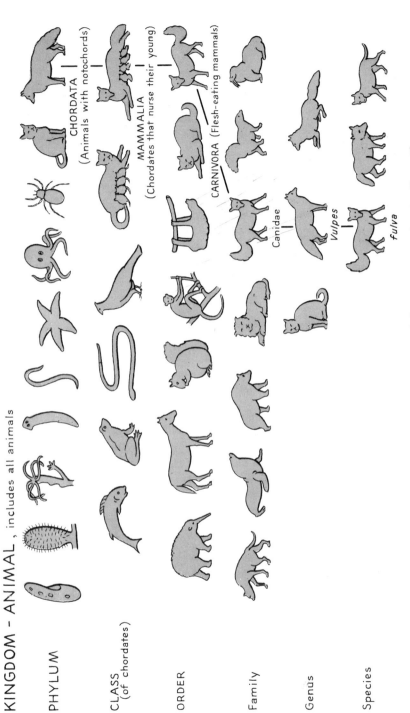

KINGDOM - ANIMAL, includes all animals

PHYLUM

CHORDATA (Animals with notochords)

CLASS (of chordates)

MAMMALIA (Chordates that nurse their young)

ORDER

CARNIVORA (Flesh-eating mammals)

Family

Canidae

Genus

Vulpes

Species

fulva

Figure 6.5. As the classification proceeds, the animals become more and more alike until finally a very similar group is to be observed within a species.

Only the major features and phyla of the animal kingdom are outlined in the table below. Certain units in the outline have not been assigned any subdivision title: namely, diploblastic, triploblastic, acoelomate, or coelomate. These terms are descriptive of the arrangement of body layers and will be discussed fully in later chapters in connection with the problem of the transformation from the acellular to the many-celled condition. The table is meaningless by itself, but its full significance will be appreciated after we consider the features of the various phyla which are listed.

A Taxonomic Preview of the Animal Kingdom

SUBKINGDOM PROTOZOA Acellular (one-celled organisms).

Phylum Protozoa Acellular or colonial animals, no tissues or organs: *Paramecium, Amoeba.*

SUBKINGDOM METAZOA Many-celled animals, cells specialized into tissues, or into tissues and organs.

Primarily Diploblastic (two body layers, with tissue-grade organization).

Phylum Porifera Asymmetrical sessile animals with flagellated canals, skeleton of spongin and/or spicules: sponges.

Phylum Coelenterata Radially symmetrical, two distinct body layers, with a third layer slightly developed in some, gastrovascular cavity, nematocysts: *Hydra,* corals, *Aurelia.*

Primarily Triploblastic (three body layers, with organ-grade organization).

Acoelomate (lacking a body space within the mesothelium).

Phylum Platyhelminthes Bilaterally symmetrical, *gastrovascular cavity,* mesothelial layer, flame bulbs: *Planaria.*

Phylum Nemathelminthes Bilaterally symmetrical, pseudocoel, true alimentary canal, cuticle, longitudinal muscles only: vinegar eel, *Ascaris.*

Coelomate (having a body space within the mesothelium).

Phylum Annelida Bilaterally symmetrical, segmented, true coelom, ventral ladder-type nervous system, nephridia: *Neanthes (Nereis),* earthworm.

Phylum Mollusca Bilaterally symmetrical, nonsegmented, shell formed by mantle, ventral foot sometimes divided into arms, nephridia: clam, squid, snail.

gure 6.6. Some animals have a completely different outward appearance at different times their lives. The larval caterpillar bears little similarity to the handsome butterfly, and yet the utterfly is the adult form of the caterpillar. (Courtesy Ernst Kraus.)

Phylum Arthropoda Bilaterally symmetrical, segmented, externally jointed appendages, well-developed exoskeleton, hemocoel, ventral lader-type nervous system: lobster, grasshopper, spider.

Phylum Echinodermata Five-part radial symmetry, nonsegmented, hydraulic system, spiny skinned: starfish, sea urchin.

Phylum Chordata Bilaterally symmetrical, segmented, endoskeleton, notochord, dorsal-tubular nervous system, gill slits at some stage: fish, frog, lizard, bird, man.

REFERENCES

ATES, MARSTON, *Animal Worlds*. Random House, New York, 1963.

URNETT, ALLISON L., and THOMAS EISNER, *Animal Adaptation*. Hope, Rinehart, and Winston, New York, 1964.

RIVER, E. C., *Name That Animal*. The Kraushar Press, Northampton, Massachusetts, 1942.

ALL, T. S., *A Source Book in Animal Biology*. McGraw-Hill Book Company, New York, 1951.

ANSON, EARL D., *Animal Diversity*. Prentice-Hall, Englewood Cliffs, 1961.

EGNER, ROBERT W., *Parade of the Animal Kingdom*. The Macmillan Company, New York, 1935.

YMAN, L., *The Invertebrates: Protozoa through Ctenophora*, Vol. I, Chapter II. McGraw-Hill Book Company, New York, 1940.

INSEY, A. C., *The Gall Wasp, Genus Cynips*. Indiana University Studies, Vol. XVI, pp. 17–77. Bloomington, Indiana, 1930.

AYR, ERNST E., GORTON LINSLEY, and ROBERT L. UNSINGER, *Methods and Principles of Systematic Zoology*. McGraw-Hill Book Company, New York, 1952.

ORDENSKIÖLD, E., *The History of Biology*. Alfred A. Knopf, New York, 1932.

NGER, C., *A History of Biology*. Henry Schuman, New York, 1950.

7

The Transition | From Acellular

to Many-Celled

Animals

•

To solve the problem of the forms of living things is the aim with which the naturalist of today comes to his work.   How have living things become what they are, and what are the laws which govern their forms?—William Bateson, 1894

Every biologist has some detective blood in his veins.   Presented with a "body," the Sherlock Holmes in us whispers, "How was it done?" or "How has this happened?"   In this discussion, we not only have a "body" to explain, but the dark secrets of the body itself.   No modern mystery story is more fascinating to us than the enigmatic origin of the many-celled animals, the Metazoa.   There exists no documentation of their creation because, as we will see later, this happened approximately *one billion years ago;* but just as in any good mystery story, there are clues to the mystery, and from these clues an investigator can reconstruct a reasonable theory to fit the facts of the case.   The "body" in our mystery is the *cell,* because the protoplasmic mass of the metazoan is sliced into hundreds or even trillions of these units, and the "facts" which must be explained are directly related to the behavior of these units.   *First,* the metazoans are partitioned, or subdivided, into cells, a condition which is in marked contrast to the organization of the acellular protozoans.   *Second,* the cells of the metazoans are arranged in layers; some of the animals, the *diploblastic,* have two layers, while others, the *triploblastic,* have three layers.   *Third,* a division of labor takes place between the cells and between the layers of cells in the metazoans.   Accordingly, as such division implies, there is a structural separation of the functions of nutrition, respiration, excretion, reproduction, and coordination.   In triploblastic animals, special *organ systems* are devoted to most of these functions, including those of respiration and excretion.   *Fourth,* with few exceptions the metazoans have a definite *anterior-posterior* axis, and consistently move with

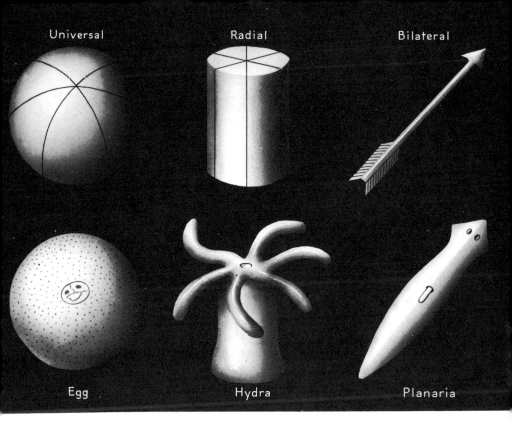

Universal   Radial   Bilateral

Egg   Hydra   Planaria

Figure 7.1. Planes of symmetry. Many animals have no definite body symmetry. A few have universal symmetry. Some have radial symmetry, in which the body may be divided into several similar parts by radial cuts. The most common body form is bilateral symmetry, in which only one cut will divide the body into similar parts (a head and tail end, and right and left sides).

one end, the anterior, forward. About the anterior-posterior axis the bodies of the animals are arranged symmetrically, usually in either a bilateral or a radial fashion.

The many-celled animals confront us, therefore, with a quadripartite mystery requiring an explanation for (1) the subdivision of protoplasm into cells, (2) the formation of layers, (3) a division of labor with the development of specialized structures, and (4) the formation of an anterior-posterior axis. These problems will be studied, beginning with the *structure of the cell* and progressing in sequence through indirect *cell division* (mitosis), *embryonic development*, and finally *tissue organization*. In addition, it is impossible to resist the temptation to speculate briefly on the probable ancestors of the Metazoa.

PROPHASE • Mitosis begins with prophase during which a series of events occur simultaneously in both the nucleus and the cytoplasm. Within the nucleus, the reticulum condenses to form a coil of darkly staining threadlike *chromatin*. The thread progressively becomes more condensed and finally

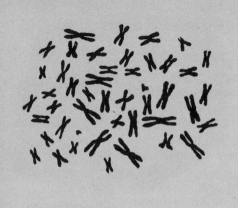
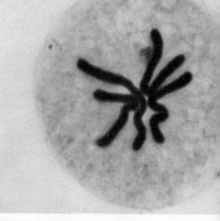

(a)   (b)

Figure 7.2. The number and size of chromosomes vary according to the organisms. These pictures illustrate large numbers of small chromosomes in man (a) and small numbers of large chromosomes in Ascaris (b). The recent work of Joe Hin Tjio and Albert Levan indicates that the correct chromosome number in man is 46. [(b) courtesy Clarence Flaten.]

breaks up into a number of distinct bodies, the *chromosomes*. Each chromosome is composed of two strands called *chromatids*, and the number of chromosomes is constant for all cells of a given species. There may be, for example, only two chromosomes in cells of certain parasitic worms or as many as several hundred may be present in some animals. The accompanying table lists a few representative organisms with the number of chromosomes present in each. While the chromatin threads are forming in the nucleus, a *centrosome*, typically

Chromosome Number in Some Representative Organisms			
Ascaris univalens	2	Honeybee	32
Garden pea	14	Mouse	40
Corn	20	Man	46
Bullfrog	26	Crayfish	200

composed of a *centriole* surrounded by a *sphere of cytoplasm*, usually appears adjacent to the nucleus. The centrosome divides, a centriole going with each of the resulting centrosomes, and the two centrosomes move apart around the periphery of the nucleus and eventually occupy positions directly opposite each other. Fibers or threads, called the *aster rays*, radiate from each of the centrosomes to form the *asters*, and similar threads connect the two centrosomes with each other. Coincidentally with these cytoplasmic developments, the nuclear membrane disintegrates and the newly formed chromosomes are free in the cytoplasm. Biologists do not always agree as to the precise limits of the prophase and metaphase stages of mitosis and this is understandable since the process of mitosis is continuous. We deem it advantageous, however, to consider the preceding events as indicative of prophase.

METAPHASE • The chromosomes now move to a position equidistant between the two centrosomes and line up in a *metaphase,* or *equatorial, plate.* They apparently adhere to the surface of a very gelatinous region of the cell, the *mitotic spindle,* which is broadest in the region of the equatorial plate and tapers at each end to the area of the centrosomes. *Spindle fibers* extend over the surface of the mitotic spindle and attach the chromosomes to the centrosomes in the aster. It is now apparent that the two chromatids which comprise each chromosome are held together by a *centromere,* and the spindle fibers attach to the chromosomes at the centrosome region. In late metaphase, each of the centromeres divides, thus freeing the two chromatids from each other. The chromatids immediately begin to move apart with a movement that is not random but is in the direction of the centrosomes and seemingly along the suface of the gelatinous spindle. When there is an obvious separation of the chromatids, the cell is considered to be in the next stage of division, the *anaphase.*

ANAPHASE • The movement of the chromatids away from each other and toward the centrioles and, therefore, toward the ends of the cell continues at an accelerated pace during anaphase. The spindle fibers and the aster rays may begin to disappear during the late anaphase in some cells, and occasionally the plasma membrane and the cytoplasm in the region of the equatorial plate may begin to indent or constrict. Constriction is always evident by the time the chromatids have moved to the ends of the cell.

TELOPHASE • The final step in mitosis is characterized by events that are essentially the reverse of those occurring during prophase. The two sets of chromatids revert to a network of chromatin threads which fuse and nuclear membranes are reformed. The centrosomes, asters, and spindle fibers disappear, the chromatin threads within the two new nuclei gradually forming a typical reticulum. The mitotic process is concluded by the complete constriction of the cytoplasm into two cells. The two cells usually have equal amounts of cytoplasm and each will contain a nucleus with an equal number of chromatids.

INTERPHASE • Immediately after mitosis and before the next division the cell is sometimes called a "resting cell," or is said to be in a resting stage. This is one of the most fallacious statements in biology, because it is during this period that the cell performs its most active synthetic processes. The term *interphase* is a more apt designation for this period. We recall that at prophase each chromosome is made up of two chromatids but that during anaphase the chromatids separate with the result that at telophase each nucleus receives only one chromatid. There is, therefore, only half as much chromatin material present at the end of the telophase as there was at the beginning of prophase, but the *number of chromosomes remains the same.* A remarkable process, however, takes place in the nucleus during interphase. The chromatids are duplicated with an exactness which is one of the most remarkable phenomena in biology.

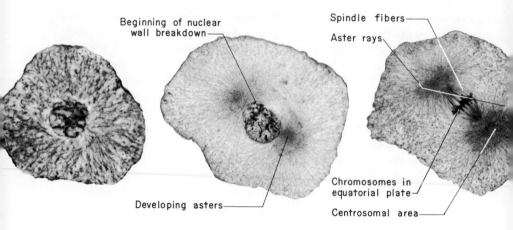

Figure 7.3.   The embryo of the whitefish has many cells which undergo mitosis simultaneously. It is excellent, therefore, for the study of mitotic cell divisions.   It should be noted, however, that mitosis in the whitefish embryo is slightly atypical since centrioles are not present.   (Courtesy Clarence Flaten.)

Each chromatin thread does *not* split into two parts, but *a new thread is created from the surrounding nuclear material!*   An exact duplicate is produced of each chromatid and as a consequence a new chromatid is formed parallel to the old chromatid and becomes attached to it by a centromere.   New chromosomes, each composed of two chromatids, are now ready for the next prophase.   The tremendous biological significance of chromatid duplication will be discussed later in detail.

Further study of mitosis

Variations exist in the details of mitosis as we have presented them.   We observed previously, for example, that in *Paramecium* the nuclear membrane does not disintegrate during mitosis, that centrosomes and even aster rays may be absent in some animals, and that in other cases, the cytoplasm may not be divided equally between daughter cells.   Variations in chromosome behavior occur with the result that one nucleus may receive more than the normal complement of chromosomes, and another nucleus may receive less.   Except for these relatively uncommon events, the variations in the details of the process are not especially significant.

We could spend a lifetime studying the biological, physical, or chemical problems involved in mitosis, with little hope of acquiring more than a superficial knowledge of a single aspect.   In fact, as yet very little is known about the stimuli which initiate cell division.   Chemical substances, age, temperature, the relation of the surface to the volume of the cell, the relation of the volume of the nucleus to the volume of the cytoplasm, injury, and the kind of tissue are but a few of the factors which influence mitotic divisions.   Tumor and cancer

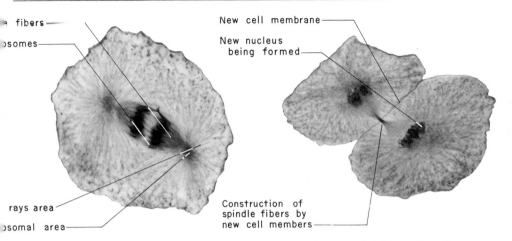

fibers —
)somes
rays area
)somal area

New cell membrane
New nucleus
being formed
Construction of
spindle fibers by
new cell members

Figure 7.4.   Figures 7.3 and 7.4 clearly show the several stages of mitotic cell division.   The cell on the left in Figure 7.3 is shown in the interphase stage, often called the "resting stage," prior to undergoing cell division.   (Courtesy Clarence Flaten.)

cells frequently will go "wild" and divide so rapidly that the constriction of the cytoplasm cannot keep pace with the multiplication of the nuclei and abnormal multinucleated masses of protoplasm are produced.   The relative time devoted to each phase of the mitotic cycle varies from organism to organism as the accompanying table indicates for representative forms.   The importance of

Duration of Mitotic Cycle, in Minutes*			
	Fruit fly (embryonic cells)	Chick (mesenchyme)	Plant†
Prophase	3.6	30–60	36–45
Metaphase	0.5	2–10	7–10
Anaphase	1.2	2–3	15–20
Telophase	0.9	3–12	20–35
Interphase	2.9	30–120	. . . . .
Total	9.1	67–205	78–110

*Modified from Schrader, 1944
†Arrhenatherum

mitosis in heredity will be considered later, but we should remark at this time that the chromosomes actually contain the hereditary factors, the *genes*, and are responsible for the transmission of these hereditary factors from one generation to the next.

The mechanical aspects of mitosis have excited the curiosity of physicists and chemists as well as of biologists.   Many attempts have been made, with little success, to construct models of mitosis.   The possibility that the movement of chromosomes can be explained as a result of differences in electrical charge has been investigated, and both microsurgery and distortion of the cell by subjecting it to hydrostatic pressures have been employed as methods of analyzing the action of the mitotic spindle.   This much is known: the mitotic spindle is more jellylike than the surrounding cytoplasm and can be whirled about in the cell by pushing it with a microprobe.   Mazia and others have been able to digest cytoplasm and isolate the mitotic spindle as an independent structure which then can be studied free from the remainder of the cell.   The spindle apparently is more fluid (sol) at its pointed ends adjacent to the centrosomes and more gelatinized (gel) in the region of the chromosomes.   There is evidence in both plants and animals that the chromosomes are held to the spindle by the spindle fibers and are moved toward the centrosomes along the surface of the spindle. The initial separation of the chromosomes is probably a result of some elastic pull by the fibers.   There is a flowing of material along the spindle due to the transformation to the sol state at the centrosome and formation of a new gel in the region of the equatorial plate.   The situation is analogous to the movement which would be observed if we were able to embed a marble on an inverted cone of ice which is melting at the pointed end, but to which additional ice is being added at the large end by a continuous freezing process.   The marble would remain adherent to the same group of ice crystals on the cone but would gradually be pushed toward the small end of the cone as a result of the melting of the ice at the tip and the freezing of new ice at the base of the cone. Thus the marble would move in a definite direction.

Mitosis clearly is a dramatic and highly significant biological event.   The true importance of the process can not be fully appreciated until we discuss problems of embryogeny and inheritance.   The end results, however, may be sum-

Figure 7.5.   Plant cell division.   The essential features of cell division are the same in both plant and animal cells.   Note in the division of these Narcissus cells that centrioles are absent and that new cells are formed by the growth of a partition [see (d)] (a) Prophase: 1. chromosome. (b) Metaphase: 1. equatorial plate.   (c) Anaphase: 1. Spindle fibers.   (d) Telophase: Note the partition.   (Courtesy Clarence Flaten.)

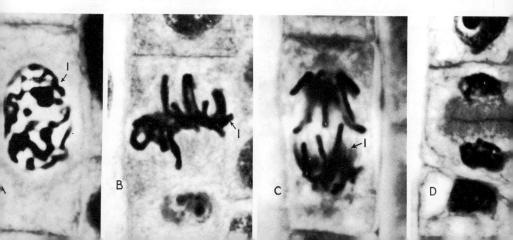

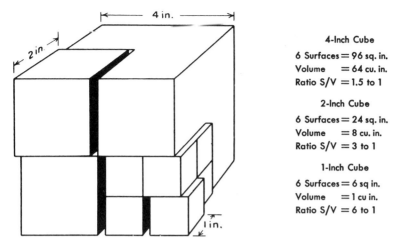

4-Inch Cube
6 Surfaces = 96 sq. in.
Volume   = 64 cu. in.
Ratio S/V = 1.5 to 1

2-Inch Cube
6 Surfaces = 24 sq. in.
Volume   = 8 cu. in.
Ratio S/V = 3 to 1

1-Inch Cube
6 Surfaces = 6 sq in.
Volume   = 1 cu in.
Ratio S/V = 6 to 1

Figure 7.6.   Surface-volume relationships.   With each subdivision of a cube, surface area is added.   Thus, the ratio of surface to volume is increased as is shown to the right.   The S/V ratio of cells is improved at mitosis by the subdivision of cells.

marized here for emphasis.   Two new cells are present after mitosis where only one existed previously.   The new cells, with a few exceptions, are of equal size. The nucleus of each new cell, because of the separation of chromatids during mitosis, will contain equal numbers of chromosomes and, therefore, the same complement of hereditary factors.   Even more important, the chromosome number is equal to that of the parent cell from which each new cell was derived. Finally, the surface area in proportion to the volume of the protoplasm is greater in the new cells than it was in the original cell and, therefore, a more efficient exchange of materials through the plasma membrane is facilitated.   The ratio of nuclear volume to cytoplasmic volume also is more favorable.

Amitosis

Not many years ago it was thought that amitosis was a common type of division in cells that were reproducing rapidly, and many of the divisions of *Amoeba* were thought to be amitotic.   We know now, as a result of better techniques and more careful study, that some mitotic divisions may occur rapidly and in a slightly atypical fashion and can be easily confused with amitosis.   It is now generally agreed that most cells which divide amitotically are *dying cells*, and there is little biological importance to be attributed to the process.   The possible exception to this generalization may be the amitotic division of certain embryonic cells.   During amitosis, the nucleus as well as the cytoplasm constricts, chromosomes do not appear, and any equal allotment of nuclear and cytoplasmic materials to daughter cells is purely incidental.

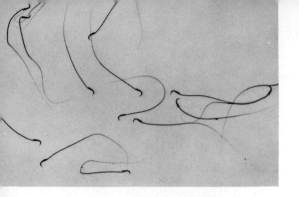

Figure 7.7. Rat sperm. These male cells are the specialized counterparts of the ovum. (Copyright by General Biological Supply House, Inc., Chicago.)

The formation of layers of cells

The second set of facts which has to be collected and analyzed in our mystery of "How was it done?" is concerned with the fate of the cells after they undergo division and after their number has been greatly increased. The cells of the Metazoa are not haphazardly arranged but are organized in layers. At first only one layer, but subsequently two or even three layers, will be formed, and it is from these plastic sheets of protoplasm that the tissues and organ systems of the adult animals will be developed. This history of an animal from the time it begins life as a fertilized ovum until it emerges in its adult form is known as *embryology;* history, especially embryological history, does repeat itself in an astounding way in the metazoans. The early developmental stages of the jellyfish, the starfish, the mouse, and man are amazingly alike, yet there is no confusion in the final product. This similarity allows us considerable freedom of choice in the selection of an animal that will illustrate embryological development, and because the embryos are easy to secure in large numbers, the development of the starfish or sea urchin is often studied. Before studying embryological history, however, it is important to understand the development of reproductive cells.

Reproductive Cells

Maturation of reproductive cells

As the details of mitosis were ascertained, it became obvious that mitotic divisions were present in all organisms. A number of investigators observed, however, that a slightly different type of cell division occurs during the development of the reproductive cells. This is called *meiotic division,* or *meiosis,* and it results in the production of mature sperm or egg cells which have only one half as many chromosomes as the other cells of the body. It is not surprising to find a mechanism present for reducing chromosome numbers in reproductive cells. Unless a reduction occurs, the union of a sperm with an egg will provide the embryo with twice as many chromosomes as are present in its parents, and after only a few generations the chromosome number would be astronomical. A brief discussion of the life history of the *germ cells* (sperm or egg cells) is in-

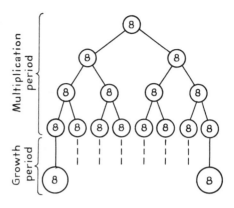

Figure 7.8. During the multiplication and growth periods of its development, the fruit-fly sperm increases only slightly in size. The chromosome number is constant (eight), for all divisions are mitotic.

cluded here only as an introduction to embryonic development. Later, a more detailed account of the chromosomal changes during meiosis will be given in order to provide an understanding of the role of the chromosomes in inheritance.

Reproductive cells have several distinct periods during their life history. These periods are comparable in all organisms and can be illustrated by describing the events in the fruit fly, *Drosophila melanogaster,* the germ cells of which contain eight chromosomes. The first phase in the development of both sperm and egg cells is a *multiplication period.* This is an interval during which the germ cells multiply rapidly by mitosis and each daughter cell receives the full number of eight chromosomes. The second phase in the history of the reproductive cell is the *growth period* during which the reproductive cells increase in size. The growth is slight in male germ cells but usually is pronounced in female germ cells due to the accumulation of yolk. A hen's egg at this time will increase from a microscopically small object to a macroscopic structure. The accompanying simplified diagram summarizes the events during the multiplication and growth phases of the development of reproductive cells. The third period is the one in which the most significant events take place in the germ cells. This is the *maturation period* and only two divisions occur during this interval. The first division is a *reduction* or *meiotic* division during which the chromosome number is reduced by one half. The second division in the maturation period, however, results in an equal allotment of chromosomes to the daughter cells, and therefore may be termed an *equational* division.

The mechanics of reduction division

Superficially, a cell which is undergoing meiosis resembles a cell in mitosis. An animal cell, for example, will have the typical mitotic figure with aster rays and spindle fibers. The stages of prophase, metaphase, anaphase, and telophase are easily recognized but, as we will note later (p. 108), prophase is much more complex in meiosis than it is in mitosis. The chromosomes at the beginning of

STAGES OF PROPHASE

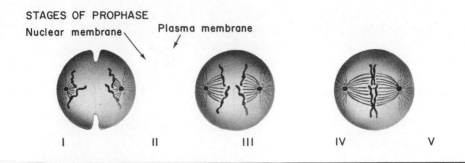

FIRST MEIOTIC DIVISION

SECOND MEIOTIC DIVISION

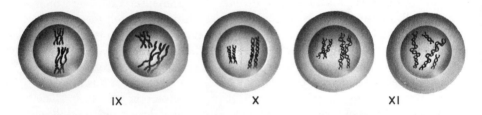

Figure 7.9. Meiosis. I: This diagram depicts a cell with four chromosomes. These are elongated threadlike bodies at the beginning of prophase and each chromosome consists of two
intertwining chromatids. II: Like chromosomes (homologous) pair up, or *synapse*. Since each
pair will have four chromatids, these pairs are often designated as *tetrads*. III: Pairing is complete at this stage, and the chromosomes are thicker and more tightly coiled. IV: The chromosomes now "open up" and the centromeres are evident; however, they *do not* split. V: The
chromosomes are shorter in this stage, which is the terminal phase of prophase. It can be observed in both stages IV and V that there were regions at which the chromatids of homologous
chromosomes crossed (chiasmata). VI: Metaphase of first division in which the chromosomes
line up in pairs. The nuclear membrane disappears. VII: Anaphase of first division, at which
time the homologous chromosomes are separated. VIII: Early telophase. The two chromatids
(dyads) of each chromosome move to the opposite ends of the cell, and the chromosome number
accordingly is reduced to one half. IX: The metaphase of the second division, in which the
chromosomes line up on the equatorial plate. X: Anaphase, at which time the centromeres
divide and the chromatids of each chromosome separate. XI: The chromatids move to the opposite ends of the cell. Since only one of the four original chromatids of each tetrad goes into
the mature reproductive cell, each is sometimes referred to as a *monad*.

the prophase of meiosis are coiled threadlike strands with characteristic enlargements of varying size along with the strands and, as in mitosis, these threads are composed of two *chromatids*. It is very significant, however, that when the prophase of the first maturation division is terminated and metaphase begins, the chromosomes line up in *pairs* in the equatorial plane. Since each of the two chromosomes is composed of two chromatids, a four-part body, sometimes called a *tetrad*, is present at the beginning of metaphase. Such paired chromosomes are called *bivalents*. It is convenient to designate the metaphase of the first division as metaphase I to distinguish it from the metaphase of the second division. Metaphase I obviously is very different from the mitotic metaphase because in the former there are two chromosomes lined up side by side instead of a single row of chromosomes as found in mitosis.

The reduction of chromosome number is accomplished during anaphase I and telophase I by the separation of the paired chromosomes. Thus each of the daughter cells will receive only one member of each pair of chromosomes. The eight chromosomes of the sperm cell of the fruit fly, for example, emerge from prophase as four pairs; and each of the two new sperm cells will receive only one of each pair, or four chromosomes. Essentially, the chromosome pairs separate, but the chromatids of chromosomes *do not separate* during anaphase I and telophase I. The result is that the new sperm cells have only half the number of chromosomes of the original parent sperm cell and each chromosome has two chromatids. In contrast with tetrads, the chromosomes at this time are often designated as *dyads*. Figure 7.10, which shows the maturation

Figure 7.10. The maturation period of sperm development.

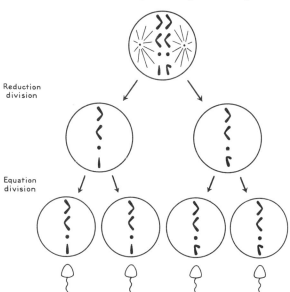

Reduction
division

Equation
division

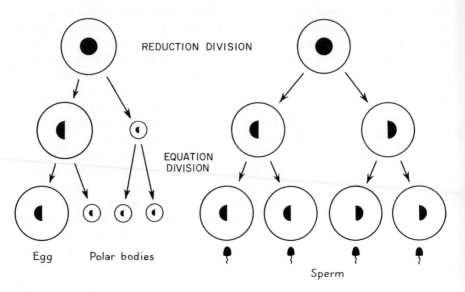

Figure 7.11. The maturation of egg and of sperm cells and the relationship of the polar bodies to the egg are shown. These are egg cells with minute amounts of cytoplasm.

period of sperm development, illustrates this in the simplest possible fashion. We should note that the chromosomes are not shown as double bodies but simply as pairs in this diagram.

After the first of the maturation divisions, the four chromosomes, each composed of two chromatids, line up in the equatorial plate of metaphase II and a typical mitotic division occurs. The two chromatids separate during anaphase II and telophase II and each of the daughter sperm cells receives one chromatid. These chromosomes are called *monads*. Since each chromatid represents one chromosome, the chromosome number will be four in each of the sperm cells. The second maturation division, therefore, is the equational division.

There is one important difference in the maturation of sperm and egg cells that we should also note at this time. Four functional sperm cells can be formed from each of the immature sperm cells that existed at the end of the growth period. Only one functional and three small nonfunctional egg cells develop, however, when the egg matures. The three small egg cells have normal chromosome numbers but possess only minute amounts of cytoplasm. The nonfunctional egg cells are called *polar bodies*, because they remain attached for a period of time to the surface (pole) of the functional egg cell. This peculiar division of the egg into cells of dissimilar size permits the reduction of chromosomes to take place but retains within one functional cell the food (yolk) necessary for the early nutrition of the embryo.

Embryonic Development: the New Individual

Embryogeny

It should be remembered that among the Protozoa mitosis results in the creating of new individuals. Mitosis in the many-celled animals merely subdivides the organism into more and more cells, and embryonic development does not begin in most animals until after the male reproductive cell, the *sperm*, has entered the cytoplasm of the egg cell. The head of the sperm is concentrated nuclear material, and as we observed in the conjugation of *Paramecium*, the male nucleus contains only one half the adult number of chromosomes. The nucleus of the egg cell likewise has the half number, so that the combination of sperm nucleus with egg nucleus, which technically is true *fertilization*, endows the embryo with a full set of chromosomes. It is important to keep this fact in mind, because this is significant in the subsequent determination of the characteristics of a new individual.

Many animals and plants can begin embryonic development without the fertilization of the egg. This surprising turn of events, noted previously, is *parthenogenesis* (literally, virgin birth) and is very common among insects. The problem of the stimulus to development has been subjected to experimental analysis, and at least in some animals the stimulus may be supplied by cooling or dehydrating the egg cells for a short time, then replacing them in a normal environment. It has been possible to remove egg cells surgically from virgin rabbits, place them in salt solution, and then implant them in other female rabbits, where they have developed. "Fatherless" bunnies have been born as a result of this experiment. It is disturbing to masculine ego that the male is unnecessary in the process of forming a new generation, but in these

Figure 7.12. These photographs of the formation of a polar body show that the chromosome distribution is normal. (Copyright by General Biological Supply House, Inc., Chicago.)

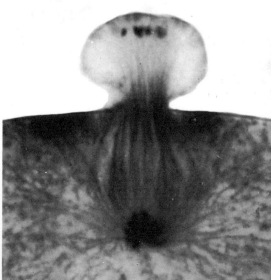

experiments a dish of salt water was as effectual as a buck rabbit.

The difficulties of survival which beset a miniature animal are appalling, and the chance of any given egg becoming an adult is remote. In this connection, the importance of the amount of food material stored in the egg cell cannot be overemphasized. Organisms that develop from egg cells having only a small amount of food material (*yolk*) in the cytoplasm of the egg cell grow rapidly to minute, free-living stages, or *larvae*, that can feed themselves. Embryos with a large amount of yolk develop more slowly, becoming larger, more complex animals. Thus we find that animals which produce eggs with small reserves of food usually lay them by the hundred thousands. Conversely, only a few eggs with large quantities of yolk will be formed, and these are often surrounded by a case, or shell, and deposited in a protected place. The two methods of ensuring that there will be a new generation have the same end result. Relatively few of the small eggs, but a proportionately large number of the large eggs will survive; so the numbers of new animals will be roughly comparable in both cases. There are, as might be expected, exceptions to this generalization: for example, most mammals have few eggs, and these contain minute quantities of yolk. Such eggs develop within the female, however, where they are protected and nourished.

CLEAVAGE • The mitotic divisions that begin embryonic life constitute *cleavage*, so called because the ovum is cleaved (subdivided) into units by the constrictions which form the cell membranes. Nuclear behavior is typical of mitosis, but the size and arrangement of the cells which result are influenced by the original organization of the egg cell and by the amount of yolk present. Cleavage, therefore, may produce cells of very dissimilar size, and the subsequent fate of these cells in the embryo may be very different. Eggs with a small amount of yolk uniformly distributed throughout the cytoplasm have the resultant cells equal in size, at least during the early stages of development. Mitosis frequently is synchronized during cleavage, so that the increase in the number of cells progresses as a doubling at each division: 2—4—8—16—32—64—128. Most embryos, however, lose this synchronization by the 64-cell stage, primarily because the cells on the lower side of the embryo, at the *vegetal pole*, usually have larger amounts of yolk which act as a mechanical hindrance to the constriction of the protoplasm, and these cells cannot keep pace with those on the upper side of the embryo, at the *animal pole*. Certain animals, of which man is an example, lack this synchronization, so that 3-cell and 5-cell stages are common.

Chemical changes take place in the egg upon the entrance of the sperm. The sperm nucleus enlarges, apparently by absorbing water from the egg cell, and a *fertilization membrane* forms an outer covering for the ovum. This membrane makes a protective sheath about the embryo during the early cleavage stages, and in addition, perhaps aids in preventing the entrance of additional sperm into the egg. The first division may be vertical, separating the embryo into right and left halves, or may be horizontal, dividing the egg into upper

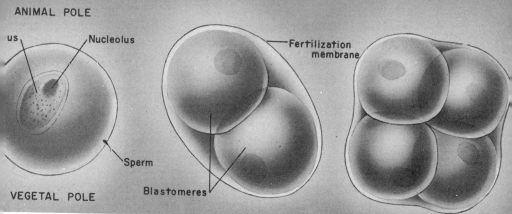

ANIMAL POLE

us
Nucleolus

Fertilization
membrane

Sperm

VEGETAL POLE

Blastomeres

Figure 7.13. These drawings, (a) and (b), depict the changes which occur during the cleavage of the starfish embryo from the fertilized egg to the morula stage of development. Note that there is only a slight change in the size of the embryo.

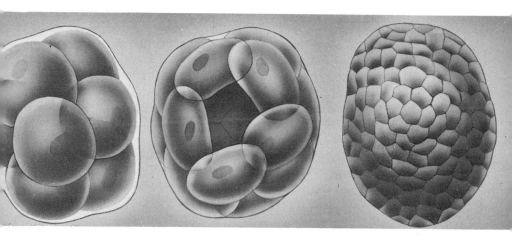

In (c) the left-hand drawing illustrates a gastrula as it would appear normally, with the surface of the ectoderm visible. The right-hand drawing, however, diagrams the details of the structure of a gastrula, with its layers and cavities.

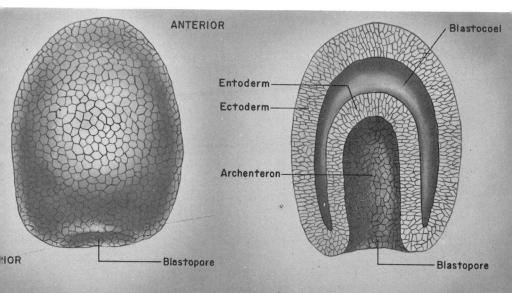

ANTERIOR

Blastocoel

Entoderm

Ectoderm

Archenteron

IOR

Blastopore

Blastopore

and lower halves.   If the yolk is concentrated in the lower, or vegetal, pole of
the egg cell, the first two cells of a horizontal division will be of unequal size.
This condition is very common, because very few eggs have an equal cleavage.
Mitotic divisions take place with great rapidity in an embryo, and the cells
during cleavage become smaller and smaller as their number is increased by
successive cleavages.   The embryo has a distinct ball-like appearance at the
16-cell or 32-cell stage, which is often referred to as a *morula* (berry).

Motion pictures taken by time-lapse photography during cleavage show that
the cells do not behave as inert marbles but constantly roll and tumble over
each other.   This observation is significant, because after about the 32-cell or
64-cell stages, the cells rearrange themselves as a result of the migration of
the interior cells to the surface to form a hollow ball, the *blastula* (little germ).
The hollow cavity inside the blastula is known as the *blastocoel*.   Previous to
the formation of this blastula, the cells do not grow in size, and at the 64-cell
stage the embryo may be slightly smaller in volume than the original uncleaved
egg.   When the cells of the blastula begin to increase in size, the synchronization of mitotic divisions is lost and the cells show distinct differences.

BLASTULATION AND GASTRULATION • The formation of the blastula, *blastulation,*because of variation in growth and in the specialization of cells, marks the
end of cleavage and the beginning of a new process in development.   Cell multiplication does continue, of course, but more important events are now shaping
the young animal.   It is the upper, animal-pole cells that divide more rapidly
at this time, and because of overgrowth in this region and the pressures developed, we now can observe the folding in of the lower, vegetal-pole cells.   This
appears first on the embryo as a tiny pit or pore on the surface of the blastula,
the *blastopore,* and this pit marks the site at which the cells are folding into
the cavity of the blastula from the surface.

This transformation into a two-layered condition is known as *gastrulation.*

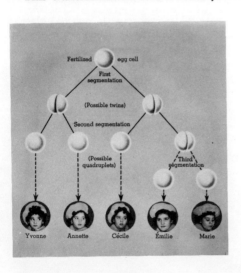

Figure 7.14.   Quintuplets.   A subdivision of an embryo into two parts early in
development can result in the development of identical twins.   When more
than two subdivisions occur, the result
may be identical triplets, quadruplets, or
even quintuplets.   (Courtesy King Features Syndicate, Inc.)

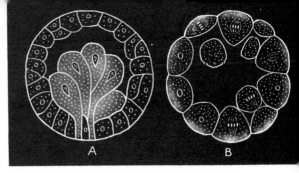

Figure 7.15. Formation of the entoderm by polar ingression (a) or by delamination, or splitting off, of the inner edges of the cells (b) occurs frequently in Metazoa.

A   B

It can be seen best by cutting an embryo at this stage, and it will be observed that the embryo is a *two-layered* structure, the *gastrula* (little stomach), composed of an *ectoderm* (outer skin) and an *entoderm* (inner skin). At this time many embryos escape from the fertilization membrane and become free-living animals. Such embryos, or *larvae*, move about by action of the cilia which are formed on their outer layer and swim with the animal pole forward. This means that an anterior-posterior axis has been developed. The beating of the cilia not only propels the animal through the water, but in addition creates currents of water which sweep food particles into the blastopore where they are taken into the cavity formed by the inner layer of cells. This primitive feeding mechanism makes it possible for the embryo to be independent and, barring accidental death, for it to grow and continue its transformation into an adult.

EMBRYONIC LAYERS • The inner layer of embryonic cells, the *entoderm*, forms the lining of the embryonic digestive tract, the *archenteron* (*arch* = primitive; *enteron* = gut or digestive tract). The opening into the archenteron, of course, is the *blastopore*. The skin and sense organs of the organism will be formed from the outer layer, the *ectoderm*. Although the appearance of the gastrula is modified by different amounts of yolk present, all these essential structures are recognizable in the embryonic development of all the metazoans.

Figure 7.16. Specializations of epithelial tissues. Special sensory structures may be developed in an epithelium: for example, the taste buds (a) are such structures. Glandular epithelium in the thyroid gland (b) shows another of the several specializations of epithelial tissues. [(a) Copyright by General Biological Supply House, Inc., Chicago; (b) courtesy Clarence Flaten.]

(a)   (b)

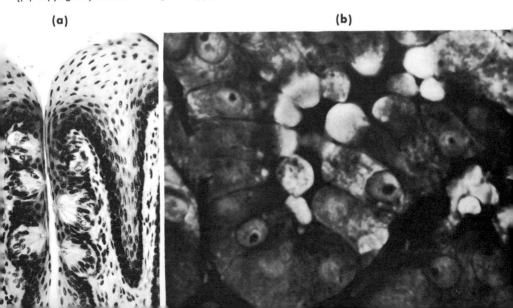

The Metazoa, therefore, by the processes of *cleavage, blastulation,* and *gastrulation* (Figure 7.13), acquire the basic features which distinguish them from the acellular animals.

Restricted areas of the body now may be seen to have diverse environments and to become adapted to these environments. The ectoderm, being on the surface, is the first to be in contact with the environment, hence the locomotion of the organism is one of the prime responsibilities of this layer. It is not surprising, therefore, to discover that the sense organs, the nervous system, the skin, and some parts of various locomotor structures will be developed from the ectoderm. The entoderm, being far removed from most environmental stimuli, has thrust upon it the responsibility for nutrition. That the digestive system and the glands associated with digestion and related functions should be developed from the entoderm seems to be a reasonable division of labor. Later we shall observe that in many phyla of animals a third layer will develop *between* the ectoderm and entoderm. This important third layer is the *mesoderm,* but we will discuss its formation at a more appropriate time.

Embryogenesis of frog

We chose to describe the early stages of embryonic development of echinoderm embryos because of their relative simplicity. Most animals, however, have eggs which contain moderate to large amounts of yolk. A high yolk content in an egg is advantageous because it provides readily available food for the developing embryo, but it also is a heavy inert material which mechanically hinders the processes of embryogenesis. The bird egg is one of the most extreme examples of a yolked egg that can be found in the animal kingdom. The shell and "whites" of the hen's egg are actually membranes formed to protect the egg itself—that portion we usually inexactly call the "yolk." As the term implies, the bird egg is predominately yolk and only the small white disc on the surface is protoplasm. It should be apparent that the entire egg (yolk and disc) cannot cleave to form blastomeres of equal size as does the sea star egg. The development of the bird egg is so extensively modified because of its high yolk content that we will not attempt to describe its embryogenesis. Instead, we use as our example an egg with an amount of yolk intermediate in quantity between the sparsely yolked echinoderm and the heavily yolked avian egg. Fortunately, frog eggs are abundant and are excellent illustrations of the moderately yolked condition. Equally fortunate is the fact that experimental studies of the embryonic development of the frog have provided valuable information for analyzing embryogenesis. We will consider this information in detail in its broad biological aspects later.

Organization of egg

The frog egg has several prominent features that are evident before it leaves the ovary. A darkly pigmented area covers slightly more than half the egg, and the remaining portion of the egg has a light creamy color. The lighter area is the region where the yolk is more concentrated. The egg has not completed its meiotic divisions when it is released from the ovary, and the first meiotic division occurs in the upper part of the oviduct with the formation of an atypical oocyte, the *first polar body*. This cell contains the same number of chromosomes as the ovum but has only a minute amount of cytoplasm. As the egg continues its passage through the oviduct to the uterus, the second meiotic division begins but is arrested in the metaphase stage, and division does not resume until fertilization occurs. The male deposits sperm over the eggs as they are released by the female and fertilization must take place quickly because a thick protective jelly coat forms rapidly about the egg in the water. The jelly is the result of the swelling of a membrane which was deposited about the egg in a "dehydrated" form in the ovary. The egg is free to turn within its jelly coating and the rotation brings the pigmented area to the top. The center of the pigmented area marks the *animal pole* and opposite this on the lower (yolk) side of the egg is the *vegetal pole.*

A remarkable event can be observed immediately after the egg is fertilized. Part of the pigment at the junction of the nonpigmented area migrates and this movement results in the development of a grey crescent-shaped region. This area, which has been aptly named the *grey crescent,* is of great significance in the development of the frog embryo.

Cleavage

The union of the male and female pronuclei is followed by the first cleavage division of the egg. This division begins as a furrow at the animal pole and progresses to the vegetal pole to create the first two blastomeres. The second cleavage division occurs at right angles to the first and also extends from animal to vegetal pole. The first four blastomeres are comparable in respect to content of pigmented and nonpigmented cytoplasm but, because of the location and shape of the grey crescent, this region is not quartered.

The third cleavage division is very different from the first two since its furrow is horizontal, and thus an upper and a lower cluster of cells is formed. The three cleavage divisions produce eight cells of which the upper four are smaller, heavily pigmented, and contain less yolk than the lower four. This is the first major expression of the hindrance provided by the high yolk concentration in the lower part of the egg. Succeeding divisions further emphasize the effect of the yolk because the cells in the upper half of the egg cleave rapidly whereas those in the lower half cleave slowly. Marked size differences and differences in the number of blastomeres are very obvious in the two hemispheres after only a few cleavage divisions have occurred.

Blastulation and gastrulation

The cells of the upper hemisphere of the embryo continue to cleave with great rapidity and begin to extend over the larger yolk-laden cells. An internal

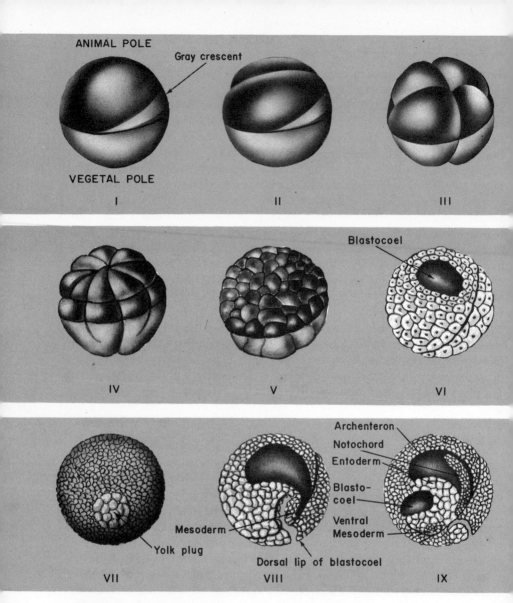

Figure 7.17. Frog Embryogenesis. I: The darkly pigmented upper hemisphere and the lighter, heavily yolked lower hemisphere show clearly. The *grey crescent* is evident at the junction of the two areas. II–III: These stages are shown at slightly different angles to illustrate that cleavage proceeds more rapidly in the upper hemisphere. IV: The marked difference in the size of the blastomeres is evident at this stage, during which there are approximately sixteen-cells. V–VI: These figures show an *early blastula* stage in surface and cutaway views. VII: The yolk-plug stage is reached when the small cells of the upper hemisphere grow over the lower yolk-laden cells, forcing them to the interior. VIII: This cutaway lateral view demonstrates the beginning of *gastrulation*. The dorsal lip of the blastopore appears first and presumptive notochord (mesodermal) cells begin to grow forward below the ectoderm. IX: This sketch shows the beginning of the ventral lip of the blastopore. Note that the blastocoel has been displaced and a new cavity, the archenteron, is now present.

examination of the embryo after 8 to 10 hours of development will show the presence of a small internal cavity, the *blastocoel*. This cavity is not centrally located but is in the upper half of the embryo with the larger yolk-laden cells comprising its floor.

The next major embryonic event occurs during the interval from 20 to 24 hours after fertilization and is marked by the appearance of a small groove slightly below the grey-crescent area of the vegetal half of the embryo. This groove is the first evidence of the *blastopore*. Actually it is only the *dorsal lip* of the blastopore and is the point at which a few of the small animal-pole cells begin to invaginate. This is the beginning of endoderm formation and the blastopore marks the future posterior end of the animal. Once started in its development, the lip of the blastopore extends ventrally and laterally forming first a semicircle and then a complete circle. Cell movements are much more complex at this stage than any observed in the echinoderm embryos. Invagination is a minor event in the frog and the endoderm develops primarily by two other processes: the first involves the rolling under of cells at the blastopore, or *involution*; and the second is an overgrowth of cells, or *epiboly*. The action of the last two processes produces the gastrula which in its early stage has a small remnant of yolk cells in the center of the blastopore. These cells are referred to as the *yolk plug*, but, in the late gastrula stage, the "plug" is completely covered by an overgrowth of the animal-pole cells. All the vegetal-pole cells, therefore, are incorporated internally and the blastopore remains only as a slit-like opening.

Organization of embryo

A re-examination of the early gastrula stage will provide some observations which will be of considerable importance later when we discuss the question of the regulation of development (p. 138). The first portion of the endoderm is formed by the cells of the dorsal lip of the blastopore. If the embryo is marked with dyes, or if time-lapse motion pictures are taken of the blastopore region, we can observe an interesting movement of cells. Cells from the region of the grey-crescent area migrate into the blastopore to comprise the middorsal roof of the developing archenteron. This region of cells is spoken of as the *chordameso-derm* because the *notochord* and some of the mesoderm develop from it. The notochord, as we will observe later, is the central axis for animals in the phylum Chordata of which man is a representative organism. The ectoderm immediately above the chordamesoderm thickens, forms longitudinal folds, and fuses in the midline to form a tube which becomes a *dorsal tubular nervous system*. The cells from the region of the grey crescent which migrated by way of the dorsal lip of the blastopore to become part of the chordamesoderm actually "organize" the formation of the nervous system. This is true not only in the frog, but also in other Chordates.

Extensive experimentation with frog embryos has established that the blasto-meres become specialized by the very beginning of cleavage. It is possible to locate areas in the undivided egg which will be associated only with certain adult tissues or organs. The embryogenesis of the frog, therefore, is in marked contrast to that of the sea star. Furthermore, the relationships between the nuclei and cytoplasm in the frog have afforded a valuable system for the analysis of developmental processes. We will discuss these relationships in more detail in connection with the regulation of cellular activity by the nucleus.

The embryo as an organism

It should be apparent that an embryo deserves status as an organism equal to that accorded an adult. Free-living larval stages of many animals are aggressive predators or voracious herbivores. Notable among these are the immature stages of insects. All embryos must perform the functions of nutrition, respiration, excretion, and coordination. Indeed, as will be noted subsequently, some embryos even reproduce! Elaborate specializations of cells or organs are observed frequently in embryos, especially among complex parasitic forms. Also is commonly found that developmental stages of parasites are more typical of their respective phyla than are the adults. It will be evident in our subsequent studies of different animal groups that the embryos are often as adaptable to environmental conditions as are the adults.

Tissue Organization: Specialized Cells

Tissues

Groups of similar cells, specialized to perform specific functions, constitute *tissues*. The specializations in tissues involve the development of structures both within cells, *intracellular*, and between cells, *intercellular*. Considerable

Figure 7.18. Ambystoma and human skin. Stratified squamous epithelium. Note the very thick cornified layer of the skin, right, and the presence of large skin glands in Ambystoma, left. In Ambystoma you may distinguish the skin glands (a), surface squamous cells (b), and basal columnar cells (c).

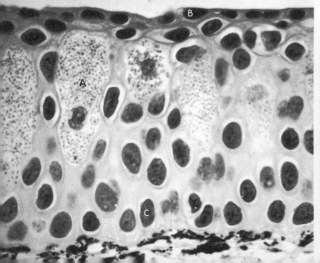
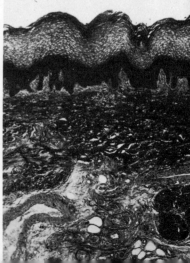

Figure 7.19. Protoplasmic bridges. Groups of cells often are able to function in an integrated fashion as a result of intercellular bridges, strands of protoplasm which provide a structural continuity. (Copyright by General Biological Supply House, Inc., Chicago.)

variation is found in the quantity and nature of the special structures which, taken together, compose these tissues. The specialization of some tissues is chiefly intracellular; that of others, intercellular. The classification of the tissues is based to a considerable extent on these differences. The four major types of tissues are as follows.

1. *Epithelial tissues* are those which cover surfaces and line cavities. They are primarily cellular, with only small amounts of cementing intercellular substance, and intracellular specialization is an important feature.

2. *Contractile tissues* are the muscle tissues, which, as a result of the presence of intracellular contractile fibrils, have the ability to shorten. There are only small amounts of intercellular materials present.

3. *Conductile tissues* are the nervous tissues, and because they possess intracellular conductile fibrils, they are able to relay impulses from one part of an organism to another. These also are characterized by limited quantities of intercellular substances.

4. *Connective and supportive tissues* are the most versatile of all the tissues. The predominant characteristic of these tissues is an intercellular substance in the form of fibrils, fluid, or salts.

Epithelial tissues

These tissues are varied in cellular composition but always possess a minimum amount of intercellular substance. The epithelia are classified primarily by the shape of the cells which compose them and, to a lesser extent, by their intracellular structures.

The *cuboidal* and *columnar* tissues usually are only one cell-layer thick, and the individual cells are cubical or columnar in form. Frequently, because of the pressure of adjacent cells, the shape may be somewhat distorted. The cuboidal epithelia are found in many glands, while the columnar epithelia are found in the lining of ducts and of the alimentary canal. The columnar cells also are frequently glandular, modified into "goblet," or ciliated, cells. The cilia on the surface of an epithelium beat in such a fashion that particles may be moved toward the exterior of the body. The linings of respiratory passages and reproductive ducts may be ciliated.

The *squamous epithelia* (*squamosus* = scaly, or flattened) are of two types: the *simple* and the *stratified*. The simple squamous epithelium is composed of a single layer of much-flattened cells, which therefore constitute an extremely thin protoplasmic veneer over the structures they cover or line. Fluids pass readily through the simple squamous epithelium which is important as a lining for blood vessels or other structures where fluid exchange is necessary. The stratified squamous epithelium is many cell-layers thick, and only the superficial layers are of simple squamous cells. Columnar cells are found within the deeper layers of the tissue. This tissue is especially valuable where surfaces are subjected to considerable wear, such as the surface of the human body. New cells gradually reach the surface as old cells above them are eroded away. The outermost cells are dead and frequently contain chemically inert *keratin granules* which are insoluble in all but strong acids or alkalis and thus constitute a chemically inert sheath for the body. This epithelium, therefore, is one of the major reasons that a long-distance swimmer or a Saturday-night bather does not go into solution during the course of such activity. Thickenings, or *calluses*, occur in stratified squamous epithelium as a result of continued pressure or wear in localized areas. Also, the separation of the epithelium from the underlying tissues leaves a space which will fill with fluid to form a *blister*, and if damage is done to small blood vessels in the area when the separation occurs, a *blood blister* will appear.

Small amounts of the *cementing substance* constitute the intercellular material of the epithelia. This substance is often perforated by strands of protoplasm that run from one cell to another and bring large numbers of cells into direct protoplasmic continuity with each other. Such strands may be considered to be intercellular bridges. Figure 7.19 shows these intercellular strands very clearly.

Figure 7.20. Smooth and striated muscle. The cigar- or spindle-shaped smooth-muscle cells (a) are in sharp contrast with the rectangular, striated muscle cells from heart tissue (b). [(a) Courtesy Clarence Flaten; (b) copyright by General Biological Supply House, Inc., Chicago.]

(a)   **(b)**

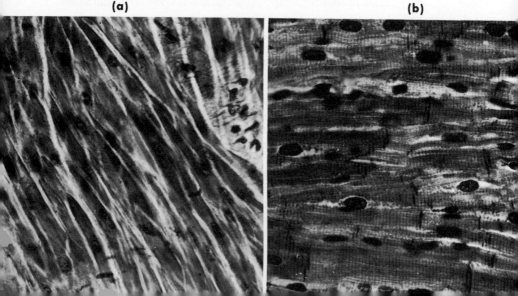

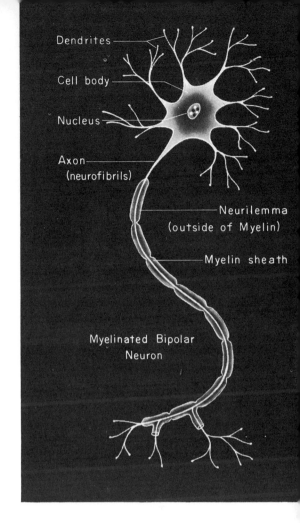

Figure 7.21. The structures of a typical nerve cell (see text, p. 126).

Contractile, or muscle, tissues

These tissues make possible (1) the movements of the body in locomotion; (2) the movement of the blood, body fluids, and secretions; and (3) the mechanical work performed by various parts of the organism. The two types of muscle tissue are the *smooth*, or nonstriated, and the *striated*, or banded. It is also common to find the muscle tissues classified as *voluntary* or *involuntary*, depending on whether or not they are under the control of the will.

Smooth muscle is found in the walls of the blood vessels, the alimentary canal, the viscera, and the reproductive organs. Small bundles and even single cells may be found in the skin, and in mammals such cells are connected to the bases of the hairs. The contraction of these muscles will "stand the hair on end." Also, in the squid the muscle cells may connect with pigment cells, and by their contraction or relaxation change the shape of the pigment cells, causing waves of protective color to sweep over the animal. Smooth-muscle cells are elon-

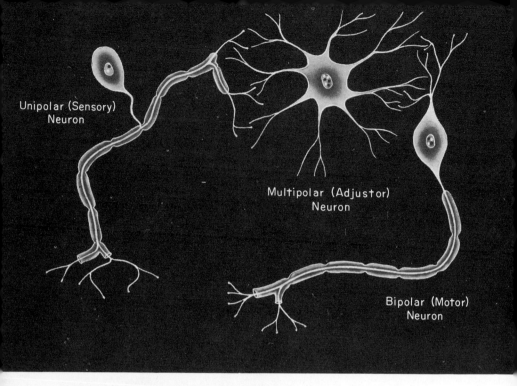

Figure 7.22. Types of nerve cells and their relationships (see text, p. 126).

gated and spindle shaped. A single centrally located nucleus is present. When the cells have been prepared for microscopical study, very delicate, densely packed contractile *fibrils* can be observed within the cell. These are not seen, however, in living cells in tissue culture, perhaps because they transmit light as does the remainder of the cytoplasm. The smooth-muscle cells usually are in the form of layers or sheets, and several of these may be present in an organ, in which case the fibers in the layers run in various directions. These cells will respond slowly to stimuli, are capable of being stretched considerably and will contract forcibly. This is called *involuntary muscle* because it is not under the control of the will.

Striated skeletal muscle is very different from smooth muscle in most of its features. It is found connected to the movable appendages of the body and to the skeleton. Striated muscles consist of long, cylindrical bands (*fibers*), in which the mass is not subdivided into distinct cells by cross partitions. The muscle fiber is considered to be either a single multinucleated cell or a group of cells fused into a long contractile band. The *myofibrils* found within a striated muscle fiber are distinct and possess pronounced *cross striations*. Small muscle fibers of this type have a diameter of 10 to 20 microns, and myofibrils are usually 1 to 2 microns in diameter. Alternating light and dark bands, the *discs*, give a striking appearance to the myofibrils, while imparting to the muscle its striated appearance. The most complicated cross striations are found in insect muscles, which contract very rapidly. Skeletal-muscle fibers are bound together in bundles of varying size and are joined to the skeleton at their ends by connective-tissue fibers of the *tendons*. Striated skeletal muscles are called *voluntary* because they may be contracted at will.

Striated cardiac muscle is a type of muscle found in the hearts of the vertebrates. This muscle is faintly striated, and possesses qualities of both smooth and skeletal fibers. It contracts slowly in comparison with skeletal muscle and forms in thick sheets or bands that run parallel to the surface of the heart. It can be stretched extensively, and the greater the amount of stretch, the greater will be the resultant contraction. The most dramatic feature of cardiac muscle is its automatic rhythmic contraction, or *beat*. It is important to note that the contractions begin in early embryonic life, before there is any blood to be pumped and before any nerves are connected to the heart. Contractions will continue after the heart has been removed from the body and even after the heart has been cut into strips. No distinct cell membranes separate the cardiac muscle cells from each other, and the cells interlace. Here we should mention an important feature of muscle tissue. Not only will individual cells contract when stimulated, but also the contractions of one fiber will stimulate adjacent fibers to contract. A wave of contraction can be propagated which may move the entire length of an organ, such as the intestine. This contraction wave is very important in the invertebrates because it affords a simple device to move blood through the muscular tubes which constitute the blood vessels and hearts of invertebrate animals.

Conductile, or nervous, tissues

These exploit to the fullest extent that property of protoplasm which we have called *irritability*. The cells which make up nervous tissue have become highly specialized for what is termed *awareness*, and for the *conduction* of impulses from one part of the organism to another. *Receptors* for all types of stimuli have been developed in the animal kingdom. These range from simple *hairs* on the skin, which connect at their bases to sensitive nerve endings, to more complicated *balancing organs*, and eventually to the almost unbelievably complex, light-sensitive, image-forming *eye*. Most of the receptors are a complex of tissues and can be discussed better when we consider coordination in the various phyla; at this time the cellular structure of nervous tissue will be our chief concern.

Nervous tissue is predominantly cellular. There is intercellular fatty material around the cells and their processes. A special type of connective tissue holds the various elements, or cells, together; except for this, the intercellular material is at a minimum. The typical nerve cell consists of a cell body and one or several processes, or outgrowths, which extend from it. A *process* is made up of a central cylinder containing *neurofibrils*, surrounded by a sheath of one layer, the *neurilemma*. A second, fatty sheath, the *myelin*, when present appears to serve as an insulating shield, much like the rubber covering on a lamp cord. The very thin neurofibrils are the "wires" which relay the messages. Three types of nerve cells, the *neurons,* can be found in many of the phyla: (1) neurons which have a single process, the *unipolar nerve cells;* (2) cells with two processes, the *bipolar nerve cells;* and (3) those cells which contain many processes, the *multipolar nerve cells.*

A bipolar nerve cell illustrates the basic features of any neuron. The longer of the two processes is the *axon;* the shorter is the *dendrite.* The axon is microscopic in diameter, except in a few rare instances, but may be several feet long. A neuron—for example, in man—may reach from the lower region of the spine to the tip of the big toe; or in an elephant, from the spinal cord to the tip of its ponderous leg. Groups of nerve-cell bodies are called *ganglia,* and the nerves act as "cables," being composed of bundles of nerve fibers. Ganglia may be classified as either *sensory* or *motor,* depending on whether they are carrying messages to or from the central nervous system, respectively. Aggregations of multipolar cells generally are found in the central portions of the nervous system, where they serve as "switchboards" for the communication system. The complexity of nervous coordination may be said to begin with the elementary nervous system of the jellyfishes, where it is composed of a loose network of scattered nerve cells, and to progress in complexity through increasing concentrations of cell bodies to the highly centralized and complex nervous system of man and his close relatives. We shall observe these developments when we study the various phyla.

Connective and supportive tissues

These tissues in the triploblastic animals are derived almost exclusively from the third embryonic layer, the *mesoderm* (p. 116), and they constitute the great-

Figure 7.23. The white fibrous tissue (a) is composed chiefly of bands of heavy nonelastic fibers, in contrast to the areolar tissue (b), which has both nonelastic (wavy) fibers and elastic (smaller straight) fibers in a loose network. (Courtesy Clarence Flaten.)

(a)   (b)

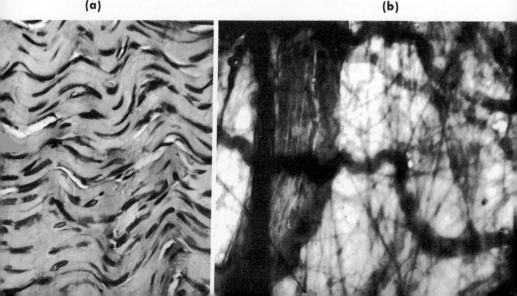

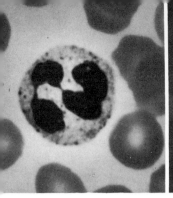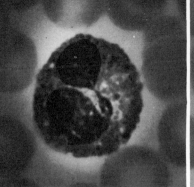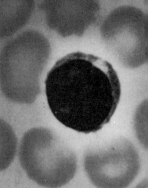

Figure 7.24. White blood cells and red blood cells. Three different kinds of white cells are shown. (Copyright by General Biological Supply House, Inc., Chicago.)

est amount of body substance in these forms. Such tissues are well defined by their name, since they connect various organs and give the body its supporting frame. Their most predominant single feature is the presence of fibers, which may be of two types: (1) the *white nonelastic* fibers; and (2) the *yellow elastic* fibers.

White fibrous connective tissues, such as *tendons* and *ligaments*, are composed of heavy bundles of white fibers, which, according to our best information, are laid down by special cells, the *fibroblasts* (fiber-formers). Arranged in flexible bundles, these heavy fibers are tough and resistant to being stretched and torn. They are, therefore, especially advantageous for attaching the muscles to the bones and make it possible for such unions to withstand great traction. The intercellular substance is a watery, gelatinous, cohesive material.

Yellow fibrous connective tissue is found in fewer places in the organism, but is important because of the flexibility it allows. It can be found connected to vertebrae, and in the tendons of the vocal cords and of the trachea. A very interesting "neck ligament" of cattle is a heavy band of elastic connective tissue which will elevate the head when the tension of the neck muscles is relaxed. The elastic fibers can be stretched but "snap back" when tension is released. The arrangement of fibers and cells is comparable to that in the white fibrous connective tissue.

Areolar connective tissue is distributed throughout the body and combines the features of both nonelastic and elastic tissues, as it is found in the form of a mat of interlacing nonelastic and elastic fibers. Flexibility and toughness are given the tissue by the white fibers, and elasticity by the yellow fibers, which return it to its original position when tensions are released. Fibroblasts are present, of course, as is also the gelatinous substance. There are, in addition, large numbers of free-moving amoeboid scavenger cells and fixed scavenger cells, the *phagocytes* (eating cells), scattered throughout the tissue. These cells engulf foreign matter and are a very important part of the body defense mechanism. Areolar tissue holds the skin to underlying areas, holds organs in position, and forms large supporting membranes. A large amount of fluid is present in areolar tissue.

Adipose connective tissue may be derived from areolar connective tissue as a result of the gradual accumulation of fat droplets within certain of the cells. This intracellular accumulation of fat can distend the cells and reduce the cytoplasm to a thin rim in which the nucleus makes a distinct bulge. Ordinary methods of preparing tissues for microscopical study will dissolve the fat, leaving the cell with a characteristic "signet-ring" appearance. Intercellular substance is in the form of a gelatinous material and fibers, but the tissue is primarily cellular. Adipose tissue has several extremely important functions: (1) layers of adipose tissue below the skin serve for *insulation*; (2) pads of adipose tissue make excellent shock absorbers (for example, behind the eye); and (3) adipose cells are important reservoirs of food, because the fat can be utilized during periods of starvation. Many animals form large stores of fat, in this way, sometimes in definite *fat bodies*, which supply the necessary food reserve to carry through periods when food is scarce.

Blood is sometimes classified separately as *vascular tissue* but is included here as a connective tissue. Blood is the source of supply of fluid for the body cells, and although the intercellular substance is fluid, the water content actually is comparable to that in areolar tissue. Blood cells are varied, but basically they are numerous free-moving *amoeboid cells*, sometimes called the *white blood cells*, which are phagocytes. The vertebrates also have *red blood cells* containing the pigment *hemoglobin*, which has the ability to combine with oxygen. Many of the animals without backbones possess hemoglobin or a related substance, *hemocyanin*, but these substances are usually dissolved in the fluid, or *plasma*, of the blood. In a few instances, however, they can be found in cells.

Bone and cartilage, the supportive tissues, are the primary skeletal supports and framework for the vertebrates and are almost exclusively limited to such skeletal forms. Some cartilage, however, does appear in small amounts in a

Figure 7.25. Supportive tissues—bone and cartilage. The difference in the arrangement of cells in bond (a) and in cartilage (b) is shown clearly. The fibers are obscured by the deposition of the salts which harden these supportive tissues. [(a) Copyright General Biological Supply House, Inc., Chicago; (b) courtesy Clarence Flaten.]

(a)   **(b)**

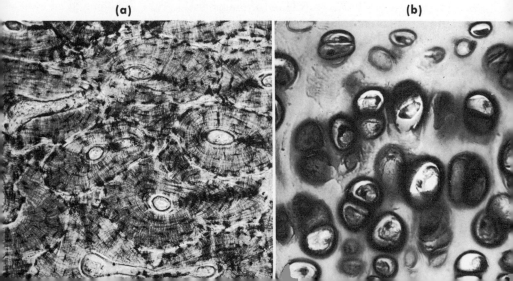

few of the invertebrates. The intercellular substance of bone is characterized by the presence of *fibers*, *mucoid substance*, and *calcium-phosphate* salts. When bone is burned, only the salts are left; but if bone is placed in a weak acid such as vinegar (acetic acid), the salts are dissolved, leaving only the fibrous matter. A bone so treated may be tied in a knot. Bone may be deposited in the form of *plates*, as in the skull, or in the form of *hollow rods* (containing bone marrow), as is illustrated by the long bones of the arm or leg. The cells which form bone are arranged in a very characteristic manner, and as the bone fibers and salts are formed or secreted, the formative cells are trapped within the newly formed bone.

Cartilage is more versatile than bone, due chiefly to the nature of the fibers which are present. These may be heavy white fibers comparable to those in bone, or yellow elastic fibers, or extremely fine white fibers. The last two types of cartilage are *fibro*, or *elastic, cartilage*, and *hyaline cartilage*. The cartilage cells not only make the fibers and mucoid substance but also are responsible for the deposition of considerable quantities of salts. The skeleton of the embryo of the vertebrate is composed of cartilage, which is later replaced by bone. It should be emphaisized that this is *replacement* and not transformation. Some animals, such as sharks, retain the cartilage in the adult skeleton and do not have bones.

Reticular tissue is sometimes recognized as a special type of fibrous connective tissue. It is made up of an interlacing network of very fine white fibers which differ from those of white fibrous connective tissue not only in their size, but also in the fact that they branch. Reticular tissue forms the framework for the cells of many glands, especially those of the lymphatic system, such as lymph nodes. It is considered, therefore, as one of the supportive tissues.

Invertebrate tissues

The basic tissues which we have been considering, with the exception of bone and cartilage, are found throughout the animal kingdom. The invertebrates, however, have some modifications of the tissues which are not present, or are relatively uncommon, in the vertebrates. Among the invertebrates *pigmented tissues* and tissues containing *unicellular glands* are common; and muscle tissue is usually of the smooth-muscle type, although notable exceptions occur among the shellfish and insects and their relatives. The diploblastic animals, which do not have mesoderm, must develop their contractile cells from epithelial elements, as the jellyfish *epithelio-muscular* cells demonstrate. Such cells cover surfaces, but at their base these have long processes which contain contractile fibrils. The skeleton of the invertebrates, with a few exceptions, is on the outside and is called an *exoskeleton*; it is a nonliving secretion formed by the cells of the epithelium. It may be a very tough membrane,

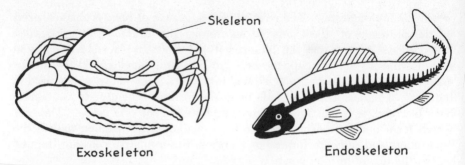

Figure 7.26. An exoskeleton provides a protective and supportive covering for an animal, much like the armor worn by a medieval knight. An endoskeleton, conversely, is an internal framework about which the animal is constructed. (After *Biology in Daily Life*, Curtis and Urban, Ginn and Co.)

and if hardened by the addition of salts, as in the Arthropoda, it makes a very effective skeleton.

Organs

We should note in conclusion that the tissues of the Metazoa (except for the sponges, the Porifera, and the jellyfishes and their relatives, the Coelenterata) are grouped together to form *organs* and *organ systems*. An organ is defined as a group of tissues working together to perform a common function. A good example is the *stomach*, which is covered and lined with an *epithelium*, has its mass composed of *contractile tissues* (muscles) and *connective tissues*, and is well supplied with *blood* and *nervous tissue*. Its special function, of course, is for *nutrition*. The development of organs permits greater flexibility of body organization and results in a more effective division of labor among the parts of organisms.

Origin of the Metazoa

In seeking to understand the ancient origin of the four distinctive features of the Metazoa, our detectivelike search immediately finds its attention focused

Figure 7.27. The flagellates show the transition from an acellular to a multicellular condition.

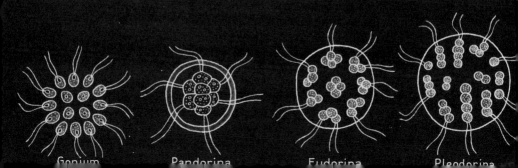

Gonium   Pandorina   Eudorina   Pleodorina

on the class Flagellata of the phylum Protozoa. You will remember that flagellates form colonies—that is, they subdivide into cell units, even though we persist in thinking of such cell units as individuals. Division of labor, the second feature, is also present, since both nutritive and reproductive individuals may be present in colonies of the flagellates. The third feature, layer formation, is less obvious, but both solid and hollow balls of cells are common. The development of an anterior-posterior axis, the fourth feature, is also common among the flagellates, as well as among other protozoans. These resemblances of the flagellates to the Metazoa caused zoologists more than a century ago to speculate that the metazoans might have been derived from the Flagellata. We now realize that such similarities between phyla may be disconcerting with respect to classification, because it is difficult to separate the organisms into their respective phyla. These resemblances, however, can supply valuable evidence for the interrelationship of organisms. Flagellates may be said to be the "kissing cousins" of the metazoans, distantly related and nice to have around.

It is possible to find organisms within one group of flagellates, the order Phytomonadina, which show gradations from the acellular condition to the presence of thousands of cells, from no division of labor to the formation of a body and reproductive cells, and from platelike masses to hollow balls of cells. *Polytoma* is a single-celled, or acellular, organism. *Gonium* varies, from 4 to 16 cells. *Pandorina* is a solid ball of 16 cells, while *Pleodorina* is a mass of 128 cells embedded in jelly and shows specialization. *Volvox* may have from a few hundred to as many as 20,000 cells; it has both *asexual and sexual reproduction; embryonic development* occurs; and a well-developed *anterior-posterior axis* is present in addition. Except for the existence of the intermediate forms cited here and still others which could have been included, *Volvox* would have to be classified as a metazoan animal. It must be emphasized that each of the above animals is an adult present-day form and that the common protozoan ancestor from which the early metazoans derived must have lived long, long ago. Most biologists agree, however, that metazoan ancestors must have been similar to these modern, adult protozoan forms, and that logically the Metazoa could have developed according to the pattern we have sketched. It will never be possible to have complete information on the subject, and we shall have to be satisfied with such circumstantial evidence as can be accumulated. *Volvox* is especially important as a piece in our jigsaw puzzle, because in this protozoan all the basic metazoan features have developed, except that *Volvox* lacks more than one layer of cells.

The spectacular similarity of the events in embryogenesis among metazoans to the curious parallel which can be drawn to these events among the flagellates was certain to attract attention. As early as 1828, the pioneer embryologist, Karl von Baer, observed that animals are essentially similar early in their embryonic development; but he added the important qualification that it is the *process* or *pattern* of development which is common to animals, and that the embryo of a "higher" form never resembles the adult of a "lower" form, only the embryo of the latter. The dynamic but scientifically shallow Ernst Haeckel seized upon the first statement of von Baer but ignored the second, and with a fertile imagination, invented in the middle of the nineteenth century the Theory of Recapitulation which took the biological world by storm. Briefly stated, Haeckel's hypothesis was that an organism in its embryonic development retraces its ancestral history. According to this theory, the ovum would correspond to an *acellular flagellate*, the morula to some form like *Pandorina*, the blastula to *Volvox*, and from *Volvox* it would be theoretically possible to derive the gastrula (provided, of course, an adult organism could be found which existed as a simple two-layered sac). The failure to find such an adult form led Haeckel to create a hypothetical form, the *Gastraea*, to fill this need. If Haeckel's theory were correct, then it should be possible to answer all questions of animal ancestry and evolution merely by studying the embryonic development of appropriate forms. Today, however, the pendulum of biological opinion has swung to the other extreme, and it is the second phase of von Baer's observation which is given credence: that it is the *process* or *pattern* of development which is common to animals. Any resemblance between the embryos of phyla of animals living and dead is to be correlated with developmental *patterns*, not with any direct ancestral link. Some animals, however, become so highly modified in their later embryological stages of development that it is only by studying earlier embryological stages that we can discover close relatives. Such studies in comparative embryology will always be an important tool for the biologist and will be discussed later.

We began this chapter with the remark that all of us have a little of Sherlock Holmes in our makeup. We may feel justified at the conclusion of this chapter in repeating the statement Holmes so often made, "Elementary my dear Watson," because we have many of the answers to our initial question, "How was it done?" The mystery of cell multiplication which maintains the same number of chromosomes from cell to cell was solved by knowledge of *mitosis*. The secret of the constancy of chromosome number from generation to generation was clarified by the analysis of *meiosis* and *fertilization*. The enigma of the formation of many cells from a single cell was resolved by an understanding of *embryogenesis* and *tissue formation*. Unfortunately, to describe how these things were done is not an adequate explanation of the mechanisms which have made it possible for these things to "happen." The mechanisms are not *elementary*. Fortunately, we are on the threshold of unlocking the doors which hide these secrets. Subsequent chapters will describe the results of deductive and inductive reasoning in biological detective stories which would have made Conan Doyle envious of their excellence. The reader will, however, be kept in suspense at this time unless he or she chooses to peek at the later chapters which will provide additional clues for unraveling the mysteries of inheritance and the regulation of cell differentiation.

REFERENCES

BAKER, J. R., "The Cell Theory," *Quarterly Journal of Microscopical Science, 90,* 1949.

BRIGGS, ROBERT, and THOMAS J. KING, "Changes in the nuclei of differentiating endoderm cells as revealed by nuclear transplantation," *Journal of Morphology, 100,* 1957, pp. 269–312.

DE ROBERTIS, E. D. P., W. W., NOWINSKI, and F. A. SAEZ, *General Cytology,* pp. 1–61. W. B. Saunders Company, Philadelphia, 1948.

HUGHES, ARTHUR, *The Mitotic Cycle.* Academic Press, New York, 1952.

HYMAN, L. H., *The Invertebrates: Protozoa through Ctenophora,* Vol. I, pp. 1–21, 248–283. McGraw-Hill Book Company, New York, 1940.

LEVINE, LAURENCE, *The Cell in Mitosis.* Academic Press, New York, 1963.

MARSLAND, D., "The Action of Hydrostatic Pressure on Cell Division," *New York Academy Science Annals, 51,* 1951, pp. 1327–1335.

MAXIMOW, A. A., and W. BLOOM, *A Textbook of Histology,* (5th ed.). W. B. Saunders Company, Philadelphia, 1948.

MULLER, H. J. C., C. C. LITTLE, and L. H. SNYDER, *Genetics, Medicine, and Man,* pp. 6–18. Cornell University Press, Ithaca, New York, 1947.

PEASE, D. C., "Hydrostatic Pressure Effects upon the Spindle and Chromosome Movement," *Biological Bulletin, 91,* 1946.

SCHRADER, F., *Mitosis.* Columbia University Press, New York, 1944.

TJIO, JOE HIN, and ALBERT LEVAN. "The Chromosome Number of Man," *Hereditas,* Band 1–2, 1956.

WHITMAN, C. O., "The Inadequacy of the Cell Theory of Development," *Journal of Morphology, 8,* 1893.

WILSON, E. B., *The Cell in Development and Heredity* (3rd ed.). The Macmillan Company, New York, 1937.

ZEUTHEN, ERIK, *Synchrony in Cell Division and Growth.* Interscience Publishers, New York, 1964.

8

Phylum

Porifera

●

From the point of view of the student of animal structure and functions, sponges offer many points of interest as representing the simplest type of cell republic found in any animal above the Protozoa.—E. A. Minchin, from Lankester's Treatise on Zoology, 1900

If it is true that the meek shall inherit the earth, then the Porifera have established a prior claim on this planet. The sponges are probably the least aggressive of all animals. They live a submerged existence in fresh water, the shallow seas, or the abysmal ocean depths. The bright colors of many, and the green coloration of those which have microscopic plants living in them as guests, misled biologists for centuries into thinking that the sponges were plants. This idea was also supported by the fact that adult sponges have absolutely no locomotion and are almost completely insensitive to external stimuli. The honor of a place in the animal kingdom was not accorded them until 1836, and even as late as 1867 their position among the Metazoa was in doubt. At that time some competent zoologists thought that the sponges were merely aggregations of flagellate protozoans, but in 1875 T. H. Huxley proposed that they should be considered as a side branch of the Metazoa and suggested for them the appellation of Parazoa (side animals). This is their accepted designation today, because we find no other metazoans which remotely resemble them, and their closest relatives are among the protozoans, the colonial Flagellata. Because of these very facts we have no difficulty in separating the Porifera from the other phyla of Metazoa.

Body form

The sponges are little more than a loose accumulation of cells within a thin-walled epithelial sac. They have no organs, and their tissues are limited to an epithelial covering of flattened cells and a lining of flagellated cells. Sponges vary in size from small animals approximately one-half inch high to large, liver-like masses ten to twelve feet tall.   The flaccid substance of the animals is strengthened by *spicules* of calcium carbonate or silica, or by organic fibers of *spongin,* and numerous canals that serve as channels for the circulation of water run throughout the entire body.   Minute openings, the *pores,* on the surface of the sponge admit water into the canals, and a larger opening, the *osculum,* is the excurrent aperture.   Food particles are trapped by the sponge cells as the water flows over them, and because of this unusual feeding mechanism the sponges are often referred to as animals that "sit and sift."   It may be obvious from this limited preview that there is considerable validity in the statement that the Porifera are animals of a *cellular grade of organization.* We shall see that the cells in addition retain a high degree of individual freedom of action and a very considerable amount of flexibility in the way in which they may alter their structure.

The arrangement of the canal system and basic body structure can be illustrated by using a simple type of sponge for comparison.   The sponges with the fewest complexities of body structures are those of the *asconoid* type.   The body is vase shaped, and because it can be cut into a number of similar parts by radial slices (like cutting a pie), it is said to have *radial symmetry.* The asconoid body wall is thin, covered on the outside and lined on the inside by a flattened epithelium.   A gelatinous *matrix* is present between the layers, in which are found large numbers of free-moving cells, the *amoebocytes,* which

Figure 8.1.   Sycon, Class 1, is often used to demonstrate sponge structure.   Shown in (b), Venus' flower basket, Class II.   Silicon spicules form the beautiful skeleton of this deep-sea sponge.   Other sponges are shown in Figure 8.6.   [(a) Courtesy Dr. A. M. Winchester, Stetson University; (b) courtesy Clarence Flaten.]

(a)   **(b)**

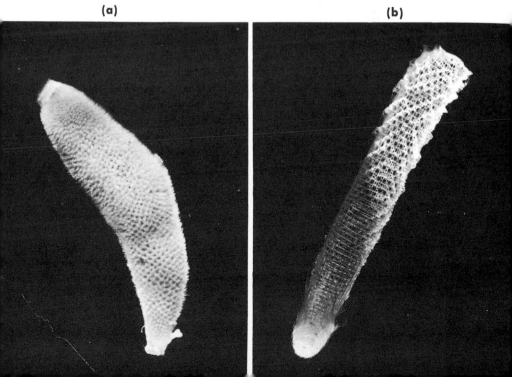

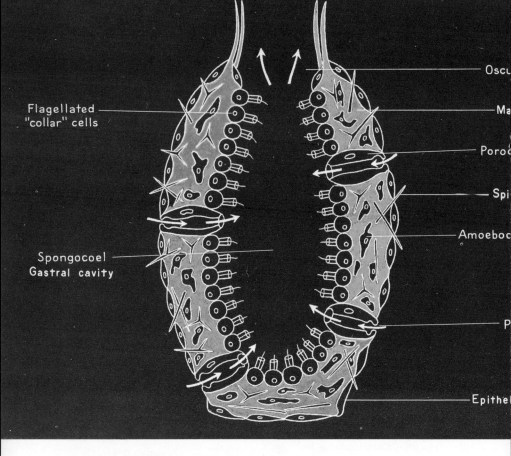

Figure 8.2. An asconoid sponge. This illustrates the simplest type of canal system in the sponges. The relationship of the central spongocoel to the pores is shown clearly.

have their origin from the covering layer, the *epidermis*. The wandering amoebocytes, the spicules, and the matrix compose the *mesenchyme*. Spicules and spongin make an interlacing network, thus forming the skeleton of the sponges, and both are secreted by special amoebocytes in the mesenchyme. There is a large central cavity within the asconoid sponge which has been named the *gastral* or *cloacal cavity;* however, it is neither a digestive nor an excretory cavity in the true sense, and Miss Hyman has suggested with excellent logic that it merely be called a *spongocoel* (sponge cavity). That terminology will be followed here.

The greater portion of the epithelium which lines the spongocoel is composed of an interesting cell type, the "collar" cells, or *choanocytes*, which have a tall collar and a flagellum. The epidermis and the lining epithelium of the collar cells are pierced by numerous openings, the *pores*, which in the asconoid sponges are actually intracellular canals within a single cell, the *porocyte*. The

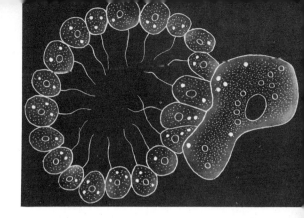

Figure 8.3. Amoebocyte feeding. Amoeboid cells of the sponges, as shown in this diagram, can pick up food particles from the "collar" cells for transportation to other regions of the sponge.

single large opening from the spongocoel to the exterior is the osculum, as we previously noted. It is usually protected by a fringe of long spicules and ringed by a "drawstring" of specialized contractile mesenchyme cells which narrow or close the osculum when they contract.

Nutrition

We have already commented upon the sifting done by sponges and have observed that their nutrition is dependent entirely on the flow of water through the canal system and the spongocoel. A precise picture of nutrition in the sponges has not yet been obtained, but the major features are fairly clear. Sponges are *holozoic*, and although they may feed partly on suspended or dissolved organic matter, small organisms are the chief food source. The beating of the flagella of the collar cells creates a current of water which continuously sweeps through the sponges; and although very little pressure is created, the rate of flow may be considerable. Various estimates have been made of the amount of water which circulates in this way. In small sponges of about 8 cubic centimeters, as much as 20 to 25 quarts will be filtered in a day, so it can be seen that a large sponge mass of several feet in diameter must pass enormous quantities of water daily. The passage of the water actually is associated with a filtration process, because the collar cells ingest small organisms that are trapped on the collar, and it is probable that some amoebocytes can also remove food directly from the passing currents. Little digestion occurs in the collar cells, and the food particles are passed to the inner ends of the cells, where they are *ingested* by the amoebocytes. Digestion takes place in food vacuoles within the amoebocytes. This process is comparable to that described for *Amoeba*. A typical set of digestive enzymes for proteins, carbohydrates, and lipids has been extracted from sponge tissues. The amoebocytes distribute the food to various parts of the organism and may also become storehouses for food reserves of glycogen or lipoprotein.

Respiration

Sponges are *oxybiotic* and hence need a relatively large amount of oxygen in their surroundings. If placed in an environment where the oxygen content

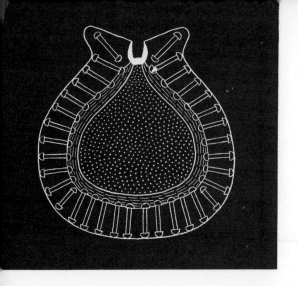

Figure 8.4. A structure which permits sponges to survive adverse environmental conditions. It is composed of a group of cells encased in a protective membrane and a sheath of spicules. The cells can emerge, when conditions are favorable, and develop into a new sponge.

is low, the sponge may depress its metabolic rate and be able to survive for a considerable period; however, the oxygen consumption is greatly elevated when the normal amount of oxygen is restored. It has been shown that in some sponge forms the oxygen consumption in the region of the osculum may be considerably higher than at the base of the sponge, which would indicate a gradient of metabolic activity.

Excretion

Very little is known concerning the excretory products of the sponges. Ammonia is probably the chief form of nitrogenous waste, and the limited observations which have been made have not demonstrated the presence of urea. It is possible, in the light of our knowledge of other animals, that additional nitrogenous compounds are excreted, but further investigation is needed. The amoebocytes, along with their other duties, ingest nitrogenous wastes and then, interestingly enough, these cells themselves may be discharged from the sponges, thus effectively riddling the animal of waste products! This is an unusual excretory method, but we shall encounter the same phenomenon in the starfishes and other forms, which use amoeboid cells in the same way. Carbon dioxide is excreted as part of the respiratory process, and since the cells of the sponge are constantly inundated, this is accomplished effectively. Undigested food material is discharged, or egested, into the spongocoel and is carried out through the osculum by the water leaving the sponge.

Reproduction

Both asexual and sexual reproduction occur in Porifera, and each has several remarkable features. Sponges are capable of forming new individuals from very small pieces of the parent substance, from any region of the body! Classical experiments by H. V. Wilson in the early 1900's beautifully illustrated this

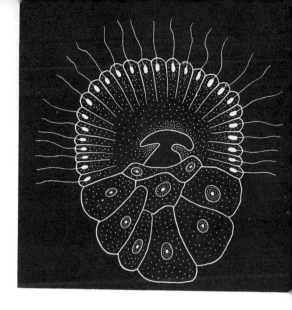

Figure 8.5. Amphiblastula. This is a ciliated larval stage peculiar to sponges. As development proceeds, the ciliated cells become the inner layer of the animal. These cells of the amphiblastula are not comparable, therfore, to the ciliated ectodermal cells of many other embryos.

remarkable ability. Pieces of sponge may be squeezed through silk cloth, which separates the individual cells; and if such cells are allowed to fall on a glass slide, they will migrate together to form a cell mass. This clump of cells then will grow into a new sponge, by asexual reproduction, forming the specialized structures of the adult as it grows, with the amoebocytes primarily responsible for this development.

The sponge may, under adverse environmental conditions, sometimes undergo great reduction in body mass, and from the small nodule of cells that remains a new sponge can be reproduced when conditions are again favorable. A procedure somewhat similar to that noted above is followed in the formation of the *gemmule*, which is an aggregation of amoebocytes surrounded by a protective membrane and spicules. Fresh-water sponges reproduce regularly by means of gemmules, and although the body of the sponge is unable to stand low winter temperatures, the gemmule is very resistant to adverse climatic conditions. New sponges are formed as the amoebocytes are released from the gemmule through a pore. This is followed by an aggregation of the cells and subsequent regeneration of the adult form. Or the gemmule may become an *amphiblastula*, a flagellated larva which swims about for a time, then settles down and transforms into the adult.

Sexual reproduction occurs in all the sponges, and certain features of the process are peculiar to these animals. Egg cells are formed from amoebocytes, and these egg cells accumulate food material in the cytoplasm and enlarge. It is not entirely clear, however, how the sperm originate; and the process may vary among the different sponges. Sperm cells arise from amoebocytes (and possibly also from the choanocytes, or collar cells), and by divisions of the original amoebocyte cell a *spermatocyst* may develop which contains sperm surrounded by a capsule of flattened cells. The sperm are discharged into the canals and are carried by the water currents into other sponges, where they have a remarkable history. The sperm are taken into the cytoplasm of a

139

choanocyte or an amoebocyte, where they lose the flagellated tail, and the engulfing cell becomes a *nurse cell*. The sperm nurse cell migrates to the egg cell, and while in contact with it the sperm is transferred and fertilization is accomplished. Why the nurse cell does not digest the sperm as it would a foreign organism poses an interesting biological question.

Cleavage begins immediately after fertilization, and the egg develops to the blastula stage while still in the gelatinous matrix. After flagella develop on the blastula, it emerges from the osculum as a free-swimming larva, and a short time later settles down, attaches itself, and develops into the adult form. There is an unusual feature in the development of the *gastrula stage* of the sponges. The flagellated portion of the embryo is the anterior end, but it is this end which invaginates to become the lining, whereas the posterior region becomes the epidermis. The animal is wrong-side out when compared with other metazoans, and it should be noted also that the layers of the Porifera probably should not be compared with the corresponding adult layers of the other Metazoa.

The versatile behavior of the amoebocytes in the sponges is one of the most impressive illustrations of the adaptability of protoplasm to be found anywhere in the animal kingdom. We have noted that these cells aid in the digestion and distribution of food, participate in excretion, can form either sperm or egg cells, and, as nurse cells, can transport the sperm to the egg for fertilization. The amoebocytes, in addition, produce the gemmule and make possible asexual

Figure 8.6.   The cactus sponge, Class III. The giant "cup sponge," Class III, has a spongin skeleton. [(a) Courtesy American Museum of Natural History; (b) courtesy Clarence Flaten.]

(a)   **(b)**

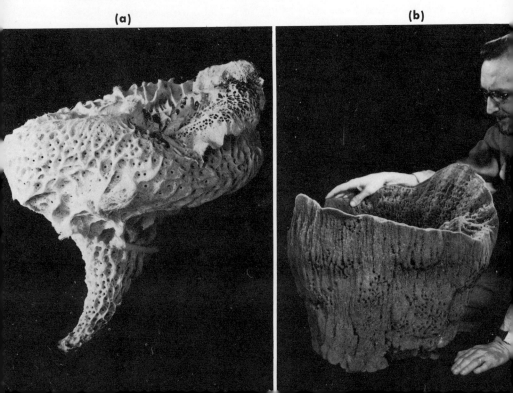

reproduction.   We will observe later in other phyla that each of the functions performed by these remarkable cells is usually allocated by other organisms to specialized cells.

Coordination

The sponges are very sluggish in their reactions, and a severe injury will elicit little response other than contraction or withdrawal of the protoplasm in an area a few millimeters distant from the site of damage.   The cells which encircle the osculum are more sensitive and will contract when stimulated, drawing together to close the opening.   G. H. Parker has called these *simple effectors*, because they respond (produce an effect) when stimulated directly, and for this reason a sponge is said to have an *independent effector-type nervous system*.   It is very generous, however, to dignify such a simple mechanism with the title "nervous system."   It is not until we get to the study of the coelenterates that we find a true system of nervous coordination.   The coelenterate nervous system, which is called a receptor-effector-type nervous system (p. 167), is really a nerve net, for no central ganglion is present.   The pore cells of the sponge, like the osculum cells, may respond to stimuli and close their intracellular canals.   In those forms in which pore cells are absent, the movement of the epidermal cells may partially or almost completely close the external openings into the canals.   The behavior of the amoebocytes in the sponges indicates that they will respond to local stimuli, but each behaves as though it were an independent amoeba.

Other Sponge Body Forms

Our description of the organization of the cells and tissues of the Porifera thus far has been confined to the asconoid type.   The basic relation of the cells and the layers is the same in other sponges, except that the canal systems become much more elaborate.   The asconoid type of sponge can never reach very large size because the surface area devoted to collar cells is small in proportion to the total body mass, and as the volume of the animal increases, a point is reached at which the collar cells cannot cause enough water to circulate to meet the functional needs of the animal.   Other sponges have solved this difficulty by folding the body wall, which results in a marked increase in area.   These folds are further supplemented by reducing the size of the spongocoel and also by creating special flagellated chambers.   The sponges which have a relatively simple folding of the epidermis and flagellated epithelium are spoken of as *syconoid*, and those with the more elaborate folds and chambers as the *leuconoid* type.

The horizontal folds of the *syconoid type* form a number of parallel, alternating canals.   The external, *incurrent canals* are covered by epidermal tissue and have as their inlet the external pores; thus they end blindly toward the interior, or center, of the sponge.   The internal, *radial canals* are lined with a flagellated epithelium and have as their outlet the internal pores which open into the spongocoel; thus they end blindly toward the exterior of the sponge. What would correspond to the original wall in the asconoid sponge is, in the syconoid sponge, reduced to a thin layer between the two canals and is pierced by very small pores, the *prosopyles*. Water enters the incurrent canals through the external pores, passes through the prosopyles into the radial canals, from the radial canals into the spongocoel by way of the internal pores, and thence to the exterior through the osculum.

The *leuconoid* sponges are so complexly folded that without the existence of the syconoid type it would be difficult to understand how their canal system could arise. There are extra folds of the epidermis which create large chambers often called *subdermal spaces*, from which canals lead to multiple *flagellated*

Figure 8.7. (a) Spicules. Such skeletal structures vary in shape and in chemical composition. (b) Sponge ova. Three sponge ova can be seen located adjacent to the canals. (c) Sponges often grow on other animals, serving to camouflage the animal which carries them and, in turn, being carried to fresh feeding areas. (d) Marine sponges grow in profusion in the shallow warm waters of the ocean. [(a) Courtesy American Museum of Natural History; (b) copyright by General Biological Supply House, Inc., Chicago; (d) courtesy Fenjohn Company.]

(a)   (b)

(c)   (d)

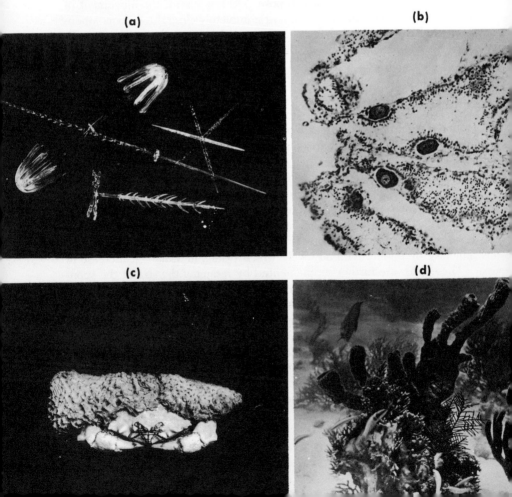

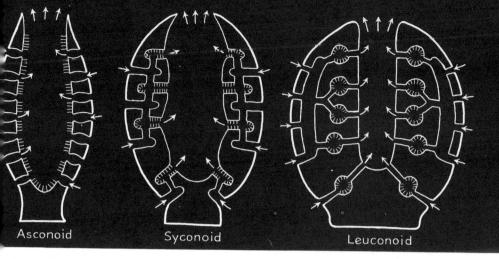

Asconoid   Syconoid   Leuconoid

Figure 8.8. Types of canal systems.   The variation in the complexity of the canal systems of sponges and the circulation of water through them is shown in the simplified diagram.

chambers lined with collar cells.   Other canals lead from the flagellated chambers to the *excurrent channels*, and these in turn connect with the osculum. The folding of the body during the formation of the excurrent channels may result in the obliteration of the spongocoel.

The formation of spicules and spongin presents one of the most interesting activities of the Porifera.   Spicules begin as small intracellular deposits of calcium carbonate or silica in cells known as *scleroblasts*, located in the matrix. The scleroblast is binucleate at the time the spicule first appears, but as the spicule grows, the nuclei move apart and the cell soon divides into two cells. One cell, the *founder*, establishes the length and form of the spicule, and the

Figure 8.9.   Spicule formation.   The form of a spicule is determined primarily by founder cells, and additional layers of calcium carbonate are deposited by the thickness.

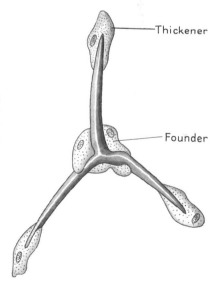

Thickener

Founder

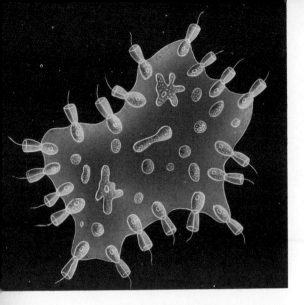

Figure 8.10. Proterospongia. This colonial protozoan may be regarded as a possible connecting link between acellular animals and sponges. The colony has collar cells which are embedded in a gelatinous material through which amoebocytes wander.

other, the *thickener*, deposits additional layers of salts around the spicule. Triradiate spicules are formed when three scleroblasts come together, and later each scleroblast divides into a founder and a thickener. The six-pronged spicules, however, start within a multinucleated protoplasmic mass. Spongin is also formed intracellularly and originates within the *spongioblasts*. These, each with a small secretion of spongin within the cytoplasm, arrange themselves in a row, and later the spongin in the separate cells fuses to form the *spongin thread*, after which the spongioblasts degenerate. They differ in this respect from the scleroblasts, which migrate back into the mesenchyme (p. 136) after they have finished their construction job. The geometric precision of spicule formation is an illustration of a biological problem which we shall encounter many times in the animal kingdom. How do formative cells "know" the size and shape of the spicule they are to create? For example, one class of sponges has six-rayed spicules, but these are never present in other classes. If we could understand the mechanism which controls so exactly this cellular activity, we should have a clue to one of the most important problems in biology: namely, the development of organic form—a problem which we comprehend so poorly at present.

The natural history of the sponges also contains several items of interest. Many of the Porifera secrete a thick mucus on the surface, and secretions that are very distasteful or even toxic liberated. Fishes generally are repelled by these secretions, and consequently many invertebrates live for protection in the cavities of the sponges or in the irregular spaces between sponge masses. Some animals acquire bits of sponge on their surface, and as the sponge grows, it supplies an excellent camouflage (Figure 8.7). The flagellated reproductive cells are considered by some zoologists to indicate a relationship between the Porifera and the Flagellata, but even more intriguing is the Protozoan flagellate organism, *Proterospongia*. This organism has collar cells embedded in a gelatinous matrix which also contains amoebocytes. The two cell types reportedly

Figure 8.11. Fresh-water sponges are much less common than the marine type. They grow as irregular masses, often colored brown or yellow, and sometimes have acellular green plants growing within them which give them a bright green color. (Courtesy American Museum of Natural History.)

can transform themselves from one into the other. This flagellate appears to be very closely related to the probable ancestral type of the Porifera.

Classification of Porifera

Phylum Porifera Animals primarily of cellular-grade organization, without organs but with epithelial tissues. Body has pores opening into a canal system, and has certain canals or chambers lined with flagellated collar cells, the *choanocytes*. Skeleton of spicules or spongin.

CLASS I. CALCAREA. Sponges with calcareous, calcium carbonate spicules, which are separate, and with one, three, or four rays. Primarily individual animals of small size, with radial symmetry. Examples: *Leucosolenia, Sycon.*

CLASS II. HEXACTINELLIDA. Sponges with spicules of silica (glass sponges). Spicules are six-rayed and frequently form networks. Animals usually are radially symmetrical. Examples: *Euplectella* (Venus' flower-basket), *Pheronema.*

CLASS III. DEMOSPONGIAE. A complex group, with skeleton of spongin or spicules of silica or both. Spicules are absent, or are either single-rayed or four-rayed. Canal system is of the leuconoid type. Examples: *Spongilla* (fresh-water sponge) and *Spongia* (bath sponge).

REFERENCES

BROWN, F. A., (ed.), *Selected Invertebrate Types*, pp. 72–84. John Wiley & Sons, Inc. New York, 1950.
HYMAN, L. H., *The Invertebrates: Protozoa through Ctenophora*, Vol. I, pp. 284–364. Mc Graw-Hill Book Company, Inc., New York, 1940.
LANKESTER, RAY, (ed.), *Treatise on Zoology*, Part II, pp. 1–178. Adam and Charles Black, London, 1900.
MACGINITIE, and N. MACGINITIE, *Natural History of Marine Animals*, pp. 108–116. McGraw-Hill Book Company, Inc., New York, 1949.
WILSON, H. V., and J. T. PENNY, "The Regeneration of Sponges from Dissociated Cells", *Journal of Experimental Zoology, 56*, 1930, pp. 73–147.

How to

Make the Most

of Tissues

•

9

Phylum

Coelenterata

(Cnidaria)

Over the structure of the cell rises the structure of plants and animals, which exhibit the yet more complicated, elaborate combinations of millions and billions of cells co-ordinated and differentiated in the most extremely different ways. Hertwig, quoted from Woodruff, Animal Biology, 1937

One who successfully makes the most of limited talents is always greatly admired by others, and for this very reason the colenterates deserve respect. They lack organs and are composed only of tissues, but during the course of millions of years the Coelenterata have molded and adapted these tissues in such a variety of ways that today they are one of the most successful groups of organisms. Historically they have much in common with the sponges, because their true animal nature was realized only in recent times; and for many years they were called Zoophyta (animal-plants) because they were thought to be intermediate between the plant and animal kingdoms. The confusion concerning their status was in part due to the presence of two body forms, the *polyp* and the *medusa*, both of which may occur during the lifetime of a single animal, and in part due to the formation of complex colonies, in which many of the animals are so highly specialized that they are unrecognizable as separate individuals unless their embryonic development is studied. The presence of peculiar "stinging threads" in the coelenterates was known to Aristotle, and their name, *Cnidaria* (thread animals), is a recognition of this characteristic feature. The combination of two layers of tissues and stinging threads is sufficient to distinguish the coelenterates from all other phyla.

One of the most important reasons for devoting our attention to the Coelenterata is the fact that they demonstrate the great adaptability of organisms and give evidence that nature has been constantly conducting "experiments." The flexibility of body form among the coelenterates is so great that individuals

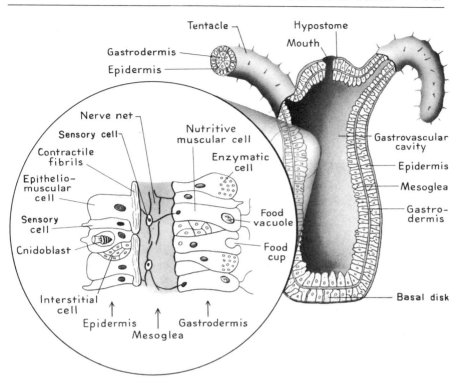

Figure 9.1.   The anatomy and cell types of Hydra, with an enlarged view of the body wall.

are specialized to perform functions that are accomplished by organ systems in the other Metazoa. It will be worth while for us to study these polyps, medusae, and colonial forms in order to understand this flexibility in the development of the limited potentialities of the two-layered body plan.

The Polyp Form

Body form or Hydra

The modest, minute *Hydra* is one of the few coelenterates that have been able to invade the fresh waters successfully. *Hydra* probably is second only to the amoeba in its popularity in the zoology laboratory, and this is because it is a hardy animal with a captivating behavior and performs readily. *Hydra* has *radial symmetry*, distinguished by an elongated tubular body which can be divided into a number of similar parts by radial cuts through the mouth region. Its structure is that of the simplest type of polyp, with an outer layer, the *epidermis*, and an inner layer, the *gastrodermis*, between which is a thin, jellylike *mesoglea*. It is imperative that we pause here for a few words about terminology.   We shall limit the use of the terms *ectoderm* and *entoderm* entirely to embryonic stages, because these are formative layers of the embryo and are not synonymous with the outer and inner layers of the adult, which will be called *epidermis* and *gastrodermis*.   There are at least three good reasons for this important distinction: *first*, the outer and inner layers of the adult are highly specialized structures with cells that have both structural and functional modifications; *second*, in the Metazoa most of these cells have lost their embryonic potentialities—that is, cannot be transformed into other cell types; *third*, the epidermis and gastrodermis may be composed of cells that were contributed by more than one of the embryonic layers.   This is especially true of the lining of the alimentary canal of certain animals, in which the ectoderm of the embryo may give rise to a considerable portion of the lining.

The tubular body of *Hydra* begins with the *basal disc* and terminates in a circlet of hollow *tentacles* which surround a slight elevation, the *hypostome*, through which the *mouth* opens into a central space, the *gastrovascular cavity*, which constitutes a high percentage of the total volume of the animal.   This is the only cavity present in the coelenterates and serves both for digestion and distribution, hence the name "gastrovascular cavity."   Polyps other than *Hydra* may have folds present in the cavity, and these are an important feature of the polyp of the sea anemone, which we will discuss later.   The body surface of *Hydra* contains numerous stinging capsules, the *nematocysts*.   These capsules are more numerous on the tentacles and appear as masses, the stinging "batteries."   *Hydra* may move by a creeping motion of the basal disc, but its most effective movement is by means of a series of looping "handstands."

Figure 9.2.   Hydra in cross section.   (Courtesy Clarence Flaten.)

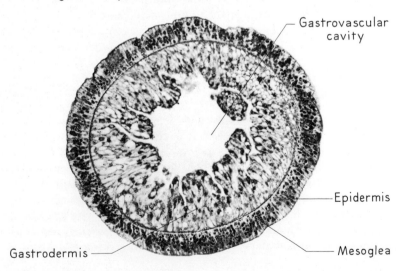

Gastrovascular
cavity

Epidermis

Gastrodermis

Mesoglea

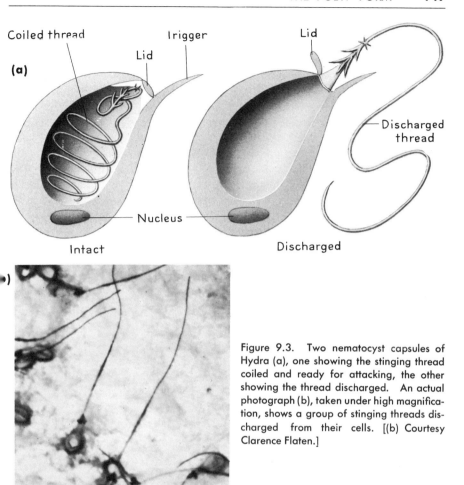

Figure 9.3. Two nematocyst capsules of Hydra (a), one showing the stinging thread coiled and ready for attacking, the other showing the thread discharged. An actual photograph (b), taken under high magnification, shows a group of stinging threads discharged from their cells. [(b) Courtesy Clarence Flaten.]

CELL TYPES • The microscopic structure of the cell layers will serve to emphasize the complexity of the epidermis and gastrodermis. The most important epithelial cell type in the coelenterates is the covering, or supporting, cell, which in *Hydra* has an elongated base with contractile fibrils and is designated as an *epitheliomuscular cell*. The fibrils in these epidermal cells run lengthwise, whereas those in the gastrodermal cells are arranged circularly. Contractions of the epidermal fibers shorten or bend the animal, but contractions of the gastrodermal cells will constrict and lengthen it. The cells of the two layers, therefore, act as opposing sets of muscles. The outer margin of the epitheliomuscular cell is granular, and fuses with the adjacent cells into a tough surface for the animal. On the basal portion of the cells are processes which anchor the cells to the mesoglea. Several other cell types are interspersed among the epitheliomuscular cells: notably, the cnidoblasts, the interstitial or mesenchymal cells, the sensory receptor cells, and the sensory nerve cells. The basal disc of *Hydra* is composed entirely of cells with coarse granules, the *glandulomuscular cells*, which secrete mucus.

The *nematocysts* are so remarkable and so varied in their structure that it is impossible to give a brief account of them; as many as seventeen different types have been described. They are formed by special cells, the *cnidoblasts* (thread-formers). Basically, the nematocyst is a capsule in which there is a coiled *thread*, often with an enlarged region, the *butt*. The surface of the nematocyst has a projecting *trigger*, the *cnidocil*. The nematocyst thread is everted on discharge and may either lasso or pierce the prey. Thus the animal being attacked is immobilized either by being "tied" down with loops of thread or by being injected with poison. Nematocysts can be used only once and must be replaced after their discharge. They are formed anew by the transformation of the interstial cells into cnidoblasts, which produce the new nematocysts. Those found in the tentacles are formed a considerable distance from their final position, which they reach by migration.

The interstitial cells are frequently called *mesenchymal cells* and retain the properties of embryonic cells. They are small, rounded cells with relatively large nuclei and can transform into any of the other cell types. The interstitial cells, in addition, contribute to the formation of buds during asexual reproduction. The interstitial cells originate during embryonic development from either the ectoderm or the entoderm and may be arranged in groups among the other cells.

The *sensory receptor cells* are more numerous on the tentacles and around the mouth but are present everywhere on the body, with the possible exception of the basal disc. These cells are elongated, and the outer edge terminates just below the epithelial surface, with a small tip or spine projecting above the epitheliomuscular cells. The base of the receptor cell has from one to several neurofibers, which extend to the *sensory nerve cells*, making up the *nerve net*. The nerve cells proper are bipolar or multipolar cells which are located chiefly in the inner regions of the epidermis, although a few appear in the gastrodermis. These are *not* continuous with each other but have small gaps between the ends of the fibers of different cells. We will discuss the significance of this nerve network in relation to nervous coordination.

There are marked similarities between the gastrodermis and the epidermis, but some specialized *gastrodermal cells* which are associated with digestion appear in the gastrodermis. Elongated glandular cells which secrete mucus as an aid to swallowing may be observed in the hypostome region. The dominant cell type is the *nutritive-muscular cell* which ingests food particles and is the counterpart of the epitheliomuscular cell of the epidermis. Digestive enzymes are secreted by *enzymatic cells*, which are enlarged at the ends adjacent to the gastrovascular cavity and drawn out into very thin protoplasmic strands toward the mesoglea. The nutritive-muscular cells usually possess two flagella, which

(a)

(b)

(c)

(d)

Figure 9.4. The modest sea anemone is handsomely shown above. Note the mouths in the two anemones in (a). The unusual photograph (d) shows, as in Figure 8.7, how two animals may form a mutually helpful partnership. (Courtesy F. Schensky.)

help to keep the fluid and particles circulating within the gastrovascular cavity. Groups of interstitial cells and scattered receptor cells also are present in the gastrodermis, but nematocysts are absent.

Body form of *Metridium* (sea anemone)

The polyp of the sea anemone possesses much greater specialization than that of *Hydra*, yet the basic structural relationships are easily recognizable. The animals are exclusively marine and much larger, with a body composed

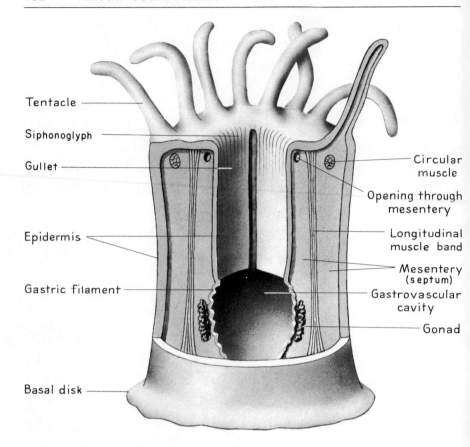

Tentacle

Siphonoglyph

Gullet

Epidermis

Gastric filament

Basal disk

Circular muscle

Opening through mesentery

Longitudinal muscle band

Mesentery (septum)

Gastrovascular cavity

Gonad

Figure 9.5.   A cutaway view of Metridium, the sea anemone.

of a *basal disc*, a *column*, and an *oral disc* which may have several hundred hollow tentacles.   The most striking difference in structure between the two types of polyps occurs in the internal organization, which is greatly modified in the anemone.   The embryonic ectoderm in the adult animal folds inwardly to form a *gullet*, which extends as a tube for a considerable distance into the gastrovascular cavity.   This cavity is divided by partitions, the *septa*, into a series of chambers which are continuous below the gullet.   The *primary septa* are complete, reaching from the wall of the body to the gullet.   Other septa are incomplete and are found between the complete, or primary, septa.   The incomplete septa reach varying distances into the gastrovascular cavity; the longer ones are the *secondary septa*, the shorter ones, the *tertiary septa*.   The covering of the septa is gastrodermal and is composed of glandular cells with numerous cilia or flagella.   The edges of the septa are very much folded, thickened, and extended to form the *gastric filaments*.   Peculiar threads, the *acontia*, are continuations of the gastric filaments and are found in the basal-, or pedal-, disc region. These threads are armed with nematocysts. When the anemone is disturbed, the threads can be protruded through minute pores in the body wall, and the discharge of the nematocysts can drive away an intruder. On the faces of the septa are the *gonads*, which produce either sperm or eggs.

The musculature of the anemone is much more highly developed than in *Hydra*. The contractile fibers are independent cells and no longer associated with the epitheliomuscular units. Longitudinal muscle bands, the *retractors*, appear in the walls of the septa, and their contraction will shorten the animal, even to the extent of pulling the oral disc and tentacles inside the polyp. A strong band of circular muscle encircles the anemone at the margin of the oral disc and when contracted will close the mouth opening tightly. Circulation of water and feeding are a result of the combined action of the cilia and the muscles. Ciliated grooves, the *siphonoglyphs*, usually are present at both sides of the gullet. The cilia of these beat downward to force water into the gastrovascular cavity; but in the central portion of the gullet, between the siphonoglyphs, the ciliary beat is upward, so that water is forced from the animal. During feeding, the tentacles carry food to the gullet, and the cilia of the central gullet reverse the direction of their beat. This ciliary action, aided by muscle contractions, carries the food particles into the gastrovascular cavity. The layer between the epidermis and the gastrodermis should be called *mesenchyme* in the anemone, because it is definitely cellular, and with the formation of fibers actually becomes a fibrous connective tissue. The anemone and its relatives probably should be considered three-layered, or *triploblastic*, animals.

The Medusa Form

Body form of *Gonionemus*

This jellyfish is relatively simple, but will demonstrate the essential features of medusoid organization. The medusa differs from the polyp because of a decrease in the relative distance between the basal disc and the mouth, and a corresponding lateral expansion. Furthermore, the amount of mesoglea is tremendously increased, with the effect that the medusa assumes a bowl shape, with marginal tentacles around the rim of the bowl. The similarity of its appearance to the head of the mythical Medusa, the lady with snake hair, gives the obvious name to this body form. The outer convex surface of a medusa is the *exumbrella;* the inner concave surface, the *subumbrella;* and both surfaces are covered with the epidermis, which is folded into a shelf at the point of junction of exumbrella and subumbrella to form the *velum.* A tube, the *manubrium,* covered with epidermis and lined with gastrodermis, projects into the subumbrella space. The mouth opens at the end of the manubrium and at its base there is a slightly expanded "stomach" which is continuous with four radial canals extending to the outer margins of the animal, where they connect with a

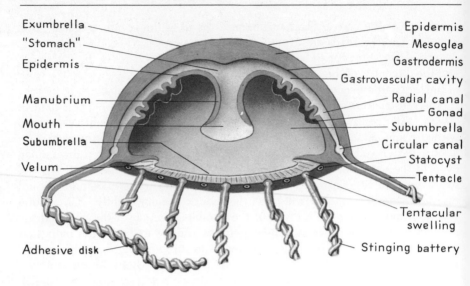

Figure 9.6.   A cross section of the small jellyfish, Gonionemus.

circular canal.   The manubrium, stomach, radial canals, and circular canal constitute the *gastrovascular cavity.*

The rim of the jellyfish has well-developed tentacles into which the gastrovascular cavity may be said to extend.   Rows of nematocysts, the *stinging batteries,* are found along the tentacles, and near the tip of each there is an *adhesive disc* which enables *Gonionemus* to attach to plants or to the ocean bottom when at rest.   The nematocysts originate in formative cells in the tentacular swellings at the upper base of the tentacles and migrate downward to their eventual position on the tentacles.   Circular muscle fibers are well developed in the epidermis and the velum.   These, along with the radially arranged fibers, make possible the "pulsating" contractions of the jellyfish by which it moves through the water in a jet-propelled fashion.   Sensory structures are found along the rim of the animal and are of two special types.   The first is a light-sensitive *pigmented area* which is present on the tentacular swellings.   There may even be a thickening of the surface over the pigmented area, which serves as a lens.   The second sensory structures are the *statocysts* (Figure 9.7), which are special balancing structures, each constructed as a small sac, usually with a brush of cilia on the

Figure 9.7.   The statocyst is a most ingenious device for achieving balance—good enough to be carried over into many, much more advanced animals such as the lobster.

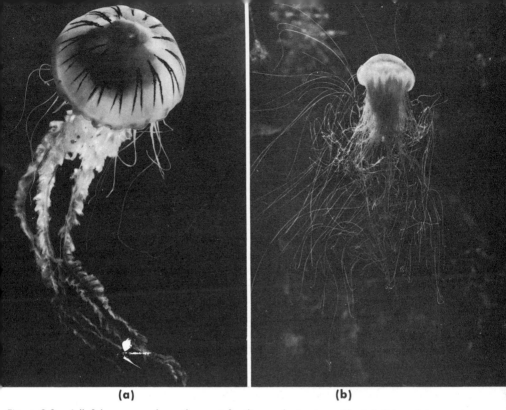

(a)　　　　　　　　　　　　　　　　(b)

Figure 9.8.　Jellyfishes are perhaps the most familiar coelenterates.　The jellyfishes shown below are handsome representatives of a class whose geological history dates more than 500,000,000 years into the past!　The four large, fluted streamers on the jellyfish in (a) are the extended oral arms which surround the animal's mouth and are used to capture food.　Note the profusion of tentacles that wave delicately below the animal in (b).　[(a) (Courtesy Dr. W. K. Fisher, Hopkins Marine Station.]

inside, upon which rolls a small stone, or *statolith*, a calcareous body produced by the animal.　Pressure of the stone on the cilia will, of course, vary according to the position of the animal, and impulses from the statocysts enable the animal to right itself.

The reproductive organs, the *gonads*, follow the course of the radial canals, but are epidermal in origin and project into the subumbrella.　The problem of reproduction in both the polyp and medusa will be considered later.　*Gonionemus* is small; exclusive of tentacles it is usually smaller than the diameter of a dime.　Some of the Scyphozoan jellyfishes reach impressive size, however, and have been reported with bodies in excess of 10 feet in diameter, with tentacles 100 feet long.　These are, therefore, among the largest invertebrate animals, and this is remarkable when it is recalled that the jellyfishes often are 94 to 96 per cent water.　The salts, proteins, carbohydrates, and lipins make up 4 per cent or less of the total body substance in these animals; thus, in some cases, the protoplasm of the jellyfish may be more dilute than the medium in which it is swimming!

The Colony Form

The Obelia colony

One of the most remarkable phenomena in the entire animal kingdom has been the development of colonial organization among the coelenterates. Some of these colonies are extremely complicated, with individuals adapted to perform functions which would be the responsibility of organs or organ systems in other metazoans. The *Obelia* colony, which is exclusively marine and seldom is more than a few inches high, will serve nicely to illustrate a simple type of colonial organization in the *Coelenterata* (see Figure 9.9).

The colony begins its existence as a small animal similar to *Hydra*, which reproduces by budding. The important feature of this budding process is the fact that the buds do not separate but remain attached and grow from a central stem in a branching fashion resembling the growth of a plant. The individuals that form by the budding process are called *polyps* because they are similar in structure to the *Hydra* polyp. As the polyps grow, the epidermis secretes a flexible protective covering, the *perisarc*, which covers the entire colony and is expanded into cups about the polyps. At the base of the polyp the perisarc is ringed, which increases the flexibility of the colony, allowing it to adjust to the movement of water currents and permitting the individual members of the colony a certain freedom of bending. A division of labor among the individuals in the colony develops early, and two types of individuals can be recognized. One of these is the *feeding polyp,* and the other the *reproductive polyp;* the former are much more numerous than the latter. All the polyps in the *Obelia* colony are connected by a *gastrovascular cavity* lying in a cellular tube called the *coenosarc,* which is formed by a fusion of the epidermis and the gastrodermis, but which, of course, is lined with gastrodermis.

The feeding polyps are similar to *Hydra* in their general form, and are composed of epidermis, mesoglea, and gastrodermis. There is an elevation, the *hypostome,* at the free end of the polyp, through which the mouth opens into the gastrovascular cavity. The tentacles are solid, very numerous, and well equipped with nematocysts. The transparent, vaselike portion of the perisarc which protects the feeding polyp is called the *hydrotheca,* and frequently the tentacles may be observed to be drawn into the cup of the hydrotheca to form a compact, protecting mass about the hypostome. The reproductive polyp is in the form of a central stalk, the *blastostyle,* which is enclosed within the *gonotheca,* a sac formed from the perisarc. The central blastostyle, by a process of budding, forms *medusae* (minute jellyfishes); and thus the reproduction of the *Obelia* colony is typically *asexual reproduction.* The oldest medusa will be found at the tip of the blastostyle and the youngest at the base of the blastostyle, near the stem of the colony. The mature medusae are freed from the blastostyle and pass to the outside through an opening at the tip of the gonotheca. This opening may be closed by a lid or by the end of the blastostyle itself.

The *Obelia* medusa is very small in size and differs considerably from the appearance of *Gonionemus;* nevertheless, it can be recognized easily as a jellyfish.   Reproduction in *Obelia* is by the process known as *alternation of generations* (see pp. 164–165).

Polymorphism

The *Obelia* colony actually has three types of indivuals: the feeding polyp, the reproductive polyp, and the medusa.   Such a colony, therefore, is said to

Figure 9.9.   The Obelia colony, since it has both feeding and reproductive polyps, is sometimes spoken of as dimorphic (having two forms).   The medusa, however, is really an additional form; hence, Obelia is actually trimorphic (having three forms).   (Courtesy Clarence Flaten.)

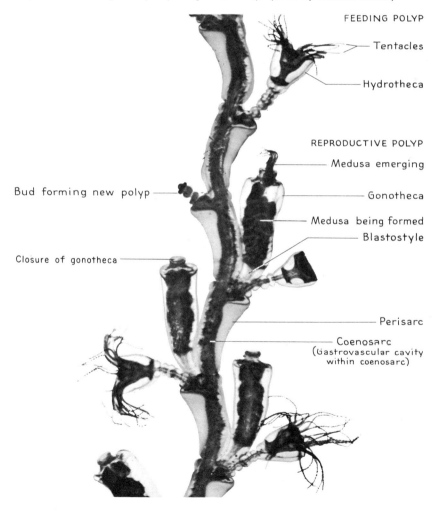

exhibit *polymorphism* (several forms); it would be better to say, however, that it has *trimorphism* (three forms).   Polymorphism has been developed in some other coelenterates to a much more elaborate degree than it has in *Obelia*.   The *Portuguese man-of-war* and some closely related organisms have polymorphism which involves both medusae and polyps.   A colony is suspended from a large gas-filled float, or bladder, which develops originally from a single medusa; this float is used as a sail.   Tentacles, which in the case of the Portuguese man-of-war may sometimes reach a length of 60 feet, extend from this float.   These tentacles have *feeding polyps* and *protective polyps*, with a tremendous number of nematocysts.   Other individuals in the colony are especially well equipped with sensory cells and are called the *tactile*, or *sensory, polyps*.   Other colonial forms may have *swimming medusae*, reduced in form to *contractile bells* which propel the colony through the water in a remarkable fashion by the combined effort of the tiny jets of water that they eject.

The remarkable degree to which polymorphism has been developed in the colonial forms means that these animals have lost their individuality and are entirely dependent for their existence upon the welfare of the colony as a whole. It is very difficult to delimit a colony from an individual in such cases, and actually the practical effect is that the entire colony behaves as an individual.

The advantages of colonial existence to the coelenterates are extensive. Animals living in large groups are able to protect themselves more effectively, as can be demonstrated by the fact that a giant Portuguese man-of-war can do considerable damage to, or perhaps kill, a human being.   The nutrition of a colony is more efficient than that of a single individual, because if a few of the feeding polyps secure food, it is partly digested and distributed through the gastrovascular cavity, where it is available to other individuals who may not have had the opportunity to feed.   An attached colony can grow and develop in a protected place, free of many of the environmental disturbances which could cause difficulty to a free-swimming organism.   The free-swimming medusa stage, however, makes possible the distribution of the colonies, because, as the medusae swim about, they have the opportunity to establish new colonies in other protected areas.

The corals

More than a century ago Charles Darwin, then a young man in his early twenties, was intrigued by the coral organisms and their ability to form the islands of the South Seas.   The coral animal is very similar in its general construction to the sea anemone and may exist either as a solitary animal or in colonies.   The body wall of the coral is much thinner than that of the anemone, and the animal protects itself by withdrawing into a calcium carbonate cup which is secreted by the cells of the basal disc.   The single, or solitary, coral secretes only small cups, but the colonial forms build large branching or encrusting masses of coral.   Whereas the solitary corals live in the colder or deeper waters of the ocean, the colonial animals live only in the warm seas and thrive

Figure 9.10. The beautiful but deadly Portuguese man-of-war is an excellent example of polymorphism and the degree to which colonial development may advance in the coelenterates. There are many different kinds of individuals present but, since the different members of the colony can no longer exist independently, it is more reasonable to think of the entire colony as a single individual. (Courtesy American Museum of Natural History.)

best at temperatures of about 30° centigrade. Such colonial corals construct the tremendous masses of the islands and the reefs of the South Pacific and have built up the Keys of our Florida coast.

Coral is formed by the basal disc of the individual coral animal, but the exact mechanism of secretion is not clearly understood. The form of the coral is that of a cup, into which the small coral animals, seldom more than an inch long, can withdraw themselves. The colonial corals reproduce only asexually—by either budding or fission—and the individual animals in the colony are connected by extensions of the basal portion, through which the common gastrovascular cavity runs. The complex pattern presented by the corals is a result of two processes: *first,* the irregularities in the form of ridges in the coral are due to the folds in the basal disc, which, in turn, are a reflection of the arrangement of the septa; *second,* the form of the entire coral mass is due to the manner of budding, which varies among the different species. The coral may bud to construct flat plates, branches, or a very convoluted mass, as in the brain coral.

The temperature adjustment of the colonial corals is so delicate that the animals are able to live only at depths down to about 100 to 150 feet, because the water below these depths becomes too cold for them to carry on their normal metabolism. An important fact about coral islands which interested the young Darwin, and has attracted the attention of so many investigators since his time, was the observation that coral skeleton may be found at depths of hundreds or even thousands of feet. When it is remembered that the coral animal can live only at a maximum depth of about 150 feet, the question immediately arises as to how we can explain the presence of skeletal coral formations at depths of a thousand or more feet.

Several theories have been advanced to explain the origin and form of coral islands and reefs. Two theories have special merit, and perhaps the best explanation involves features of each theory. The first, known as the *subsidence theory*, was formulated primarily by Darwin; the second is the *submerged-bank theory*. The idea advanced by Darwin was that a coral island or reef began as a growth on the edge of the sloping land mass, and as the land slowly sank into the sea, the sloping shore was gradually submerged. Coral would be able to grow just below the surface of the ocean and could keep pace with a slow rate of subsidence, with the result that over a period of hundreds of years new coral would be gradually superimposed layer upon layer above the old coral. The deeper portion of the mass would contain only skeletons, however, because the animals would die as they sank into the deeper, colder waters of the sea.

The submerged-bank theory is somewhat similar to the idea advanced by Darwin but postulates that coral began to grow on a submerged *shelf* of land. If this submerged plateau gradually sank deeper into the water, then the coral might be able to grow rapidly enough to keep pace with the submergence. We know now that coral growth thrived in shallow seas of relatively recent geologic time, and that ocean depths have frequently changed. As glaciers melted, for example, oceans deepened; but as glaciers grew, the oceans became more shallow.

The Great Barrier Reef of Australia is one of the most remarkable coral formations in the world. This reef is nearly 1200 miles long and lies off the continent of Australia at distances varying up to 90 miles. There is a channel between the reef and the continent which can be navigated by ship, and as a matter of fact, the reef was originally discovered by the English explorer, Capt. James Cook, who was sailing on the inside channel but did not realize the presence of the reef until he had wrecked his boat on it. Borings taken in the Great Barrier Reef have extended to depths of 300 to 400 feet before sand bottom was reached. Similar borings on the islands of Funafuti and Samoa have reached depths of over 1000 feet. These observations indicate the great mass of calcium carbonate that has been secreted by coral animals, and give some evidence of the age of these islands and reefs. The rate of formation of coral is variable, and may range from as little as 0.2 inch to as much as 8 inches per year. Various estimates have been made as to the length of time which would have been required to build up masses such as the island of Samoa; these estimates range from 10,000 to 30,000 years. This means, of course, that this coral was formed during what we know today as the Glacial period and supports the theories that are based on fluctuations of ocean depth. A combination of the subsidence and the submerged-bank theories offers the most reasonable explanation for the formation of coral land masses, especially when we consider the fluctuation in ocean depth due to the action of glaciers. It also seems probable that many coral formations originated on submerged banks.

Other colonial coelenterates may form large plumes or fanlike masses, which to the inexperienced eye look like plant growth; examples of these are the sea

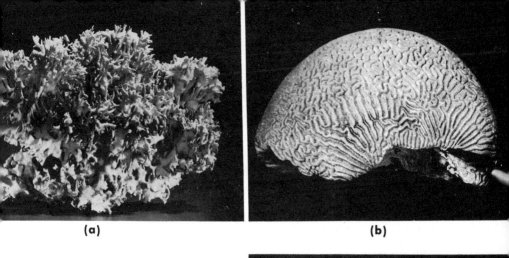

(a)   (b)

Figure 9.11. The photographs (a) and (b) show, respectively, the lacy coral structure of the stinging coral Millepora and the massive structure of a brain coral. The ghostlike, transparent star coral animals in (c) look quite similar to the anemones shown in Figure 9.4 but, unlike the anemones, these build houses of rock in which to live. [(a) (c) Courtesy American Museum of Natural History; (b) courtesy Clarence Flaten.]

(c)

plumes, sea fans, and sea pens. These branching colonies are striking in appearance, and, when interspersed among the colored corals in warm water, give the appearance of a beautiful underwater garden. Fantastic marine jungles formed by the growth of these organisms can be seen off the Florida coast and the island of Bermuda, where they are the most attractive and artistic contributions of the animal kingdom.

Body Functions of the Coelenterates

The functions of the coelenterates are not as diverse as the variations in body structure might suggest. It must be remembered that the basic form of the Coelenterata is that of a two-layered sac, and the mesoglea (or in the anemone, the mesenchyme) is a mass of material with a very high water content but with a small number of cells. The relatively large size of the gastrovascular cavity in proportion to the total volume of the animal makes its possible for all cells to be in contact with a water environment. Thus an exchange of materials in the form of fluids, gases, or waste products is easily accomplished through the cell

membranes.   The coelenterates have developed no special respiratory structures.   The advances in structural organization, therefore, have been the acquisition of the gastrovascular cavity specialized for nutrition, a nerve net for
coordination, and gonads for reproduction.   It must be concluded that coelenterate architectural design is superior to that of the Porifera, but that much of
the function in these organisms is still the responsibility of the individual cells.
The advances which have been made, however, represent important milestones
along the evolutionary path.

Nutrition

The coelenterates are holozoic and carnivorous in their nutrition; and we
should not be misled by the fact that some of the animals possess green plants
which live among their cells as guests, because coelenterate nutrition is never
holophytic.   The capture of food is made possible by the action of the nematocysts and the tentacles.   Jellyfishes, sea anemones, and the larger colonial
animals can eat relatively large organisms.   Fishes are frequently captured by
the jellyfishes and the Portuguese man-of-war.   *Hydra* is able to capture and
gradually ingest animals actually much larger than itself.   Such organisms are
immobilized by the toxin or bound by the filaments of the nematocysts, and
Hydra literally wraps itself around its food material.   Digestion begins in the
gastrovascular cavity but is completed within the cells of the gastrodermis.
Some digestive juices are secreted into the gastrovascular cavity by the enzymatic cells, but these enzymes appear to act entirely on proteins.   The digestion
of food in the gastrovascular cavity proceeds until the mass of food material has
been broken down into a thick soup, after which the cells of the gastrodermis
engulf the small particles by the formation of food cups, in a manner almost

Figure 9.12.   At the left we have a soft coral showing the profusion of polyps which can make
up a single coral colony.   At the right is a branching coral with some of its polyps extended.
[(a) Courtesy Clarence Flaten; (b) courtesy Fenimore Johnson Laboratories.]

(a)   (b)

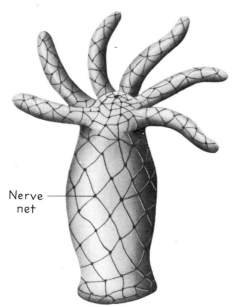

Nerve net

Figure 9.13. Nerve net of Hydra. Special straining techniques are used to demonstrate the netlike nature of the nervous system. This highly simplified diagram illustrates the greater concentration of the nervous system in the region of the mouth.

exactly like the formation of food vacuoles in an amoeba, and thus intracellular digestion in the gastrodermis is very similar to that in the amoeba. The food cup is first acid and later alkaline, and the digested food materials may be stored in the form of fats or carbohydrates within the gastrodermal cells. Undigested food particles are then egested into the gastrovascular cavity and are eliminated from the animal through the mouth. Enzymes for protein and fat digestion have been demonstrated in the coelenterates, and some Coelenterata are also able to digest sugars, but starch is apparently not digested. It must be emphasized that the important phases of digestion are accomplished *intracellularly* in the coelenterates.

Respiration

The respiration of the coelenterates is oxybiotic, but there are no special respiratory structures in the phylum. The exchange of oxygen and carbon dioxide is through the plasma membranes of the individual cells, as in protozoans and sponges. This mechanism is effective because the wall of the body is thin, and since all the coelenterates are aquatic, the entire organism is covered with water. The arrangement of the gastrovascular cavity, and its large size in proportion to the total volume of the animal, ensure that the internal cells as well will be bathed with a current of water. The water is constantly circulated in the gastrovascular cavity by the body movements and also by the beating of the flagella which protrude from the gastrodermal cells. The radial canals in the jellyfishes aid in the circulation of water, and as part of the gastrovascular cavity they are, therefore, part of the respiratory system. A number of measurements have been made of the rate of oxygen consumption in the coelenterates; and although the actual figures are of no special import, it is rather interesting to discover that—in spite of the large size of many of the jellyfishes—their oxygen consumption is low. It will be remembered that most of the body mass of the jellyfish is mesoglea, in which there are very few cells present. Since the number of cells, in proportion to the body size, is very small in the jellyfishes, one therefore would not expect to find a very high rate of oxygen consumption.

Excretion

Very little specific information is available concerning excretion in the coelenterates. No special excretory structures exist, although in a few cases the radial canals open to the outside by pores and are adapted for excretion. It has also been reported that special loops of the gastrovascular cavity are present in some of the colonial forms and that these have excretory function. This, however, remains to be studied in greater detail. The excretion of the nitrogenous waste compounds apparently is in the form of ammonia, and a few investigators have reported that traces of urea and uric acid can be found. These two substances, however, do not constitute a very high percentage of the nitrogenous waste compounds. Carbon dioxide and water, the other two important waste substances, are excreted from the animal through the plasma membranes of the individual cells. Excretion, therefore, in the coelenterates is essentially the same as in *Amoeba* or *Paramaecium*—that is, it remains the responsibility of the individual cells which constitute the tissues of the coelenterates.

Reproduction

Asexual and sexual reproduction are both common in the Coelenterata. *Hydra* illustrates both types in a single animal, because this organism reproduces by budding and also by the formation of eggs and sperm. *Hydra* forms buds originating from an outgrowth of the two layers of the body wall, sometimes with extra interstitial cells. These buds grow, develop the epidermal and gastrodermal tissues, form tentacles, and remain attached for a period of time to the parent body as active miniature animals. The buds eventually separate from the parent at the base to become independent organisms. The interstitial cells of the epidermis also specialize to form sperm or egg cells. Each hydra may form either eggs or sperm; in some species both sperm cells and egg cells can be formed in a single individual. When *testes*, forming sperm, and *ovaries*, forming eggs, are both present in one animal, we speak of such an organism as a *hermaphrodite*. We shall find many examples of hermaphroditism in the animal kingdom. The term itself is a combination of the names of the god Hermes and the goddess Aphrodite; thus an animal which possesses the gonads of both sexes has both male and female characteristics. The ovaries are formed toward the

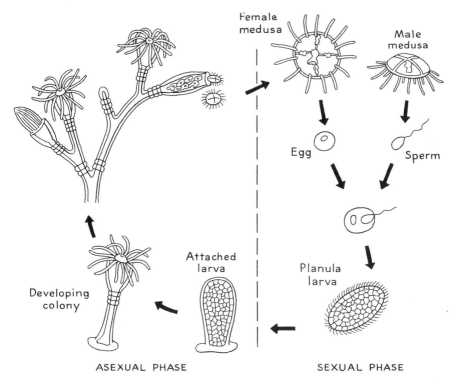

Figure 9.14.   Alternation of generations, showing the sexual and asexual phases in Obelia.

basal disc of *Hydra;* the testes, between the ovaries and the mouth region. Many sperm are developed in a testis, but only one egg in an ovary.   The sperm are released into the water, where they swim about until they finally penetrate the wall of the ovary and one sperm fertilizes the egg, which then begins embryonic development within the ovarian wall.   Two envelopes are formed about the *Hydra* embryo at the gastrula stage, after which it is freed from the parent and remains on the bottom in a quiescent state for a period of time before completing its development.

The discussion of reproduction probably should be concluded with a few words concerning the alternate appearance of both sexual and asexual generations among some of the Coelenterata.   This phenomenon, known as *alternation of generations,* is illustrated by *Obelia* (see Figure 9.14).   Individuals in the *Obelia* colony reproduce only by asexual means: the feeding polyps are budded from the central stem, and medusae are budded from the blastostyle.   After the medusae have been freed into the water, they reproduce by sexual means, forming either sperm or eggs, which combine in the water to initiate embryonic development.   Thus an asexual generation is followed by a sexual generation,

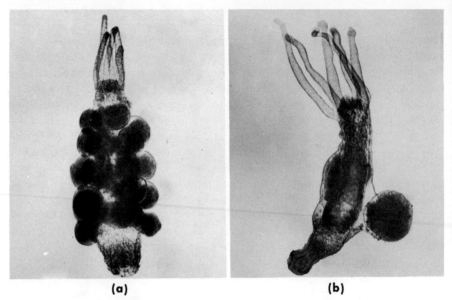

(a)   **(b)**

Figure 9.15. Left: A male Hydra with testes. Right: A female Hydra with a developed ovary. (Courtesy Clarence Flaten.)

which in turn is followed by an asexual one. The "children" do not resemble their parents but only their grandparents. *Aurelia* and other jellyfishes have a greatly reduced polyp stage which reproduces asexually. The larger animal in this series is the medusa stage, which reproduces sexually. In *Obelia* it is the medusa stage which is reduced in size, while the polyp stage, in the form of the colony, is relatively large. Alternation of generations is an interesting biological fact, but its significance is obscure.

Nervous coordination

The biggest structural advance made by the coelenterates over the forms we have examined previously has been in the development of nervous coordination. The nervous system is composed of receptor elements, the *sensory receptor cells* and the *sensory nerve cells*, which make up what is called a *nerve net*. The nerve net is composed of cells located at the base of the epidermis; the cells are either bipolar or multipolar neurons. There also may be a lesser nerve net located in the gastrodermis of some of the coelenterates. The tips of the nerve fibers of the nerve net are in close proximity to each other but do not actually make protoplasmic contact. Impulses can be carried in either direction along the nerve fibers of the nerve net and will "jump the gap" between the ends of the respective nerve fibers. The receptor cells receive stimuli and relay impulses to the sensory nerve cells of the nerve net. The numerous processes of the nerve-net cells in turn relay the impulses throughout the body, and this transmission is slow and *diffuse*—that is, goes in all directions. The diffuse nature of the nerve net has been illustrated many times by the simple experimental procedure of making zigzag cuts in the body wall of an animal. It takes the impulse longer to reach a given point after such a series of cuts has been made, but the impulse will eventually reach the spot in which an effect will be produced—provided, of course, that the animal is not completely cut into two pieces. The diffuse nature of the transmission is evidence that the nervous system of the Coelenterata is not centralized. There may be a greater concentration of nerve cells in the region of the hypostome, but this cannot be considered a "head" region for the animal. The coelenterate type of nervous coordination, as noted previously, is called a *receptor-effector-type nervous system*, and measurements have been made of the rate at which an impulse moves along the nerve fibers. The speed varies from 10 to 100 centimeters per second, and although this may appear to be a rapid rate of transmission, it is very slow when compared with the rate of transmission of impulses in man, which move at the rate of 10,000 to 12,000 centimeters per second.

The behavior of the coelenterates is complex, and their responses to stimuli are varied. Many experiments have been performed on the coelenterates, testing their responses to light, gravity, contact, and food. In general it should be said that the responses to food are the most definite of all. Among the coelenterates the jellyfishes, as might be expected, are the most responsive to stimuli. The reaction of the jellyfishes to light is not very marked, but they tend to avoid the bright sunlight and select a light area of medium intensity. Experiments have been performed with the jellyfishes, testing the action of their balancing organs, the statocysts. It can be shown, by placing weights on one side of a jellyfish so as to tilt it, that the animal makes a definite righting reaction. The righting reactions apparently are influenced by the position of the statolith, or stone, within the statocyst and by the impulses which it relays through the animal as a result of its contact with the cilia. Most of the coelenterates make definite responses to contact, and in the jellyfishes the manubrium may be directed toward a point of contact in a typical feeding reaction; the same response also is performed by the tentacles of *Hydra*. Finally, it should be said that there is an inexactness of nervous response in the coelenterates, as is illustrated by the fact that portions of an animal respond nearly as well and in the same general fashion as does the entire animal.

Regeneration and other body adaptations

The coelenterates in general, and *Hydra* in particular, have contributed toward the solution of biological problems through their remarkable ability to generate. It is possible to cut *Hydra* and other related forms into pieces and to observe the development of these pieces into new animals. It has been noted that if a piece is cut from the mid-region of *Hydra*, the portion nearest the hypostome grows a new mouth and ring of tentacles, and that part which was nearest to the base forms a new basal disc. On the other hand, if a very short piece is cut near the mouth region, the tentacles already present will remain

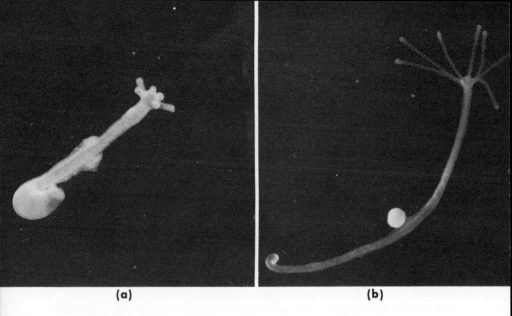

(a)   (b)

Figure 9.16. Left: The partially contracted male Hydra shows developing testes massed about its central region. Right: The fully extended female Hydra shows a developing ovary on its upper central region. Compare these with the specimens in Figure 9.15. (Courtesy Clarence Flaten.)

and a new set of tentacles will develop on the cut side. A similar short piece taken from the basal region, however, does not develop into a new animal. It is difficult for these pieces to survive. There appears to be, therefore, a definite organization of the animal along an axis running from the hypostome to the base, and the suggestion is made that this organization is a result of variation in the metabolic activity between the two extremes of the animal's body. There are several experimental techniques which can be used to test this hypothesis. Animals may be cut and two pieces joined end to end; if the two

Figure 9.17. Regeneration experiments with Hydra have added much to our knowledge of the processes of development, organization, and repair which take place in other many-celled animals. In (a) we have only a clump of cells. This clump develops to the stage, shown in (b), where tentacles and internal organization have been established. In (c) the animals are almost completely re-formed. (Courtesy of *Life, Time,* Inc. Copyright by *Life* photographer Fritz Goro.)

(a)   (b)   (c)

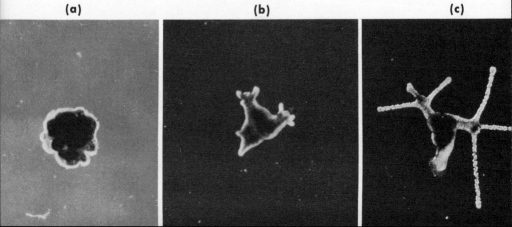

sections are from the region of the hypostome, they fuse, and an animal will be developed with a hypostome and ring of tentacles at either end.   This animal usually separates eventually in its mid-region to form two complete animals. If a sizable piece of *Hydra* taken from the basal region is studied by placing the end near the hypostome in soil, so that its metabolic rate and oxygen consumption are lowered, the portion that would normally develop a mouth constructs a new basal disc, indicative of a lower metabolic rate.   Conversely, if a section from the basal region is treated so that the original basal disc is given an extra amount of oxygen, that portion develops into a new mouth region with a ring of tentacles.   This difference in the metabolic activity ranging from one end to the other is called an *axial gradient;* we shall speak of this later in discussing the flatworms, where the subject has been studied in great detail.

Two further observations of some significance have been made on *Hydra* and other Coelenterata.   Occasionally, under adverse environment, the *Hydra* will gradually decrease in body mass and become transformed into a *reduction mass,*which may later regenerate a new hydra.   This is comparable to a similar situation which we observed in the sponges.   The similarity of the epidermis and the gastrodermis in *Hydra* influenced experimenters to try turning the animals inside out, and such experiments have been done successfully many times.   It is noticed that if the animal is turned wrong-side out and prevented from returning to its normal condition, the epidermis will transform into a gastrodermis and the gastrodermis into an epidermis.   This is not accomplished by a complete reorganization of the original layer, but rather as a result of migration of gastrodermal cells to the new inside and a similar migration of epidermal cells to the new outside of the animal.   This is, therefore, not a demonstration of the interchangeability of the two layers, but merely of the great flexibility which exists in the organization of the animal and the freedom with which individual cells may move about.

Figure 9.18.   Some metazoans, as well as acellular organisms, may reproduce asexually by fission.   This unusual photograph shows an anemone undergoing fission.   (Copyright by Douglas P. Wilson, F. R. P. S. Marine Biological Laboratory, Plymouth, England.)

Classification of Coelenterata (Cnidaria)

Phylum Coelenterata Primarily diploblastic animals of tissue-grade organization. Radial or biradial symmetry, with tentacles and stinging threads, the *nematocysts*. Only one internal cavity, the *gastrovascular cavity*.

CLASS I. HYDROZOA. With either polyp or medusa body form, or both. The animals have radial symmetry. Gastrovascular cavity not divided by partitions. Mesoglea noncellular. Examples: *Hydra, Obelia, Gonionemus.*

CLASS II. SCYPHOZOA. Only medusae (jellyfishes), or polyplike larvae reproducing medusae by budding. Four-part radial symmetry. The mesoglea is cellular. Members of this class are found'only in marine waters. Examples: Jellyfishes, *Aurelia, Cassiopeia.*

CLASS III. ANTHOZOA. Poly body form only. Gastrovascular cavity divided by partitions which also bear nematocysts. Mesoglea is a fibrous connective tissue. Solitary and colonial forms are present: all are confined to marine waters. Examples: *Metridium* (sea anemone), *Meandrina* (brain coral).

REFERENCES

BROWN, F. A. (ed.), *Selected Invertebrate Types*, pp. 85–135. John Wiley and Sons, New York, 1950.
GARDINER, J. S., *Coral Reefs and Atolls.* The Macmillan Company, London, 1931.
HARMER, S. F., and A. E. SHIPLEY, (eds.), *Cambride Natural History, "Coelenterata"*, Vol. I, pp. 245–411. Macmillan and Company, London, 1909.
HYMAN, L. H., *The Invertebrates: Protozoa through Ctenophora*, Vol. I, pp. 365–661. McGraw-Hill Book Company, New York, 1940.
LENHOFF, HOWARD M., and W. FARNSWORTH LOOMIS, *Biology of Hydra.* University of Miami Press, Coral Gables, Florida, 1961.
MAYER, A. G., *The Medusae of the World.* Carnegia Institution of Washington, 1910.
ROUGHLEY, T. C., *Wonders of the Great Barrier Reef.* Charles Scribner's Sons, New York, 1947.

10

The Development

of a Head

Phylum

Platyhelminthes

•

The organic individual presents two problems, the problem of pattern, and the problem of material.—Child, The Origin and Development of the Nervous System

When Linnaeus classified the worms he placed them in a single phylum, the Vermes. This phylum included all the animals of wormlike appearance, namely those whose body was many times longer than it was broad. It is surprising that such a careful observer as Linnaeus should have placed all the worms in a single group, because they are so divergent in structure and appearance that today they have been subdivided into at least six phyla. We will consider three of the more important of these phyla, beginning with the simplest: the flatworms, or Platyhelminthes.

The structural design in these animals is significantly improved over that which we saw in the coelenterates and is marked by two important new features: (1) a third body layer, the mesoderm, which is extensively developed; and (2) a true bilateral symmetry, with an anterior and posterior end, a right and left side, and dorsal and ventral surfaces. The characteristics of the phylum are illustrated very well by interesting but unobtrusive little flatworms, the planarians; and the one commonly used in laboratories, *Dugesia (Euplanaria)*, will be the subject of most of our discussion. These worms are from ½ to 1 inch long, and specimens are easily secured because they can be found in large numbers on the bottom of almost any fast-flowing small stream.

The Planarians

Body form

The external characteristics of planarians, although not too obvious, are so definite that once they have been seen there should be no difficulty in iden-

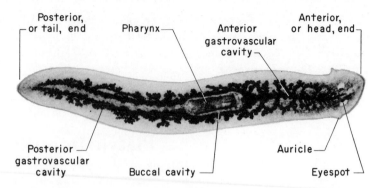

Figure 10.1.   The planarian, a regular inhabitant of streams and ponds, is often overlooked because of its small size and retiring habits.   Its structure is typical of that of the free-living flatworms.   In this photograph the gastrovascular cavity is very obvious because the animal was fed with colored food.   (Courtesy Clarence Flaten.)

tifying specimens.   *Dugesia* and other planarians belong to the class Turbellaria, so named by Ehrenberg in 1831 when he observed that the animals created a "turbulence" in the water about them.   This agitation is produced by the cilia, which cover most of the surface of the body and are an aid in locomotion. The body is, of course, wormlike and flattened.   There are lateral projections at the anterior end of the animal, usually spoken of as *auricles*, but in some of the relatives of *Dugesia* these are long enough to be considered tentacles. The most distinctive feature of the dorsal, or upper, surface of *Dugesia* is the presence of two *eyespots* at the anterior end.   These are light-sensitive pigmented areas; and because the pigment of the eyespots is located in the midregion of the dorsal surface, the animal has a homely, cross-eyed look.

The ventral, or belly, surface of the planarian has an opening, the *mouth*, through which the *pharynx* can be protruded, and the pharynx is the only opening into the gastrovascular cavity.   Posterior to the mouth is another smaller opening, the *genital pore*.   Some planarians are almost colorless, but usually they have a redish-brown or black pigmentation.   When the animals have fed, they are colored by the contents of the gastrovascular cavity, which can be seen readily through the thin body wall.   The animals move about with a seemingly effortless, gliding motion which is a consequence of the action of the cilia on the ventral surface.   The head turns slowly to the right or left, probing the area, and if an obstacle is encountered, the planarian may climb over it or bend the body acutely to turn away from, or to pass around, the object.

A more detailed study of the epidermis and gastrodermis demonstrates that the flatworms possess several unique characteristics.   The epidermis of planarians and that of many other flatworms is an epithelium whose cells are of cuboidal type.   It may be ciliated over the entire body or only on the ventral side and lateral margins. Gland cells which secrete mucus for protection or as an aid to locomotion are common. Special structures, *rhabdites*, are often very numerous; these rodlike bodies are arranged either singly or in bundles at right angles to the surface of the epidermis, but their function is not definitely known. It is possible that the rhabdites may be released from the body and dissolved in the water surrounding the animal to create a protective chemical covering. They also have been claimed to be excretory bodies. Certain secretions of the epidermis are obviously distasteful to other animals, and a planarian which has been captured often will be spat out hurriedly by its captor. It is very interesting to note that some flatworms may be found to have nematocysts in the epidermis. These nematocysts, however, are not formed by the worms themselves but are secured from coelenterates that have been eaten for food. The nematocysts are digested free of surrounding tissues, are transferred from the gastrovascular cavity, and are finally deposited at the surface, where they function as they would in their normal position in the coelenterate!

The mouth opens into a *buccal cavity*, through which the pharynx is protruded. The buccal cavity and the surface of the pharynx are covered with epidermis, which is folded inward during the formation of the cavity. The gastrodermis of flatworms is less complicated in its cellular organization than it is in most of the coelenterates. The cell types primarily are *granular storage cells* and the club-shaped *phagocytic cells* which ingest and digest food particles. *Glandular cells* in the gastrodermis of the pharynx also secrete a mucus as an aid in swallowing. There is a possibility that the pharyngeal secretions may be toxic and thus immoblize the prey. This, however, needs experimental verification.

The development of a third layer in the embryo, the *mesoderm*, is the important contributing feature which makes possible the greater complexity of

Figure 10.2. A cutaway view showing the gastrovascular cavity of a planarian.

Anterior trunk of
gastrovascular cavity

Buccal cavity

Pharynx

Mouth

Opening to
pharynx

Posterior trunks of
gastrovascular cavity

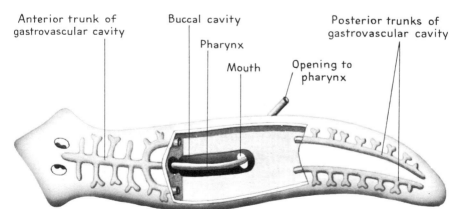

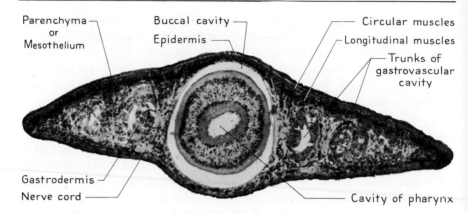

Figure 10.3.   A planarian in cross section.   (Courtesy Clarence Flaten.)

the Platyhelminthes.   It is this third embryonic layer which forms the *muscles, reproductive organs, excretory organs,* and *connective tissues* in most of the triploblastic (three-layered) animals.   The third layer, therefore, is highly differentiated in the adult organism.   Unfortunately, there is no generally accepted term for mesoderm in the adult which compares with the relationship in terminology between the entoderm and the gastrodermis, or between the ectoderm and the epidermis.   We will frequently employ the term *mesothelium* for the adult derivatives of the mesoderm and will take the liberty of using this term with a broader connotation than is generally accorded to it.   A portion of the mesothelium, the *parenchyma,* in planarians is a complex connective and supportive tissue, composed of an interlacing network of protoplasm and irregular fluid-filled spaces.   This protoplasm is a multinucleated mass, without partitions of either cell walls or plasma membranes, and is termed a *syncytium* (cell together).   Such multinucleated masses of protoplasm are relatively common in the animal knigdom.   *Amoebocyte cells,* comparable with those seen in sponges, wander through the parenchyma, and *pigment granules* are also scattered in it.   The latter are not found within cells but are suspended in the fluid of the parenchymal spaces.

Two major layers of muscle develop from the mesoderm: an outer, *circular layer* beneath the epidermis and an inner, *longitudinal layer.*   The antagonistic action of these muscle layers produces elongation or constriction of the body.   The performance is reminiscent of the action of the epitheliomuscular cells of the epidermis and the nutritive-muscular cells of the gastrodermis of *Hydra.*   *Dorsoventral* bands of muscle are also present in *Dugesia,* and their contraction effects further alterations of body shape.

In spite of their singular qualities, the flatworms retain certain characteristics of the coelenterates.   There are, for example, no special respiratory structures, and the digestive system is a gastrovascular cavity.   The advances in body construction in the flatworms have been the establishing of *organ systems*, of definite *muscle layers*, and a *centralized nervous system*. These improvements in body architecture will be analyzed in conjunction with the discussion of the performance of the basic functions.

Nutrition

The planarians are holozoic, almost exclusively carnivorous, and are able to capture and eat animals much larger than themselves. *Dugesia*, for example, attacks and captures immature insects, small earthworms, and even fast-swimming water fleas. It wraps the anterior portion of the body tightly around its prey and thus immobilizes it. The proboscis is then protruded from the buccal cavity, and by forceful contraction of its muscles the animal exerts a sucking action on the tissues of the captive, with the result that small chunks of meat are detached. These are taken into the pharynx and passed into the gastrovascular cavity by a wave of contraction that moves along the pharynx. The entire gastrovascular cavity can be filled with foodstuff within an hour after the animal begins feeding. *Dugesia* (a triclad planarian) possesses a gastrovascular cavity with three trunks: one long trunk extends forward from the pharynx to a region between the eyespots, and two trunks with many branches project posteriorly. The branches may be interconnected, so that a complex network of gastrovascular tissue is created.

Very little if any digestion occurs within the cavity of the digestive system, but food particles are ingested rapidly by the phagocytic cells which line the gastrovascular cavity. These cells form food cups comparable to those found in *Amoeba* or in the cells of the gastrodermis of *Hydra*. Digestion of proteins and fats occurs within the food cup, but it is questionable whether starch is digested. The food particles, after having been broken down and digested within the food cups of the phagocytic cells, are passed by diffusion throughout the body. This would appear to be inefficient method of nutrition, but the many-branched gastrovascular cavity and the spongy construction of the parenchyma make the distribution throughout the body mass relatively easy.

The basal portion of the gastrodermal cells stores large quantities of fats, which can be used as a reserve supply of food, and the granular storage cells also probably store proteins as an additional food reserve. The ability to

Figure 10.4. Gastrodermis of a planarian. Digestion is primarily intracellular: food particles are ingested and digested by the phagocytic cells, and food can be stored for later use in the granular cells.

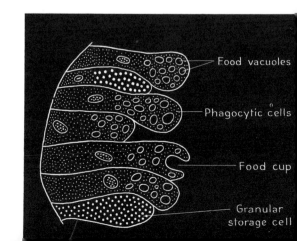

accumulate food, particularly proteins, is remarkable in planarians, and the animals may survive a year or more without feeding. Body size during this starvation period may decrease to as little as ⅟₅₀₀ of the original volume, which demonstrates that body tissues as well as food reserves are used.

An interesting nutritional relationship exists in some small marine flatworms, the Acoela, which harbor plants among their body cells. These plant cells use the carbon dioxide and nitrogenous compounds excreted by the acoels; in return they contribute oxygen and, presumably, carbohydrates. This is a remarkable mutual-benefit relationship, but the older acoels gradually come to depend entirely upon the plants for their own food, and a type of reverse parasitism then ensues, the plants being parasitized by the host in which they live. The end result is fatal to both, because the plants are unable to continue to support successfully both themselves and the worm.

Respiration

The respiration of planarians is oxybiotic, and detailed studies have been made of the rate of oxygen consumption. The oxygen needs are higher in young planarians (a condition common to young animals) during digestion of food materials and after a period of starvation when the animal's size is reduced. Extensive studies have shown that the amount of oxygen consumed is highest at the head end and lowest at the tail end of the animal and that there is an intermediate rate of oxygen consumption in the mid-body region. It will be pointed out later that this variation in the rate of oxygen consumption between the head end and the tail end of the animal is evidence for an *axial gradient*, which we discussed briefly in the preceding chapter. Utilization of oxygen can be inhibited by treating the animals with cyanide, and this indicates the presence of an oxidative enzyme system comparable to that in man. This is another of the many examples of similarity of functions which occur throughout the animal kingdom. The amount of oxygen consumed in planarians has been estimated to be between 0.2 and 0.3 cubic centimeter per gram per hour, exclusive of the variations noted above.

The thin body wall of *Dugesia* and other planarians permits rapid exchange of oxygen and carbon dioxide between the environment and the tissues. The irregular fluid-filled body spaces also facilitate interchange of the oxygen and carbon dioxide within the body. Planarians have probably achieved nearly the maximum body size which can be attained with such a simplified method of gaseous exchange.

Excretion

The excretory system in the Platyhelminthes is a new development, because such a system was not found in either the Porifera or the Coelenterata. The basic structure of the excretory system is a complicated arrangement of *flame bulbs* and *excretory tubules,* the latter with openings, the *excretory pores,* lead-

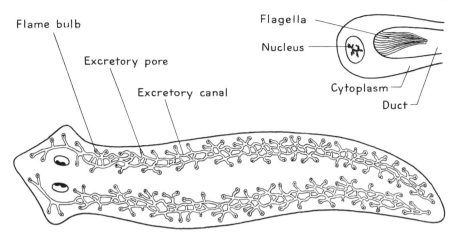

Figure 10.5.   Excretory system of a planarian, with an enlarged view of a flame bulb.

ing to the outside. The system operates almost exclusively for the elimination of water and is better developed in the forms which live in fresh water than in those which live in salt water. The flame bulbs develop from a single cell that hollows out to form a bulb at one end and a hollow tubule at the other. The bulb end, containing a nucleus, projects without any opening into the parenchyma, while the tubule is connected by a duct with the *excretory canal*. A clump of flagella, or sometimes a single flagellum, extends from the bulb end of the tubule into the duct. The movement of the flagella produces a flamelike flickering when observed in a living animal. Fluid accumulates in the flame bulb by diffusion from the tissue spaces of the parenchyma, and the current created by the flagella moves the fluid through the excretory canals to the outside.

The method of elimination of nitrogenous wastes in planarians is not clearly understood, but small quantities of waste may be dissolved in the water which is eliminated through the excretory canals. Nitrogenous waste compounds apparently are deposited as insoluble granules in the parenchyma and may contribute to the body pigmentation of the flatworm. We mentioned earlier that the rhabdites also may contain concentrated excretory products, but evidence for this is not conclusive. Carbon dioxide is eliminated through the body wall, in conjunction with the respiratory activity of the animal.

Reproduction

Both asexual and sexual reproduction occur in the flatworms. Some planarians are primarily asexual, and others primarily sexual; in the case of *Dugesia*, asexual reproduction is prevalent. Most of the flatworms are hermaphroditic, and both eggs and sperm mature simultaneously in a single individual, but

Ovary ⌐   ⌐Oviduct   ⌐Copulatory sac

          ⌐Sperm duct   ⌐Penis

          ⌐Yolk gland   ⌐Genital chamber

          ⌐Testis   ⌐Genital pore

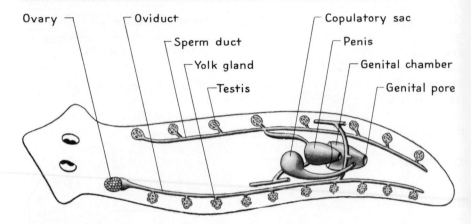

Figure 10.6.   Reproductive system of a planarian.   For simplicity, the female reproductive system is shown on only one side and the male reproductive system on the other.

self-fertilization rarely occurs.   Asexual reproduction is accomplished by fission, with the animal constricting posterior to the pharynx.   The constriction eventually separates the animal into two pieces, with the anterior portion developing a new tail, and the posterior portion a new head.   The formative material for the new parts is to be found in special cells of the mesothelium which retain embryonic potentialities.   A second or third constriction is initiated in some planarians before the first one has been completed, so that a chain of developing individuals may be observed.   Asexual reproduction may continue for several years without the intervention of sexual generations, and a thousand successive asexual generations have been reported over a period of eleven years.

Considerable diversity exists in the reproductive organs of the several flatworms, and for that reason it is difficult to give a description of a "typical" reproductive system.   *Dugesia*, however, is fairly representative of the various forms.   Generally, two *ovaries* are located in the head region of the animal. These are connected by *oviducts* with the *genital pore*, which is situated on the posterior ventral surface of the animal.   Numerous *testes* are found along the sides of the body, and each testis is connected by a very fine tube to a *sperm duct*.   The sperm ducts are paired, and each runs posteriorly to the genital-pore region where the sperm are stored.   The genital-pore region is complicated, because it receives the ducts from both the ovaries and testes, has a *copulatory sac* for the reception of sperm from another individual, and also has a *penis* by means of which sperm are transferred to the mate.   The stored sperm are inactive but are activated when transferred into the second animal.   The sperm, after being deposited in the copulatory sac during mating, migrate up the oviduct, where they fertilize the ova as they complete their passage down this tube.

The presence of numerous *yolk glands* which are joined to the oviduct is characteristic of the reproductive system. These glands release yolk cells, which migrate into the oviduct and aggregate posteriorly in the region of the genital pore. During the passage of the fertilized ova along the oviduct, the yolk cells accumulate about the ova. This is a rather unusual situation, because in most animals the yolk is deposited within the cytoplasm of the egg. The fertilized eggs finally are covered by a secretion which hardens into a capsule and which will contain several ova when laid, or ejected. The capsule is deposited in a protected place, and all the ova develop simultaneously.

Coordination

The flatworms have made a significant advance over the coelenterates in the development of a *centralized nervous system*. This nervous system begins with a concentration of nerve cells in the anterior region: the *brain* and two *nerve cords* which extend posteriorly from the brain to the tail end of the animal. There are numerous cross connections between these two nerve strands, as well as projections which extend laterally. The two cords, with the cross strands, give the nervous system the appearance of a ladder, and hence this is often spoken of as a *ventral ladder-type* nervous system. A centralized nervous system has many advantages over the nerve net, because stimuli received from the sense organs are conveyed rapidly to other parts of the body in a direct, coordinated fashion. The nerve net, which was characteristic of the coelenterates, has not been lost entirely but is still present in the planarians, although of secondary importance.

Numerous sensory receptor cells and sense organs are present in planarians, and receptor cells which extend processes to the surface of the animal constitute the simplest type of sensory structure. The *auricles* on the head are generally sensitive to light, touch, or chemical stimuli; and although the head acts as the coordinating center for the entire animal, it does not seem to be

Figure 10.7. Nervous system of a planarian. This is a ventral ladder-type nervous system, but it differs from the ladder-type nervous systems of the earthworm and of the insects.

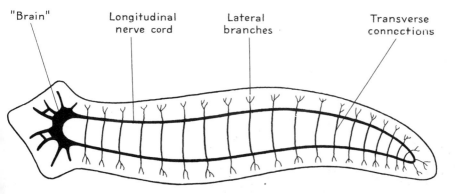

"Brain"   Longitudinal   Lateral   Transverse
               nerve cord   branches   connections

too important, because planarians continue to move about actively after the brain has been removed. The most highly developed sense organ is the *eyespot*, in which there is a concentration of nerve cells partially covered by a pigmented cup, and the entire area is especially receptive to light. The arrangement of the pigment in the cup is such that light can strike the sensitive cells only from a given direction. The animal, therefore, is able to orient itself to the light that reaches it from various points in its surroundings.

We can easily perform several simple experiments to illustrate some of the behavior patterns in a laboratory. *Dugesia* normally lives in streams where there is a moderate current of water, and its response to a water current is precise. This can be demonstrated by directing a jet of water from the tip of a pipette at various parts of the animal. If the pipette is pointed toward the tail end of the animal, the planarian will turn so that its head is directed toward the pipette; if the current is pointed toward the side of the animal, it will like-wise turn its head toward the current. Planarians also orient themselves toward bits of meat placed in the water near them and will move toward the meat. This is definitely a response to a chemical stimulus. The adjustment of pla-narians to light is also very definite. The animals select a region of dim illumi-nation and turn away from a strong source of light; they even do so after the eyes have been removed, although the reaction is much slower. This indicates that the general body surface possesses sensory receptors for light, but these receptors are not as efficient as the eyespots for light detection. Planarians, in addition, may be taught simple associations. If an experimental setup is devised in which the planarians are allowed to select a dark or a brightly lighted region, we can observe that the animals tend to move into the dark area. By inserting an electrical device which shocks the animals when they move into the dark region, they can be taught to avoid the dark. This avoid-ance response will persist for a considerable period of time after the device

Figure 10.8. Movement and response of a planarian. The planarian (a) is gliding steadily away from the surface film of the water, which it had met head-on. The animal, having com-pleted its turning maneuver (b), again encounters the surface film at another place (c). It then contracts more vigorously, preparatory to making another change of direction, as in (a). (Courtesy Clarence Flaten.)

(a)   **(b)**   **(c)**

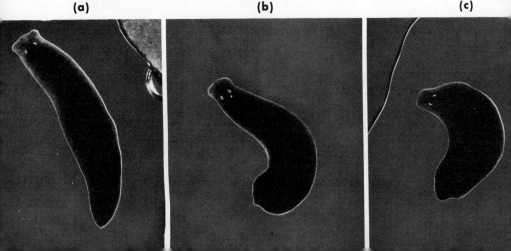

has been turned off, which demonstrates that the planarians have "learned" to make the simple association of darkness with a disturbing stimulus.

Experimentation with planarians

Planarians also have made important contributions to the study of several biological problems. We have noted that the head end of the planarian can be shown to consume oxygen at a rate higher than the tail end. This was confirmed indirectly many years ago when certain poisons were added to the water in which the planarians were swimming. The heads of the animals were the first to disintegrate as a result of the action of the poisons. Since it is known that the region of the body having the highest metabolic rate will be the first area affected by a poison, this simple experiment confirmed the fact that a difference in oxidative rate exists between the two ends of the animal.

The division of planaria asexually by fission suggested to investigators many years ago the possibility of analyzing this process experimentally to determine whether there is a correlation between the variation in oxidative rate and body organization. These experiments have led to the development of the axial-gradient theory of body organization and metabolism. This imposing term merely means that the metabolism of the animal varies along an anterior-posterior axis, and that cellular activity is higher in the head and gradually diminishes toward the tail. A striking illustration of this gradient can be shown by severing a planarian in the mid-region. We observe that the cut edge of the anterior half will grow a new tail, and the cut edge of the posterior half will develop a new head. An animal cut into three approximately equal parts will develop a tail on the anterior third, a head on the posterior third, and the middle third will reform a head at its anterior margin and a tail at its posterior end. It can be concluded, therefore, that a head always develops in the area with the higher oxidative rate and a tail in the region of the lower oxidative rate. Additional information on this problem of organization can be secured by cutting the animal differently. If a planarian is split lengthwise from the head end about halfway down the body length, and if the two pieces are kept apart for a period of about 24 hours, each split half will regenerate a portion of the head, with the result that a two-headed animal develops. An interesting extension of this experiment is possible by splitting each of the two heads and as a consequence a four-headed animal can be formed. The experiment has been carried much further, with as many as eight to sixteen heads being formed on a single planarian.

An evaluation of these experiments shows that there is an over-all organization of the body, and this recalls the quotation at the head of this chapter. That statement emphasizes that both *pattern* and *material* are essential to organic form. It is also obvious that an animal must be considered as a whole, and that the fate of an individual cell is determined primarily by its position in the organism. When we re-examine the cell theory in the light of these observations, it again is apparent that cells are not predominant in body structure.

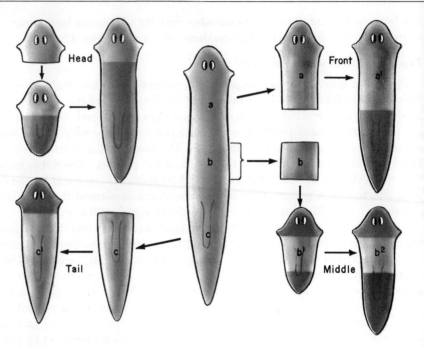

Figure 10.9.   Regeneration.   This diagram illustrates the fate of pieces of planarian which are cut from various regions of the body.   The darker areas represent regenerated regions. (Courtesy Hugh Spencer.)

Figure 10.10.   Regeneration.   These are actual photographs of animals which were operated on by a student in an introductory zoology course.   The picture in (a) corresponds to (b) in Figure 10.9.   The lighter areas are the regenerating head and tail (note the tiny eyespots). The photograph in (b) corresponds roughly to piece a in Figure 10.9, and the regenerating tail region is clearly delineated.   The photograph in (c) shows an animal which was split lengthwise approximately one third its length with two heads developing.   (Courtesy Clarence Platen.)

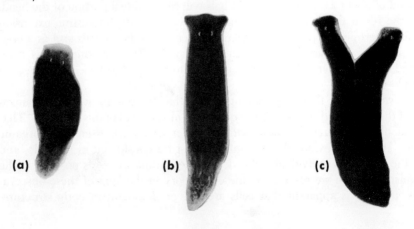

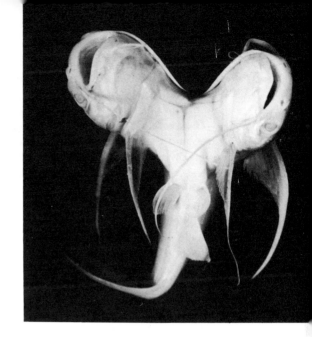

Figure 10.11. Two-headed catfish. The fact that regeneration is not confiner to animals in the "lower" phyla is illustrated by this two-headed catfish. It must have suffered a split head during embryonic development and, like the planarian in Figure 10.10 (c) regenerated each of the split parts. (Courtesy Frank Piper.)

They are the plastic materials out of which the organism makes its functional units in the form of tissues or organs.

These experiments with planarians may seem to be overemphasized, but the conclusions can be extended to forms as remote from the planarians as the birds and mammals. We find evidence that an axial gradient exists in the embryonic development of these two groups. Probably everyone has seen two-headed animals in side shows; the development of these monsters can be interpreted in the light of the experiments on planaria. It is known that if the embryonic head region of a chicken, for example, is split experimentally, two heads may be formed. Likewise, as a result of similar experiments performed in the embryonic tail region, the material in the posterior portion of the embryo can be separated, or modified in its relation to the other parts of the body, and extra limbs may develop.

Planarians have made important contributions to the study of *aging*. Well-fed planarians will continue to grow for a long time, but as they increase in size their metabolic activity gradually diminishes. Oxygen consumption in these larger, older animals is lower than it is in the younger, smaller animals. The well-fed planarians will die after a period of time unless their metabolic activity is increased experimentally, or unless they undergo fission. Some of the older animals will fragment—that is, they undergo multiple fission—each of the pieces becoming a new worm. Measurement of the oxidative rate of these small animals derived from the old worm shows that rejuvenation has taken place: the metabolic rate is high, and they are young planarians. If an old animal is starved so that its body size is decreased rapidly, an increase in the rate of oxidation is observed. Starvation, therefore, rejuvenates these animals also. These facts indicate the existence of a problem which correlates general metabolism with age, and the experimental results, though not fully understood, clearly suggest that if the proper relation of surface area to volume is maintained, aging and death do not occur.

One of the most important problems in human biology today is that of old age. The average age of the human population has increased greatly in a few decades, and the study of old age (*geriatrics*) is occupying a great deal of the attention of biologists and the medical profession today. Any investigation, therefore, which will contribute to an understanding of the problems of metabolism in the aged is advantageous. It is probable that our homely little animal, the planarian, will give us important clues which may make it possible for older people to live more productive and happier existences in their later years.

It should be stressed, in conclusion, that experimentation with planarians illustrates one of the most important contributions which zoology has made to the field of scientific investigation. Our knowledge can be expanded by observation and experimentation with simpler animals, and this knowledge can be applied to the interpretation of problems which arise in more complex organisms. Thus we are able to study processes which would be almost impossible to investigate in man or his close relatives, even should more elaborate experimental procedures be devised than are available today.

Other Flatworms

Although the planarians are appreciated for their contributions to the understanding of biological problems, other flatworms also are of concern to man. Certain ones, such as the *flukes* and the *tapeworms*, are of great economic importance because they parasitize both man and his domestic animals. The flukes and the tapeworms are complicated organisms, and many of them have bizarre embryonic or larval forms. A fluke and a tapeworm will be used to illustrate the essential features of these other groups, but their embryonic forms will be discussed later, when we consider the general problems of parasitism (Chapter 17).

Flukes

All the flukes (class, Trematoda) are parasitic organisms, and their body structure is adapted to a parasitic existence. Any one of several flukes would illustrate the features of this class, but we will select for our consideration the liver fluke. This animal is recognizable on the basis of its external features as a member of the Platyhelminthes. There is, however, no true epidermis, but the mesothelium secretes a protective *cuticle* about the outside of the animal. This cuticle and the presence of oral and ventral suckers, or adhesive organs, characterize all flukes. In addition, the mouth has moved forward and is located as an opening in the oral sucker. Internally the animals possess typical flatworm organization, but the muscle layers are better developed than are those of planarians. An outer circular-muscle layer, a middle

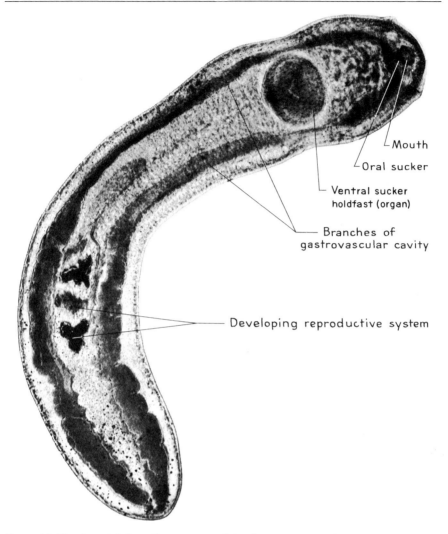

Mouth

Oral sucker

Ventral sucker
holdfast (organ)

Branches of
gastrovascular cavity

Developing reproductive system

Figure 10.12.   Larval fluke.   This immature fluke illustrates some of the specialization for parastic existence which is to be found amoung the flatworms.   The large ventral sucker used to hold the fluke to its host (the animal parasitized) is especially noteworthy.   (Courtesy Clarence Flaten.)

longitudinal-muscle layer, and the usual dorsal-ventral muscles are present, but an internal diagonal-muscle layer has been added.   The gastrovascular cavity is somewhat modified; a very short pharynx connects directly with large *pouches* which project posteriorly.   These pouches usually are called *caeca* and may be extensively branched.   The caeca create additional storage space for food material in the flukes.

All respiration is accomplished through the body surface, and the excretion of water is performed by flame bulbs and excretory tubules in a manner comparable to that of the planarians. The development of the parenchyma is more extensive than in *Dugesia*, and the irregular fluid-filled spaces may fuse to constitute a very primitive circulatory system. The importance of such a system will be evident later when we come to consider the functions of circulation in other triploblastic animals. The sense organs of the fluke are reduced, but the nervous system is essentially the same as that of the planarians. The animals have a ventral ladder-type nervous system, and sensory structures in the form of fine branches of the receptor cells reach into the cuticle. The sexes are separate in the blood flukes, but the majority of the other flukes are hermaphroditic. Those flukes which are internal parasites also have complicated life histories, with larval forms that reproduce asexually in the larval stages. These details, however, can be discussed more profitably when the parasites are considered as a group.

Tapeworms

The tapeworms (class, Cestoda) are among the most distinctive animals in the animal kingdom. They demonstrate the acme in parasitic adaptation, because their energies are devoted almost entirely to reproduction, and their degenerative changes are extensive. As a reflection of their adaptation, we can make the following observations: (1) the gastrovascular cavity is completely absent; (2) sensory structures have almost disappeared; and (3) hooks and suckers have been developed elaborately. The tapeworms are obviously more highly modified than the flukes, and with the loss of the digestive system they must depend entirely on the host, not only for food but even for the digestion of that food.

The name *tapeworm* is descriptive of the body appearance of these animals. They are flattened, elongated, tapelike animals with a small *scolex* and a series

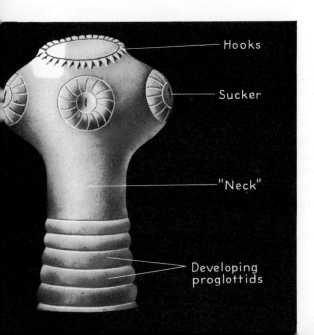

Hooks

Sucker

"Neck"

Developing
proglottids

Figure 10.13. Scolex (head) of a hog tapeworm, showing the elaborate development of hooks and suckers as "holdfast organs." Note the proglottids (also see Figure 10.14).

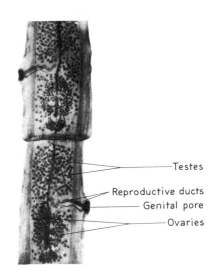

Testes

Reproductive ducts

Genital pore

Ovaries

Figure 10.14. Tapeworm proglottids. Two tapeworm proglottids are shown. In this form the genital openings on adjacent proglottids are on opposite sides. The hermaphroditic condition is evident from the presence of both ovaries and testes and from the fact that ducts of both sexes are present. An account of the structure of a proglottid is given in the study of parasitism, Chapter 17. (Courtesy Clarence Flaten.)

of segments, the *proglottids*. The scolex is equipped with *suckers* and, in some tapeworms, with a circlet of *hooks*. It serves as a "holdfast organ," to prevent the host from dislodging the animal from its position in the alimentary canal. The scolex is continuous with a narrow "neck" which produces, or "buds off," the proglottids. The youngest proglottid, as a result, is the one nearest the scolex and the oldest proglottid is at the extreme end of the worm. The hog tapeworm may reach a length of 10 to 12 feet, and the broad tapeworm a length of 30 to 40 feet. The proglottids in a single host may number as many as 3000 to 4000!

The surface of the tapeworm is protected by a cuticle, beneath which are circular and longitudinal muscle layers. The general constitution of the body wall, therefore, is comparable to that of the fluke. Two *nerve cords* and two *excretory canals* extend the length of the body. The excretory canals are interconnected at the posterior portion of each proglottid by a transverse *excretory duct*. *Flame bulbs* are joined to the excretory canals, and the organization of the excretory system is comparable to that of the planarians.

Perhaps the most remarkable feature of the tapeworm is the relationship of its segmentation to the development of the reproductive system. The worms are hermaphroditic, and each segment, or proglottid, of the tapeworm contains a complete set of male and female reproductive organs. This reproductive system is embedded in the parenchyma, and there are numerous *testes* and a single pair of large *ovaries*. The testes are connected by small tubes to a large *sperm duct* which opens at the *genital pore*. The female portion of the reproductive system is much more complex than is the male portion. A *yolk gland* is situated near the posterior margin of each proglottid, and a pair of ducts leads from this yolk gland to the *uterus* and to the *vagina*. The vagina parallels the sperm duct, and the sperm enter the vagina at the genital pore and pass toward the uterus.

Self-fertilization apparently can occur within a proglottid, but it seems more likely that the bending of the worm brings proglottids from various regions of the body close together, with cross-fertilization usually occurring. When the eggs are discharged, they are fertilized by the sperm which have been stored in the enlarged portion of the vagina. These fertilized eggs receive *yolk cells* from the yolk gland. A shell is formed about the eggs and yolk cells by the *shell gland.* The fertilized eggs pass into the uterus, which is a large, median saclike structure that develops many branches as the embryos mature. The testes degenerate, and the remaining portions of the female reproductive system degenerate as the uterus hypertrophies (increases). The greatly distended uterus eventually fills practically the entire space within a "ripe" proglottid. This ripe proglottid finally is broken free of the animal and discharged with the fecal material of the host, liberating thousands of embryos. It has been estimated, for example, that the beef tapeworm in a 10-year period may lay 2,500,000,000 eggs!

Since the tapeworms have a segmented appearance, a question of considerable theoretical interest is raised: namely, is this true segmentation? *Segmentation* has been defined as the condition in which there is serial duplication of parts. Since the reproductive organs and the excretory organs are duplicated serially, it must be granted that the tapeworms fulfill the terms of the definition, but a complicating factor is introduced by the fact that the proglottids are budded from the scolex. It will be observed later that the segments are formed from the posterior (tail) region in other segmented animals. Miss Hyman, however, is of the opinion that this difference is of no significance.

Classification of the Platyhelminthes

Phylum Platyhelminthes   Flatworms which are bilaterally symmetrical and triploblastic, but without a coelom. Possessing a gastrovascular cavity, and an excretory system with flame bulbs.

Class I. Turbellaria. Free-living flatworms with undivided body and ciliated epidermis. Examples: *Dugesia, Bipalium* (the land planaria).

Class II. Trematoda. The Flukes. External and internal parasites. Without an epidermis or cilia, and possessing a cuticle, but with the body undivided. Usually with one or more suckers. Life cycles may be complicated as an adaptation to parasitism. Examples: Liver fluke, blood fluke.

Class III. Cestoda. The Tapeworms. Internal parasites exclusively. Without an epidermis or cilia, and possessing a cuticle. Body usually divided into many segments (proglottids). Suckers and hooks may be present on the anterior end. Examples: Broad tapeworm, hog tapeworm.

REFERENCES

Brown, F. A. (ed.), *Selected Invertebrate Types*, pp. 141–208. John Wiley & Sons, Inc., New York, 1950.

Child, C. M., *Patterns and Problems of Development*, pp. 1–165. University of Chicago Press, Chicago, 1941.

Harmer, S. F., and A. E. Shipley, (eds.), "Platyhelminthes and Metazoa," *The Cambridge Natural History*, Vol. 2, pp. 3–91. Macmillan and Company, Ltd., London, 1922.

Hyman, L. H. *The Invertebrates: Platyhelminthes and Rhynchocoela*, Vol. II, pp. 52–333. McGraw-Hill Book Company, Inc., New York, 1951.

Lankester, Ray (ed.), *A Treatise on Zoology*, Part IV, pp. 1–147. Adam and Charles Black, London, 1901.

Wardle, R. A., and J. A. McLeod, *The Zoology of Tapeworms*, pp. 3–44. University of Minnesota Press, Minneapolis, 1952.

11

Worms

and More Worms

Phylum

Nemathelminthes

●

It is amazing the complexity of the nematodes—the variety of specific organization in so small a space is marvelous.—Jacques Loeb

The phylum Nemathelminthes° illustrates some of the troublesome problems encountered by a taxonomist when he endeavors to place animals in definitive classification groups. We implied in the previous chapter that Linnaeus was lax when he cataloged all the worms into a single phylum, the Vermes. We must say in his defense, however, that even had he examined them carefully, he would have had difficulty, because many of the characteristic features of worms are discernible only upon microscopic examination. Microscopes were known during Linnaeus' time but were poor instruments, and there was little interest among biologists in their use. Furthermore, the study of microscopic features as an aid in classification did not seem important until many years later.

We have tried to avoid some of the various taxonomic complications by subdividing the phylum Nemathelminthes into three classes, following the plan outlined by Miss Hyman, but omitting several of the less well-known groups of worms. These classes frequently are given rank as phyla, but the class distinction employed here is convenient and can be justified on the basis of the many features which the worms possess in common. The three classes which we will consider are: (1) Rotifera; (2) Nematoda; and (3) Gordiacea. We will consider the remaining large group of worms later as the phylum Annelida.

The Nemathelminthes have achieved several structural advances over the flatworms. The animals generally are elongated, cylindrical forms, although a few are spherical. A well-developed *cuticle* is typical and, in the case of some

° A better name probably is Aschelminthes (cavity worms), as Miss Hyman points out, but the better-known name, Nemathelminthes (thread worms), is used here.

nematodes, this cuticle is shed several times during growth. They possess a body cavity, the *pseudocoel*, partially within the mesothelium; this, however, is not a true coelom. The development of a *true alimentary canal* in each of the three classes is a significant improvement over a gastrovascular cavity. The alimentary canal is a tube extending the length of the animal, with a mouth and an anal opening. This tubular plan makes possible a greater division of labor in the digestive system. The rotifers have retained *flame cells* for excretion, but the nematodes have a unique excretory structure of their own, and the gordiacea have no recognizable excretory system. One remarkable feature, very common in the phylum, is the fact that the body is composed of relatively few cells and, especially, that this number is constant. Each cell has been counted in the rotifers and actually located on a "cell map." The number of cells in each gland, for example, is constant and, once the body form has been established, the cell number does not increase. The number of cells in the different species of rotifers ranges from 900 to 1000, but the number of cells in the nematodes is greater.

The rotifers and the gordiacea are of little economic importance, but their theoretical significance is considerable. Some rotifers are smaller than many protozoans, and others no larger than the average-size protozoan. This intrigues us because the rotifers, despite their minute size, have a very intricate body organization. Ehrenberg is usually given credit for classifying the rotifers separately from the protozoans, a distinction which he made in the late 1830's. However, in 1812, Dutrochet had named them Rotifera and recognized that they were distinct from the protozoans. He also made the remarkable

Figure 11.1.   Though generally unobserved and unknown, the microscopic rotifers are common inhabitants of fresh-water ponds and streams.   They are also found, but less commonly, in salt water and even in places only temporarily wet, such as rock crevices.   (a) A floating rotifer; (b) a rotifer feeding on an alga plant.   (Courtesy American Museum of Natural History.)

(a)   **(b)**

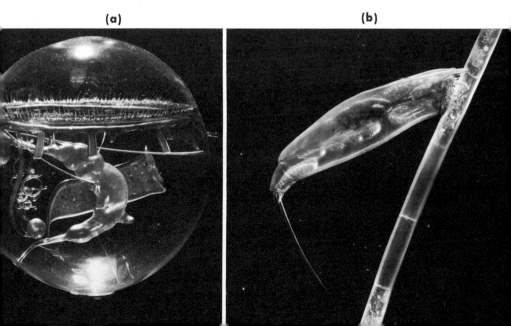

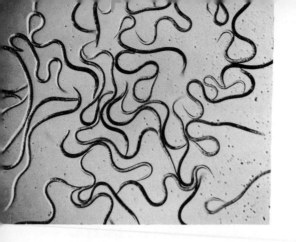

Figure 11.2. The tiny vinegar eels, Turbatrix aceti, of typical nematode body form, are found in vinegar, sometimes in great numbers. Though of minute size, they give birth to living young. (Copyright by General Biological Supply House, Inc., Chicago.)

observation that the organization of these microscopic animals is more complex than that of the coelenterates!

The nematodes are of tremendous economic importance to man, and their body organization is also of interest. The nematodes have been much maligned, because many text and reference books speak of them as though they were exclusively parasitic. It is true that certain infamous parasites are nematodes, but the majority of these worms are free-living animals. The outstanding student of nematodes is an American, N. A. Cobb, who for many years has campaigned for the animals, contending that they deserved more important consideration than was usually accorded them in the study of the animal kingdom. Indeed, the nematodes have contributed much to our knowledge of biological problems. The first demonstration of the fertilization of an ovum was made by Otto Bütschli on the egg of the nematode many years ago, and some of the most exact and precise studies on embryonic development were done on nematodes in the last century by Theodor Boveri. Although relatively few species have been described, it is estimated by Miss Hyman that there are probably 500,000 species of nematodes. The nematodes usually are of very small size, although larger than the rotifers. They are found in all regions of the earth, from the greatest depths of the oceans to the tops of the highest mountains, and it has been estimated that as many as several billion per acre may live in the top few inches of soil. Many of these animals exist on decaying matter; others are carnivores. The nematodes are known to be extremely important in the disposal of dead organisms and the consequent return of organic matter to the earth in a form which may be used again by other organisms.

The parasitic nematodes must be given major consideration, because some of the most important parasites of man are found in this group, for example, Ascaris and the hookworm. It has been estimated that $100,000,000 worth of damage is done annually to livestock in the United States as a result of nematode infections. The nematodes often are parasitic in plants as well as in animals.

One common form of nematode that will illustrate the basic structures of the class is called the *vinegar eel*. This tiny animal, usually two to three milli-meters long, lives in cider vinegar, which has a high content of acetic acid. The worm thrives when the acetic-acid content is about 6 per cent but is able to withstand concentrations of the acid as high as 13 to 14 per cent. Any-one who likes vinegar on salads will find it difficult to be a vegetarian, because there is always the possibility of ingesting many thousands of vinegar eels. Fortunately, there are no ill effects on human beings from the inadvertent ingestion and digestion of this animal protein.

The gordiacea are known to all boys who have a curiosity about living things. These worms are called the *horsehair snakes* and are often discovered in small vessels containing water and are sometimes mistakenly thought to have developed from horsehairs.

Rotifera

Body form

The body of the typical rotifer is an elongated cylinder with a broad *anterior end*, sometimes called the "head end," a *neck* area, a somewhat expanded *trunk* region, and a tapering *tail*, with a *foot*. Some of the rotifers are saclike, or spherical. The most prominent external feature of the rotifers is the presence of a single or double band of cilia in the head region. This is called the *wheel organ* and gives the animals their designation of "wheel animalcules." When a rotifer is observed under the microscope, the cilia seem to beat in a rotating

Figure 11.3. This drawing illustrates general rotifer body form. Rotifers have many shapes, but all are bilaterally symmetrical, and all, in spite of their microscopic size, have complex structures.

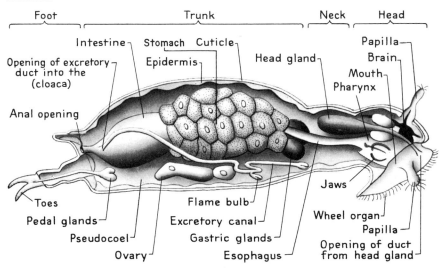

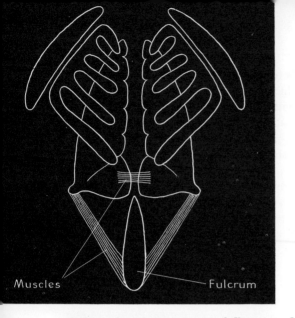

Figure 11.4. The jaws of the rotifer are complex. The upper and lower jaws differ in shape and muscular articulation so that they can grasp, cut, and grind.

Muscles Fulcrum

fashion; but this is an optical illusion and results from the fact that the effective stroke of the cilia is fast, whereas the recovery stroke is slow. The entire surface of the rotifer is covered with a semirigid protective cuticle, often of a slightly yellowish color. This cuticle, composed primarily of protein, is secreted by the epidermis and may be thinned in many places to permit flexibility. The epidermis of the rotifer is a syncytium—i.e., a multinucleated protoplasmic mass.

Sensory fingerlike projections, the *papillae*, or *antennae*, occur on various parts of the animal; these may be dorsal antennae, paired lateral antennae, or caudal (or tail) antennae. Ciliated *tips*, *bristles*, and other papillae occur at various points on the surface of the animal and are also sensory. The head region of some of the rotifers contains one or two pigmented areas, the "eyes," which may have a thickened *lens* over them for the focusing of light rays. The eyes are not image-forming but are very sensitive to light. Special *pedal glands* are present in the tail region, and these secrete a sticky substance which enables the rotifers to attach themselves by means of the foot. They may attach themselves temporarily, remain attached, or swim about actively. The muscles are not arranged in layers, which is more common in the worms, but are in the form of bands. The musculature, however, is very well developed. The basic arrangement of structures of a typical rotifer can be illustrated by *Notommata*, a relatively common and easily collected form.

Nutrition

The rotifers are holozoic and are very adaptable in their feeding habits. The animals secure food by three different methods: *first*, the wheel organ creates a current which sweeps small organisms into the mouth opening; *second*, the rotifer may expand its mouth region and engulf organisms; and *third*, certain rotifers may remain attached throughout their life and act as animated traps by expanding the head region to produce a funnel, into which unwary organisms swim and are trapped. The importance of the wheel organ is obvious in all three types of feeding.

The mouth of the rotifer opens into a *pharynx*, which is equipped with *jaws*. These jaws are horny bodies which work on a fulcrum and enable the animal to tear the prey into small pieces. The smaller particles are then passed into a short *esophagus* which connects with the *stomach*, usually composed of only 30 to 40 cells. Digestive enzymes are secreted into the cavity, or *lumen*, of the stomach; and digestion appears to be exclusively extracellular. Rotifers undoubtedly are able to use both proteins and fats, and possess enzymes for the digestion of these substances. There is a question, however, as to whether they can digest starches; and digestion, therefore, seems comparable to that observed previously in flatworms. Additional investigation is needed on the digestive processes of the rotifers. Undigested food materials are passed along to the *intestine*, which is a short, simple tube connected posteriorly with an enlargement, the *cloaca*. The cloaca represents a new development not previously encountered in the animal kingdom, but it is a very common feature of many triploblastic organisms. The term *cloaca* means "sewer," and it is the portion of the body into which the undigested food material, the excretory products, and often the reproductive cells are emptied. The cloaca empties to the outside through the *anal opening*. There is an extension of the body posterior to the anal opening, which, by definition, is a *tail*. This particular feature is not common to all animals and is encountered for the first time in the rotifers.

Respiration

Respiration in the rotifers is oxybiotic, and the exchange of gases is very simple. The body size is small, and the total mass of tissue in proportion to the

Figure 11.5. (a) A group of colonial rotifers. These colonies are often brilliantly colored and show a fantastic variety of shapes. Their relative size can be judged from the hydra at the extreme left. (b) Both colonial and individual rotifers are shown in this photograph. The hemispherical rotifer at the top left of (b) is engulfing a worm. (a) Courtesy American Museum of Natural History.

(a) **(b)**

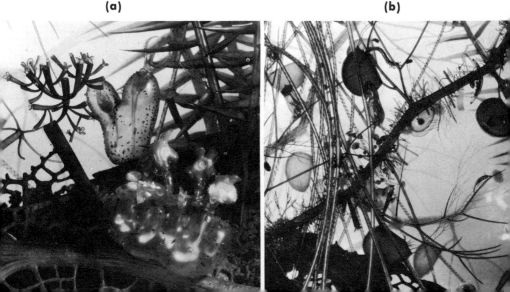

total amount of the body surface is such that enough oxygen can diffuse through the body wall to supply the needs of the organism.   Carbon dioxide can also be eliminated by diffusion through the body surface.

Excretion

The rotifers possess an excretory system somewhat comparable to that of the flatworms, although there are certain slight structural differences in the features of the system.   Typically the excretory system consists of flame bulbs and two excretory canals, lateral in position, which connect posteriorly with the cloaca. There may also be a cross, or transverse, connection between the two canals in the head region.   The excretory canals are spaces within a syncytial protoplasmic mass; and the flame bulbs are not true cells but are structures also developed in the syncytium.   The functioning of the flame-bulb system is for the elimination of water, and in some of the fresh-water forms a contraction of the posterior region, and hence expulsion of water from the flame bulbs through the cloaca and anal opening, occurs one to four times per minute.

The amount of water eliminated is remarkable in proportion to the body size; it has been estimated that a quantity of water equivalent to the total volume of the rotifer may be excreted every nine minutes.   Very little is known concerning the nitrogen excretion of the rotifers, but it seems improbable that any complicated nitrogenous compounds would be excreted.   The most likely nitrogenous excretory compound is ammonia.

Reproduction

The reproductive organs of the female rotifer are composed of an *ovary* which is syncytial, and a *yolk gland* which is also syncytial and is fastened to the ovary by a membrane.   This membrane extends posteriorly to the cloaca, and in its posterior portion serves as the oviduct.   The egg cells, as they are discharged, receive yolk from the yolk gland and are markedly increased in size by the time they reach the cloaca.   The male is a much simpler animal than the female among most of the rotifers, often only about one tenth the size of the female, and does not grow after reaching maturity.   The *testis* is a rather simple saclike structure, connected by a *sperm duct,* which is often ciliated, directly to the *genital pore* region.   Frequently the cloaca is absent in the male.

Mating is accomplished either by the insertion of the end of the sperm duct into the cloaca of the female and the transfer of the sperm by this means, or by the penetration of the sperm directly through the body wall of the female into the body cavity.   Fertilization occurs internally, and embryonic development begins within the body.   The female lays three types of eggs: (1) a large egg with a thin membrane, called the *summer egg,* which develops without fertilization into females; (2) a *small egg,* which develops without fertilization into males; and (3) a thick-shelled *dormant egg,* which is fertilized, and which develops into a female after a resting period.

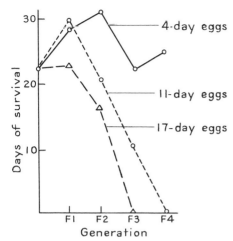

Figure 11.6.   Aging in rotifers.   See text discussion below.

The reproduction of the rotifers by means of unfertilized eggs enables the animals to produce large numbers of individuals during the periods when food and temperature are optimal.   Experiments have been performed on rotifers in an endeavor to control the type of egg which will be laid, and in general the results indicate that anything which alters the physical conditions very markedly for a short period of time will result in the formation of dormant eggs.   Males have not been discovered in some of the rotifers, and there is a possibility that certain species reproduce entirely by parthenogenesis.

Figure 11.7.   The arrangement of the major muscle bands and the main features of the nervous system are shown in this rotifer, Hydatina.

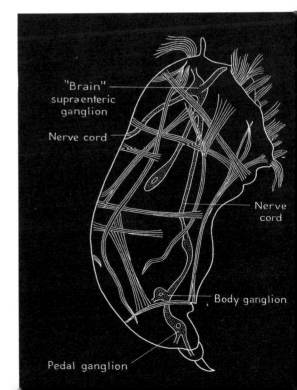

The average life span of a rotifer ranges from 10 to 40 days. Recent experiments by A. I. Lansing, however, have indicated that if successive generations of rotifers are grown using only the eggs of young animals, the life span may be considerably lengthened. If, on the other hand, successive generations are reared using the eggs of old animals only, the life span will be shortened. This can be seen quickly by referring to Figure 11.6. Rotifers were selected from a colony which had an average life span of 20.4 days, and successive generations were grown from parents of different ages. In one group, the first generation and succeeding generations were divided from eggs of young parents that were only 4 days old when the eggs were laid. In another group, all generations were grown from eggs of middle-aged parents, 11 days old. In the third group, all generations were grown from eggs of senile animals, 17 days old. It will be observed that the 17-day group died out (did not reproduce) by the third generation. The 11-day group died out by the fourth generation. The 4-day group not only survived, but the life span was lengthened in three of the four generations. Rotifers, therefore, appear to be another group of organisms which will enable us to acquire additional information concerning the problems of aging.

Coordination

The nervous system of the rotifers bears some resemblance to that of planarians, but there is no nerve net present. There is a concentration of nerve cells in the region of the pharynx, often called a *suprapharyngeal ganglion,* but which we shall call throughout this book a *supraenteric ganglion.* This is the "brain" of the rotifer. A pair of ventral nerves runs the length of the body from this brain, and some forms possess a pair of lateral nerves in addition. The sense organs were mentioned previously in connection with the body form of the rotifer. The antennae and the bristles on the body serve as sensory structures, apparently for tactile purposes. *Ciliated pits* in the head region of the rotifers probably serve in addition as chemical receptors, and the eyes, or eyespots, are light-sensitive and aid in the orientation of the animal. There has not been an extensive study of the behavior of the rotifers, but they should be excellent experimental animals for research on the problems of the behavior of animals with a simple nervous system.

Nematoda

Body form

Cobb objects to the designation of the nematodes as wormlike animals, pointing out that many of them actually are cylindrical. The typical nematodes,

---

*The "brain" of different triploblastic animals is variously located. In some cases it is in the region of the pharynx, and in other cases in the region of the esophagus. The term *enteric,* therefore, has merit in being nonspecific and making it possible to call *supraenteric* the comparable anterior ganglia, or "brain," of the different animals.

however, are wormlike; they are elongated animals, usually pointed at both ends.   These animals possess a very well-developed cuticle, which is formed by a syncytial epidermis comparable to that observed in the rotifers.   It often is ringed throughout the length of the body, giving the misleading appearance of segmentation.   The cuticle may be in three layers: (1) the outermost, the *cortex*, is composed of a chemically inert substance, *keratin;* (2) the middle layer, of a sulfur-rich fibroid composition, is called the *matrix;* and (3) the inner, *fibrous layer* contains fibers comparable to those seen in connective tissue.   The construction of the cuticle is so excellent that it actually constitutes an exoskeleton for the nematodes.   It is not surprising, therefore, that the animals *molt*, or periodically shed the old exoskeleton and form a new one.   Body growth occurs

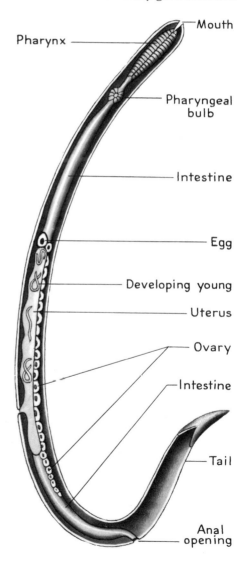

Figure 11.8.   In the vinegar eel, as in the rotifers, a complex body construction is present in a minute organism. This animal is a better example of basic nematode body form than is the larger and better-known Ascaris worm.

Mouth

Pharynx

Pharyngeal bulb

Intestine

Egg

Developing young

Uterus

Ovary

Intestine

Tail

Anal opening

during this transition while the new cuticle is being formed and can still be stretched. The cuticle serves as an excellent protection for those members of the class which are parasitic, and the keratin layer, being very inactive chemically, protects the animals from the digestive juices or other harmful substances in the animal that is being parasitized.

The nematodes possess a true alimentary canal, with mouth and anal openings and specialized regions. A well-developed body cavity, the *pseudocoel*, is much more extensive than that observed in rotifers. Giant cells are found within the pseudocoel, and these extend long processes which fuse to form a protoplasmic network in the cavity. Since specimens that have been fixed for microscopic study are often torn and distorted, the long processes of the giant cells may not be seen. One of the remarkable features of the nematodes is the complete absence of cilia; even the male reproductive cells are not ciliated but have amoeboid motion. The nematodes and the arthropods are the only two major groups in the animal kingdom in which cilia are absent. Another feature of considerable interest is the nematode musculature: they possess only longitudinal muscles. The contraction of these muscles imparts a peculiar jerky motion to the animals when they are swimming. This movement can be readily seen by observing vinegar eels, either in the vinegar or on a slide. The animals possess glands in the tail region which secrete a sticky substance that helps to hold the

Figure 11.9. Ascaris cross section. The extensive pseudocoel is not an empty space but contains the expanded ends of the muscle cells and also fluid, which coagulated during the preparation of the cross section. (Courtesy Clarence Flaten.)

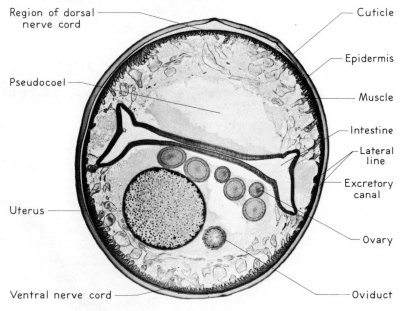

Region of dorsal nerve cord

Cuticle

Epidermis

Pseudocoel

Muscle

Intestine

Lateral line

Excretory canal

Uterus

Ovary

Ventral nerve cord

Oviduct

animal in place. These glands are comparable to the pedal glands of the rotifers, and Cobb has compared them with the spinning glands of spiders; indeed, he refers to them as "spinnerets." Nematodes vary greatly in length, from ¹⁄₁₀₀ inch to about 40 inches, but the average female is 2 to 3 millimeters long and the male only about half as long.

Nutrition

The alimentary canal of the nematodes begins with a *mouth*, which is often equipped with *teeth*, and in some cases with a *spear* which can be protruded to penetrate the prey. The mouth region joins a *pharynx* which is muscular and often is in two parts. The muscle contractions of the pharynx cause it to expand, thus producing a sucking action that draws food into the alimentary canal. The pharynx connects with an *intestine*, usually composed of a single layer of cells, which extends to the posterior part of the body, where it connects with a short, flattened tube, the *rectum*. The latter, in turn, opens to the outside through the anal opening. There is a postanal continuation of the body, a *tail*. The usual complement of digestive enzymes has been described for the nematodes, but again there is a question as to the ability of nematodes to digest starch.

Respiration

The free-living nematodes are both oxybiotic and anoxybiotic in their metabolic activity. The small body size permits a full exchange of oxygen and carbon dioxide through the cuticle, which is completely permeable. The relatively large spaces of the pseudocoel also aid in the distribution of the gases through the body. The parasitic forms apparently are able to exist for long periods of time either in the absence of oxygen or in the presence of low oxygen concentrations. They survive during the absence of oxygen by anoxybiotic respiration, but after the restoration of oxygen to their surroundings they oxidize the by-products previously formed. Since cyanide inhibits their respiration, it is probable that an oxidase system is present which is comparable to that previously noted in planarians, and also to that which is operating in man.

Excretion

The nematode excretory system remains a puzzle. One or more *giant cells* with long processes extend to an excretory pore in the anterior region of the animal and appear to be the only excretory structures. The processes hollow out to form the *excretory canals*. This simplified system accounts for the excretion of fluid and probably of some nitrogenous materials. There are no flame bulbs present in the nematodes. The animals adapt themselves rapidly to any changes in the concentration of the surrounding medium, but the mechanism of this adjustment is not clearly understood. Probably, however, it does not involve the functioning of the excretory cells.

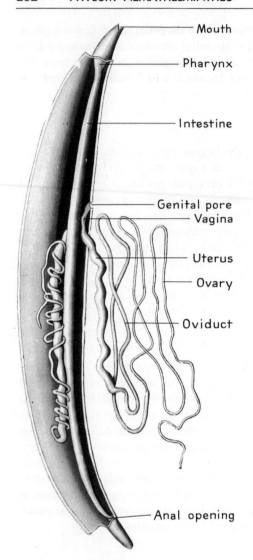

Mouth

Pharynx

Intestine

Genital pore
Vagina

Uterus

Ovary

Oviduct

Figure 11.10. Ascaris is one of the largest of the parasitic nematodes, and the elaborate development of its reproductive system reflects its parasitic existence.

Anal opening

Reproduction

The sexes usually are separate in nematodes, but some hermaphroditism occurs. Eggs may develop outside the body of the worm or may develop within the oviduct of the female and hatch as self-sufficient young worms. The gonads show considerable variation but are often in the form of long, tubular structures. Either one or two *testes* may be present in the male, and either one or two *ovaries* in the female. The reproductive cells in some forms develop along the entire length of the gonad, but typically they are made only at the terminal portion of the reproductive organ. The covering epithelium of the testis or the ovary continues either as the *sperm duct* or as the *oviduct,* respectively. A sac-like portion of the oviduct also serves as a *sperm receptacle* to retain the sperm deposited by the male. If the young develop within the female, that portion of the oviduct in which they develop is spoken of as the *uterus.*

The ovary or the testis may be as long as the body of the worm, or longer; the latter condition results from the fact that the gonads can be coiled compactly within the pseudocoel. The typical male nematode contains *spines,* or *setae,* in the area of the genital opening, which are used to spread the genital pore of the female so that the sperm may be inserted. The vinegar eel and *Ascaris* both illustrate the basic structure of the reproductive system.

Some of the nematodes are hermaphroditic—that is, they possess both ovaries and testes. The relationship of the ovaries and testes, however, is different from that which we encountered previously, because the testes form first and produce sperm, while the ovaries mature later. This condition is called *protandry,* or "first male." A peculiar type of parthenogenesis also occurs in some nematodes, which is of considerable interest when we remember the earlier discussion of the effect of sperm on the development of the egg. The sperm enters the egg and cleavage is initiated, but the sperm nucleus does not combine with the egg nucleus. Since the correct definition of fertilization is "a union of male and female nuclei," the mere entrance of the sperm to initiate cleavage cannot be fertilization; therefore, this peculiar developmental process in these nematodes must be considered parthenogenesis.

Coordination

The nervous system of the nematodes is complex. In *Ascaris* there is a *dorsal* and a *ventral nerve cord,* as well as lateral thickenings, designated as *lateral lines.* There is a *nerve ring* about the anterior part of the alimentary canal in the head region, and numerous fibers extend to the palps surrounding the mouth. There may be, in addition, ventral-lateral nerve cords in nematodes. The number of nerve cells is constant in the nerve cords, as in the other parts of the nematode body, and has been counted in some species. The longitudinal muscles have contractile fibers in their basal portion next to the epidermis, but the medial portion of the muscle cell is expanded into a protoplasmic bulb, from which processes reach through the pseudocoel to the nerve cords. It is probable that direct conduction occurs over these protoplasmic strands. Simple tactile sense organs, such as *bristles* and *spines,* are present in the nematodes. Eyespots are present in many members of the class, and in some there is a *lens* over the eyespot for the concentration of light rays. The parasitic nematodes, however, have lost most of the sense organs.

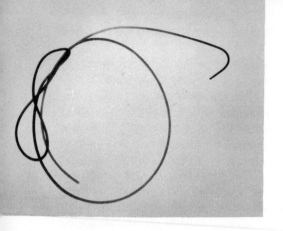

Figure 11.11. The horsehair snake, Gordius, has no obvious external structures and in its typical "knotted" condition does closely resemble a tangled horsehair. (Courtesy Clarence Flaten.)

Gordiacea*

The gordiacea, or *threadworms,* are found in almost any type of water habitat, sometimes in large numbers. The young develop within the body of some arthropod, usually an insect such as a cricket, a grasshopper, or a beetle, and their complete development may require several months. The fact that such parasitized insects often die in small ponds, pools, or even small containers of water permits the adult worm to emerge from the dead host into the necessary aquatic environment. One who discovers a horsehair snake in a pan of water seldom notices the dead grasshopper or cricket which served as the host.

The body of the threadworm is greatly elongated and of small diameter. It may be 36 inches long but only ⅒ inch in thickness. The adults are sluggish in their movements, and since only longitudinal muscles are present, they have the same peculiar locomotion that was observed in the nematodes. There is a well-developed cuticle secreted by an epidermis, and molting may take place, especially during larval development. The animals are typical "cavity worms," possessing an extensive pseudocoel, which contains a rather compact mesh of cells with interlacing processes. The spaces between cells are small and irregular. The presence of cuticle, longitudinal muscle, the pseudocoel, and a mesh of cells is reminiscent of nematode construction and supports the allocation of these worms to a class standing in the phylum Nemathelminthes. *Gordius,* so named because it typically entwines itself into a Gordian knot, depicts very well the characteristics of the class.

The alimentary canal of the threadworm is degenerate, does not open to the outside, and apparently is not used for digestion at any time during the life of the worm. Particularly during larval life, the worm must absorb food through the body wall. It appears that secretions from the surface of the body of the larva digest the tissues of the animal which is being parasitized. Digestive enzymes have not been demonstrated in the alimentary canal.

No specialized respiratory or excretory structures are to be found in the

*Often called phylum Nematomorpha (thread form).

threadworms. Respiration is by direct diffusion of oxygen and carbon dioxide through the cuticle. It has been suggested that excretion is accomplished by the mid-gut region of the alimentary canal. The basis for this conjecture rests on the similarity of the appearance of this region with that of certain special excretory tubules of insects. Direct evidence, however, is lacking. The reproductive system is comparable to that of nematodes. The gonads are long cylindrical tubes and may be branched in the females. An ovary of the branched type may release 3000 to 4000 eggs at any one time. Strangely enough, in some threadworms the ova may be formed in the loose network of pseudocoel cells, and in these animals a definitive ovary is lacking. The sexes are separate. Coordination in the threadworms is poorly understood, although the details of the nervous system have been determined. The usual ring of nerve fibers is found around the anterior end of the alimentary canal, and there is also a ventral nerve cord. Sense organs are poorly developed, consisting primarily of bristles or spines. A very rudimentary light-sensitive organ is present in some of these worms.

Classification of Nemathelminthes

Phylum Nemathelminthes   Triploblastic, wormlike animals with a true alimentary canal. A well-developed cuticle appears, and a pseudocoel is present. The animals generally have longitudinal muscles only. The nervous system is comparable with that of the Platyhelminthes, but without a nerve net and frequently with the addition of lateral nerve cords.

CLASS I. ROTIFERA. Generally elongated microscopic animals with constant cell number. A cuticle is present, and the muscles are often arranged in single muscle bands, not in layers. A single or double band of cilia in the head region, the wheel organ, is the most prominent diagnostic feature of this class. The excretory system has flame bulbs. Many reproduce only by parthenogenesis. Examples: *Hydatina, Trochosphaera, Notommata.*

CLASS II. NEMATODA. Usually elongated cylindrical animals, with a very complex cuticle, a true alimentary canal, and a pseudocoel. Longitudinal muscles only are present. Sexes are usually separate in these animals, but some hermaphroditism does occur. The excretory system is unique, composed of single excretory cells with an intracellular excretory tubule. Examples: *Tubatrix aceti* (vinegar eel), *Ascaris lumbricoides.*

CLASS III. GORDIACEA. Threadworms, with the larval stages parasitic. Lacking an excretory system, but with a well-developed cuticle and a pseudocoel. Example: *Gordius robustus* (horsehair snake).

REFERENCES

Cobb, N. A., "Some Recent Aspects of Nematology," *Science, 73,* 1935.

Harmer, S. F., and A. E. Shipley (eds.), "Nemathelminthes and Chaetognatha," *Cambridge Natural History,* Vol. 2, pp. 99–173, 197–231. Macmillan and Company, Ltd., London, 1922.

Hyman, L. H., *The Invertebrates: Acanthocephala, Aschelminthes, and Entoprocta,* Vol. III, pp. 53–151, 197–471. McGraw-Hill Book Company, Inc., New York, 1951.

Lansing, A. I., "A Transmissible, Cumulative, and Reversible Factor in Ageing," *Journal of Gerontology, 2,* 1947, pp. 228–239.

Lansing, A. I., "Some Physiological Aspects of Ageing," *Physiological Review, 31,* pp. 274–285.

Wesenberg-Lund, C., *Contributions to the Biology of the Rotifera,* Vols. I and II. A. F. Host and Son, Copenhagen, 1923–1930.

12

Room to Grow | The Coelom

•

One may describe some one part throughout the principal genera, and in this
manner an instructive comparison is perfectly effected.—Goethe, 1817

We have remarked on several occasions that the amount of surface area in
proportion to the volume of the animal is extremely important, because surface
area controls the movement of materials into and out of the tissues of the organism. The ratio of surface to volume thus imposes a definite limitation on the
size of animals, since the surface is the major route for acquiring materials or
eliminating waste products. The development of the third embryonic layer,
the *mesoderm*, inflicts a new problem on animals as far as functional relationships are concerned. The connective and supportive tissues of the adult develop from this layer, and cells of these tissues are far removed from the surface.
The exchange of waste materials and the acquisition of oxygen become more
difficult because of the remoteness of the cells from the surface. Organisms
which develop the mesodermal layer must, therefore, make adjustments in order
to compensate for the lack of an adequate and accessible surface for such exchange or acquisition. This adjustment is accomplished by the development
of a cavity, or cavities, within the mesoderm. We have already observed this
in the interlacing network of cells, with irregular fluid-filled spaces, in adult
flatworms, and in the pseudocoel of the threadworms. Although the cells are
bathed with a fluid which permits internal exchanges, neither of these two systems is very effective. Consequently, few of the flatworms or nematodes ever
reach a large size.

The body cavity, or coelom

The body cavity within the *mesothelium* (the adult derivative of the mesoderm) is fully developed only in *coelomate* animals. The mesothelium develops
in such animals from two embryonic layers: one of these layers, the *somatic*

207

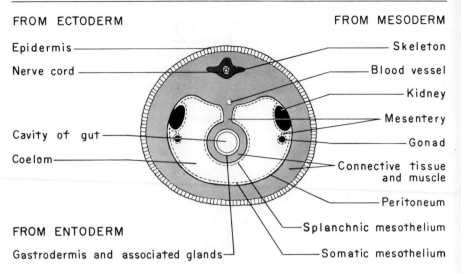

FROM ECTODERM   FROM MESODERM

Epidermis —————————————————————— Skeleton

Nerve cord ———————————————————— Blood vessel

————————————— Kidney

————————— Mesentery

Cavity of gut ——————————

Coelom—————————— Gonad

————— Connective tissue
and muscle

——————————— Peritoneum

FROM ENTODERM   —Splanchnic mesothelium

Gastrodermis and associated glands—   —Somatic mesothelium

Figure 12.1. A section through the body cavity of a vertebrate animal illustrates the relationship of the coelomic cavity and mesothelium to the órgan systems.

mesoderm, is associated with the epidermis, whereas the other layer, the *splanchnic mesoderm,* adheres to the gastrodermis. The body cavity bounded by these layers is the *coelom.* The innermost cells of both somatic and splanchnic layers form an epithelial lining for the coelom. These cells are usually flattened and constitute the *peritoneum.* A coelom thus may be defined more fully as *a body cavity within the mesothelium, between the alimentary canal and body wall, and lined by a peritoneum.*

In order to acquire a complete understanding of the relationship of the coelom to body organization, it is necessary to refer to an early stage in embryonic development. The original embryonic cavity, of course, is the *blastocoel,* or space within the blastula. This cavity is largely obliterated by the ingrowth of the entoderm, and we observed in *Hydra* that it may be filled by a small amount of jellylike mesoglea. The distance between the ectoderm and entoderm, however, may be considerable. A large amount of gelatinous mesoglea is present in the jellyfishes, but it has few cells. Its metabolic activity, therefore, is extremely low.

The distance separating the gastrovascular cavity and the epidermis in the flatworms, or Platyhelminthes, is relatively great, and this region represents the original blastocoel. It was noted on several occasions that only irregular fluid-filled spaces remain, and that these are in an interlacing network of mesothelial cells. This condition is referred to as *acoelomate* (without a coelom). The need for greater surface area in these animals is compensated for in part by the extensive branching of the gastrovascular cavity.

The Nemathelminthes are somewhat intermediate in the development of the body cavity. They are acoelomate, but the pseudocoel cavity may be very extensive and is bounded on one side by somatic mesothelium. The intercellular spaces, in general, are more extensive than in the flatworms.

The development of the coelom is marked by the complete disappearance of the blastocoel. (There is an exception to this in the insects and their relatives, which will be considered briefly in Chapter 15.) The mesoderm in the coelomate animal invades the remnant of the blastocoel, and since the somatic mesoderm fuses with the ectoderm, and the splanchnic mesoderm fuses with the entoderm, the blastocoel is obliterated in the process.

Origin of the mesoderm

The origin of the mesoderm differs in the various coelomate groups. Two major types of mesodermal formation are recognized, and in some instances both types may appear in a single group. (Both these types of mesodermal formation are shown in Figure 12.3.) The *enterocoelic* (intestinal cavity) type of mesodermal formation is characterized by the development of pouches as outfoldings from the embryonic gut, or archenteron. These pouches grow into the blastocoel and are gradually constricted at their junction with the gut, so that they eventually are separated. The pouches gradually expand, and the blastocoel disappears. It is important to note that one layer of each pouch becomes associated with the gastrodermis and the other layer with the epidermis. Especially significant is the observation that the splanchnic layers of each pouch meet above and below the alimentary canal to form supporting membranes for the alimentary canal. These membranes which attach the intestines to the walls of the abdominal, or coelomic, cavity are the dorsal *mesentery* and the ventral

Figure 12.2.   With the specialization of the body cavity, animals show a corresponding specialization of body plan and the ability to reach a larger size. The diploblastic animal gives way to the acoelomate animal. In the coelomate or pseudocoelomate animal, however, the body cavity becomes distinct from the alimentary canal.

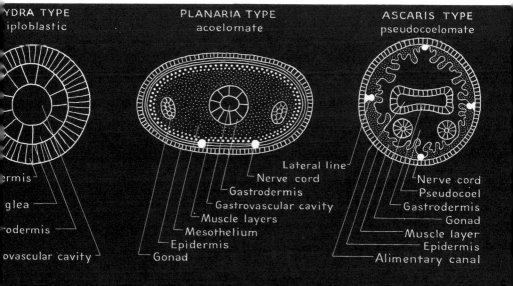

YDRA TYPE
iploblastic

PLANARIA TYPE
acoelomate

ASCARIS TYPE
pseudocoelomate

Lateral line
Nerve cord
Gastrodermis
Gastrovascular cavity
Muscle layers
Mesothelium
Epidermis
Gonad

Nerve cord
Pseudocoel
Gastrodermis
Gonad
Muscle layer
Epidermis
Alimentary canal

rmis

glea

odermis

ovascular cavity

mesentery of the digestive tract.   Any organs projecting into the coelom are supported by similar mesenteries.

The second type of mesodermal formation, *schizocoelic* (split cavity), is a result of the formation of mesodermal bands during early embryonic development.   Certain cells in the region of the blastopore multiply rapidly and grow forward as cords of cells between the epidermis and gastrodermis.   These cords soon split; the two sheets of cells which result become associated with the ectoderm and the entoderm; and the cavity formed between them is the coelom. It is not possible to distinguish in adult animals between coeloms formed by the two processes.

Development of the gonads

There is a close association between the coelom and the development of both the reproductive organs and the ducts of the reproductive system.   Cells from the walls of the coelom multiply and push the peritoneum upward in a fold to form a decided bulge on the wall of the coelom, with a thin covering of peritoneum stretching over the cells.   This is the most primitive type of gonad formation in a coelomate animal.   The question as to the origin of the germ cells remains a problem of considerable interest to the zoologist.   It was originally thought that all the reproductive cells originate in the embryo from mesodermal tissue.   This will be noted subsequently in our discussion of other coelomate phyla.   It is now known, however, that the reproductive cells can be recognized early in embryonic development, even during cleavage.   Such cells migrate into the region where the gonads will form, and it is from these "primordial" germ cells that the reproductive cells of the adult animal arise.   It is possible, therefore, that in some forms the reproductive cells may have a dual origin—that is, some reproductive cells may arise from the mesodermal cells near the gonad site, while others arise from primordial germ cells which migrate to the gonad site.   Regardless of the origin of the reproductive cells, there is no doubt as to the intimate relationship between the coelom and the formation of the gonads.

Segmentation

Several of the coelomate phyla have developed a serial duplication of organs within the body of the animal; such duplication is called *segmentation*.   Segmentation is found only in the coelomate animals (with the exception of the tapeworms), and the question of the origin of segmentation is of considerable interest to the zoologist.   We shall not discuss at length the theories of the origin of body segments, but it should be pointed out that this is an important feature of the annelids, the arthropods, and the chordates.   It seems probable, in the light of our best information, that segmentation arose in the ancestors of the coelomates as a result of two factors: (1) a serial duplication of internal structures such as the gonads and excretory organs; and (2) serpentine body movements,

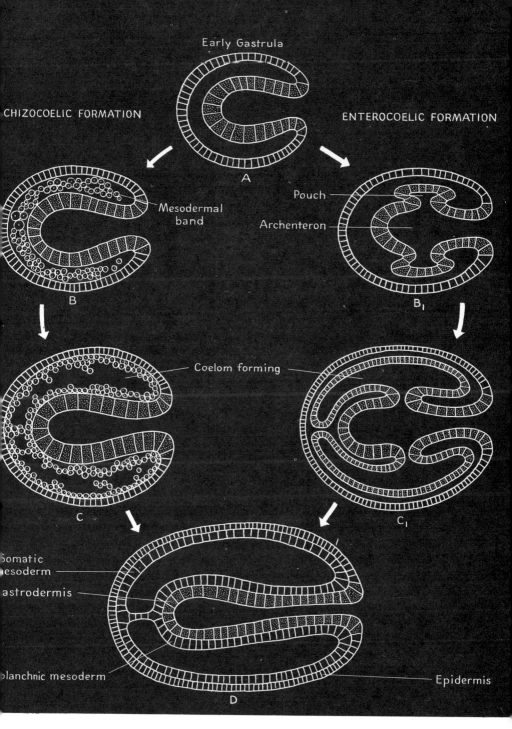

CHIZOCOELIC FORMATION

ENTEROCOELIC FORMATION

Early Gastrula

A

Mesodermal band

Pouch

Archenteron

B

B₁

Coelom forming

C

C₁

Somatic mesoderm

Gastrodermis

Splanchnic mesoderm

Epidermis

D

Figure 12.3.   A diploblastic gastrula can form a coelom by the splitting of bands or mesodermal cells (schizocoelic, or split cavity) or by the outgrowth of pouches from the archenteron (enterocoelic, or intestinal cavity).   Figure (D) represents the end result.

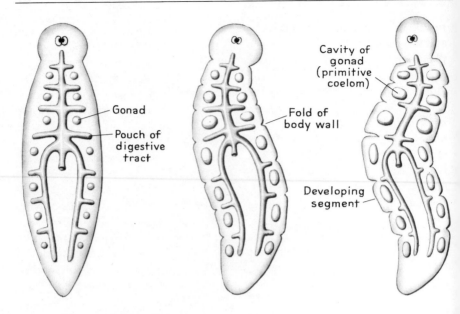

Figure 12.4. Segmentation may have originated in the locomotion of ancient planarian-like animals, which involved the continual folding of the animals' body.

which would cause bending. This clearly would occur most easily at the points of least resistance—between the internal organs. The external folds produced in the body wall, if accompanied by a development of musculature, could result in segmental division of the body.

Advantages of coelom formation

There are several important values which may be ascribed to the presence of a coelom. *First*, it is significant that opportunity is afforded the alimentary canal to increase greatly in length by coiling within the coelomic cavity. We will observe later that in many instances the length of the digestive tract is several times greater than the length of the animal. Increased gut size would seem to have been adequately provided for in the flatworms by the acquisition of pouches in the gastrovascular cavity, even though no coelom is present to allow coiling. This is not a comparable situation, however, because the pouches are blind sacs and are all alike. The elongated tube of the alimentary canal, on the other hand, allows only one-way passage of the food. Also, the greater length makes it possible for specialized regions to develop, with a division of labor for storage, grinding, digestion, and absorption, as well as for elimination of undigested food without mixing with newly ingested nutrient material.

The *second* important values which results from coelomic growth is a greater elaboration of duct systems. The principal ducts are those of the excretory and reproductive systems, and their development is closely associated with the walls and the cavity of the coelom.   It will be recalled that the excretory systems of planarians and rotifers are composed of flame bulbs and excretory tubules. This acoelomate excretory system has been called a *protonephridial system* (first kidney), and the ducts develop from embryonic ectoderm.   The typical excretory system of the coelomate animals, however, is referred to as a *metanephridial system* (last kidney), and generally develops from the embryonic mesoderm.   There is a resemblance between the two systems, because some of the metanephridia end blindly in the coelom, as do all the protonephridia.   It is important to note, however, that the metanephridium is usually called a *nephridium;* it has a ciliated funnel opening into the coelom, into which coelomic fluid will be carried, and provides for more efficient drainage of waste material.

A *third* advantage accruing from the presence of a coelom is that the increased surface areas have removed all practical limitations on body size.   It is noteworthy that the coelom increases in volume as the body size is augmented; and even more important is the fact that the coelom is fluid filled.   This *coelomic fluid* is circulated as a result of body movements and contains within it free *amoeboid* cells with varied functions.   The coelom, therefore, assumes a

Figure 12.5.   This larval insect, a caterpillar, is a typical segmented animal. Its "humping" locomotion is characteristic: some legs hold fast while the body in between is elevated and moved forward; the animal progresses by section. (Courtesy Clarence Flaten.)

paramount role in providing a fluid medium for the internal cells of the organism. The cells which cover the alimentary canal or which are adjacent to the epidermis could not carry on their metabolic activities without this circulating coelomic fluid.

The *fourth* useful function performed by the coelom is closely associated with the foregoing problem of providing a fluid medium. This is the development of a *circulatory*, or *blood vascular, system* from the mesothelium of the coelom. The vascular system in its simplest organization is composed of tubes with valves which allow movement of the blood in only one direction. Certain regions of the tubes acquire contractile properties as the circulatory systems become more complex; such regions are called *hearts*. The larger vessels branch repeatedly to form minute tubes, the *capillaries*, many of microscopic size, which penetrate all parts of the organism. These tiny vessels make possible the delivery of oxygen, food materials, and secretions to the cells; they also accomplish the removal of carbon dioxide and waste products from the cells.

It should be obvious in summary that the coelom represents an important advance in structural organization. It provides room to grow and, especially when coupled with segmentation, permits a remarkable division of labor in the various regions of the body. We have made repeated reference to the fact that cells need a fluid medium if they are to live; the coelomic fluid provides this medium. Finally, the development of the excretory, reproductive, and circulatory systems, as well as muscular and connective tissues, from the walls of the coelom is an impressive contribution. The subdivision of the triploblastic animals into acoelomate (including pseudocoelomate) and coelomate types, therefore, has a real functional siginificance.

REFERENCES

Goodrich, E. S., "On the Coelom, Genital Ducts, and Nephridia," *Quarterly Journal of Microscopial Science*, 37, 1897.

Hyman, L. H., *The Invertebrates: Platyhelminthes and Rhynchocoela*, Vol. II, pp. 18–50. McGraw-Hill Book Company, Inc., New York, 1951.

Kellicott, W. E., *A Textbook of General Embryology*, pp. 329–363. Henry Holt and Company, Inc., New York, 1927.

Lankester, Ray (ed.), *Treatise on Zoology*, Part II, pp. 1–37. Adam and Charles Black, London, 1900.

13

Serial

Duplication

Phylum

Annelida

●

The plough is one of the most ancient and valuable of man's inventions; but long before he existed, the land was in fact regularly ploughed, and still continues to be thus ploughed by earthworms.—Charles Darwin, The Formation of Vegetable Mould, 1837

If there is one bird that everyone knows, it is the robin, and no less familiar is the unpretentious earthworm; in fact, the earthworm is so common we seldom think of it as an important animal. Yet it is studied throughout the world as a representative of the phylum Annelida, and it holds a unique distinction as an "average animal." This eminence is accorded to earthworms because all the major organ systems are established, because the relationship of the coelom to body organization is so typical as to be almost diagrammatic, and because segmentation has been developed. The earthworm is widely used to illustrate the structural and functional features of the phylum, but it is not the most representative annelid because it is specialized for a cave existence in tunnels of its own construction. The marine clamworm is more representative of the group, and we will therefore consider its most important features. Furthermore, as a marine worm it is typical, because all the annelids are aquatic. Even the terrestrial earthworm could be considered aquatic, since the surface of the body must be kept moist at all times or the animal dies. The leech will be studied briefly also, in order to illustrate additional structural modifications which can be correlated with a semiparasitic mode of life.

The annelids are of biological and economic importance chiefly because of the work done by the earthworms, and this activity is considerable. In 1837 Charles Darwin published a brief account of his observations on the formation

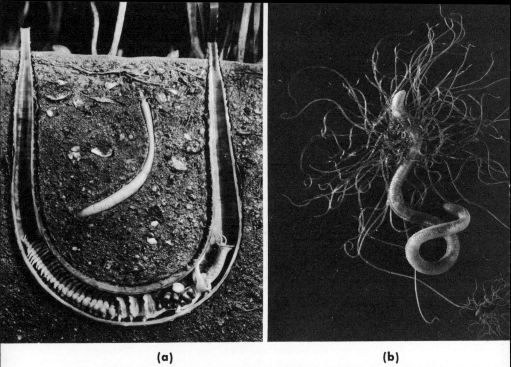

(a)   (b)

Figure 13.1. The annelid worms in this figure show an unexpected variation in form. In (a) the tube worm, Chaetopterus, builds its burrow in the mud of the ocean floor, its body secretions forming a tough lining inside the tube. The fringed worm, Cirratulus, shown in (b), is also a tube-dwelling worm. Note the profusion of weird tentacles which catch microscopic food and serve as gills. (Courtesy American Museum of Natural History.)

of "vegetable mould" by earthworms and later described additional data in his book, which is a classic in zoological literature. Darwin pointed out that earthworms eat their way through the earth and drop their excrement behind them in the tunnels as castings and also deposit their castings on the surface of the ground at the opening into the burrow. The worms are extremely important, therefore, in improving the soil by this method of fertilization. He estimated that from 10 to 18 tons of castings per acre were deposited annually by earthworms, and that there might be 50,000 worms per acre. The practice of "earthworm farming" by scattering earthworms on barren ground has become an important method of rebuilding the soil. The procedure is especially effective where strip mining or erosion has exposed sterile subsoil, because each year as much as 0.2 inch per acre of rich castings may be spread on the surface by the worms. Earthworms burrow to a depth of as much as two feet, and the porous condition so created in the earth gives it a spongy nature which helps to prevent surface runoff of rain water and thus to check erosion. Multitudes of other small oligochaete worms live in the mud on the bottoms of ponds and lakes. These are important in the breakdown of organic matter and as food for other aquatic organisms.

Less than a century ago physicians were commonly known as "leeches." This appellation resulted from the practice, which was prevalent until recent years, of drawing blood from patients by applying leeches to their veins. The technique was simple; a large leech was used if the blood-letting was to be profuse, and a small leech if the bleeding was to be slight. Leeches formerly were sold by the millions annually, but there is little demand for their services today. The sale of leeches is confined to congested areas of some of the larger cities, where they are sold for the purpose of removing the blood which accumulates in "black eyes."

Segmentation, the most obvious trait of the Annelida, results from the presence of rings, which give the phylum its name (*annulus* = ring). Each segment is bounded internally by partitions, the *septa*, and typically each segment contains paired excretory and reproductive organs. Annelids have a well-developed cuticle, as well as both the outer (circular) and inner (longitudinal) sets of muscles. The coelom is a prominent cavity lined with a peritoneum of squamous epithelium, except that in the leeches the coelom is filled with a loose connective tissue. An alimentary canal, with a mouth and an anal opening and with several highly specialized regions, is typical of the phylum. The nervous system is composed of a ventral pair of nerve cords with a pair of ganglia in each segment of the body; however, these cords and ganglia fuse in the adult forms of most annelids and appear as a single ventral cord. An important new feature in the phylum is the appearance of a *closed circulatory system*.

A few additional comments about segmentation are in order at this time. If serial duplication were perfect, all segments, or *somites*, of the body would be alike; but this condition is never realized. The head and tail ends, at least, are

Figure 13.2. The earthworm, although adapted to a cave existence, has the basic features of other annelids. Especially noteworthy here are the positions of the septa, the nerve cord, the coelom, and the arrangement of the muscles. (Courtesy Clarence Flaten.)

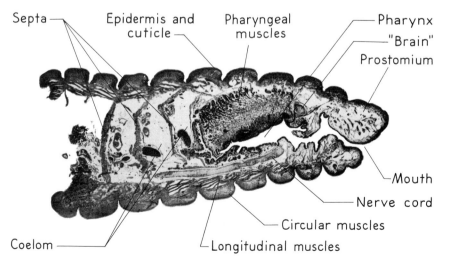

Septa — Epidermis and cuticle — Pharyngeal muscles — Pharynx — "Brain" — Prostomium — Mouth — Nerve cord — Circular muscles — Coelom — Longitudinal muscles

different from the other segments.   Three advantages of segmentation can be seen in the study of the annelids and may be compared with those which result from the subdivisions of protoplasm into cells: (1) there is increased opportunity for division of labor among the segments; (2) the septa give additional strength to the body and aid in holding the internal organs in position; and (3) additional surface area is provided by the septal walls and external projections.

The Clamworm*

Body form

This marine worm reaches a length of 12 or more inches, is often brightly colored a bluish-green or reddish-orange, and has striations in the cuticle which give an iridescent sheen to its surface.   The animals live much of their time in burrows in the sand but frequently emerge and swim about actively, either by movements of lateral appendages, the *parapodia,* or by swimming undulations of the body.   Usually there are more than 200 segments to the body, but the number is not constant; parapodia are attached to each segment except the first and the last.

The body architecture of the clamworm is typical of that of many coelomate animals.   A tough but flexible cuticle is secreted by the epidermis, which in this instance is not a syncytium but is *cellular.*   Immediately below the epidermis are two muscle layers: the outer, circular layer and the inner, longitudinal layer. These two muscle layers, together with the peritoneum, are derivatives of the somatic mesoderm and are, of course, external to the coelom.   The digestive tract has a layer of circular muscle adjacent to the gastrodermis and an outer layer of longitudinal muscle covered by peritoneum.   These two layers consti-tute the inner wall of the coelom.   They are derived from splanchnic mesoderm.

The first segment of the worm is the *peristomium* and, as the name implies, it encircles the mouth.   A forward projection from the first segment, the *prosto-*

Neanthes (formerly Nereis) viridens.

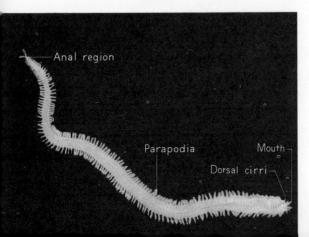

Anal region

Parapodia

Mouth

Dorsal cirri

Figure 13.3.   This photograph of a clam-worm illustrates two important features of locomotion: the flexing of the body and the rhythmic movement of the para-podia.   (Courtesy Clarence Flaten.)

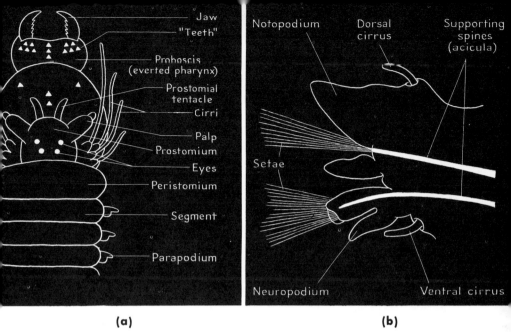

(a)   **(b)**

Figure 13.4.　Shown in (a) is the head of a clamworm with pharynx everted; in (b) parapodia of clamworm.

mium, is an important feature of the anterior end, and both the prostomium and the peristomium of the clamworm contain well-developed sense organs. The prostomium has *eyes, tentacles,* and *palps;* and the peristomium possesses *cirri,* one pair of which, the *dorsal cirri,* may fold posteriorly as far as the ninth segment. The well-developed parapodia are complex appendages which serve not only for locomotion but also for respiration. They are not uniform in size and are usually larger in the mid-body region.

Nutrition

The clamworm tends to select meat (is carnivorous) but will eat almost anything. The alimentary canal begins with the *mouth* and *buccal cavity,* which is ringed by the peristomium and is continuous posteriorly with a very muscular pharynx. These regions are lined by a cuticle, and, in addition, the pharynx has teeth and powerful jaws. The muscles of the pharynx in some cases are contracted, causing the pharynx to be everted, and the pharynx is then spoken of as a *proboscis.* This modification enables the jaws to act as pincers to seize the prey. A short esophagus connects the pharynx to the intestine, which is constricted slightly in each segment by the septa. The intestine eventually terminates in a short rectum, which opens to the outside through the anus and, like the anterior part of the digestivt tract, is lined with a cuticle.

The outer longitudinal and inner circular muscle layers of the intestine are well developed and act antagonistically to each other. A wave of contraction can be produced which progresses from anterior to posterior along the intestinal wall and acts to push the food through the alimentary canal. This is called the *peristaltic wave.* A pair of *digestive glands* opens into the esophagus, and these

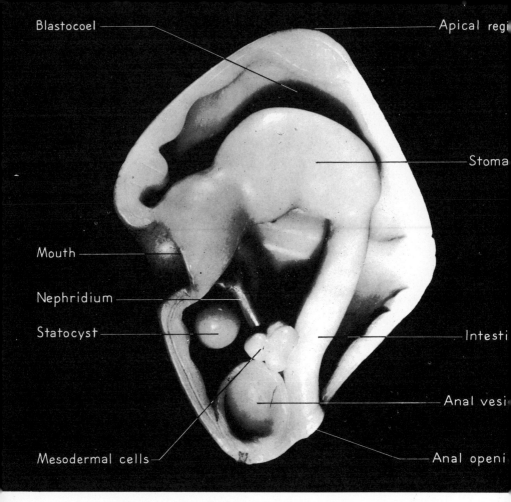

Blastocoel — ——— Apical regi

Stoma

Mouth —

Nephridium —

Statocyst— Intesti

Anal vesi

Mesodermal cells— Anal openi

Figure 13.5.   Model of trochophore larva.   (Courtesy Clarence Flaten.)

glands, as well as the walls of the intestine, secrete enzymes.   Practically all digestion and absorption of foods occurs in the intestine.

Respiration

The clamworm is oxybiotic but may exist for a time in the absence of oxygen. The worm secures its oxygen and eliminates carbon dioxide through the lobes of the parapodia, which are well supplied with blood vessels.   Respiration is very efficient, and the worm is able to remove as much as 70 per cent of the dissolved oxygen from the water which passes over its surface.   When living in low oxygen concentrations, or in the absence of oxygen, it breaks down food materials anoxybiotically, with the formation of lactic acid, which can be excreted.   The clamworm has *hemoglobin,* an iron-protein compound, in the blood, which combines chemically with oxygen in an unstable union.   In the presence of excess carbon dioxide, this oxygenated hemoglobin, or *oxyhemo-*

globin, will break down, with the liberation of oxygen. Since the internal cells and tissues are constantly forming carbon dioxide, the oxygen will be released from the hemoglobin at the interior cells but will combine with the hemoglobin at the parapodia, where carbon dioxide concentration is low. In this way the oxygen is transported from the body surface to the interior of the body. Because of its red color and its function in respiration, hemoglobin is called a *respiratory pigment,* but in these animals it is probably much less important as an oxygen carrier than it is in man. The clamworm probably transports less than 50 percent of its oxygen in combination with hemoglobin, the remainder being carried dissoloved in a chemically free (uncombined) state in the fluid of the blood.

Excretion

The functional unit of the annelid excretory system is the *nephridium,* which has a close relationship with the coelom. Typically, there is a pair of nephridia for each segment. Each nephridium consists of two parts, a *ciliated funnel* and a *coiled tubule.* The nephridium is actually located in two adjoining segments; the funnel projects through the septum separating the two segments, into the cavity of the anterior segment; and the tubule is situated in the segment posterior to the funnel. Each segment, therefore, will have a pair of nephridial funnels and two nephridial tubules from the segment anterior to it. Each tubule empties to the exterior by way of a *nephridial pore* on the ventral side of the segment. Excretory products enter the nephridium in two ways: *first,* coelomic fluid which contains waste materials will be swept into the tubule by the action of the cilia on the funnel; and *second,* since the tubule is well supplied with blood vessels, the cells of the tubule will remove excretory matter from the circulating blood.

Reproduction

The sexes are separate in the clamworm, and the reproductive cells develop from the wall of the coelom in the posterior half of the animal. This region in some worms is so modified during the breeding season that such worms (called *heteronereis*) were classified as different species for many years before it was recognized that they were merely sexual stages. The eggs and sperm are discharged into the water by the rupture of the body wall, and the worms usually die, although in some species the anterior (nonreproductive) segments may regenerate a new tail end. The sexual behavior is remarkably regular in some of the animals; the *palolo worm* of the South Seas, for example, comes to the surface to breed on one night of the year in November. The natives gather them at this time and have a feast, which provides an important supplement of animal protein to their diet.

The embryos of clamworms develop into a characteristic free-swimming, ciliated *trochophore larva,* which is of great theoretical significance because a similar larva is found in the Mollusca and thought by some to have been present in the ancestral forms of the Arthropoda. The *apical region*, or *apex*, of the trochophore is the part from which the prostomium develops, and the segments develop in the larva opposite the apical region and posterior to the mouth.

Coordination

The clamworm nervous system may be said to center in a *ganglionic mass*, or "brain," which is located in the prostomium. More exactly, the "brain" is the result of fused ganglia and is called for convenience a *supraenteric* (over-the-gut) *ganglion*. A pair of ventral nerve cords runs posteriorly from the brain, and each segment of the body contains a pair of ganglionic enlargements of the cord. As in the case of the brain, the segmental ganglia are fused in the adult worms, and the double cord therefore appears as a single strand. The only obvious evidence of the original paired condition of the nervous system is to be found in the *circumenteric* (around-the-gut) *nerves* which encircle the pharynx. A nervous system of this type is found in the earthworm and is also encountered in the arthropods. Because of its location and its basic paired structure, it is often spoken of as a *ventral ladder-type* nervous system.

The major sensory structures in the clamworm are the *palps*, the two pairs of *eyes*, the *cirri*, and the *nuchal pits* on the upper surface of the head. The eyes are composed of light-sensitive cells, with a superficial lens which serves to converge the light rays. The nuchal pits are chemical receptors, but the functions of the palps and cirri are not known definitely; they probably are tactile receptors and may be sensitive to chemicals as well.

The brain is a coordinating center, and although the animal moves about in an almost normal fashion when the brain is removed, the responses to stimuli are abnormal. The brain appears to act primarily as an inhibitory center. The rate of conduction along the nerve cord is relatively slow, but special *giant nerve cells* are also present in the cord, and these cells, which may run the entire length of the cord, can transmit impulses rapidly. The speed of the impulse in some of the marine worms may be several hundred centimeters per second, or approximately one tenth as fast as conduction in man. Although not all annelids send messages so swiftly, the nervous system of the clamworm obviously is a distinct improvement over that found in other phyla of worms.

Circulatory system

The circulatory system is of great functional significance and is elaborately developed in the first coelomate group we are considering. As, we mentioned previously, the circulatory system functions in nutrition by delivering food to all body cells, in respiration by the transportation of oxygen and carbon dioxide, in excretion by supplying the nephridia and the coelom with fluid in which waste products are present, and perhaps most important of all, by providing a *fluid medium* for all cells of the organism. The circulatory system, therefore, furnishes a means of *chemical coordination* of body activities.

The actual structure of the circulatory system in the various relatives of the clamworm is extremely variable, and we will accordingly limit our discussion to the major blood vessels only. The most obvious vessels are the *dorsal*, above the alimentary canal, and the *ventral*, below the alimentary canal. Paired *lateral vessels* in each segment connect the ventral vessel with the dorsal. The muscular walls of the dorsal vessel set up peristaltic waves which propel the blood forward to the esophageal region, where the vessel splits and turns ventrally to form a capillary network on the wall of the esophagus. The capillaries subsequently join to make lateral vessels, which in turn fuse to become the ventral vessel, in which the blood flows posteriorly. The lateral vessels receive respiratory branches which bring oxygenated blood from the parapodia, and the ventral vessel sends enteric branches to the alimentary canal, respiratory branches to the parapodia, and nephridial branches to the nephridia.

These major vessels are structurally prominent, but they are not the physiologically important ones. The vessels of greatest functional significance are the microscopic *capillaries*, which are lined with a single layer of squamous cells, and represent the very fine subdivisions of the major vessels. The thin layer of protoplasm constituting the wall of a capillary permits the diffusion of food, fluids, and gases to the cells and tissues in exchange for waste materials. Significant aspects of the capillary system will be considered in detail later, but it is important to note that the total length of the capillaries is many times greater than that of all the major vessels combined.

The Earthworm*

Body form

The earthworm is a modified annelid highly adapted to a cave existence. Sense organs are reduced, and there is an absence of the cirri, palps, and eyes which would be a nuisance to a burrowing animal. The parapodia also have been lost, but the earthworm has four pairs of spines, or *setae*, on each segment for locomotion. The segments are obvious externally, and the worms are covered with a thin protective cuticle. The red color of the body is due both to pigmentation and to the hemoglobin in the capillary network of the skin.

Nutrition

The alimentary canal of the earthworm shows greater specialization than that of the clamworm, and its modifications can be correlated with its omnivorous diet (p. 216). The mouth opens through the peristomium into a very muscular pharynx, much as in the clamworm. Muscle fibers run from the pharynx to the body wall, the expansion of the pharynx exerts a strong suction

---

Lumbricus terrestris.

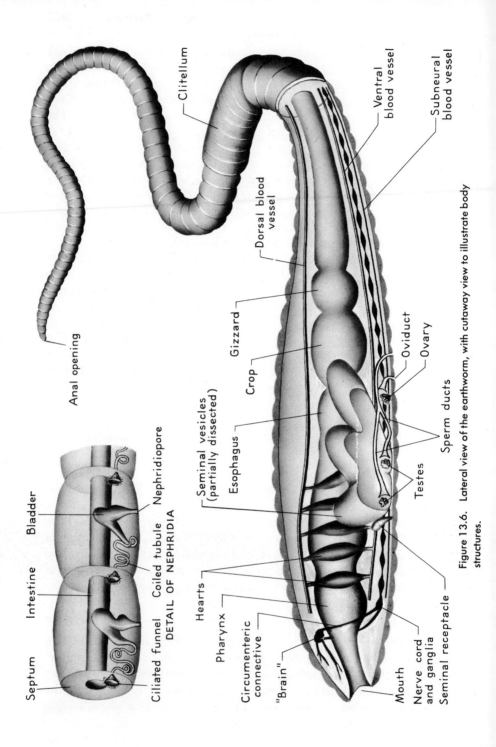

Anal opening

Clitellum

Dorsal blood vessel

Ventral blood vessel

Subneural blood vessel

Gizzard

Crop

Oviduct

Ovary

Esophagus

Sperm ducts

Seminal vesicles (partially dissected)

Testes

Hearts

Pharynx

Circumenteric connective

"Brain"

Mouth

Nerve cord and ganglia

Seminal receptacle

Septum   Intestine   Bladder

Ciliated funnel   Coiled tubule   Nephridiopore

DETAIL OF NEPHRIDIA

Figure 13.6. Lateral view of the earthworm, with cutaway view to illustrate body structures.

by means of which food is ingested. There are no teeth or jaws, but the worms regularly swallow small stones which help grind up the food. A narrow esophagus connects the pharynx to an enlarged storage sac, the *crop*, and three *calciferous glands* are associated with the esophagus. Darwin showed that these glands probably perform two important functions in nutrition: *first*, the plant food which is digested by earthworms has a high calcium content, and the calciferous glands, by secreting the calcium into the esophagus, actually serve to excrete this element by eliminating it from the body fluids; *second*, the calcium helps to counteract the organic acids in the food, making it possible for the digestive enzymes, which are comparable to human pancreatic secretions, to act more effectively. Food passes from the crop into the *gizzard*, where contractions of the heavy muscular walls, aided by the stones which were swallowed, pulverize the food. Posterior to the gizzard is the *intestine*, where most of the digestion and absorption occurs, and which extends the remaining length of the animal to the *anal opening*.

A significant structure, the *typhlosole*, is present in the intestine. This is a fold of the dorsal wall, which projects into the intestine and performs several important functions: *first*, it slows the passage of food so that it may be acted upon for a longer time by the digestive fluids; *second*, it increases the surface area for the secretion of digestive enzymes; and *third*, it increases the area for absorption of the products of digestion. Modifications of the alimentary canal (such as folds, processes, sacs, and coiling) to accomplish these functions are common in other organisms and are usually better developed in herbivores than in carnivores. The muscle layers of the intestine of the earthworm are poorly developed in comparison with those of the clamworm, but weak peristaltic waves do occur.

Respiration

The earthworm secures its oxygen by diffusion into the skin capillaries through the cuticle. It is much less efficient in removing oxygen from its surroundings than is the clamworm, but since its movements are not as rapid or sustained as are those of the latter, its oxygen need is not so great. The earthworm consumes only about one tenth as much oxygen as the clamworm. The cuticle is readily permeable to both oxygen and carbon dioxide but does not permit the rapid diffusion of the gases that would occur if the cuticle were absent. Hemoglobin, in the form of oxyhemoglobin, aids in the transportation of oxygen to the tissues, where the release of oxygen, as we described for the clamworm, occurs in the presence of any slight excess of carbon dioxide.

Excretion

Nephridia are the primary excretory structures in the earthworm, and they are almost identical in structure and action with those of the clamworm. Waste material enters the ciliated funnel from the coelom and passes into the coiled

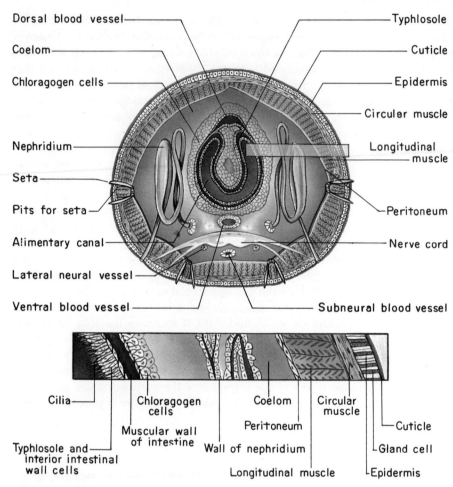

Dorsal blood vessel

Coelom

Chloragogen cells

Nephridium

Seta

Pits for seta

Alimentary canal

Lateral neural vessel

Ventral blood vessel

Typhlosole

Cuticle

Epidermis

Circular muscle

Longitudinal muscle

Peritoneum

Nerve cord

Subneural blood vessel

Cilia

Chloragogen cells

Coelom

Circular muscle

Muscular wall of intestine

Peritoneum

Cuticle

Typhlosole and interior intestinal wall cells

Wall of nephridium

Gland cell

Longitudinal muscle

Epidermis

Figure 13.7.   This drawing of an earthworm in cross section shows very clearly the relationship of its internal structures.

tubule from the capillary network.   An enlargement, the *bladder,* occurs at the point where the tubule opens to the outside.   This bladder serves as a temporary storage sac.

The peritoneum covering the intestine and portions of the major blood vessels is modified in earthworms to form a *chloragogen* layer.   Waste materials accumulate in the chloragogen cells, which eventually separate from the intestinal wall and float freely in the coelomic fluid.   Some of these detached cells are ingested by the amoebocytes of the coelom, which in turn migrate later to the superficial tissues, disintegrate, and deposit their contents in the form of a protective pigment.   Other chloragogen cells are swept into the ciliated funnel of the nephridia and thence to the outside.   The form taken by nitrogenous waste materials is not clearly understood, but from 10 to 50 per cent is probably in the form of ammonia, and from 12 to 86 per cent as urea.   Considerable quantities of amino acids also may be excreted by the earthworm.

Reproduction

The reproductive system of earthworms is radically different from that of clamworms, and these modifications can be correlated with two important features of the earthworms' existence: *first*, the worms live in a restricted area; and *second*, they cannot discharge their sex cells into water, yet the embryos must be protected from dehydration.   The earthworms are hermaphroditic; both eggs and sperm are formed simultaneously in a single individual, but self-fertilization does not occur.   Two pairs of testes and a single pair of ovaries are located in the anterior region of the earthworm, and reproductive ducts are present.   Two pairs of small sacs, the *sperm receptacles*, located in segments 9 and 10 from the anterior end, receive the sperm from the mate during copulation.   The cells of the epidermis are very glandular in five segments (usually numbers 32 through 36) and constitute the *clitellum*, which secretes a *cocoon* in which the eggs are deposited after mating.   We will give a brief account of copulation to illustrate the relationship of the various parts of the reproductive system of these worms.

During copulation, two worms press their anterior ventral surfaces together, with their heads pointing in opposite directions, and the clitellum of each secretes a thick mucus covering which forms a tube about the animals.   Sperm are discharged from the openings of the sperm ducts in segment 15 and enter the sperm receptacles (in segments 9 and 10) of each animal, where they are stored.   After the worms separate, each clitellum secretes a band of mucus which moves slowly toward the head and, as it passes the opening of the oviducts in segment 14, the ova are deposited in this band.   The mucus band continues to slide forward slowly and, as it passes segments 10 and 9, the sperm are discharged from the receptacles and fertilize the eggs.   The band finally slips off over the head end of the worm and closes at each end to make a cocoon (often

Figure 13.8.   Earthworms copulating. (Courtesy Charles Davis.)

incorrectly called the worm egg) to protect the forming embryos from drying.

It should be apparent that it is advantageous for animals that occupy a limited territory to be hermaphroditic, because when *any two* individuals meet it is possible to have cross-fertilization, and this increases the reproductive potentiality. A comparable situation of limited territory also exists in the case of internal parasites, where hermaphroditism is common, as we will observe later. The earthbound earthworms can have no free-swimming larval stage, but this is not peculiar since even fresh-water animals rarely have larval stages comparable to those of marine organisms.

Coordination

There is an absence of prominent sense organs, but receptors consisting of small groups of cells, some of which are sensitive to light and others to touch or chemical stimuli, are scattered over the body. Light-sensitive cells are located on the dorsal surface and are concentrated especially in the anterior and posterior parts of the worms. Cells with tactile "hairs" which protrude above the surface are the touch, and possibly the chemical, receptors. Darwin determined that the earthworm exercises considerable choice in the selection of food, and it is probable that simple taste receptors exist in the mouth or pharyngeal region. Earthworms are not responsive to sound but react violently to vibrations. Darwin demonstrated this experimentally by placing pots of worms on a

Figure 13.9. Circulatory system of the earthworm. The nephridium has been omitted from one segment for the sake of clarity. Certain minor blood vessels also are not included in the diagram.

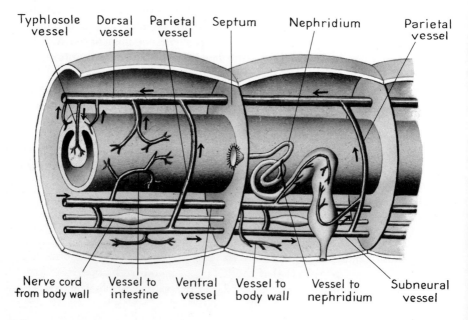

Typhlosole vessel   Dorsal vessel   Parietal vessel   Septum   Nephridium   Parietal vessel

Nerve cord from body wall   Vessel to intestine   Ventral vessel   Vessel to body wall   Vessel to nephridium   Subneural vessel

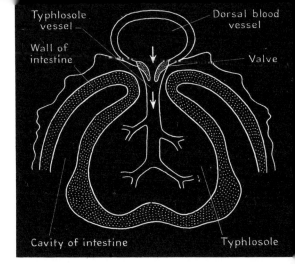

Figure 13.10. Valve in typhlosole blood vessel.

piano and striking the keys, with the result that the worms withdrew rapidly
into their burrows; but there was no response when the same keys were struck
while the worms were beside the piano. It was clear, therefore, that the vibrations were being perceived, or "felt," by the tactile organs; that they could not
be "heard" because no hearing organs are present.

The nervous system is strikingly similar to that of the clamworms and fundamentally is composed of a ventral-ladder-type nerve cord with ganglia in each
segment. The double cord and the ganglia fuse in the adult earthworm as in
the clamworm, but the basic condition can still be recognized in the so-called
brain region. The "brain" is composed of a pair of supraenteric ganglia, with
cross connections which lie immediately above the anterior part of the pharynx.
The brain develops from the ganglia of the prostomium. Circumenteric connectives encircle the pharynx to join the subenteric, a large ganglion below the
pharynx; this ganglion is apparently formed by the fusion of the three ganglia
of the first three segments. The nerve cord continues posteriorly, and the
ganglia in each segment send three pairs of lateral nerves to the body and the
viscera. One branch is in the anterior region of each segment; the other two
are in the posterior region. The brain controls the behavior of the entire worm
in a fashion comparable to the action observed in clamworms, but the subenteric
ganglion primarily controls the peristomium and pharynx. The removal of the
latter disrupts the feeding and the burrowing of the earthworm; but it may be
said that feeding and burrowing are essentially one process since the animal
literally eats its way through the soil. As in the clamworm, giant nerve cells are
present in the nerve cord, and rapid conduction of impulses over the length of
the worm is the responsibility of these cells.

Circulatory system

Thousands of earthworms have been dissected in zoological laboratories, but
it is only in the last few years that the details of blood circulation have been
understood. Recent investigations based on observations of blood movement

Figure 13.11. The dark areas within the body of this leech are the blood-filled pouches which connect with the intestine. The smaller, anterior sucker and the larger, posterior sucker are prominent. (Courtesy S. T. Brooks.)

in living worms after an injection of India ink have made it possible to determine the direction of blood flow. The major blood vessels are the same as those observed in the clamworm, with a large *dorsal vessel,* which exhibits peristalsis, and a *ventral,* or *subintestinal, vessel.* A *ventral subneural vessel* is joined to a pair of *parietal vessels* in each segment, which in turn empty into the dorsal vessel. The body wall, the wall of the alimentary canal, and the nephridia are supplied by branches from the ventral vessel, and the typhlosole in the intestine receives a branch from the dorsal vessel in each segment. Drainage from the body wall is by way of small vessels into the parietal vessel, and vessels from the alimentary canal empty into the dorsal. The nephridial blood vessels drain into the parietals. Simple valves control the direction of blood flow and, in the case of the dorsal vessel, allow it to both receive blood from and supply blood to the intestine. The capillary network is extensive, and it serves for gaseous exchange in the skin, to pick up nutrient materials from the alimentary canal, and to convey waste materials to the coelom and nephridia.

The Leech*

This annelid worm is modified for what constitutes partial parasitic existence. The body is somewhat flattened and, unlike the segmentation of the clamworm or the earthworm, a constant number of 32 segments is present. Only 26 of these segments are obvious, because the 6 posterior ones fuse into the posterior sucker. The leech possesses two suckers—one anterior, the other posterior—and the mouth opens in the anterior sucker. The jaws of leeches are of a rasping

Hirudo medicinalis.

type and leave a three-rayed puncture when they penetrate the surface of the animal on which the leech is feeding. A special secretion, *hirudin,* prevents the blood of the host from clotting when ingested, which makes ingestion easier. The crop of the leech has 11 pairs of pouches which enable the animal to store great quantities of blood when feeding. If it has been able to fill the crop sacs, a leech may be able to survive for as long as a year without additional food.

The leeches are hermaphroditic; they have 10 pairs of testes and a single pair of ovaries. Cross-fertilization occurs, and a cocoon is formed about the developing eggs. The sperm may, in some instances, be deposited in capsules on the surface of the mating partner, after which the body wall is eaten away by enzyme action, and the sperm enter the body by this hypodermic method. The features of the leeches are comparable to those of other annelids with respect to nephridia, nervous system, and muscle layers. The coelom, as we noted earlier, is filled with a loose tissue through which run strong dorsal-ventral bands of muscles, and the blood vessels appear as irregular spaces, or *sinuses,* in the coelomic tissue.

The Proboscis Worm

It is difficult to imagine how the coelomate animals could have appeared suddenly in the animal kingdom as descendants of acoelomate worms—for example, the Nemathelminthes studied in Chapter 11. The problem is so exasperating that zoologists have searched diligently for an animal or a group of animals of intermediate structure which could help resolve the problem. Intermediate forms are always hard to find, but in this instance the search has been partially rewarded. The *proboscis worms,* or *nemertines,* offer some clues concerning the possible structure of the ancestors of the coelomates; they may help to explain the transition from unsegmented to segmented animals and from acoelomate to coelomate animals (Figure 12.12). They do not possess a coelom

Figure 13.12. The simple exterior of the nemertine, or proboscis, worm hides a very complicated internal structure. The animal in this picture has its proboscis slightly protruded. (Courtesy Clarence Flaten.)

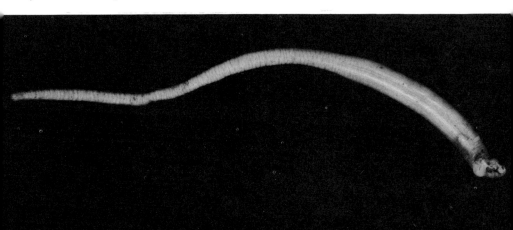

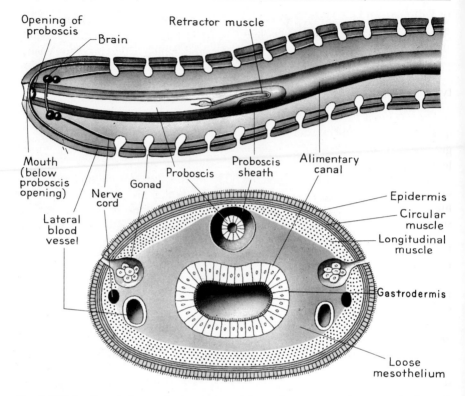

Figure 13.13. Dorsal view and cross section of the proboscis worm, showing its body structures.

and have many characteristics of the flatworms; but at the same time they have developed organ systems typical of the coelomates: a true alimentary canal, a circulatory system, and a more complex "brain" and nervous system.

The proboscis worms have been difficult to classify. They have been considered as classes of different phyla and especially as a class of flatworms. Primarily as a result of the work of Max Johann Schultze in 1850, they are now dignified with the designation of a phylum; and the classification seems to be amply justified.

The worms vary greatly in size, from a few inches to a reported 100 feet in length. Most of them, however, are small animals. Their most distinctive feature is the presence of a *proboscis*, from which they derive their name. This is a tubular structure, often armed at the end with a spear which can be swiftly and accurately thrust from the body to pierce or lasso prey. The proboscis lies in a *sheath* dorsal to the alimentary canal, and when protruded it is actually turned wrong side out. A muscle attached to the base of the proboscis contracts to pull it back into the sheath. The body of the worm may be cylindrical or flattened, and the surface is entirely ciliated, the cilia being outgrowths of an epidermis of columnar epithelium. The similarity of the body covering to that of the flatworms is obvious. Immediately below the epidermis are layers of circular and longitudinal muscle, and surrounding the digestive system is a connective tissue of mesothelium comparable to the parenchyma of flatworms. Amoebocytes wander through the parenchyma.

Similarity to the flatworms ends, however, when the details of the digestive, vascular, and nervous systems are considered. The digestive tract has both a *mouth* and an *anal opening*, and one-way passage of food occurs. The digestive tract may be a very simple tube in some nemertines, or a highly specialized one in others. A mouth, an esophagus, a stomach, an intestine with pouches, and an anus are recognizable in some proboscis worms. Muscles may be associated with the digestive tract, but these usually are poorly developed, a condition comparable to that found in the round worms.

The proboscis worms are the "lowest" animals to possess a true circulatory, or vascular, system and, as in the case of the digestive tract, considerable variation exists in the degree of development. The simplest type is composed of a pair of lateral vessels which run one on each side of the alimentary canal; these are fused with each other above the proboscis sheath in the anterior end and below the anus in the posterior end. A dorsal vessel is also present in those forms with more complicated vascular systems, and numerous trunks connect the lateral and dorsal vessels. Typically, there are amoeboid cells present in the circulating fluid, which usually is colorless, although in a few cases hemoglobin is present. The walls of some of the major vessels are contractile, but body movement accounts for most of the circulation of the blood.

A close association exists between the excretory and circulatory systems. The animals have a rotonephridial system with flame bulbs, and the bulbs frequently penetrate into the blood vessels. Excretory tubules may be well developed and empty to the outside by excretory pores.

The nervous system is much better developed in the nemertines than in the flatworms. The "brain" of many nemertines is composed of two ganglia above the proboscis sheath and two below. These ganglia are interconnected, and the ringlike arrangement of nerves is superficially comparable to their disposition in annelids. The brain is joined to two lateral nerve cords, and in a few of the worms a dorsal nerve cord may also be present. The sense organs are much more elaborate than in the flatworms. Special *tactile receptors* are scattered over the worm and are especially prominent anteriorly and posteriorly. Grooves, or nuchal pits, which behave as *chemical receptors*, are present in the anterior end, as are also *pigmented cups*, or "eyes." These vary in number from 2 to 200 or more and are light-sensitive rather than image-forming.

Reproduction is both sexual and asexual. Some forms are hermaphroditic, frequently exhibiting *protandry* (the production of first sperm and then eggs by the same gonad). The gonads are flask-shaped bodies, located usually in the intestinal region, and are formed by mesothelial cells of the parenchyma.

Each gonad opens by a *gonopore* through the lateral body wall. Asexual reproduction is remarkable in some nemertines. The animals often break into two pieces, and each regenerates the necessary parts for a complete animal. One species fragments into many small pieces, and each regenerates a complete worm—one of the most amazing reproductive phenomena to be found in the animal kingdom.

This brief account of the proboscis worms may be summarized by noting the important position that these animals hold in the relationship of acoelomate to coelomate forms. The body structure clearly is more nearly related to that of the flatworms, and the retention of a parenchyma-filled body space is disadvantageous to them, since it prevents the full development of organ systems. The worms, however, have evolved an alimentary canal, a circulatory system, and a more complex nervous system. Their organization, therefore, indicates a pathway which could have been followed by the ancestors of the coelomates.

Classification of Annelida

Phylum Annelida   Segmented worms with a well-developed coelom and nephridia for excretion. A true alimentary canal, with specialized regions, is present, and the nervous system is of a ventral ladder type. A cuticle as well as circular and longitudinal muscles are found.

CLASS I. POLYCHAETA.   Mostly free-living marine annelids with well-developed parapodia. Sexes usually separate, and the prostomium is equipped with sensory structures. Examples: *Chaetopterus* (a tube-dwelling worm), *Neanthes* or *Neris* (clamworm, or sandworm).

CLASS II. OLIGOCHAETA.   Mostly terrestrial or fresh-water worms, without parapodia, but with locomotor spines. Hermaphroditic, and the head is without elaborate sensory structures. Examples: *Tubifer* (a tube-dwelling worm), *Lumbricus* (earthworm).

CLASS III. HIRUDINEA.   Flattened worms with suckers; are semiparasitic and hermaphroditic. A constant number of 32 segments is present, of which 6 form the posterior sucker. Example: *Hirudo medicinalis* (medicinal leech).

CLASS IV. ARCHIANNELIDA.   Marine worms with only faint external traces of segmentation. Head tentacles are present, and ciliated area also appear externally. Usually parapodia and setae are absent. Example: *Polygordius*.

Phylum Rhynchocoela   Acoelomate, with true alimentary canal and a circulatory system. A proboscis for capture of food. Example: *Cerebratulus* (proboscis worm).

REFERENCES

BELL, A. W., "The Earthworm Circulatory System," *Turtox News*, 25, 1947.

BROWN, F. A. (ed.), *Selected Invertebrate Types*, pp. 271–309. John Wiley & Sons, Inc., New York, 1950.

DARWIN, CHARLES, *The Formation of Vegetable Mould through the Action of Worms, with Observations of Their Habits*. Murray, London, 1881.

GROVE, A. J., "On the Reproductive Processes of the Earthworm, *Lumbricus terrestris*," *Quarterly Journal of Microscopical Science*, 69, 1925.

HARMER, S. F., and A. E. SHIPLEY, (ed.), "Oligochaeta and Hirudinea," *Cambridge Natural History*, Vol. 2, pp. 347–410. Macmillan and Company, Ltd., London, 1922.

HYMAN, L. H., *The Invertebrates: Platyhelminthes to Rhynchocoela*, Vol. II, pp. 459–528. McGraw-Hill Book Company, Inc., New York, 1951.

14

The Shellfishes

Phylum Mollusca

•

The Mollusca also afford a very good instance of the progressive modification and evolution of organic structure.—Paul Telseneer, A Treatise on Zoology, 1906

The family tree of the Mollusca has as its roots ancestors who thrived in ancient seas 300 to 500 million years ago and as its branches modern descendants who are spread over the entir earth. The mollusks, in the form of the squid and the octopus, are among the most remarkable animals that have ever existed. The clams and oysters, however, are secondarily adapted for a sedentary life and, at a casual glance, appear to have little in common with the squid. The wide superficial differences between the various mollusks are not accompanied by comparable extensive changes in the internal structure. The basic features of all the mollusks are apparent upon careful dissection, and the variations in the anatomy merely illustrate the structural adjustments which have been made during the long period of years that the mollusks have inhabited this planet. As a phylum the Mollusca are one of the best-known animal groups, because some of its members have been considered delicacies by prehistoric and both modern human gourmets, and because their shell is such a unique diagnostic feature, the like of which appears in few other animal forms.

There are four major divisions to the molluscan body: (1) the *head*, which contains the "brain," the sense organs in the form of eyes or tentacles, and the mouth with a rasping, tonguelike structure, the radula; (2) the *foot*, which is a muscular locomotor organ with considerable variation in structure; (3) the *mantle*, which is a fold of the body wall, and contains the epithelium which secretes the shell, and which also serves as a cover for the body organs; (4) the *visceral mass*, which lies above the foot and is composed of the digestive, excretory, circulatory, and reproductive organs. The four basic divisions of the body, however, are considerably modified in the different classes of Mollusca. One part may be almost entirely suppressed but another part developed to a very high degree; the squid, the snail, and the clam will serve to illustrate some of these variations. The chiton will be used to delineate the basic organization of the molluscan body. The functions of the different mollusks, however, will be considered together. The squid and the octopus have the foot subdivided to form the arms and the tentacles, of which there may be eight or ten, and the sense organs of the head are very well developed. The head of the clam and the oyster has been effaced completely, but the foot is a prominent organ, into part of which the visceral mass protrudes. The visceral mass of the snail is coiled above the foot, and the mantle is arranged in such a fashion that a spiral shell is formed. The clam is a highly modified organism, adapted for a quiet, sedentary life, but the squid is an active, aggressive animal. The differences between the squid and the clam demonstrate the great adaptability of the various mollusks. It should be noted that the mollusks are coelomate, but that they posses a *reduced coelom* which is limited almost entirely to the space

Figure 14.1.   Modifications of body structure of representative mollusks.

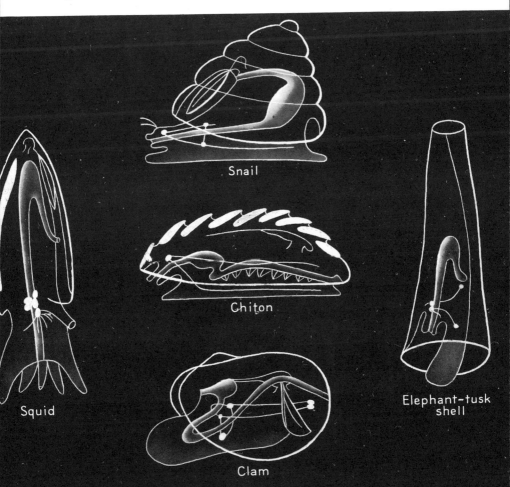

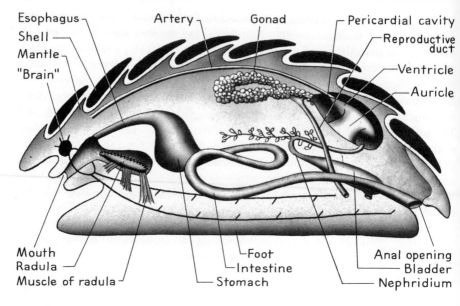

Figure 14.2.   Sectional drawing, showing body form and structures of the chiton.

about the heart, the *pericardial cavity*.   The illustration above presents the modifications of the parts of the body in five representative mollusks.

The Chiton

Body form

The chitons are marine mollusks with a clear-cut bilateral symmetry and a strong ventral foot equipped with mucus-secreting glands.   The visceral mass of the chiton is covered by the *mantle,* which also extends laterally in folds beyond the foot.   The mantle secretes overlapping plates of *shell* on the dorsal surface of the chiton; there are usually eight of these plates.   The groove between the mantle and the foot serves as a respiratory chamber, because numerous ridges on which the *gills* are located project into this space.   There are no eyes or tentacles in the head region, and no actual head exists.   The chiton for this reason is not a typical mollusk, but if it were not for this structural inadequacy, it might well serve as an ancestral type for the phylum Mollusca.

Chiton also possesses a *radula, nephridia,* and a *reduced coelom,*and as we will note later, it has a trochophore larva.   With all these features it might very well serve as the ancestral type for the phylum *Mollusca* were it not for the existence of some structural inadequacies.   There are no eyes or tentacles in the head region and, indeed, there is no true head.   The chiton for these reasons cannot be considered to be the "typical" mollusk.

The arrangement of the viscera is relatively simple: the *mouth* opens into a pharyngeal cavity which contains the radula and is connected posteriorly by the esophagus to the saclike stomach. Posterior to the stomach is the long intestine, which terminates at the anus. Excretion is accomplished by a pair of glandular folded tubules, the nephridia, or kidneys, which start with a ciliated funnel in the pericardial cavity and extend posteriorly to form the bladder, emptying to the outside through pores near the anus at the posterior end of the animal. This relationship of the kidneys to the pericardial cavity is typical of the Mollusca. The nervous system is composed of a circumenteric ring about the esophagus, and in addition there are anterior branches, two posterior nerves, and a pair of connecting nerves which encircle the mantle. Numerous cross connections are present, so that the nervous system appears as a ventral ladder type, but without the ganglionic enlargements that are so obvious in the annelids. Dorsal to the alimentary canal is a three-chambered heart, lying within the pericardial cavity: the single ventricle pumps the blood throughout the body by a series of arteries. The blood is returned through large irregular spaces, the sinuses, and through the veins to the heart's two auricles.

The sexes are separate in the chiton, and the gonads, like the heart, are dorsal to the alimentary canal. The reproductive organs may be paired in some chitons, or fused to a single median organ in others, and the ducts open posteriorly, just in front of the kidney openings. The eggs and sperm are shed into the sea water, where the fertilized egg develops into a trochophore larva. This is similar in many of its features to the trochophore of the annelids and possesses a ciliated band about the equator and a tuft of cilia on the prostomial region, or acron. The foot appears very early in the larval development. The larval excretory system has flame bulbs; these, however, are replaced by the nephridial-type kidneys when the larva transforms into an adult.

The Clam*

Body form

The clams have world-wide distribution and are present in large numbers in both fresh and marine waters. Although there are differences in the color and thickness and in the shape and size of the shell, the body parts arc so similar that several clams, such as the marine mollusk Venus or the fresh-water Unio, can be used concurrently to illustrate common structural features (see Figures 14.4, 14.5, 14.6, 14.7). The shell consists of two parts, or valves, which are joined at the dorsal surface by the hinge ligament. A swelling on each valve at the anterior end of the ligament is the umbo, which marks the oldest part of the shell. The mantle secretes new layers of shell at the fresh margins of the umbo, and this produces concentric lines on the surface, marking the successive

*Description applies primarily to members of the genus Unio.

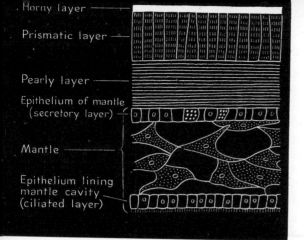

Figure 14.3. The complex nature of both shell and mantle is indicated by this diagram of shell–mantle relationship.

periods of growth. The shell is composed of three layers: an outer, *horny layer* of material like that which forms the hinge ligament; a middle, *prismatic layer*, in which crystals of calcium carbonate are laid down in thin sheets; and an inner, *mother-of-pearl layer*. The edge of the mantle secretes the horny and prismatic layers, but the mother-of-pearl layer is formed by the surface of the mantle. Foreign particles lodged between the mantle and shell stimulate the epithelium to form a mother-of-pearl coating about the particles, and in this way pearls are formed.

Figure 14.4. This drawing shows the relationship of the clam's gills to the mantle, mouth, and foot.

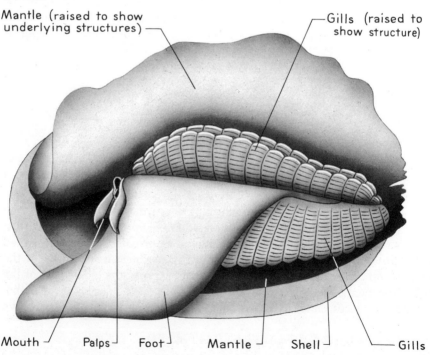

Mantle (raised to show underlying structures)

Gills (raised to show structure)

Mouth   Palps   Foot   Mantle   Shell   Gills

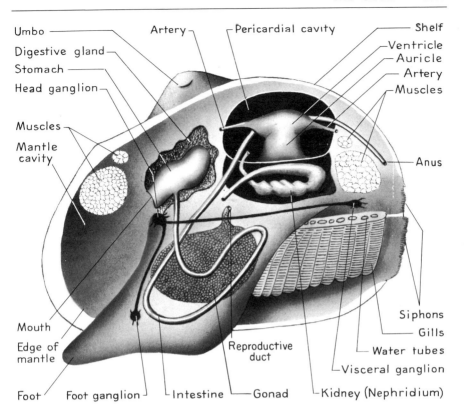

Figure 14.5. The relationship of the clam's basic structures (see also Figure 14.7).

The careful removal of one valve discloses that the mantle covers the body of the clam like a curtain. Two large, strong *adductor muscles,* one anterior and the other posterior, hold the clam shell closed; and in addition, *protractor* and *retractor muscles* attach the foot to the shell and may pull it forward or backward, making locomotion possible. The two halves of the mantle enclose a large space, the *mantle cavity,* in which the visceral mass is located and from which the foot can be protruded at the anterior, or ventral, edge. The posterior margins of the mantle are thickened, and when brought together form short tubes, the dorsal and ventral *siphons.* These siphons in some clams (for example, the "gapers") may be drawn out together into a long, tubelike "neck" and function as a part of the feeding mechanism.

Two pairs of *gills* project from the dorsal mass of the viscera into the mantle cavity, much like the pages of a book between its covers; one pair is found on the right, the other on the left. Immediately above the foot is the *mouth,* surrounded by fleshy lobes, the *palps,* but there is no radula present in the clam. The esophagus connects the mouth with the *stomach,* which is embedded in a

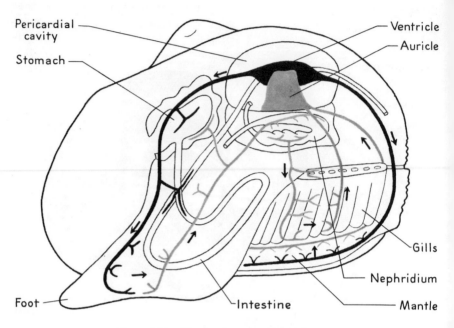

Pericardial cavity
Stomach
Ventricle
Auricle
Gills
Nephridium
Foot
Intestine
Mantle

Figure 14.6.   The circulatory system of the clam.

large *digestive gland* and connected to it by a duct.   The stomach opens posteriorly into the intestine, which makes several loops in the foot before continuing dorsally through the pericardial cavity (actually through the ventricle of
the heart) to the *anus,* which opens into the region of the dorsal siphon.   The
effective length of the alimentary canal is increased by the coiling of the intestine.   Sexes are separate, and the gonad surrounds the intestinal loops in the
foot.   The *reproductive ducts,* considered to be part of the coelom, open dorsally
into the gill passages, or *suprabranchial chambers.*

The circulatory system is well developed in clams.   A muscular *ventricle*
pumps the blood forward and backward through arteries, and the blood is returned to the ventricle by way of the right and left *auricles.*   The *arteries* open
into irregular spaces in the tissues, the *sinuses,* from which the blood returns to
the auricles through a system of *veins.*   The heart, as was previously indicated,
lies in the pericardial cavity, which is also part of the coelom.   The kidneys,
sometimes called nephridia, are comparable to those of the chiton; they consist
of a pair of glandular coiled tubes opening into the pericardial cavity at their
anterior ends and into the gill passages at their posterior ends.   The dorsal portion of the kidney is a thin-walled bladder lined with cilia that create a current
of water for the movement of the waste material.

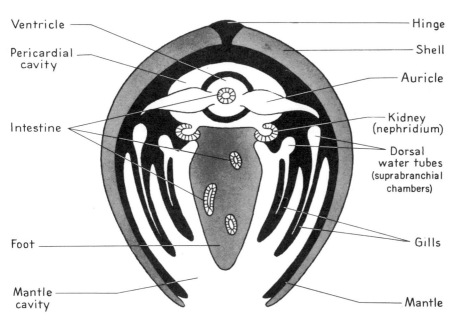

Figure 14.7.   The basic structures of the clam in cross section.

The clam nervous system is much reduced when compared with that of the chiton.   Three ganglia and two pairs of nerve cords are present: the *head ganglion,* with a circumenteric loop about the esophagus, is connected by a pair of nerves to the *pedal ganglion* and by another pair of nerves to the *visceral ganglion* in the region of the posterior adductor muscle.   Sense organs are greatly reduced: light-sensitive areas are present on the edge of the mantle, chemical receptors in the mouth region, and a pair of balancing organs in the foot.   These sense organs are comparable to the statocysts of other mollusks.

The feeding, respiratory, and reproductive activities of clams are dependent upon the flow of water through the mantle cavity.   The gills and mantle are ciliated, and the beating of these countless microscopic projections maintains a current of water which flows in by the ventral (incurrent) siphon, through the mantle cavity, over the gills to the dorsal gill passages, and thence posteriorly to leave the clam by way of the dorsal (excurrent) siphon.   Small particles of food in suspension in the water are entangled by mucus secreted by the surface of the gills and are carried by ciliary action to the palps, where they are ingested. Heavy particles of undigestible matter, such as sand grains, drop from the gills and palps to the lower portion of the mantle to be expelled.

The Squid*

Body form

Squids are active, predatory marine animals which swim by body undulations and by jet propulsion. The shell is a greatly reduced "pen" and is buried in the body, with the result that the muscular mantle becomes the surface covering of the animal. The body is cone-shaped, and the mantle is expanded into triangular *fins* at the pointed end of the animal; these expansions are used for swimming and as rudders. The *arms* and *tentacles*, a *funnel*, and a *head* project from the large end of the body cone, and the mantle in this region is modified into a *collar*, which interlocks with the visceral mass to close the opening into the mantle cavity. The squid, therefore, differs radically in its appearance from most other mollusks because of its adaptations for rapid movement and the reduction of its shell.

The question of symmetry in the squid presents an annoying problem because, although the animals are bilaterally symmetrical, the elongation of the body is actually in a dorsal-ventral direction! The pointed end of the animal where the fins are located is usually posterior as the animal swims but is actually the *dorsal* side. The base of the cone, where the head is found, is usually anterior in the swimming animal but is the true *ventral* side. As a consequence of this peculiar condition, the functional upper side is the structural *anterior* side, and the functional underside is the structural *posterior* side. If you picture the squid as standing head downward on its arms, this complicated orientation will be easier to visualize.

The *funnel*, or *siphon*, is not formed by the mantle but is actually a modified portion of the *foot*, as are also the arms and tentacles! The mantle contains *circular* and some *longitudinal muscles*, but the latter are primarily concentrated in the forward (ventral) portion of the mantle. Unique *radial muscles* are also present in the mantle. The integrated action of the muscles makes possible the circulation of water in the mantle cavity. A contraction of radial muscles, with a simultaneous relaxation of the circular muscles, expands the mantle like an inflated balloon and results in the suction of water into the animal. The subsequent forceful contraction of the circular muscles, accompanied by relaxation of the radial muscles, contracts the mantle, closes the collar, and ejects the water through the funnel. A vigorous ejection of the water produces effective jet propulsion. Since the funnel can be swiveled, the squid can change direction easily: when the funnel is turned to the rear, the squid will move forward, but if the funnel points forward as water is ejected, the animal will move to the rear. A cloud of "ink" may be released through the funnel with the water to produce a protective "smoke screen" for the squid, an effective escape mechanism. There is also evidence that the ink may temporarily destroy the sense of "smell'" of the attacking animal.

*Description is primarily of *Loligo pealeii*.

A startling feature of the external appearance of the squid is the rapidity of color change. Red-brown, yellow, and violet pigments are contained in minute elastic sacs which have muscle fibers connected to their walls. The contraction of the muscle fibers, either voluntarily or involuntarily, expands the sacs about 20 times in diameter and disperses the pigments, and since the colors are located in different sacs, waves of color will sweep across the surface of the animal in a beautiful sequence. The squid is, therefore, a rare animal which can blush in many colors, either involuntarily or at will.

Figure 14.8. The basic structures of the squid are shown in this longitudinal section.

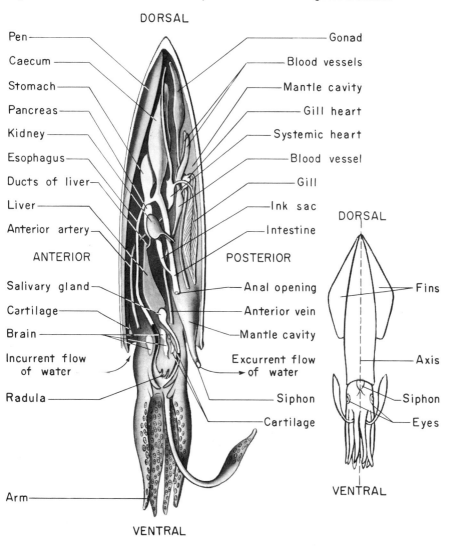

There are four pairs of arms and two tentacles about the head, and these are all equipped with suckers which enable the animal to hold the prey firmly. Organisms are usually captured by the tentacles, which are longer and somewhat retractile; these pull the prey to the mouth, where it is held firmly by the arms. Although most squid are small, giant squid have been observed which reach a total length of 30 to 50 feet, with tentacles that have a diameter equal to that of a man's arm and are equipped with suckers the size of saucers! These giant squid are among the largest animals in the world.

The internal anatomy of the squid is somewhat complicated by the long dorsal-ventral axis of the animal and by the elaborately developed organ systems which almost fill the mantle cavity. The *mouth* opens into a *pharynx* in which a reduced *radula* but well-developed *jaws* are found. The prey, which is held immobile in the arms, is torn to pieces by the jaws. The radula is of little importance in the squid. An *esophagus* connects with a saclike *stomach*, from which a slightly coiled *intestine* leads to the *anus*, located in the forward region of the mantle cavity near the mouth. The large *digestive gland* ("liver" and "pancreas") empties into the stomach, and *salivary glands* are located near the mouth. A pair of *gills* projects into the mantle cavity near the stomach, and the *ink sac* is located near the anal region.

The circulatory system is equipped with two *gill hearts* which send the blood to the gills, from which it is returned to the *systemic heart*. The blood is pumped by this organ into anterior and posterior *arteries*, thence through a *capillary network*, and returned to the gill hearts by way of anterior and posterior *veins*. A pair of *kidneys* open from the pericardial cavity of the gill hearts and empty into the mantle cavity near the anus. A very complex *brain*, surrounded by a *brain case* of cartilage, is located in the head region. There are also ganglia associated with the mantle.

Functions of the Mollusks

Nutrition

The nutrition of the Mollusca is variable, as might be expected from the great differences in habits and body structure. Members of the class Pelecypoda, such as clams, feed on microscopic floating organisms, the plankton, and on organic matter in suspension. The circulation rate of water through the clam probably does not exceed three liters per day, and the number of plankton

Figure 14.9. Representative mollusks. The frilled, octopuslike cephalopod in (a) lived 350,000,000 years ago and reached a length of 20 ft. The oyster (b) is as familiar as the clam or the snail (c). The cuttlefish (d) is in the same class as the squid and the octopus. [(a) Courtesy New York State Museum; (b) Holiday, reprinted by special permission; copyright 1952 by the Curtis Publishing Company; (c) courtesy Robert C. Hermes; (d) courtesy F. Schensky.]

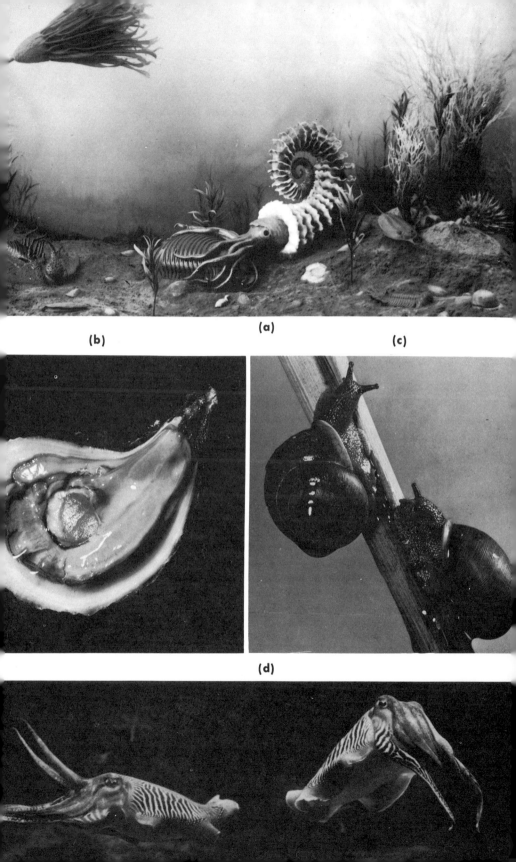

(a)

(b)

(c)

(d)

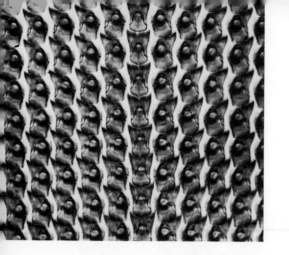

Figure 14.10. This dangerous looking and efficient structure is the radula of a snail, greatly magnified. (Copyright by General Biological Supply House, Inc., Chicago.)

organisms in this quantity of water is not adequate to meet the nutritional demands; but ample food is available in the additional amount of organic matter in suspension. The food is entangled in mucus, and this material is carried by a special ciliated *food groove* to the mouth where it is ingested. Digestion in the clams is both intracellular and extracellular, and a peculiar rodlike structure in the stomach, the *crystalline style*, is the source of starch-digesting enzymes. This style rubs against the wall of the stomach and is slowly dissolved and mixed with the food material. New material is constantly being deposited at the base of the style to compensate for this dissolution. The digestive gland participates in both the intracellular and extracellular digestion of proteins, fats, and sugars. Amoebocytes are present in the cavity of the alimentary canal, and they also ingest and digest food particles, after which they migrate into the tissue spaces. The amoebocytes can then disgorge food to the tissue cells. They are protoplasmic delivery trucks.

The chiton, the snail, and the squid are active feeders; the first two are primarily herbivores, but the squid is a carnivore. The radula, which is absent in the clam and its relatives, plays an important role in the feeding of most of the mollusks. It is a ribbonlike band, armed with teeth, and is drawn like a rasp over the food, thus scraping the material and taking it into the mouth. Evidence of its action can be seen in the form of the holes cut in leaves by snails. The special jaws of the squid have already been noted, and similar structures are present in the octopus. There is a typhlosole in some mollusks which functions, as in annelids, to increase the surface area of the digestive canal.

Respiration

There is an intimate relationship between the mantle and respiration in the Mollusca. The flow of water which carries the oxygen is controlled by the mantle in the squid, and frequently the cavity of the mantle may also contain gills, as in the clam. The moist surface of the mantle cavity in some air-breathing snails serves as a "lung," making it possible for the snail to secure oxygen directly from the air. *Respiratory pigments* are present in the mollusks, the most important of which is a copper-protein compound, *hemocyanin*, but some mollusks also have *hemoglobin*. The transportation of oxygen is both by chemical combination with the pigments and by solution in the blood plasma. The former is especially important in the squid and octopus, but the latter method apparently is more important in the snails and their close relatives. The squid may release nearly 97 per cent of the oxygen from the blood during its passage through the capillaries; this is several times more than is released from the blood in human capillaries, and it is obvious that the squid is very sensitive to slight decreases in the amount of oxygen in its surroundings. Correlated with the change in oxygen content of the circulating blood is a very striking color change which can be observed in the blood as it passes through the gills and picks up oxygen. Carbon dioxide is also carried by the blood to the gills and eliminated, but the mechanism of the transportation of this gas is not well understood. The mollusks are exclusively oxybiotic, although within the phylum there is a wide variation in the oxygen needs and, as would be expected, active forms like the squid have a much greater demand for oxygen than does the sedentary clam.

Excretion

The kidneys of the mollusks are often spoken of as *nephridia,* and in their connections with the coelom they have the same relationship as do the annelid

Figure 14.11. The hectocotylus, a modified arm with special function in reproduction, is shown in this sketch. Its appearance is so radically different from the typical arm that its presence on the animal at the time of mating is very obvious.

(a)   **(b)**

Figure 14.12. The octopus (a) is a very specialized mollusk, for it has no shell and the foot is divided into sucker-bearing "arma." Octopus eggs (a) are protected by a tough case, within which the young animals may be seen. [(a) Copyright by Douglas P. Wilson, F.R.P.S. Marine Biological Laboratory, Plymouth, England; (b) copyright by General Biological Supply House, Inc., Chicago.]

nephridia. The exact functioning of the kidneys has been incompletely analyzed, but coelomic fluid is carried through them to the mantle cavity and thence out of the animal. The kidneys are also very vascular, and waste products of the blood undoubtedly filter through the capillary walls into the kidney ducts. The wall of the pericardial cavity is glandular in some forms, and apparently secretes waste material from the blood into the pericardial cavity as an aid in excretion. Ammonia is the most common nitrogenous excretory compound in Molluscans, although they also excrete some nitrogenous waste as urea, as uric acid, or even as amino acid. Some of the land forms may excrete large quantities of uric acid, and, as we will see later, this form of nitrogenous waste is advantageous, because with it very little water is lost from the body. It is not clear, with respect to the excretion of water, how the freshwater mollusks maintain a constancy of their body fluids and avoid dilution from the increased intake of water during feeding and by osmosis.

Reproduction

Sexes are separate in most mollusks. A few are hermaphroditic and, as might be expected, these are the sessile or slow-moving forms, such as the oysters. The gonads and ducts are part of the reduced coelom, and in the hermaphroditic forms usually the gonads first are testes, changing later into ovaries—a condition which we have previously noted as protandry. Self-fertilization is impossible, except in rare instances where eggs may be formed first and held until sperm mature at a later time. The gills of clams or oysters may be modified into brood chambers, and in some clams a larval form, the *glochidium*, will attach to fish and live a parasitic existence for a period of time. The larvae after several weeks detach and drop to the bottom, where they develop into adults. This process serves to distribute the animals over a wider area than would be possible otherwise. The number of eggs released by the oyster is impressive; as many as 60,000,000 may be shed in a season by a single animal!

A remarkable sexual apparatus is formed in male cephalopods at mating time. This is a special reproductive arm, the *hectocotylus*. These structures are modified arms that may even lose their suckers, and in the case of some octopuses they actually break off and enter the mantle cavity of the female. The sperm are surrounded by an envelope to form a *sperm sac*, which passes through the funnel into the reproductive arm before being deposited in the female. The eggs of the cephalopods are covered with a protective case, and the octopus may incubate the eggs and thus protect them from enemies.

Coordination

The basic organization of the molluscan nervous system is probably best represented in the chiton; this system is reduced in clams and very elaborately developed in the squid. The squid brain is a very complex ganglionic mass which really deserves its designation as a brain because it functions as a complex coordinating center. Responses to stimuli in the squid must be rapid, and such adjustments are facilitated by *giant axons,* or nerve fibers. These are comparable with those previously described in the annelids but are even more efficient. The giant fibers are associated with paired *stellate ganglia*. They may have a diameter of one millimeter and run the length of the body. These large nerve fibers conduct impulses more rapidly than small ones; the rate of conduction over the giant fibers in the squid is in excess of 2000 centimeters per second. This speed compares favorably with the rate of nervous transmission in man and exceeds that for many other vertebrates.

The sensory receptors of the mollusks range from generalized chemical and light-sensitive areas in the clams and oysters to the image-forming eye of the squid. The light receptors in many pelecypods often are merely cells distributed

Figure 14.13. The complex structure of the squid eye is apparent in this drawing. It will be noted later that there are striking similarities between its structure and the structure of the vertebrate eye (Figure 18.11, 19.26).

along the edge of the mantle; but they are rather more complex in snails, in which a pigmented layer of cells lies beneath a cornea and lens. The squid eye is one of the most remarkable organs in the animal kingdom, along with the eye of the bird and the mammal. The squid eye possesses cornea, pupil, iris, lens, and retina; the size of the pupil can be dilated or contracted to correspond with changes in light intensity; the lens can be altered in its curvature to focus the light rays on the retina; and there is a small canal which opens to the outside from the anterior chamber of the eye to adjust for pressure differences between the interior of the eye and the outside water pressure.

Circulatory system

We clearly see, in studying the circulatory systems of the chiton, clam, and squid, that the vascular system is elaborately developed. Much experimental work has been done with the heart, which can be kept beating outside the body for long periods of time. A capillary bed or a system of blood sinuses is very extensive, even in sedentary forms like the clam. The blood may pass through two sets of capillaries or sinuses in making a circuit from the ventricle to the auricles; such a double capillary system constitutes a *portal system*. We shall encounter this arrangement again in the vertebrates.

The circulatory system of the mollusks has assumed additional significance as a coordinating mechanism. Secretions that are comparable to the hormones of the vertebrates are released into the blood stream, and experiments have shown that these have important regulatory functions. If a dark-adapted, or dark-colored, octopus has its blood stream connected with that of a light-adapted animal, the latter darkens in color, but both animals must be anesthetized to avoid nervous stimulation of the pigment sacs. Conversely, if blood from a light-adapted, or light-colored, animal is transfused into a dark one, the latter becomes lighter in color. The removal of the salivary glands causes the animals to become lighter colored. Even more striking is the effect of castration, or removal of the testes, in the male octopus. After such surgery, the reproductive arm will not develop; therefore it must be concluded that the testis secretes a chemical substance into the blood, a *hormone*, which controls the development of this secondary sex character.

The Ancestry of the Mollusca

The ancestry of the mollusks has been a major puzzle. Many of the features of the phylum, for example the nephridia and the trochophore larva, are very suggestive of a close kinship with the Annelida. The mollusks, however, are not segmented. Some light has been shed on this problem of relationship by the discoveries of the Galathea Expedition. Deep sea dredging at depths of two to three miles off the coast of Mexico by this expedition brought to the surface a limpetlike mollusk, *Neopilina galatheae*. An ancestral form of this animal, called *Pilina*, became extinct 300 million years ago. *Neopilina* has five *pairs of auricles* which are associated with five *pairs of gills*, and there are also six *pairs of nephridia*. In addition, there are two pairs of gonads and eight pairs of shell muscles. These paired organs are strongly suggestive of segmentation, and thus the organism affords a possible "missing link" between annelids and mollusks.

Classification of the Mollusca

Phylum Mollusca Soft-bodied animals with a *reduced coelom*. A ventral foot, sometimes divided into "arms," and a mantle which secretes a shell are present. The shell may be reduced, coiled, or bivalved. A radula is present in the oral region of many of the animals.

CLASS I. AMPHINEURA. Flattened, bilaterally symmetrical mollusks with eight dorsal plates secreted by the mantle. The head is reduced. Example: chiton.

CLASS II. SCAPHOPODA. Marine mollusks which possess a straight tubular shell open at both ends. Example: elephant-tusk shell.

CLASS III. GASTROPODA. Marine, fresh-water, and air-dwelling forms which have a characteristic coiled shell; occasionally, shell absent. The mantle cavity is modified for a "lung" in some forms. Eyes and tentacles are present on a well-developed head. Examples: snail, slug.

CLASS IV. PELECYPODA. Marine and fresh-water bivalves with the head greatly reduced and the radula absent. Many of these animals are sedentary. Examples: clam, oyster.

CLASS V. CEPHALOPODA. Mollusks which have a well-developed head bearing eyes, tentacles, and "arms." The body is elongated in the dorsal-ventral plane in some forms; the shell is frequently reduced or absent, and sometimes only a relatively small "pen" is present. Examples: squid, pearly nautilus, octopus.

REFERENCES

BRUUN, ANTON F., "Animals of the Abyss," *Scientific American, 197,* May 1957.

GALTSOFF, PAUL S., "The American Oyster," *Fishery Bulletin of the Fish and Wildlife Service, 64,* Washington, 1964.

GLASS, BENTLEY, "New Missing Link Discovered," *Science, 126,* No. 3265, 1957.

GRAVE, B. H., "Natural History of the Shipworm, Teredo navalis, at Woods Hole, Mass.," *Biological Bulletin, 55,* 1928, pp. 260–282.

HARMER, S. F., and A. E. SHIPLEY (Eds.), "Mollusca", *Cambridge Natural History,* Vol. 3, pp. 1–459. The Macmillan Company, New York, 1895.

LANKESTER, RAY (Ed.), *Treatise on Zoology,* Part 5, pp. 1–343. Adam and Charles Black, London, 1906.

MACGINTIE, G. E., and N. MACGINTIE, *Natural History of Marine Animals,* pp. 329–401. McGraw-Hill Book Company, New York, 1949.

SCHEER, B. T., *Comparative Physiology,* pp. 159–232. John Wiley and Sons, New York, 1948.

WARD, H. B., and G. C. WHIPPLE, *Freshwater Biology,* pp. 957–1020. John Wiley and Sons, New York, 1918.

WILBUR, KARL M., and C. M. YONGE, *Physiology of Mollusca.* Academic Press, New York, 1964.

YOUNG, J. Z., "The Functioning of the Giant Nerve Fibers of the Squid." *Journal of Experimental Biology,* 15, 1938, pp. 170–185.

15

A Biological

Success Story

Phylum

Arthropoda

●

The animal groups which we judge to have obtained the greatest biological
success are those which have the largest number of species and of individuals
occupying the widest stretches of territories, or the greatest variety of habitat,
consuming the largest amount and kinds of food, and most capable of defending
themselves against their enemies.—Buchsbaum, Animals Without Backbones,
1948

Any animals which directly or indirectly affect the pocketbook of man are
certain to arouse his interest, and for this reason the members of the phylum
Arthropoda have been a vital concern of his for many decades. The construction of a balance sheet of the activities of the arthropods proves that they
contribute to both the misery and comfort of the human race. The debit
side of the account contains such items as the transmission of diseases to man
and his domestic animals, and the destruction of buildings, crops, and stored
foods. These destructive activities cost millions of dollars annually. Minor
annoyances also must be considered: the ants which invade our picnics and
kitchens, the mosquitoes which disturb our fishing trips, and the flies which
hover about the dining-room table add considerably to man's discomfort.

On the other hand, the arthropods have a multitude of creditable activities.
The pollination of many plants is dependent upon insects; shrimps and lobsters are seafood delicacies; and minute aquatic arthropods are a major source
of food for fishes, which in turn are eaten by man. Arthropod scavengers eat
decaying organic matter, and thus contaminating materials which otherwise
would soon make the earth uninhabitable are converted to usable materials.
By-products of the activities of insects, such as silk, beeswax, honey, dyes, and
shellac, are valued in millions of dollars annually and compensate for crop destruction. Finally, many of the arthropods are important in biological research.

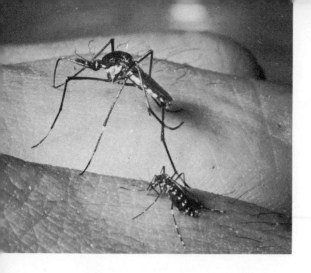

Figure 15.1. The arthropods constitute a serious challenge to man's victory over other animals. Fleas carry bubonic plague, lice carry typhus, and both have irritating and painful bites. Arthropods, however, often destroy each other. The giant cannibal mosquito shown in the figure is one example; it attacks other, often deadly, mosquitoes. (Courtesy Hawaii Department of Health; photo by Timio Funise.)

Important diseases which attack man—such as the plague, typhus, yellow fever, malaria, elephantiasis, and African sleeping sickness—are transmitted by insect carriers, or *vectors*. The control of insect vectors is a major problem, because large areas of the world are almost uninhabitable, or at best are almost unbearable for mankind, as a result of diseases carried by these arthropods. It has been estimated that at least 10 per cent of the crops grown every year are eaten by insects, and the growing plants as well as stored crops are attacked. Plagues of locusts (grasshoppers) are spoken of in the Bible, and in modern times similar plagues have destroyed crops in the western United States and devastated areas of Asia. These invasions furnish impressive illustrations of the damage which can be done by a single group of insects. Marine vessels, particularly those built of wood, suffer from the growth of barnacles, which damages the hulls of the ships and slows their passage through the water. Insects such as termites can attack and completely ruin wooden buildings, not even sparing libraries, where they devour the pages of books. Telephone poles in many tropical regions must be made of metal, because wooden poles are quickly eaten by the termites. This activity is pleasantly described in the following verse:*

> The primal termite knocked on wood,
> Tasted it and found it good.
> That is why your Cousin May
> Fell through the parlor floor today.—Ogden Nash

The pollination of plants often is wholly dependent upon bees or other insects, which carry pollen from plant to plant and make possible cross-fertilization. Darwin posed an interesting hypothesis of the relationship between the village clover crop and the number of old maids in the village. He pointed out that

---

*"The Termite," copyright 1942 by the Curtis Publishing Company.

(a)   (b)

Figure 15.2. The variation among arthropods is all the more striking because of their many common external characteristics. The caterpillar and the scorpion, shown here, each have a chitinous exoskeleton. Their segments show an obvious specialization, as do their jointed appendages. [(a) Courtesy Clarence Flaten; (b) courtesy Robert C. Hermes.]

old maids kept cats, cats ate mice; and since the mice destroyed the nests of bees, the number of bees was directly proportional to the number of cats and inversely proportional to the number of mice. The bees pollinate the clover, and the size of the clover crop, therefore, would be related to the number of old maids in the village. This is an interesting, although theoretical, example of a biological interrelationship. Arthropoda are valuable for *biological control;* that is, some arthropods destroy others. The locusts periodically increase to fantastic numbers, and it is almost impossible to stop their cross-country migration. Yet, even without the intervention of man, they die in great numbers and almost completely disappear. This destruction of the locusts is due to the parasites which attack them, parasites in the form of the larvae of other arthropods. The important action of arthropods as *scavengers* was mentioned. The return to the soil of organic waste material by the scavengers protects man from the dire consequences of organic decay. The use of insects in *scientific research* in recent years has become extremely important. We will see later that the knowledge of the basic details of the mechanism of inheritance is a result of studies which have been made on the fruit fly, *Drosophila.* Meal worms, which are larval insects and not true worms, have been used in *population studies.* The growth of meal worms in the laboratory has made it possible to analyze their food requirements and their relationship to each other and also to determine the number of organisms that can live in a limited area. These data have application to the growth of populations of many other organisms, including human populations. Seemingly remote fields such as aviation have been aided considerably by the study of the *flight mechanisms* of the insects.

There are approximately 1,000,000 described species of animals in the world today, and of those nearly 750,000 are species of Arthropoda. There can be little doubt that the arthropods compete for the position of being the dominant group on earth today. The only phyla able to challenge them in total numbers are the Protozoa and the Nemathelminthes. There are, however,

Figure 15.3.   The tarantula and the crab have many common external features.   The habits of an arthropod can be described by a study of the specialization of its appendages.   The legs of the spider and the crab, for example, look alike superficially but have important differences of structure and use. (Courtesy National Audubon Society.)   [(a) Photo by Robert C. Hermes; (b) photo by Allan D. Cruickshank.]

only a few thousand described species of protozoans, chiefly because they have not been investigated so intensively as have the arthropods.   It is probable that a detailed study will disclose as many species of Protozoa as there are species of Arthropoda, and it was noted that there are probably 500,000 kinds of nematodes.   Even should other phyla eventually prove to contain as many different species, the arthropods would retain a dominant position because of their aggressive activities.   Man clearly is confronted with a peculiar problem with respect to the Arthropoda: it is difficult for him to live with them, and yet the human race probably could not survive more than five years without them!

At least 12 classes of Arthropoda are commonly recognized, but several of these classes consist of members which are few in number and of interest primarily to the professional zoologist because they show certain structural relationships.   Only five classes of Arthropoda will be considered here.   These classes are well known to everyone, but we will select only two of the five classes, the Crustacea and the Insecta, for detailed study.   The reason for this choice is that the Crustacea are aquatic forms and demonstrate certain adaptations which differ from those of the air-dwelling Insecta.   The crayfish and the grasshopper will illustrate the respective classes, and a comprehension of the features of these animals will enable us to understand the basic structures of all the arthropods.   We will discuss major orders of insects briefly at the close of this chapter.

The classes of modern arthropods are so highly specialized that they offer little in the way of clues to the ancestry of the phylum.   A further complication is the fact that there are no larval forms comparable to those of the annelids and the mollusks to aid in the solution of this problem.   The obvious segmentation of the arthropods suggests, of course, a possible relationship with the annelids.   This is supplemented by the presence of appendages on each segment and by a similar ventral ladder-type nervous system in both phyla. Even though a trochophore larva is not present, the development of the mesoderm, segments, and coelom in the arthropod embryo is comparable to that in the trochophore. The bands of mesoderm are formed from special mesodermal cells delimited in the early "gastrula" stage (p. 210). The coelom is formed by a splitting of these mesodermal bands, and the prostomial region is not segmented.

These similarities have focused attention on a peculiar wormlike animal, *Peripatus*, because this rare organism has features in common with both the annelids and the arthropods. Its annelid characteristics include a thin cuticle which covers the body, paired and segmentally arranged nephridia, a dorsal tubular blood vessel, and ciliated reproductive organs. Its arthropod features are *claws* on the paired appendages, *tracheal tubes* for respiration, and irregular blood spaces which correspond to the *hemocoel*. Much has been said concerning the possibility that *Peripatus* represents a "missing link" between the annelids and the arthropods. This animal, however, is highly specialized and possesses many distinct characteristics of its own. It has no external body segmentation; a ventral nerve cord is present, but it is different from that of either the annelids or the arthropods; the head has only three segments; and the legs are ringed rather than jointed. Its relationship now appears to be that of a primitive animal which evolved from the same ancestral stock that gave rise to both the annelids and the arthropods. Fossil records indicate the *Peripatus* once was widespread in its distribution and that the genus has been in existence for millions of years. *Peripatus* therefore offers a problem in classification which probably is best solved by placing this unusual group of animals in a phylum of its own, phylum Onychophora.

It has been noted that the body plan of the arthropods has many features in common with that of the annelids. The arthropods, however, have exploited to a greater degree the structural possibilities of a cuticle and of segmentation.

Figure 15.4   Peripatus looks much like a worm, with its tubular body and paired, segmentally arranged ringed legs. Any similarity between this animal and a comedian in black-face make-up is purely coincidental. (Courtesy Ward's Natural Science Establishment, Inc.)

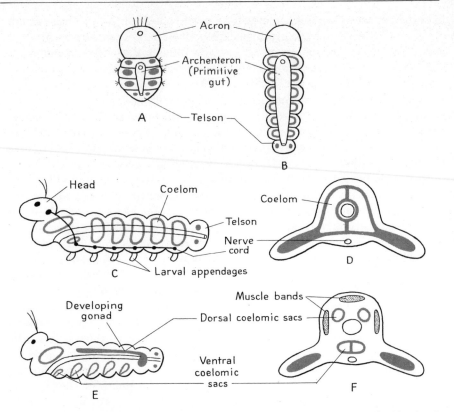

Figure 15.5.   The embryonic development of arthropods has been compared with what is known about the trochophore larva.   The result suggests that ancestral forms must have developed according to the patterns outlined in the diagram above.

The cuticle is formed of plates of material which are thinned to form external joints at the margin of each segment.   Similar joints are also present in the appendages.   A literal translation of the name *Arthropoda* is "jointed legs." These jointed legs can be distinguished easily from those of the vertebrates (the group to which man belongs) by the fact that the joints are external.   Primitive arthropods and embryonic stages of the more highly specialized arthropods have body segments which are alike and possess similar paired appendages. The appendages are modified as the larval form of the arthropod develops, and there is fusion of the body segments.   This union is accompanied by fusion of internal organs, with the result that the adult arthropod may differ radically in its external and internal anatomy from the primitive or the larval forms. The exact fate of the segments is uncertain, and this is especially true of those segments which constitute the head region of the adult arthropod.   The similarities between the embryonic stages of the Arthropoda and the embryonic stages

of certain annelids can serve as a basis for analyzing the structural relationships.
The early larva has primary segments and secondary segments, in both of which coelomic pouches are developed. At the anterior end of the animal is the *acron*, which is nonsegmented, and at the posterior end is the *telson*, a region at which new segments are formed. A pair of appendages develops on each segment. The *acron* is the region on which a pair of *first antennae* and the *eyes* will be formed. This acron, which corresponds to the acron of the trochophore, should be considered as a nonsegmented, prostomial portion of the arthropod body. The first antennae and the compound eye of the crayfish, for example, develop from this region.

It is also important to consider in greater detail the development of the cuticle. Typically, the cuticle is a thick protective layer about the entire animal, secreted by the epithelium of the body surface. The cuticle serves for the attachment of the muscles and as a protective armor plate over the animal, and is, therefore, an exoskeleton. A characteristic chemical substance, *chitin*, commonly found in the arthropod cuticle is a complex nitrogenous sugar $(C_{30}H_{50}N_4O_{19})$ which is very tough and is resistant to all but very strong chemical substances. Chitin, therefore, is the tough, flexible substance in the cuticle which provides support and chemical protection for the animal. The cuticle often is hardened by the calcium salts deposited in it, and an examination of the body region in which the hardened cuticle is found shows that there are typically three layers. The outermost layer is a thin *waxy* covering, and immediately below it is a *hardened* layer in which the salts are deposited. A third, *flexible* layer is adjacent to the epithelial cells of the epidermis. The hardened layer is lacking at the joint, and the flexible layer is thin. This thinning of the cuticle and the absence of the hardened layer permit flexibility at the joint. The situation is analogous to a leather hinge on a door. The muscle attachments are on the inner surface of the cuticle. It is the pull exerted across the joint by opposing sets of muscles,

Figure 15.6. The structure of the cuticle in cross section.

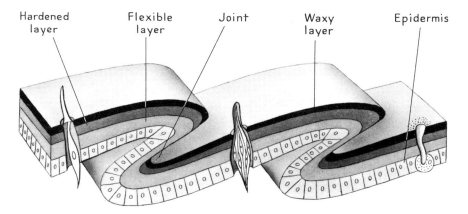

Hardened layer   Flexible layer   Joint   Waxy layer   Epidermis

therefore, which flexes and extends an appendage or bends and straightens the body segments.

The development of an elaborate musculature in arthropods is in part responsible for the breakdown of the coelomic sacs (Figure 15.5). The coelomic sacs are compressed into the dorsal and ventral regions of the animal. The dorsal remnants of the coelom develop into the gonads, and the reduced ventral coelomic sacs develop into the excretory organs of some of the arthropods. Large, irregular body spaces are created by the ingrowth of the muscles and the distintegration of the coelomic walls. These irregular spaces subsequently become filled with blood and transform into a *hemocoel*. This hemocoel is one of the characteristic features of the Arthropoda, and technically, it would be considered the original blastocoel.

The Crayfish

Body form

The exoskeleton of the crayfish (except at the time of molting) is composed of a thick, hardened cuticle, and the body is divided into two major parts: the *cephalothorax* (head-chest), and the *abdomen*. The cephalothorax results from a fusion of the head and thoracic regions, and these are approximately delimited by a transverse depression on the dorsal surface, the *cervical groove*. External segmentation is not obvious in the cephalothorax but can be determined by the location of the appendages. The abdominal region of the animal, however, is divided into six distinct segments.

A striking feature of the crayfish is the manner in which the *paired appendages* are modified to perform specific tasks. The abdominal appendages are comparable with the *basic*, or *primitive*, *type* from which the specialized appendages have developed. These appendages are known as *swimmerets* and are said to be *biramous* because they have a basal section, the *protopodite*, and two branches, the *rami*, which extend from the basal unit. The outside (lateral) branch is the *exopodite;* the inner (medial) branch is the *endopodite*. The head and thoracic appendages of the crayfish have been derived from the biramous type by loss of parts and by the addition of processes or plates. The accomplishment of division of labor by modification of the appendage is a notable example of the way in which the advantages of segmentation have been utilized by the arthropods.

The most anterior of the paired appendages in the crayfish are the *first antennae*, or *antennules*, and the stalked, *compound eyes*. These appendages are lateral to an anterior extension of the cephalothorax known as the *rostrum*, and both the first antennae and the compound eyes develop from the prostomial region, or acron. They probably should not be considered true segmental appendages, because the prostomium is a nonsegmented portion of the body. The two filaments on each first antenna do not represent the exopodite and the

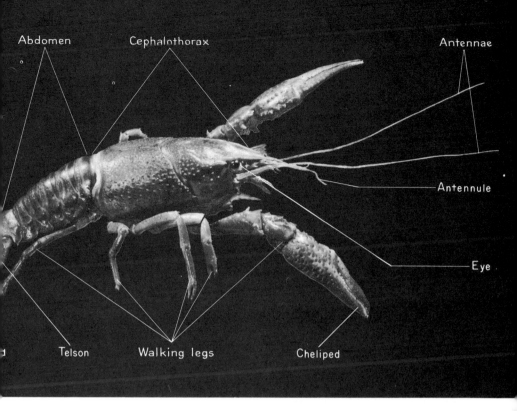

Abdomen Cephalothorax Antennae

Antennule

Eye

Telson Walking legs Cheliped

Figure 15.7.   The crayfish illustrates the typical body structures of the class Crustacea.   (Courtesy Clarence Flaten.)

endopodite, since there is only a single *filament* when the antenna first forms, the branched condition developing later.   Posterior to the eyes are the *second antennae*.   These have a long *filament* and a broad *basal plate*.   The basal plate of the second antenna is the exopodite and the long filament is the endopodite. The second antenna is a sensory organ; and in addition, the broad basal exopodite serves as a elevator, or flow surface, to determine the angle of dive when the animals are swimming.   Posterior to the second antennae are three pairs of modified head appendages which are associated with the feeding mechanism of the crayfish.   These appendages are modified to form jaws and will be considered in detail when we discuss nutrition of the crayfish.

The thoracic region of the crayfish can be identified by the points of attachment of the *five pairs of walking legs*.   The first pair is developed into the very large *pincers*, or *chelipeds*.   The second and third pairs of walking legs also develop small pincers at their ends, but the fourth and fifth pairs terminate in a simple spinelike process.   Gills are attached to the walking legs; and in addition, these have a *protective flap* which projects from the leg, separating and partially covering the gills.   It is of considerable interest to note that *fracture lines* are present at the bases of the walking legs, and that the legs break easily at these

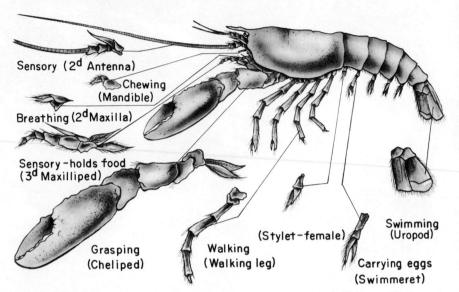

Sensory (2ᵈ Antenna)

Chewing (Mandible)

Breathing (2ᵈMaxilla)

Sensory – holds food (3ᵈ Maxilliped)

Grasping (Cheliped)

Walking (Walking leg)

(Stylet – female)

Swimming (Uropod)

Carrying eggs (Swimmeret)

Figure 15.8.   This drawing of the crayfish and its appendages shows the modifications for special functions.

points.   This feature enables the animal to detach a leg voluntarily when the leg is attacked and either injured or held captive.   The loss of appendages in this manner is known as *autotomy,* and it is an important safety device.   When a leg is detached, the loss of blood is minimized by the action of a valve at the fracture point.   New legs can be developed to replace those which have been lost by autotomy.

The abdominal appendages are the *swimmerets.*   The first and second pairs of swimmerets in the male are enlarged and stiffened and are used in transferring sperm to the female.   The first pair of swimmerets of the female is usually much reduced and, in some species, may be absent.   The remaining swimmerets in the male and in the female, with the exception of the sixth, are typical biramous appendages.   The sixth swimmerets, however, have the exopodite and endopodite greatly expanded to form the *uropod,* a broad, platelike structure.   These fanlike uropods, together with the terminal *telson,* constitute a large posterior rudder and swimming appendage for the crayfish.   The animal can dart backward rapidly by forceful contraction of the abdominal muscles, which produces a sweeping action by the uropods and the telson.   The typical backward locomotion is the origin of the common expression "to crawfish."

Nutrition

The first three pairs of thoracic appendages and the last three pairs of head appendages are modified to form jaws, and these constitute the feeding mechanism.   They overlap in such a fashion that the largest, most posterior pair of

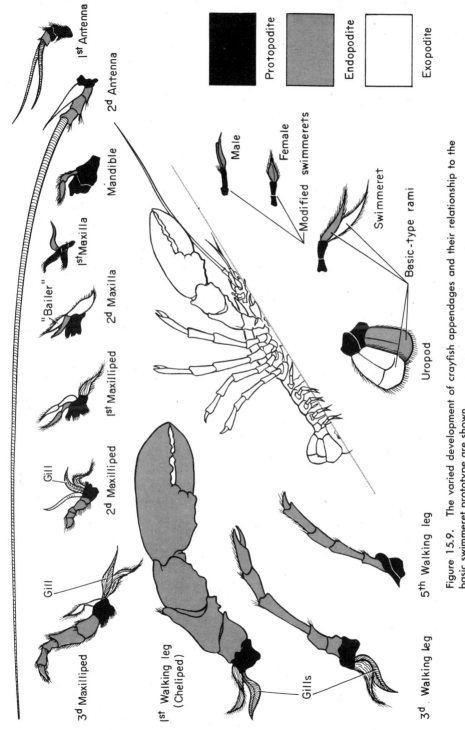

1st Antenna

2d Antenna

Mandible

1st Maxilla

2d Maxilla

1st Maxilliped

2d Maxilliped

3d Maxilliped

"Bailer"

Gill

Gill

1st Walking leg
(Cheliped)

Gills

3d Walking leg

5th Walking leg

Male

Female

Modified swimmerets

Swimmeret

Basic-type rami

Uropod

Protopodite

Endopodite

Exopodite

Figure 15.9.   The varied development of crayfish appendages and their relationship to the basic swimmeret prototype are shown.

thoracic appendages, the *third maxillipeds*, are the first to be observed. These overlie the remaining mouth parts and serve as a protective covering. The third maxillipeds grasp and tear the food material and pass it to the *second maxillipeds*, which are similar to the third, but are smaller and have a smaller endopodite. Gills are attached to the third and to the second maxillipeds, although a large *gill flap* is present on the latter. The *first maxillipeds* are also similar but are the smallest of the three pairs. The remaining three jaws are the modified head appendages, the most posterior (external) of these being the *second maxillae*, which overlie the smaller *first maxillae*. The maxillae aid in pushing the food into the region of the *mouth*, and to the heavy *mandibles*, or jaws, which grind the food. The second maxilla also possesses a special flap, the *scaphognathite*, a thin indented plate which serves as a bailer to circulate the water in the respiratory space. This structure is primarily a modified exopodite. The first maxilla is closely pressed against the mandible and has lost its exopodite. The mandible has a small palp which is a modified endopodite. The heavy, jawlike portion of the mandible probably represents a protopodite, and the exopodite is absent. The mandibles of the crayfish hold the food material in place for the tearing action of the third maxillipeds and crush it before putting it into the mouth. The mandibles in some of the larger crustacea, such as the lobsters, also serve for chewing the food.

The digestive tract of the crayfish consists of three parts (Figure 15.10). The first part is the *fore-gut*, which is subdivided into an esophagus, a cardiac stomach, and a pyloric stomach. The second part is the *mid-gut*, which is composed primarily of a complex digestive gland, or "liver," and a small portion of the pyloric stomach. The third part is the *hind-gut*, consisting of the intestine and the rectum. The epithelium which lines the fore-gut and the hind-gut is derived from the ectoderm of the embryo. It is interesting that there is a lining of cuticle in both the fore-gut and the hind-gut, and that this lining is shed at each molt.

The mouth opens into the short *esophagus*, which continues vertically to open into the floor of the *cardiac stomach*. The opening between the esophagus and the cardiac stomach is guarded by a series of *spines*, or *setae*, which prevent food from being regurgitated. The wall of the cardiac portion of the stomach secretes structures of considerable interest, the *gastroliths*, or stomach stones. These are calcareous and are covered by a cuticle, but during molting the cuticle is removed. The calcium salts stored in the gastroliths are absorbed at this time and probably are used for the hardening of certain parts of the newly formed exoskeleton and appendages. The cardiac stomach also contains *three teeth*, of which one is dorsal and two are lateral. These constitute the *gastric mill*. A complex arrangement of muscles operates these teeth, and an effective chewing of food material is accomplished. A marked constriction exists between the cardiac stomach and the next region of the alimentary canal, the *pyloric stomach*. A complex system of folds in the lining of the cardiac stomach results in the formation of a system of channels, and food material must be thoroughly ground into very small particles before it can be passed through the channels and the constriction into the pyloric stomach.

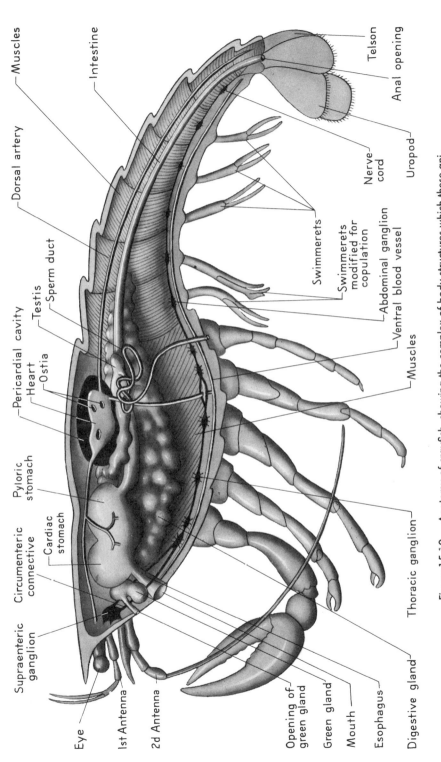

Muscles

Intestine

Dorsal artery

Sperm duct

Pericardial cavity

Testis

Heart

Ostia

Pyloric
stomach

Cardiac
stomach

Circumenteric
connective

Supraenteric
ganglion

Eye

1st Antenna

2d Antenna

Opening of
green gland

Green gland

Mouth

Esophagus

Digestive gland

Thoracic ganglion

Muscles

Ventral blood vessel

Abdominal ganglion

Swimmerets
modified for
copulation

Swimmerets

Nerve
cord

Uropod

Anal opening

Telson

Figure 15.10. Anatomy of crayfish, showing the complex of body structures which these animals have developed.

Figure 15.11. The barnacle, though its shell gives it a mollusklike appearance, is really a highly modified crustacean. Note the typically crustacean appendages of this barnacle: chitinous, jointed, bristled, and two-branched. They sweep small animals and organic particles into the barnacle's mouth. (Courtesy American Museum of Natural History.)

A large *digestive gland* is present near the pyloric stomach. This gland is divided into two parts and develops from the mid-gut. It is composed of a series of tubules which have a tremendous surface area and is the most important gland of the alimentary canal of the crayfish. It secretes digestive enzymes which flow through the complex channels into the pyloric and cardiac stomachs. The gland absorbs food from the mid-gut, and this material is digested within the gland itself. Food can be stored in the cells of the tubules of the digestive gland, and practically all the absorption of food materials is done by the walls of these tubules. The exact limits of the mid-gut are difficult to determine without examining the alimentary canal under a microscope, because part of the pyloric stomach is actually mid-gut and continuous with the intestine. The intestine, or hind-gut, extends to the posterior end of the animal, where it enlarges into a rectum before opening through the anus on the ventral surface of the telson.

The menu of the crayfish includes both plants and animals, and much of the food is scraped from the bottom. Relatively large animals are fragmented into small particles by the tearing action of the third maxillipeds. A full complement of digestive enzymes has been demonstrated for the crayfish and other crustaceans. The enzymes for splitting proteins, fats, and carbohydrates are apparently adequate in amount for any nutritional needs of the organism. Much of the digested food material may be stored in the form of glycogen, and this carbohydrate is readily mobilized when needed for emergency nutrition.

Respiration

The crayfish, an aquatic animal, possesses a well-developed set of gills. These lie in the *gill chamber* in the thoracic region, which is formed as a result of a lateral growth of the *carapace*, the part of the exoskeleton which covers the back, to form a gill cover, the *branchiostegite*. The gill chamber is open at both front and rear, but on the ventral surface is closed effectively by the thoracic appendages. The water which enters the gill chamber, therefore, must enter from either the anterior or the posterior opening. The plumelike filamentous gills are outgrowths of the body surface and are arranged in three layers. The outermost gills, the *podobranchiae*, are attached at the base of the legs; the middle gills, the *arthrobranchiae*, are fastened at the joint where the leg attaches to the body; and the innermost gills, the *pleurobranchiae*, arise from the body wall. The number of pairs of gills in the crayfish genus *Astacus* is approximately 20, but there is considerable variation in the different crayfishes, especially in the number of pleurobranchiae present. The pleurobranchiae are absent in the genus *Cambarus*, and there is a double row of arthrobranchiae.

Effective functioning of the gills in respiration is made possible by a constant flow of water over their surfaces. The movement of water is caused by action of the bailers, or *scaphognathites*, the large flat plates on the second maxillae. Each bailer has a sweeping action which forces the water through the gill chambers from posterior to anterior. Periodically the bailers reverse their beat, so that the water current moves from anterior to posterior. Small particles of debris which accumulate on the surfaces of the gills are removed by this reversal of flow, and the gills are thus kept clean.

Figure 15.12.   The principal structures of the crayfish are shown in cross section.

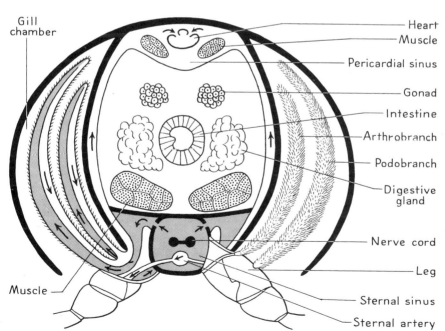

Gill chamber

Heart

Muscle

Pericardial sinus

Gonad

Intestine

Arthrobranch

Podobranch

Digestive gland

Nerve cord

Leg

Muscle

Sternal sinus

Sternal artery

The blood of the crayfish has a bluish or blue-green color. This color is due to the respiratory pigment hemocyanin, which is a copper-protein compound. The gills have very thin walls, which separate the blood from the surrounding water and permit the diffusion of oxygen and carbon dioxide. The blood enters the gills from a large ventral sinus, and the hemocyanin, like hemoglobin, forms a loose chemical combination with oxygen to serve as an oxygen carrier. Oxygen is also dissolved in the fluid as a free substance. The blood is returned from the gills through irregular channels to the pericardial sinus and thence into the heart. The oxygen-carrying capacity of the blood is about half that of the squid or the octopus, but the crayfish is able to remove oxygen from the water very efficiently. Approximately 60 to 70 per cent of the oxygen in the water flowing over the gills can be taken up by the crayfish. It has been shown that the rate of beat of the bailer is controlled by a variety of environmental conditions; it increases with a rise in temperature or of carbon dioxide concentration, and also when only small amounts of oxygen are present in the surrounding water.

Excretion

The primary structural unit of the excretory system of the crayfish is a pair of antennary, *green glands.* These are located slightly anterior and ventral to the stomach and open by ducts at the bases of the second antennae. These glands are the modified ventral coelomic pouches spoken of in describing the arthropod coelom (pp. 260, 262). The green glands consist of a ventral glandular region and a dorsal thin-walled, saclike bladder. The glandular portion of the green gland is well supplied with blood vessels, and serves both for the elimination of waste materials and for the regulation of water balance. The digestive gland is also significant as an excretory organ because it has the ability to secrete urea, uric acid, and ammonia. Approximately 60 per cent of the nitrogenous waste is ammonia, 11 per cent urea, and 10 per cent amino acids. The gills also serve to eliminate carbon dioxide and, in addition, control the passage of the ions of certain salts. The gills, therefore, are influential in main-

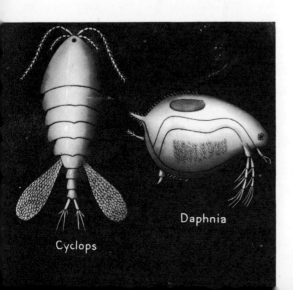

Cyclops

Daphnia

Figure 15.13. These minute, fresh-water crustaceans abound in arctic oceans as well as in fresh-water ponds and lakes. They are the basic food of fishes and are best known as water fleas.

taining proper osmotic balance.   It is probable that some excretion in the cray-fish is accomplished by the deposition of materials in the cuticle.

Reproduction

The sexes in the crayfish are separate, and the gonads are located dorsally between the alimentary canal and the pericardial sinus.   Both the testes and ovaries are Y-shaped, with the arms of the Y extending forward; the median, unpaired portion of the gonad extends posteriorly.   The thin-walled, transparent oviducts are paired and arise in the region of the pericardial sinus, whence they extend ventrally to the bases of the third walking legs.   The females of some species possess a ring-shaped *seminal receptacle*, which is located between the bases of the fourth and fifth pair of walking legs.   This receptacle serves to hold the sperm which are deposited by the male at copulation.

The reproductive system of the male is similar to that of the female, in that the sperm ducts arise in the region of the pericardial sinus and extend downward to the legs.   The openings of the sperm ducts, however, are on the bases of the fifth walking legs.   The sperm duct, in contrast to the oviduct, has a thick wall which is also glandular.   The glandular portion secretes a sticky material which surrounds the sperm and forms a capsulelike covering.

At the time of mating, the male holds the female on her back by means of the pincers and the walking legs.   The sperm, as they issue from the sperm ducts, move along a groove in the modified copulatory swimmerets and are surrounded by the gelatinous secretion of the sperm duct.   The sperm are deposited in the seminal receptacle, if there is one present in the female, and the sticky secretion from the sperm duct hardens to form a sperm plug.   The sperm are sometimes deposited in packets comparable to those which we noted in the squid.   Egg-laying occurs from one to several weeks after mating, but the sperm in the meantime remain alive and are protected by the gelatinous covering.   The sperm are released as the eggs are laid, but the exact mechanism involved in freeing the sperm from their protective coating is not known.   The emerging eggs are moved along the abdomen and are attached to the swimmerets, where embryonic development takes place.   One of the surprising features of reproduction in the crayfish is the fact that the sperm may remain alive for several months, or even for years.   This unusual situation is only rarely encountered in some other arthropods.

Coordination

We remarked previously that there is a striking similarity between the nervous system of the arthropods and of the annelids.   The crayfish nervous system is typical of that of many of the arthropods, because it is a ventral-ladder type.   The brain is a *supraenteric ganglion* and is connected to the *subenteric ganglion* by the *circumenteric connections* which encircle the anterior part of the alimentary canal.   Posterior to the fused subenteric ganglia are the *segmental ganglia* in the remaining segments of the body of the crayfish. The individual ganglia of segments 2 through 6 are fused into a single large ganglion. The remaining thoracic ganglia remain relatively distinct, and the six abdominal ganglia are not fused. The "ladder" condition of the nervous system is difficult to ascertain in the adult animal. The circumenteric connectives and the connectives which encircle the sternal artery are the only visible remnants in the adult of the paired nerve cords. Numerous nerves from the brain and nerve cord extend to the muscles and sense organs. *Giant fibers* which conduct impulses rapidly are also present in the nerve cord. Rapid coordination of muscle contractions involved in flexing or bending the abdomen is made possible by the speedy transmission of messages along the giant fibers.

The supraenteric ganglion is a *sensory ganglion* and receives nerve fibers from the sense organs in the head region: there are *antennary nerves* from the first antennae; *optic nerves* from the eyes, and in addition, nerve fibers are received from the second antennae and the green glands. The subenteric ganglion, however, is primarily a *motor ganglion*—that is, a center to relay messages to the tissues and organs. The nervous system of the crayfish functions more efficiently than that of the annelids. It is a more complex system, with a better integration of impulses. Damage to the supraenteric ganglion, or its removal, results in greater activity on the part of the animal; this is similar to the situation in the clamworm. The supraenteric ganglion, therefore, apparently acts as an inhibitory center.

The sense organs of the crayfish are remarkable and, as might be expected in such an active animal, are very efficient. The chief sense organs are the *eyes* and the *statocysts*. The eye is *compound*, consisting of about 2500 sensory units, the *ommatidia*. It is an efficient organ, being both light-sensitive and image-forming. The eye is not the only light-sensitive structure in the crayfish; there are scattered light-sensitive areas elsewhere. A crayfish which has been blinded experimentally can detect variations in light intensity. This is made possible by the presence of light receptors, particularly at the base of the tail. The statocysts are balancing organs located at the bases of the first antennae. Each small, saclike statocyst has a minute external opening, and there are many fine processes lining the sac. Sand grains are introduced through the opening of the sac and roll about upon the processes. As the animal changes its position, the sand grains are shifted slightly, touching different processes, with the result that different series of impulses are sent to the central nervous system. A *righting reflex* will follow which orients the animal with respect to gravitational pull. A classic experiment was performed by Kreidl, who placed newly molted crayfishes in distilled water in an aquarium. Since the crayfish at the time of molting sheds the lining of the statocysts as well as the sand grains contained in the statocysts, new sand grains are required to replace those lost. Sand grains were not available to the experimental animals, but Kreidl had placed small iron filings in the aquarium. These filings were introduced into the statocysts by the crayfish, simply by scraping the antennae along the bottom of the tank. Thus, the filings substituted for the sand in the statocysts. It was then pos-

Light adapted   Dark adapted

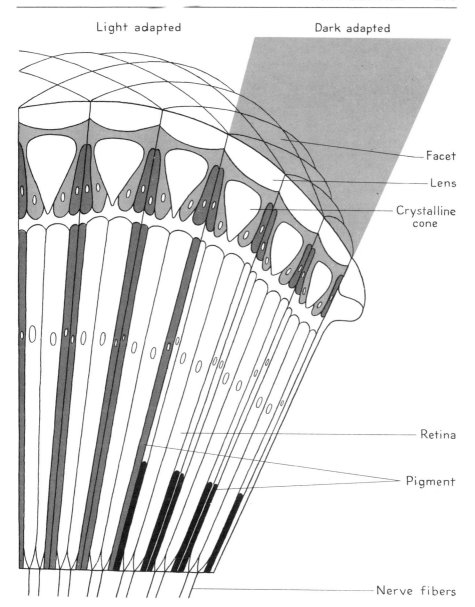

Facet

Lens

Crystalline cone

Retina

Pigment

Nerve fibers

Figure 15.14.   The compound eye is composed of many units, the ommatidia, six of which are shown in detail here.   The three on the right are shown as adapted to dim light.

sible, by drawing a magnet around the animal, to move the filings about within the statocysts, causing the animal to attempt to orient itself to the pressure of the filings.   This experiment works, however, only when the crayfish has been blinded, indicating that vision also plays an important role in orientation.

There are also many diffuse sensory structures associated with the exoskeleton of the crayfish. Some of these are relatively simple *setae*, small processes with a thin covering of exoskeleton; these respond to touch. *Chemoreceptors* are located on the mouth parts and on the branches of the first antennae. Undoubtedly special receptors are present for the determination of the degree of muscle contraction, but these receptors have not been identified structurally.

The Grasshopper

Only a few classes of animals have been able to surmount the difficulties of living in an air environment rather than in water. The most successful groups are the reptiles, the birds, and the mammals among the vertebrates, and the Arachnoidea and Insecta among the arthropods. Either of these may be used to illustrate the modifications necessary to enable an arthropod to live in an air environment. The Arachnoidea, however, have several features in common with the Crustacea just described; so to avoid repetition the Insecta will be considered as the representative group. The insects are so highly specialized, however, that it is imperative to use a relatively generalized animal to illustrate their basic architecture and functions. The *grasshopper* meets this requirement rather well, although it must be emphasized that it too has certain specialized features. The grasshopper also is relatively large, in contrast to most insects, which are small.

Body form

The parts of the insect body are well delineated in this arthropod. There are three body divisions: the head, thorax, and abdomen. Although the head is segmented, this segmentation is obscured in the adult and can be studied only with difficulty in the embryonic stages. The thorax is distinctly marked off from the head and abdomen by constrictions and is easily identified by the presence of *three pairs of legs* and *two pairs of wings*. The location of each of the three thoracic segments can be determined, because one pair of legs arises from each, and the wings are located on the second and third segments. The wingless first thoracic segment has a characteristic "collar" on the dorsal surface, which extends posteriorly over part of the second segment. The abdomen of an adult insect does not have paired segmental appendages; the grasshopper is typical in this respect, except for the presence of the terminal appendages used in reproduction. The first abdominal segment is fused with the thorax, but it can be identified by the *tympanic membrane* of the auditory organ, to be seen on each side. The three posterior segments are fused to form the external genital apparatus.

Several obvious specializations of the grasshopper are evident externally. The two pairs of wings are not alike. The first pair is leathery and is not used in flying. The second pair of wings is fanlike and folds beneath the first pair

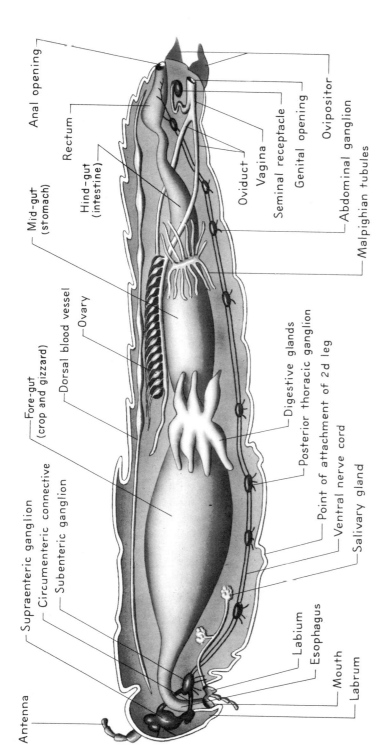

Antenna

Supraenteric ganglion
Circumenteric connective
Subenteric ganglion

Fore-gut
(crop and gizzard)

Dorsal blood vessel

Ovary

Mid-gut
(stomach)

Rectum

Anal opening

Hind-gut
(intestine)

Oviduct
Vagina
Seminal receptacle
Genital opening
Ovipositor
Abdominal ganglion
Malpighian tubules

Digestive glands
Posterior thoracic ganglion
Point of attachment of 2d leg
Ventral nerve cord
Salivary gland

Labium
Esophagus
Mouth
Labrum

Figure 15.15. The basic anatomy of the female grasshopper is shown in longitudinal section in the illustration above. The structures are typical of the class Insecta, although the grasshopper does have certain specialized features, for example the large jumping legs and the heavy membranous first pair of wings.

when at rest.   The first two pairs of legs are typical walking legs, but the third pair is greatly enlarged, and is especially efficient for jumping.

Nutrition

The grasshopper is herbivorous, and certain characteristic structural adaptations are correlated with its diet of plant food.   The mouth parts are of the *chewing* and *grinding* type, in contrast to the *sucking* type, which is to be seen in the bugs, moths, and mosquitoes.   The grasshopper head is composed primarily of the mouth parts and the muscles which are necessary to operate them. The mouth opening is bounded dorsally by a large, platelike upper lip, the *labrum;* ventrally by the smaller lower lip, the *labium;* and laterally by the heavy, powerful *mandibles.*   A second pair of jaws is located between the lower lip and the mandibles; these are the *maxillae.*   The maxillae are typical paired appendages and bear a striking superficial resemblance to some of the mouth parts of the crayfish.   Each has a flattened, platelike lobe and a medial spiny tooth and, in addition, possesses a sensory palp.   The palps on the maxillae and those on the lower lip are sensory structures for touch and taste.   Interposed in the middle of the mouth between the jaws is the "tongue" or *hypopharynx.*   The lower lip arises in the embryo as a pair of appendages, each with a pair of palps.   These appendages correspond to second maxillae but fuse in the adult to form the single lower lip.   The upper and lower lips hold the food while it is torn and chewed by the maxillae and the mandibles.

The alimentary canal in the grasshopper consists of a *fore-gut,* a *mid-gut,* and a *hind-gut.*   The fore-gut and the hind-gut are lined with cuticle, and little or no absorption of food occurs in either.   The mouth opens into a short *esophagus* (Figure 15.15), which is continuous with an enlarged *crop* used for temporary food storage, and in which digestion is begun.   The lining of the crop has ridges and spines which assist in the maceration and mixing of the food mass. A pair of *salivary glands* opens in the region of the lower lip, and the secretions of these glands serve to lubricate the food as it is ingested.   Digestive enzymes also are secreted by the salivary glands, but digestion is initiated in the crop. Posterior to the crop is the muscular *gizzard,* the walls of which are equipped with *teeth.*   The esophagus, crop, and gizzard constitute the fore-gut and are confined almost entirely to the thoracic region.   The *stomach,* which is separated from the gizzard by a constriction, is the mid-gut, and most of the digestion and absorption of food takes place in this region. There are six pairs of pouches, the *digestive glands,* at the junction of the gizzard and the stomach. One arm of each pouch extends anteriorly, the other posteriorly.   Large quantities of digestive enzymes are secreted by these glands.   The walls of the glands also absorb food, and therefore are comparable in their functions to the digestive glands of the crayfish.   The *intestine* is the hind-gut and makes up the remainder of the alimentary canal; it expands slightly, immediately anterior to the anus, to form the rectum.   The cuticular lining of the intestine is permeable to

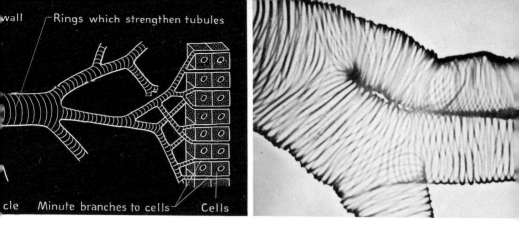

wall — Rings which strengthen tubules

cle — Minute branches to cells — Cells

Figure 15.16. The arrangement of an insect's tracheae is shown in (a), and (b) shows a section of the actual tracheae of a mosquito, greatly magnified. [(b) Courtesy Radio Corporation of America.]

water, and there is considerable absorption of water in the rectum from the undigested food residues. This is an important factor in the conservation of fluid, in the grasshopper as well as in other insects. These animals, therefore, are able to subsist for considerable periods of time with the minimum of water intake.

Respiration

The insects possess a system of *air tubes,* the *tracheae.* These tubes are invaginations of the body surface and ramify throughout the body. Most insects are oxybiotic, and the air tubes rather than the circulatory system are responsible for the distribution of oxygen to the cells. Paired openings, the *spiracles,* are located along the sides of the abdomen and on the thorax and lead into the tracheae. There are two thoracic spiracles and usually eight abdominal ones. The larger tracheal tubes are arranged in longitudinal and transverse trunks, and their walls are spirally thickened so that they remain open permanently. The spiracles, however, may open and close, and experimental work has demonstrated that the percentage of carbon dioxide in the inhaled air has a strong regulatory effect on the opening. As the carbon dioxide concentration increases, the spiracles open, and breathing movements of the abdomen are initiated. The spiracles do not close as long as the amount of carbon dioxide is as high as 20 per cent. The tracheae branch repeatedly to produce very fine *air capillaries,* only a few microns in diameter. These air capillaries penetrate among the cells and deliver oxygen directly. They perform the function in insect respiration which is usually accomplished by blood capillaries in many other organisms. The blood in most insects, therefore, is of little importance in respiration.

Excretion

The excretory processes of the insects are closely correlated with water balance, for it is difficult for any animal living in the air to avoid dehydration. The chief excretory structures are the *Malpighian tubules,* which open into the gut at the junction of the stomach and intestine. The tubules end blindly in the *hemocoel* and vary in number and length. The total surface area of the Malpighian tubules is relatively large; when few tubules are present they are long, but when tubules are short they are usually numerous. Nitrogen waste compounds are secreted as uric acid into the end of the tubule farthest from the alimentary canal, and water is reabsorbed as the secretion moves down the tubule. The uric acid, as a result of the removal of water, is precipitated in a solid or semisolid state and enters the intestine to mix with the undigested food material. This process enables the grasshopper to excrete nitrogenous waste with the minimum loss of water and is another important factor favoring the retention of water. Traces of ammonia and urea are also found in the excreta of insects.

Some insects, especially aquatic forms and bloodsuckers, may excrete large quantities of water. The water intake in such forms, either in the food or by osmosis, is so large that conservation of water is not a problem. Experimental studies with mosquito larvae demonstrate that if the osmotic relationships are altered by placing such organisms in a salt medium, the animals excrete a concentrated urine. Uric acid may also be excreted in variable amounts by *storage excretion*—that is, certain cells of the body may have crystals of urates deposited in them, and such chemically inactive deposits in the tissues are effectively removed from any participation in the metabolc processes.

Reproduction

The reproductive system of the grasshopper is typical of that found in most insects. The sexes are separate, and the reproductive organs are located in the abdomen, dorsal to the alimentary canal. The male possesses a pair of *testes* which are connected by *sperm ducts* to a *genital pore* at the posterior end of the body. These ducts, however, unite into a single *medium tube* before reaching the genital pore. *Accessory glands* which secrete the fluid in which the sperm are carried are joined to the sperm duct.

The female reproductive system is very similar to that of the male. A pair of *ovaries* is present, and each is joined to an *oviduct.* The two oviducts fuse to form a single *median vagina* through which eggs are carried to the *genital opening.* A special sac, the *seminal receptacle,* is connected with the posterior part of the vagina and serves as a sperm receptacle for the storage of sperm after copulation. The tip of the abdomen of the grasshopper is constructed as an *ovipositor,* a powerful quadripartite appendage which is used to dig a hole in the ground just before the egg laying. An unusual feature of the reproductive process of the grasshopper is the fact that as the eggs pass down the oviducts, they have a shell deposited about them. A small pore is present in this shell, through which the sperm enter to fertilize the egg.

Coordination

The nervous system of the grasshopper is a ventral ladder type, similar in many respects to that of the crayfish. There is a large ganglionic mass, the *brain*, anterior and dorsal to the esophagus. This is the *supraenteric ganglion*, and it innervates the eyes, the antennae, and the upper lip. The brain is joined to the *subenteric ganglion* by the connectives which encircle the esophagus. The subenteric ganglion controls the mouth parts. Three large thoracic ganglia associated with the control of the wings and the legs are present, and the posterior ganglion of the thorax also is fused with the first abdominal ganglion. The abdominal ganglia fuse so that only five pairs are obvious. The first abdominal ganglion is formed by the fusion of the second and third embryonic ganglia; the fifth abdominal ganglion is composed of the embryonic ganglia of segments seven through eleven.

The sense organs of the grasshopper are, of course, adapted for the reception of stimuli from the air environment. The grasshopper, as an active animal, must have a highly efficient set of receptors for the determination and interpretation of a variety of stimuli. These receptors range from the *simple hairs* and the simple eyes, or *ocelli*, to the complex image-forming *compound eye*. Neither type of eye is capable of focusing on objects, and the ocelli apparently are concerned primarily with the detection of variations in light intensity. The compound eyes, however, are able to perceive images and probably function as efficient visual organs in the grasshoppers.

Tactile hairs are widely distributed over the body and are especially prominent on the antennae, the palps, and the legs. The hairs are sensitive to vibrations and enable the insect to detect the nearness or the approach of an object. The antennae and palps, in addition to being important organs of touch, are also chemical receptors. The insect probably does not distinguish *between* smell and taste, but both the antennae and the palps are sensitive to odors *and* to taste. The chemical receptors on the mouth parts undoubtedly are sensitive to these stimuli only when in direct contact.

An elaborate *ear*, or *tympanic organ*, is located on each side of the body, at the junction of the thorax and the abdomen and should be regarded as a true ear, because it is highly sensitive to sound waves. The tympanic organ consists of a thickened ring of cuticle, over which a thin layer of cuticle, the *tympanic membrane*, is stretched like a drumhead. Under it is a series of receptor structures which are set in motion by the vibration of the membrane. The impulses which result from the motion of these sensory receptors are relayed to the sensory nervous system.

Although insects have no true voice, many different kinds of sounds are made, usually by rubbing one body part against another. The hind legs are rubbed against the wing veins to produce the characteristic clicking sound of the grasshopper. Some of the close relatives of the grasshopper have the tympanic organs located on the legs, and this is of some advantage because of the ease

(a)   (b)

Figure 15.17.   Insects have been helped in their different adaptations to life by having highly specialized sense organs. The capabilities of insect antennae (a) have not been fully explored, but they are certainly organs of touch and smell, and in some insects are also radar instruments. A male mosquito can use his antennae to detect a female a quarter of a mile away.   The compound eye of the robber fly (b) has about 4000 units; that of a dragonfly, 30,000; and that of certain ants, only 50.   [(a) Courtesy Richard L. Cassell; (b) courtesy Edwin Way Teale.]

with which the auditory organs may be directed toward the source of the sound.

It is of interest also to consider the sound-making abilities of crickets.   The cricket, a close relative of the grasshopper, produces very elaborate sounds, some of which are pleasing to the human ear.   In Japan, crickets are kept in cages and raised much as canaries are in North America.   An interesting correlation apparently exists between the rate at which the sound is made by crickets and the air temperature.   Various estimates have been made of this correlation. If the number of chirps made by a cricket, for example, is counted for a period of 14 seconds and 40 is added to the number, the resultant figure will give the correct temperature in degrees of Fahrenheit.   This calculation holds very well for temperatures above 50 degrees Fahrenheit; below that temperature, however, the cricket chirp is about 40 times per minute.

Circulatory system

The circulatory system of the grasshopper is illustrative of that of most insects. There is a prominent dorsal blood vessel, which is subdivided into an aorta and a heart.   The heart portion of the dorsal vessel is located in the abdomen and consists of a series of eight enlargements, of which each contains a pair of openings, the *ostia*. Blood enters the heart through the ostia and, as the vessel contracts, simple flap valves prevent the blood from leaving the vessel and returning to the body spaces. The blood is pumped forward through the aorta to the head region of the grasshopper.

The blood vessels open into the body spaces which constitute the hemocoel. The blood is shunted throughout the body through the irregular sinuses and spaces of the hemocoel, but flow is controlled as a result of the development of membranes which create channels. It was commented upon previously that the circulatory system is especially important in that it supplies a fluid medium for the cells of the body and also serves for the carrying of food materials. A fluid medium is, of course, critical for all air-dwelling organisms.

Insect Societies

Long before man or the great apes populated the earth, there existed great city states, cultivated gardens, and air-conditioned edifices housing thousands of busy workers. These were an expression of the community activities of bees, ants, and termites, and an account of arthropod life would be incomplete without reference to the almost fantastic social organization which has been developed by these insects. *Division of labor* among individuals is characteristic of insect societies and has led to the establishment of *castes*. This phenomenon may be introduced by a brief description of a honeybee colony, which functions as a tightly integrated state dominated by a *queen* and maintained by thousands of sterile female *workers*. The male caste, the *drones*, do nothing constructive except participate in one nuptial flight with a queen.

A bee colony may exist for many decades and may be populated by as many as 60,000 individuals at any one time. The worker bees support the colony and are responsible for building and cleaning the hive, feeding the queen and larvae, and defending against enemies. The workers as well as the queens are females and both develop from fertilized eggs, but differential feeding is responsible for the unequal growth and different development in these two castes. The queen larva is fed only a special, rich food, the royal jelly, which is responsible for her more rapid and larger growth. The worker larvae, fed a less rich diet, are sterile and hence are smaller than the queens. The fat, "lazy" drones develop from unfertilized eggs and do no work in the colony; but when a new queen appears, they perform their one function of supplying sperm for new generations. This is accomplished during the nuptial flight, when a virgin queen flies high into the air, followed by the drones. One by one the drones explode and die as their air sacs expand under the progressively lower atmospheric pressures of the higher altitudes. Finally, only one drone remains, but before his death he copulates with the queen, depositing sperm in her sperm receptacle. These sperm are all that will be used by the queen throughout her life and may last for five or six years.

After her nuptial flight the young queen returns to the hive.   Then the old queen with a retinue of workers flies away ("swarms") to found a new colony, leaving the ancestral colony to the usurper.   The workers with the old queen undertake the construction of a new hive.   Wax secreted on their abdomens solidifies into plates, and these are used to build the geometrically precise, six-sided wax cells.   Some workers scout for nectar and pollen and bring these nutrients to the colony to be used to make the food for the queen and the larvae. The youngest workers are nurses and do the actual feeding, supplying the larvae at first with royal jelly, which is digested food that has been regurgitated by the workers.   A larva which is to become a queen receives no food except the jelly; but the other larvae are transferred to a diet of honey and pollen.   The queen lays both fertilized and nonfertilized eggs; the latter, as previously mentioned, developing into the drones.

The behavior of the bees is so remarkable that it is difficult to imagine how it can be controlled by the simple supraenteric and subenteric ganglia.   The superb account of the life of the bee by Maeterlinck should be read by everyone, not only for its literary excellence, but also because it depicts so vividly the complex activities of these organisms.   Recently, the work of Karl von Frisch has added much to our understanding of bee behavior, as a result of his excellent experimental analysis of the "vision, chemical senses, and language" of the bees.   It is not possible to review all the beautifully conceived and meticulous

Figure 15.18.   The developing queen bee exhibits a characteristic head-down position, as shown in (a).   The pollen-laden worker bee in (b) has her third pair of legs pressed together to form a pollen basket as she comes in for a landing.   [(a) Courtesy M. Leonard Hutchins, State College, Mississippi; (b) Cornelia Clarke.]

(a)   **(b)**

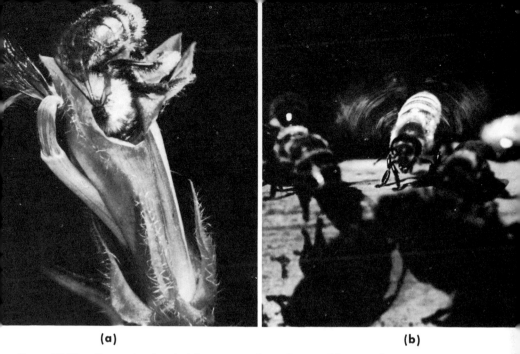

(a)   (b)

Figure 15.19.   The worker bee in (a), upon entering a flower, picks up pollen with her legs and nectar with her tongue.   This bee in (b) is fanning its wings to remove excess water from some of the honey solution stored in the hive.   This whirring motion also helps to ventilate the hive.   [(a) Courtesy Rutherford Platt; (b) Edwin Way Teale.]

experiments performed by von Frisch, but one experiment may be outlined in some detail.   The way in which bees convey information as to *distance* and *direction*, for example, is most amazing and will serve to illustrate one phase of their behavior.

Von Frisch established feeding stations at points approximately 100 to 300 yards from the hive.   The bees visited the stations where a rich sugar solution was available and performed a lively "dance" on the vertical surface of the comb when they returned to the hive.   They did not dance, however, if food was scarce or absent, but "scouts" revisited the stations periodically as if to see whether more food was available.   It was observed that the dances of the well-fed bees were not always the same: if the food was 50 to 100 yards away, the bees did a "round dance," but if more than 100 yards, they did a "wagging dance."   This dance was characterized by shaking the abdomen from side to side during that part of the dance called the "straight run."   Feeding stations were placed at distances up to 3.7 miles from the hive, and by marking the bees it was possible to show that the scouts directed other workers to the food.   This stimulated von Frisch to observe the wagging dances more closely.   He discovered that the number of "turns" in the dance varied according to the distance of the food from the hive.   Nearly 4000 observations showed that if the food was 100 yards away, there would be "9 to 10 complete cycles of the dance in 15 seconds; at 200 yards there were 7; . . . and at 3.7 miles, only 2."

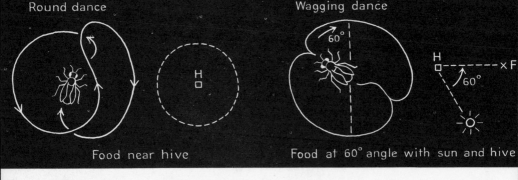

Round dance   Wagging dance

Food near hive   Food at 60° angle with sun and hive

Figure 15.20. The "scout" bees tell the other workers in the hive of available food supplies by "dancing," the pattern and speed of the dance indicating the distance and direction of the food. (After Bees, by Karl von Frisch, published by the Cornell University Press.)

A few of the counts did not exactly correlate with the distance, and it was discovered that one influential factor which produced variation was wind direction. If there was a "tail wind," the bees indicated a shorter distance; if a "head wind," a longer distance. Thus the bees really informed the other workers in terms of "flying time" rather than actual distance!

Still more remarkable is the communication of information with respect to the direction of the food, because the workers used the sun as a compass. Von Frisch and others had noted previously that the direction of the "straight run" of the dance on the vertical surface of the comb was not the same when bees returned from different feeding stations. Careful observation showed that the workers oriented in the hive to the force of gravity at exactly the same angle that they flew with respect to the sun when leaving the hive for the feeding place. For example, if the straight part of the dance was directly upward on the comb, it meant "fly in the direction of the sun"; if directly downward, "fly away from the sun." Still more astounding was the situation where the bees made a run 60° to the left of vertical, which, when translated, directed the workers to fly 60° to the left of the sun; a run 120° to the right of vertical informed the others to fly 120° to the right of the sun! Two other remarkable communication methods should be mentioned: *first*, as the day progressed, the apparent movement of the sun in the sky changed the angle with respect to sun, hive, and food, and the bees would change the angle of run accordingly; *second*, when fed regularly at a given place and time, the bees would return to this place at this time on succeeding days, thus demonstrating a time sense.

A final, most remarkable observation should be recorded. Von Frisch placed the hives horizontally, instead of in their normal vertical position. The bees then could not adjust according to the vertical axis but, instead, now indicated the direction of food by pointing the straight run toward the food. As the hive was slowly rotated, the bees did not rotate but continued to point directly at the food. They were, in effect, living compass needles. When the sun was obscured by clouds, they still indicated the proper direction. Von Frisch, however, proved conclusively that they actually were using polarized light from the sky for orientation.

This brief account emphasizes the value of carefully designed experiments, and of course illustrates one of the most amazing phenomena in the animal kingdom. Other experiments of von Frisch on color perception and chemical sense are equally remarkable and are so simply and beautifully written that they should be read by everyone interested in the living world.

The ants and termites have colonies more complex than those of the bees, both in number of castes and in functional organization. The ants, like the bees, are a female-dominated society, but greater specializations occur among workers. These may be *soldiers*, with large heads and mandibles, or *honey pots*, which become living storehouses. Workers may vary in size, and even the larvae may be used for special functions, such as forming a living needle and thread in the *leaf-sewing* ants. Ants often keep plant lice as "cows"; they "milk" them for secretions which are used for food, take them out to pasture, and guard them against predators. Elaborate gardens of fungus are cultivated and harvested; grain is gathered and stored for winter food. Some species of ants raid other colonies, steal the young, and rear them as slaves. The queen and the soldiers become the dominant members in a slave-making colony and suffer the dire consequences of slaveholding, because they cannot maintain themselves if the slave population is reduced.

The most remarkable colonies of all are those of the termites. These animals, commonly called "white ants," are not ants at all but are closely related to roaches. The feature of the termite colony which bestows on these animals the designation of "most remarkable" is the high degree of development of the caste system. There are *reproductive, soldier,* and *worker* castes, and both males and females are present in each caste. The specialization of individuals does not stop at this point, however, as there may be three grades of both soldiers and workers. The colony is organized around a "king and queen" who reside in a "royal chamber" centrally located in the termite nest. Such a nest in tropic regions may reach the stupendous size of ten feet or more in height. To found a new colony, a young termite king and queen leave the home nest together.

Figure 15.21.   Perhaps largely as a result of their efficient organization, ants are among the most successful animals in the world, being the most widespread and numbering at least 6000 species. The worker (a) is the mainstay of this organization. In (b) we see carpenter ant nest, showing ants and eggs. (Courtesy Lynwood M. Chace.)

(a)   **(b)**

(a)   (b)

Figure 15.22. Termite nest (a) showing the white queen almost bursting with eggs. Towering nests such as those in (b) may be produced by the highly specialized termite colonies. [(b) Courtesy Commonwealth of Australia Scientific and Industrial Research Organization.]

The royal couple excavate a new nest, mate, and raise the first brood themselves. Once founded, the colony is governed largely by the workers. The highly developed caste system of the termites can be described as *polymorphic*.

A final word should be said relative to the engineering abilities of the social insects. We mentioned earlier that bee colonies are built with geometrical precision. The arrangement of the openings is such that the workers, by fanning their wings, set up air currents which evaporate moisture in the hive and lower the temperature several degrees. A closed hive may have the temperature elevated several degrees in winter by the heat generated by thousands of workers vigorously beating their wings. The subterranean galleries of ants are spacious and include storehouses, nurseries for young ants, and stables for the "cows." They are constructed for maximum protection against sudden temperature changes, and drainage is designed to prevent flooding. Huge termite colonies are built to provide minimum temperature fluctuations, and the passageways and chambers are arranged for maximum air circulation and air conditioning.

A biologist may be pardoned for occasionally surveying the world through the eyes of a layman. He, in common with philosophers past and present, may speculate concerning the relative standards of insect and human societies, but such comparisons are dangerous. The *polymorphism* (p. 158) of an ant or termite colony is just as real as that in the Portuguese man-of-war. Individuality has been subjugated in both cases, and the entire colony is essentially a *super-organism*. The trivial difference of lack of physical bonds between members of an insect colony is more than offset by the functional ties which exist. The philosopher is impressed by the remarkable efficiency of an insect society. Each individual is predestined for a special task, and no deviation is possible. Old age and social security offer no problem: when efficiency decreases, an animal is liquidated and cast out or used as fertilizer. The biologist in the guise of a layman may be pardoned for wondering if totalitarian human states are not rapidly approaching the unfeeling efficiency of an ant colony, where the individual is unimportant and instinctive behavior rules.

Other Arthropods

Chilopoda

The Chilopoda are represented by the *centipedes,* or hundred-legged worms. These animals do not actually possess a hundred legs; the number usually is about 24 or 36.   Their most characteristic feature is the possession of a pair of *poison claws* located on the first body segment.   The animals are carnivorous, and the poison claws inject their poison from a pair of *poison glands* into the prey, thus killing or paralyzing the victim.   The two divisions of the centipede body, the head and the trunk, are characteristically flattened in a dorsal-ventral plane; and on each segment of the trunk, except the last two, a pair of walking legs is attached.   The head of the centipede possesses a pair of long antennae and several ocelli.   The ocelli are light-sensitive, and it appears probable that other scattered light-sensitive areas are present on the surface of the centipede. The animals react negatively to light, hence their well-known nocturnal habits. The organ systems of the centipede are very similar to those of the insects.   The alimentary canal is a relatively straight tube, with the usual fore-gut, mid-gut, and hind-gut regions.   They excrete by means of Malpighian tubules, and respiration is accomplished through tracheal tubes.   The tracheal tubes characteristically have a pair of openings in each segment of the body.

The largest centipedes are found in tropical regions, but in the temperate zone a very well-known form is the *house centipede.*   The fact that many centipedes are found in semiarid regions might suggest that they can stand considerable drying, but to the contrary, the animals are very sensitive to dehydration. This probably is the principal reason why the centipedes tend to hide in dark places in which the body can retain moisture.   The animals can survive for long periods of time completely immersed in water but die in a short time if confined to dry air.   The poisonous bite of the centipede is notorious but probably is not as serious to man as is commonly thought.   Many deaths attributed to centipede bites undoubtedly result from the fact that the person who was poisoned was

Figure 15.23.   In (a) is a centipede; in (b), a millipede.   (Courtesy Hugh Spencer.)

(a) **(b)**

Figure 15.24. This spider has already darted in and paralyzed the unfortunate grasshopper with its poison jaws. Note how it is now using its two hind legs to draw out streamers of still nearly liquid silk thread from the spinnerets on its abdomen. Even such large animals as birds and snakes may be trapped in the silk confusion of a spider's web. (Courtesy Walker Van Riper, Denver Museum of Natural History).

sick or in a weakened condition at the time; the centipede poison was merely an additional factor. A healthy individual usually can survive the bite.

Diplopoda

The Diplopoda are the *millipedes,* or thousand-legged worms. These sometimes may be mistaken for centipedes, but the features of this group are very distinct from those of the Chilopoda. The body is cylindrical, and although the animals have a large number of legs, it certainly is less than a thousand. There are two pairs of legs per segment, but the segments actually are fused in adults, and should be considered as *double segments.* The millipedes possess a pair of short antennae, and simple eyes which are arranged in groups that superficially resemble the compound eye. The body is divided into a head, a short thorax, and a trunk. The organs for digestion, respiration, and excretion are comparable to those of the centipede. The millipedes, like the centipedes, tend to select damp, dark places. They are commonly found in the field in rotted logs and beneath stones. The Diplopoda, in contrast to the Chilopoda, are herbivorous.

Arachnoidea

Probably the best-known group of arthropods, next to the insects, is the class Arachnoidea. This class includes the spiders, the mites, the ticks, and the scorpions, and often has the interesting marine animal, the *king crab,* or horseshoe crab, classified in it. Strangely enough, the spiders and their relatives have not received the attention due to them. They are almost as remarkably diversified in structure and habits as are the insects, and range from almost microscopical size to spiders with a leg spread of six to seven inches. King crabs frequently are

Figure 15.25. The multiple eyes, mouth parts, and appendages of the spider can be readily seen in this photograph. Frightening in appearance, spiders are usually helpful, not harmful to man. (Courtesy National Audubon Soceity, photo by Lynwood M. Chace.)

two feet long. Spiders are commonly thought of as "trappers," because of the extraordinary webs they construct as nets to capture prey. Many, however, are aggressive hunters, notably, the crab spiders, wolf spiders, tarantulas, and jumping spiders. They are not content to sit in a web but actively stalk and capture their prey.

The arachnids have some features which remind us of the crustaceans. The body is subdivided into cephalothorax and abdomen; excretion is by coelomic sacs or Malpighian tubules, and respiration is by either *book gills* or *tracheae*. The book gills are modified portions of the body surface which are thrown into leaflike folds through which the blood circulates. These respiratory structures are more like the gills of a crustacean than the tracheal tubes of an air-breathing insect, or the tracheal gills of an aquatic insect. There are several important distinguishing features which clearly delimit the Arachnoidea from the other classes of Arthropoda, and the *spider* may be considered as a representative animal of this group. We note that on the head there is a group of simple eyes, usually eight in number, and there is a pair of claws, the *chelicerae*, in front of the mouth. The chelicerae of the spiders are able to inject a poison into the prey and thus are often called *poison jaws*. A pair of leglike appendages, the *pedipalps*, are found immediately behind the mouth; these leglike structures serve the sensory function usually accomplished by antennae. They arc used for seizing prey and holding it while the other appendages tear the food apart. No antennae are present on the head of the arachnids, and there are no compound eyes; but the body is covered with *sensory hairs,* and these, together with the pedipalps, accomplish the function ordinarily performed by the antennae.

The cephalothorax of the spider and other arachnids contains four pairs of walking legs. The eight legs of these animals, therefore, provide an easy method of distinguishing an arachnid from an insect, which, of course, has three pairs of legs. The only appendages on the arachnid abdomen are the *spinnerets*, and these secrete the silk from which the web is formed. There are several types of glands which manufacture silk for the web. When first secreted, the silk is a fluid but it hardens when it comes in contact with the air. Some of these

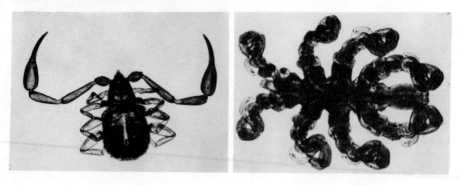

Figure 15.26. These arthropods, the pseudoscorpion and the sea spider, are members of classes not considered in the text. Weird and repelling in appearance, they are minute, each being but a fraction of an inch long. Most sea spiders are reasonably large, however. (Courtesy Clarence Flaten.)

secretions, however, remain sticky to serve as a trap for the prey that comes in contact with the web. Any small animal caught in the web is attacked by the spider, which may either poison it by biting with the poison jaws, or immobilize it by spinning an entangling mass of silk about it. The spider feeds by injecting digestive enzymes into the body of the animal which has been captured. These enzymes break down the tissues of the prey, and the liquefied material is then sucked into the alimentary canal. This sucking is made possible by the squeezing action of the pedipalps and the contractions of the heavy muscles of the *sucking stomach*. The alimentary canal has very extensive digestive and absorptive surface areas, and its function is aided by a large digestive gland. This gland secretes enzymes and, in addition, is extensively branched, functioning as a storehouse for large amounts of food. This large storage capacity makes it possible for the spider to survive for long periods between feedings.

The *scorpions* are similar in their basic structure to spiders, but the abdomen is elongated and terminates in a *poison spine*. Prey is captured when seized by the *chelicerae*, which immobilize it while poison is injected from the poison spine. The chelicerae then hold the animal firmly while it is torn to pieces by the pedipalps. Scorpions are infamous animals in the Southwest, but although their sting is very painful, it probably is not fatal as often as is commonly thought. It is possible that very old, ill persons or very young children may be killed by the scorpion poison.

The *mites* and *ticks* are small arachnids which are of considerable annoyance to human beings, because many of them are bloodsucking parasites. Perhaps the greatest danger to man from these arachnids comes from the fact that they may transmit very serious diseases. We have become aware of the importance of these animals in recent years because they infect human beings with Rocky Mountain spotted fever. These minute arachnids also do considerable damage to domestic animals; this is particularly true of those ticks which carry the

well-known Texas fever.   Most of the human dislike for the arachnids, however, is not justified.   The arachnids feed upon a variety of insects, and for the
most part are extremely beneficial to man because of the number of pests they
devour.   The dislike for the spiders probably stems from their general appearance.   The long legs, the hairy body, and the fact that they are often found in
dark places, or unexpectedly on tropical fruits, lends an element of unwelcome
surprise which arouses antagonism.

The king crabs° are sometimes designated as "living fossils," because the
present-day genus can be traced with little change back to the Triassic period,
over 100,000,000 years ago.   These animals are well known along the eastern
coast of North America, where they are very numerous.   The name commonly
given to them is "horseshoe crab" and is descriptive of their appearance.   They
have a heavy, convexly curved protective armor over the cephalothorax, which
is shaped like a horseshoe (or more properly, a horse's hoof), a single somewhat
flattened platelike cover over the abdomen, and a long spine (telson) which projects posteriorly.   Although well covered, the king crab possesses paired segmental appendages, book gills, and chelicerae—structures which are common
arthropod characteristics.

° *Limulus polyphemus.*

Figure 15.27.   The horseshoe crab has been variously classified, sometimes as an arachnid.
In this book it is considered sufficiently distinct to be in a separate class.   These photographs
show the animal in dorsal view (a) and in ventral view (b).   (Courtesy Clarence Flaten)

(a)   **(b)**

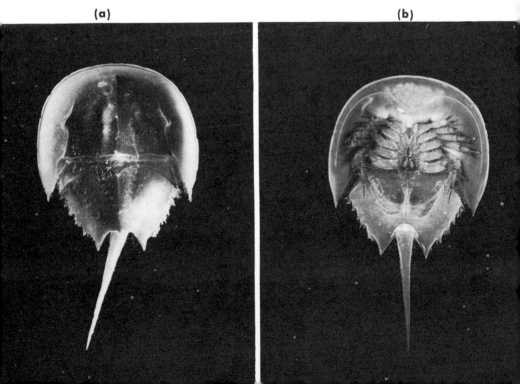

Arthropod Hormones

Considerable excitement has been aroused in recent years by the discovery of the existence of chemical coordinators, the *hormones*, in arthropods. The experiments of Wigglesworth, Brown, and Williams have demonstrated the presence of hormones affecting growth, differentiation, and pigmentation in crustaceans and insects. Workers in the field of genetics also have shown that gene-controlled chemical substances are released by various tissues and diffuse or circulate throughout the animal to influence metabolic activites in remote regions. The evidence in all cases proves that only minute amounts of these hormones are released, that their release is controlled by a variety of environmental factors, both internal and external, and that several different tissues may be involved in the secretion of the hormones.

The study of the developmental stages of the insects has been valuable for the elucidation of the problem of arthropod hormones, because most insects undergo a series of changes between the embryonic and adult stages which is spoken of as *metamorphosis*. A few, such as the silverfish and snow fleas, hatch in an essentially adult condition and are said to have no metamorphosis, or to be *ametamorphic*. The grasshopper, various bugs, and the dragonfly have a *gradual* or an *incomplete metamorphosis*. The young stages, the *nymphs* (or *naiads* if they live in water) gradually transform into adults after a series of molts. Moths, beetles, and bees have *complete metamorphosis*, in which the

Figure 15.28.   Aquatic larvae.   (a) The dragonfly (a) is shown molting, or emerging from its naiad skin, with its wings beginning to unfold. Many aquatic larvae are ravenous predators and will even attack each other, as this battle to the death in (b) illustrates. (Courtesy Robert C. Hermes.)

(a)   **(b)**

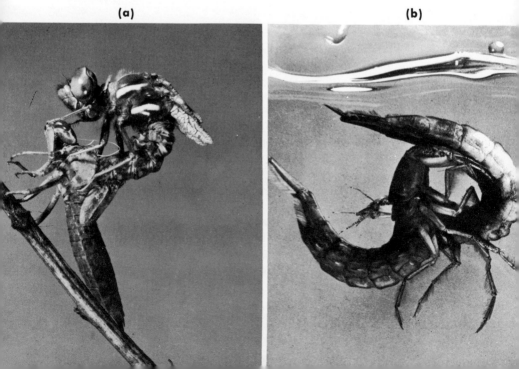

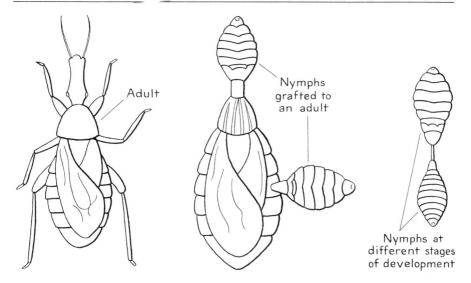

Adult

Nymphs
grafted to
an adult

Nymphs at
different stages
of development

Fiure 15.29.   The various possibilities of joining nymphs and adults, or nymphs with other nymphs, are shown in this sketch.

larval stage (for example, a *caterpillar*) transforms into a *pupa*.   This is often mistakenly spoken of as a "resting stage" but actually is a stage during which a complete reorganization of the body occurs.   The pupa in turn metamorphoses into the adult.   These differences in development have afforded opportunites for the investigation of chemical processes involved during the transformation. The experiments of Wigglesworth with bugs which have an incomplete metamorphosis and those of Williams with moths which have a complete metamorphosis have been most fruitful in this regard.

Wigglesworth experimented with a bug, *Rhodnius*, the nymphal stages of which are bloodsuckers and have a series of five molts.   Its was demonstrated that there were two hormones involved in the transformation: (1) the *juvenile hormone*, which causes the retention of the nymphal characteristics; and (2) the *growth-and-differentiation hormone*, or *Ecdysone*, which stimulates growth and the transformation of organs and tissues to the adult condition.   *Rhodnius* is a very favorable animal for experimentation, because it has a long "neck and head" which can be severed entirely from the body or cut at various levels.   The bug continues to live for months after the operation, and animals in the same stage or different stages of development may be fastened together to make experimental Siamese twins.   This operation permits an exchange of hormones between different individuals.

Brain cells of *Rhodnius* release a stimulating hormone (tropic hormone) which causes a gland in the thorax, the *prothoracic gland*, to secrete ecdysone. A special cerebral gland, the corpus allatum, secretes the juvenile hormone. The head can be cut in a manner such that the brain can be removed, leaving the corpus allatum intact, or both brain and corpus allatum can be removed. When only the brain is removed, the animal remains juvenile and undergoes extra molts. If both the brain and corpus allatum are removed, however, the nymph becomes a miniature adult. An amazing result followed the joining of headless adult with nymphs which were secreting large amounts of juvenile hormone. The headless adults molted and redeveloped certain nymphal characters. Obviously the juvenile hormone and ecdysone are autagonistic in their actions.

Experiments performed on moths by Kopec and by Williams add further information about arthropod hormones. Since the moths undergo complete metamorphosis, it is possible to make a more detailed analysis of action of the GD hormone and the juvenile hormone, both of which are present in the moths. The corpus allatum in moths also secretes the juvenile hormone. This can be demonstrated (1) by the removal of the corpus allatum, which will be followed immediately by pupation, or (2) by the implantation of the corpus allatum in caterpillars that are ready to pupate, which will prevent their transformation.

The pupa of the giant silkworm moth undergoes a long period of dormancy known as the *diapause*, which lasts for about five months at room temperature.

Figure 15.30.   Complete metamorphosis means a radical change in an insect body structure. Some insects show only a gradual or incomplete metamorphosis; others, no metamorphosis.

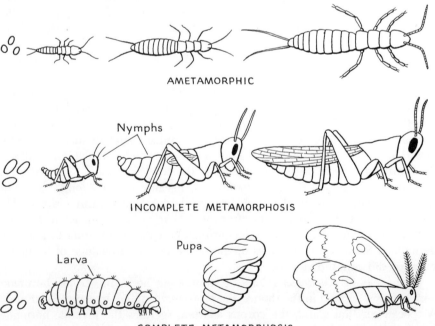

AMETAMORPHIC

Nymphs

INCOMPLETE METAMORPHOSIS

Larva

Pupa

COMPLETE METAMORPHOSIS

If these animals are chilled by being placed in a refrigerator at 3° to 5°C for one and one-half months and then are returned to room temperature, the pupae will transform into adults in about one month. Brains from chilled pupae implanted in other moths in diapause will causes these animals to transform into adults. Chilled pupae can be united surgically with the diapause pupae, which will cause the dormant animals to metamorphose to adults. The most startling demonstration involved cutting a pupa into two pieces, a head-thorax section and an abdominal section, and fastening each to a plastic cover glass. The head piece transformed into an adult anterior end, but the tail piece did not. The introduction of glandular tissue from the anterior region, however, transformed the tail portion into an adult posterior end.

The moth experiments demonstrated that the chilled brain alone was unable to elicit transformation. It was effective only when administered with pro-thoracic gland. Although this relationship was discussed in the *Rhodnius* experiments, the mechanism was discovered first in the moth. The brain hormone was shown to be a *prothoracicotropic hormone*—that is, it stimulated the pro-thoracic gland to secrete ecdysone. The absence of either the brain or the prothoracic gland, of course, will prevent the transformation of the pupa into an adult. The "chilling of the brain," therefore, merely provides a stimulus to the brain for the release of the prothoracicotropic hormone.

The experiments with insect hormones afford some valuable insights into hormone production and action. Small groups of cells secrete only very minute amounts of hormone, but the effects are far reaching. It should also be noted that the brain plays a significant role in this secretory mechanism. Since the hormones affect growth and specialization of tissues and organs, these experiments are of great value in the analysis of the complex problems involved.

It was mentioned that an ant colony might be considered a superorganism, and that its polymorphism was comparable to that noted in some coelenterates. Furthermore, it was stated that the "functional bonds" were as strong as the physical ones. These conclusions may serve to introduce the interesting speculations advanced by Wheeler many years ago. He was interested especially in the larval secretions which attracted the ant workers to the developing young, and by the fact that each ant colony had its own characteristic odor (perceived by the other ants of the colony). He demonstrated, for example, that an ant given a bath and returned to its own colony would be killed as an intruder. Wheeler suggested that such secretions should be spoken of as *social hormones;* and although they are not substances which diffuse or circulate, they do function in a colony in a manner comparable with that of hormones.

Orders of Insects

The great success of the class Insecta, the interesting biological features of their adaptability, and their versatility suggest that we should give them some additional consideration. Furthermore, we can gain a better understanding

Figure 15.31. Silverfish, order Thysanura.
(Courtesy Hugh Spencer.)

of their economic importance to man and of their role in that interrelationship
among organisms known as *biological balance* if we analyze more carefully
the different major orders of insects.

This account of the insect orders is intended only as a brief introduction to
these groups, and for that reason several relatively common orders are not included. The sequence in the presentation of the orders departs from the usual
scheme of relationship suggested by our knowledge of paleontology and embryology. The arrangement is, however, designed to demonstrate certain features which the orders have in common. The first seven orders, for example,
either are without metamorphosis or have gradual metamorphosis, and most of
them are rather closely related. The *lice*, however, are placed together merely
because they are "lice," and not because of any uniformity of metamorphosis or
evolutionary relationship.

Aptera

The apterans (*a*, not; *pteron*, wing) are the most primitive of the insects and
are not a homogenous group. More correctly, they are separated by specialists
into three orders, two of which are well known.° The members of this order
do not metamorphose (p. 292) and, as the name implies, they are *wingless*. The
silverfish, or *fish moth*, is a small, silver-colored insect with an appetite for
starch and a penchant for warm places.† Consequently, it often lives with man
and devours the binding of books or is a pest in the kitchen. The silverfish has
chewing mouth parts, as its habits might indicate.

The *springtails*, or snow fleas, also are *wingless* and *without metamorphosis*,
but they possess *sucking mouth parts*.‡ These tiny insects have two interesting
abdominal appendages: one is a "spring" on the fourth segment, which enables

° The three orders are: Protura, Thysanura, and Collembola.
† The silverfish is a thysanuran.
‡ The snow flea is a collembolan.

the animal to project itself into the air; the other is a sticky "tube," present on the first abdominal segment. The common name of the animals is derived from the "spring," but the fact that they also appear frequently in great numbers while the snow is still on the ground in the spring has given them an alternative cognomen, *snow fleas.*

Orthoptera

This famous order of insects, the orthopterans (*orthos,* straight; *pteron,* wing), includes the *grasshoppers, crickets,* and *roaches;* and perhaps little needs to be said about them here because of the discussion of the grasshopper included earlier. It is a very ancient order of insects in which the *metamorphosis is incomplete* (p. 292) and is more properly designated as *gradual metamorphosis.* A few members of the order are wingless but most possess *two pairs of wings.* The hind wings usually are folded fanlike under the first pair of leathery wings, which accordingly serve as a sheath. *Chewing mouth parts* are present. Many members of the order are noted for their "singing"; namely, the *crickets* and the *katydids.* More important are the crop-destroying "locusts" and the crickets which also appear in destructive hordes from time to time; notably, the Mormon crickets of the West.

Isoptera

Among the isopterans (*iso,* like; *pteron,* wing) are the termites, which are commonly called white ants. It is a well-authenticated fact that these voracious animals have excellent *chewing mouth parts* as well as immense appetites. The *two pairs of wings,* when present, are equal in size, but wings are absent in most of the castes of termites. *Metamorphosis is gradual.* The most famous feature of this group is their social organization, which has been commented upon elsewhere (p. 285). Paleontological and other evidence indicates that the termites are closely related to the roaches and not to the ants.

Hemiptera

The hemipterans (*hemi,* half; *pteron,* wing) are the *true bugs.* This causes zoologists great trouble since students persist in referring to all insects as "bugs" when they are not. This is a varied group of insects; and although all have *piercing-sucking mouth parts,* some are wingless, whereas others have *two pairs of wings.* The base of the first pair is thickened, and the second is membranous; when the wings are overlapped on the back, this produces the *half-wing* appearance which has given the order its name. *Metamorphosis is gradual.* Some of the hemipterans are interesting aquatic forms: *water striders, water boatmen,* and *back swimmers* probably have been observed by everyone. Many of the bugs do serious damage to plants; notably, the *squash bug* and *chinch bug.* The *assassin bugs* are predators, and the *kissing bug* is a blood-sucking insect. The

Figure 15.32. Cricket, order Orthoptera. (Courtesy Lynwood M. Chace.)

Figure 15.33. Termite (soldier), order Isoptera. (Courtesy Hugh Spencer.)

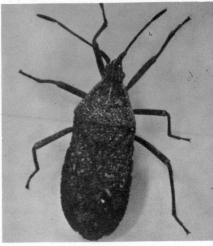

Figure 15.34. Squash bug, order Hemiptera. (Courtesy National Audubon Society; photo by Lee Jenkins.)

two most notorious hemipterans undoubtedly are *bedbugs* and *stink bugs*.

Homoptera

The order of homopterans (*homos,* same; *pteron,* wing) is of great economic importance because of the damage its members do to domestic plants. The best known are the *cicadas,* commonly misnamed "locusts," the *plant lice, scale insects,* and the *tree* and *leaf hoppers.* The *two pairs of wings* are membranous and are held in a rooflike fashion over the body. Many members of the order, however, are wingless. The mouth parts are of the *piercing-sucking type,* and *metamorphosis is gradual,* as in the hemipterans. The remarkable life cycle of the cicada is an interesting phenomenon, especially in the seventeen-year form. The young live in the ground as larvae, feeding on roots for 17 years, and when they emerge, they climb a tree, undergo a molt to their adult form, lay their eggs inside twigs of the tree, and die after a few days. Other cicadas have shorter life cycles, and since emergence from the ground occurs in a well-synchronized fashion, the appearance of the so-called locusts is usually impressive in number and voluminous in sound.

Thysanoptera

The order of thysanoptera (*thysanos,* fringe; *pteron,* wing) is a group of miniature insects. The body form is characterized by the presence of *two pairs of*

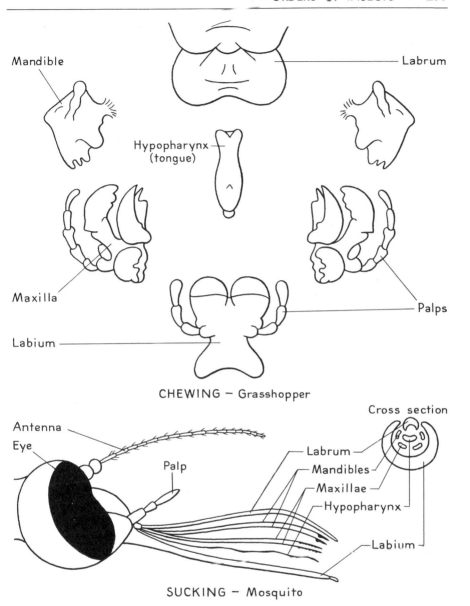

Mandible

Labrum

Hypopharynx (tongue)

Maxilla

Palps

Labium

CHEWING — Grasshopper

Cross section

Antenna
Eye
Palp

Labrum
Mandibles
Maxillae
Hypopharynx
Labium

SUCKING — Mosquito

Figure 15.35.   This drawing shows the mouth parts of typical chewing and sucking insects.

narrow, *membranous wings* which have a fringe of long "hairs." Some members of the order, however, are wingless. The mouth parts are of the *piercing-sucking type* and *metamorphosis is gradual.* The *thrips* are examples of this order.

Figure 15.36. Cicada, order Homoptera. (Courtesy National Audubon Society; photo by Dade Thornton.)

Dermaptera

The dermapterans (*derma*, skin; *pteron*, wing) comprise an interesting order of insects about which there is a great deal of fiction and not too much fact. These animals have an arresting appearance because of the formidable pair of *pincers*, or forceps, at the posterior tip of the body. It was long believed that these insects would crawl into the ear of a human being, bore into the brain, and cause death. This is, of course, pure fiction; but the appellation, *earwig*, which was assigned to the animals because of this presumed behavior, has remained. The presence of wings is quite variable among the earwigs; *none, one pair, or two pairs* may be present. The first pair, when present, is leathery, or skinlike; the second pair is somewhat like those of the orthopterans and is folded under the first pair when at rest. The mouth parts are the *chewing type*, and *metamorphosis is gradual*.

The following four orders of insects are noteworthy because they contain well-known aquatic larvae (naiads). They are important links in the food chains which involve aquatic organisms. Many fish depend either directly or indirectly on the larvae of these organisms as a source of nourishment.

Ephemeroptera, or Ephemerida

The distinguished representatives of the ephemeropterans (*ephemeros*, "living but a day"; *pteron*, wing) are the *May flies*, which swarm in the evenings in the late spring, obscure automobile windshields with their bodies, and even fill the

Figure 15.37. Earwig, order Dermaptera. (Courtesy Alfred Renfro, FPSA.)

gutters of streets.   The adults usually live less than 24 hours, hence the name which designates their ephemeral nature.   *Metamorphosis is incomplete,* and the immature insects live in the water as *naiads* (p. 292) for as long as three years. When they emerge from the water, they transform into graceful adults with *two pairs* of delicate, somewhat triangular-shaped *wings.*   When at rest, the wings are held vertically to the body.   The animals possess three filamentous projections from the tip of the abdomen, the *cerci.*   Immediately after mating, the eggs are deposited in the water and the adults die.   The *mouth parts are vestigial* in the adult.

Odonata

The fascinating insects of the Odonata (*odus,* tooth) are not "snake charmers" nor "snake feeders," as superstition has suggested, but their behavior has charmed small boys for ages.   The *dragonflies* and *damsel flies* are the characteristic members of the group and are efficient, strong-flying, beautiful insects. They have *two pairs of membranous wings* of almost equal size.   These are held horizontally by dragon flies but at an angle vertical to the body by damsel flies. They possess excellent *chewing mouth parts* and are insectivorous, consuming large quantities of mosquitoes and flies.   *Metamorphosis is incomplete;* and the larval stage is an aquatic form, or naiad.   The dragonfly naiad is one of the most remarkable immature forms to be found among the insects, if not in the entire animal kingdom.   These powerful creatures are capable of capturing small minnows.   They respire by drawing water into the rectal region and are able to utilize "jet propulsion" for locomotion by forcibly ejecting this water from the anal opening.

Plecoptera

Representative of the plecopterans (*pleco,* pleated, or folded; *pteron,* wing) are the *stone flies;* their immature forms are naiads comparable with those of the May flies and dragonflies.   Characteristically, the naiads have well-developed

Figure 15.38.   May fly, order Ephemeroptera, or Ephemerida.   (Courtesy National Audubon Society; photo by William Jahoda.)

Figure 15.39. Damsel fly, order Odonata. (Courtesy Hugh Spencer.)

"tracheal gills." *Metamorphosis is incomplete.* The adults possess *chewing mouth parts* and *two pairs of wings.* The posterior pair of wings is larger and is folded beneath the first pair, and at rest the wings are held flat over the body. A pair of long *cerci* is present at the end of the abdomen.

Neuroptera

The order Neuroptera (*neuron,* nerve; *pteron,* wing) is notable because of the remarkable variety of larval forms which are present in its members. The larva of the *dobson fly* is the *hellgrammite,* which is a large aquatic form very much favored by fishermen as bait. The *caddis fly* larvae are also aquatic; they construct "cases," often plastered over with small stones and sticks. The *aphis lion* and the *ant lion* (or doodle bug) are carnivorous nonaquatic larval forms of neuropterans. They are predacious on other insects, as their names imply. The ant lion is interesting because it constructs a funnel-shaped sand pit and buries itself at the bottom with only its powerful jaws protruding into the funnel. An insect which blunders into the trap cannot crawl out because of the sliding walls of the pit and is promptly eaten. *Metamorphosis* in the order is *complete,* and *chewing mouth parts* are the rule, although they may be modified in some forms. There are *two pairs of long wings* of approximately equal size, and there is a delicate tracery of numerous fine veins, or "nerves," in the wings, which is responsible for the naming of the order.

The popular designation of *lice* includes a diversified assemblage of insects.

Figure 15.40. Lacewing fly, order Neuroptera. (Courtesy Lynwood M. Chace.)

Actually, they have little in common except small size and, quite generally, a loss of wings. The characteristics of the orders which follow will emphasize the dissimilarities that are encountered.

Corrodentia

The order Corrodentia (*corrodens,* gnawing) includes the *book lice* and the *psocids.* These small insects may be *wingless* or may possess *two pairs of wings.* When wings are present, the hind pair is smaller than the fore. The wings are held at a rooflike angle over the body when at rest. *Metamorphosis is gradual* and, as the order name indicates, the mouth parts are of the *chewing type.*

Mallophaga

The members of the order Mallophaga (*mallos,* wool; *phagein,* "to feed") are the *biting lice.* Those with which most people are best acquainted are the *bird lice,* which are common on barnyard fowl and are often found on pet birds. Not all mallophagans are bird lice, however, since many inhabit mammals. These are *wingless* animals, and they have *chewing mouth parts.* They actually feed on bits of feathers, skin, or hair, and thus differ from the better-known lice, which suck fluids from the host. Metamorphosis is somewhat variable in the order: some have *gradual* and others, *incomplete metamorphosis.*

Anoplura

The anoplurans (*an,* without; *oplos,* sting; *oura,* tail) are the *sucking lice.* The human *head louse* and the *body louse* are the best-known members of this group. They were intimate acquaintances of man long before Bobby Burns wrote his illustrious poem. The animals are flattened dorsoventrally, and they have well-developed *claws* which enable them to hold firmly to hair and make them difficult to dislodge. The eggs deposited by these creatures are called *nits,* and their presence may afford the first indication of a visitation by the adults. The members of the order are *wingless* and have strong *piercing mouth parts. Metamorphosis is gradual.*

Siphonaptera

The siphonapterans (*siphon,* tube; *a,* without; *pteron,* wing) are the *fleas.* They are common pests not only on man, but also on other mammals. The

Figure 15.41. Head louse, order Anoplura. (Courtesy United States Department
of Agriculture; photo by V. C. Loftin.)

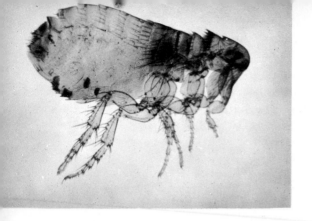

Figure 15.42. Flea, order Siphonaptera. (Courtesy Hugh Spencer.)

bodies are flattened laterally, and "spines" are present over the surface. These two specializations make it difficult for the host to dislodge the animals. The legs are adapted for jumping, especially the powerful hind legs. The animals are *wingless* and have *sucking mouth parts*. *Metamorphosis is complete*. The lice and the fleas of the order Anoplura are particularly important to human beings because they are vectors of some of man's most dangerous diseases, notably plague and typhus (p. 342).

Four major orders remain for our consideration and these include approximately 85 per cent of all the described species of insects. Not only are the members of these orders present in multitudes, but, as might be expected, they are among the most successful and adaptable. Each of these four orders, however, has gained its prominence as a result of different achievements, and each attracts our interest because of these divergences.

Coleoptera

The greatest number of described species is to be found in the order Coleoptera (*coleos*, sheath; *pteron*, wing) which includes the weevils and beetles. Many of these insects are frequently called "bugs" by the uninitiated, because within this order are the *June bugs, tumble bugs, mealy bugs,* and *lightning bugs,* all of which, of course, are *beetles!* The members of the group have *complete metamorphosis;* notable examples of larval types in the order are the *grub worms* and the *glowworms*. The presence of *two pairs of wings* is typical of the order. The first pair of wings is tough and leathery and serves as a sheath for the second pair, which are the ones used for flying. *Chewing mouth parts* are

Figure 15.43. Long-horned beetle, order Coleoptera. (Courtesy National Audubon Soceity.)

characteristic of the beetles, and in some these are snoutlike. Many of the coleopterans are of significant economic importance to man because of the damage they do. The *wood-boring beetles*, the *weevils*, the *meal worms*, and the *potato beetles* levy a heavy annual tax on man. Conversely, certain beetles render great service: the *carrion beetles* and *rove beetles* feed on decaying organic matter; the *tiger beetles*, *lady-bird beetles*, and *ground beetles* destroy great numbers of other insects. The "cost" of the beetles is more than compensated for by the "services" they perform for the welfare of mankind and of other organisms.

Lepidoptera

The lepidopterans (*lepid*, scale; *pteron*, wing), the most beautiful of all insects, deserve to be called "collectors items." Most children have passed through a butterfly- or a moth-collecting stage after being attracted by the large size and beauty of these particular animals. The group naturally splits itself into two major divisions: the *moths*, which are primarily night-flying insects; and the *butterflies*, which are chiefly day-flying. The *two pairs of wings* are membranous but are covered with scales, which come off on the hands of a careless collector as a very fine dust. *Metamorphosis is complete*, and the larval forms are the *caterpillars*, many of which are quite bizarre and with equally unusual common names. The *wooly worm*, the *tomato worm*, and the *hickory horned devil* are only a few of the better-known larvae. The wormlike appearance of these creatures is especially misleading if they are examined only casually and, of course, was responsible for their mistaken identification by Linnaeus as Vermes.

The larvae transform into pupae during metamorphosis and many spin a cocoon about themselves at this time—for example, the *silkworms*. It is during the pupal stage that a complete reorganization of the body is accomplished and, upon emergence, a phenomenal transformation from the wormlike larva to the winged adult has been accomplished. The change in the mouth parts affords a good illustration of one of the alterations which occur. The *larval mouth* is of the chewing type, whereas the *adult* possesses a *sucking mouth*, which often is a very elongated elaborate tube. This is used for penetrating deep into the

Figure 15.44. Swallowtail butterfly, order Lepidoptera. (Courtesy National Audubon Society; photo by Verna R. Johnson.)

recesses of a blossom and is coiled tightly below the head when not in use.

Lepidopterans, like coleopterans, are both advantageous and disadvantageous to man. Some are important for their role in cross-pollination of plants and in the production of silk; conversely, the *bag worms, army worms,* and *tomato worms* cause great economic loss annually because of their destruction of shrubs, trees, and other plants, and the *clothes moth larvae* cause much damage to clothing and home furnishings.

Diptera

The number of described species in the order Diptera (*dis,* two; *pteron,* wing) is the least of any of the orders included in this group. A person annoyed by the profusion of *midges, mosquitoes, sand flies,* or *house flies* which swarm about in the spring and early summer will find it difficult, however, to relegate these insects to any minor role. The numbers of adult individuals produced by a single species of midge, for example, is almost beyond enumeration. The skies in some areas of the world—for example, the arctic in the summer—become clouded with swarms of mosquitoes. Thus, although in numbers of different species this order may not be the greatest, the numbers of individual dipterans almost are beyond comprehension.

Metamorphosis is complete among the Diptera, and the larval forms of many are called *maggots.* Midge larvae and the larvae of closely related dipterans are aquatic, and these, like the larvae of other aquatic insects, are important members of the food chain in lakes and streams. The cast-off larval skin frequently serves as a case, or cocoon, for the pupa, and in these instances is designated as a *puparium.* Generally, the mouth parts are the *piercing-sucking type,* but the *biting flies* have jaws which enable them to puncture the skin of the host so they can draw up blood. As the order name indicates, the dipterans usually have

Figure 15.45.   House fly, order Diptera. (Courtesy National Audubon Society; photo by G. T. Hillman.)

Figure 15.46. Black wasp, order Hymenoptera. (Courtesy National Audubon Society; photo by W. T. Davidson.)

only *a single pair of wings*. These represent the first pair, the hind wings being reduced to a pair of knobbed strands, the "balancers," or *halteres*.

The economic importance of such a well-populated order of insects is certain to be significant. It has been mentioned that midges are an integral part of the aquatic food chain. In addition, other flies, either as adults or larvae, subsist on decaying flesh and are, therefore, necessary for the maintenance of the nitrogen cycle (p. 42). The *botflies, mosquitoes, tsetse flies,* and even the *horse flies* are parasites of considerable importance, but even more critical for man's well-being is the role of several of them as carriers of major diseases.

Any account of the Diptera would be incomplete, however, without a reverent bow in the direction of the *fruit fly, Drosophila*. This tiny organism has become an indispensable tool of the geneticists for the study of inheritance. The very characteristics of the dipterans which make them obnoxious as a group —for example, hardiness, rapid multiplication, and overpopulation—have been utilized by investigators who breed fruit flies in the laboratory for the controlled investigation of the transmission of traits from generation to generation. Without them the science of genetics could not have advanced so rapidly.

Hymenoptera

The order Hymenoptera (*hymen*, membrane; *pteron*, wing) is, in many respects, the most remarkable of all orders of insects. It is approximately equal in number of species to the order Lepidoptera, and second only to Coleoptera. Hymenopterans are perhaps second only to the dipterans in total numbers of individuals. The *ants, bees, wasps, hornets,* and *gallflies* are long-standing, even if not popular, acquaintances of everyone. The notable social

Figure 15.47. Colonial wasps, order Hymenoptera. (Courtesy Lynwood M. Chace.)

organization which occurs in the order has been described (p. 285). *Metamorphosis is complete*, and the care of the young is intimately associated with the degree of social development. Parental care may be slight, as in the mud dauber, which deposits the eggs in a rather simple "nursery" of mud construction and provisioned with small spiders the mud dauber has paralyzed with its sting. When the larvae hatch they are thus provided with fresh meat. The eggs of hornets are laid in more elaborate houses of waterproof "paper" construction. Sometimes the young are given an advantageous environment and left to fend for themselves. Certain wasps, for example, deposit their eggs within other organisms and the newborn larvae feed upon the tissues of the host. Gall wasps are interesting in this respect. Their eggs are placed in twigs and leaves and the plant so infected is stimulated to produce cancerlike growths, the *galls*, within which the larvae are protected and nourished. The species relationship between parasite and host is usually very close, and only a single species of plant is attacked regularly.

The mouth parts of hymenopterans are basically of the *chewing type*, although they may be extensively modified for sucking, as in bees. The wings are also variable, although typically the hymenopteran will possess *two pairs* of *membranous wings*. The fore wings are larger than the hind wings. Some hymenopterans, however, are wingless. Among these are the ants and even some wasps, called the "velvet ants," in which only the females are wingless.

The economic importance of the Hymenoptera was noted in part at the beginning of this chapter: honey and beeswax are products of great value produced by bees, but their activity in the cross-pollination of plants, especially clover, is of even greater value. Monetary losses due to the activities of gall wasps and wood-boring bees are considerable. The "balance sheet," however, greatly favors the "good works" of the Hymenoptera when an accounting is made of their contribution to biological balance among organisms. The destruction of other insects by the parasitic larvae of wasps is one of the most effective population controls on earth.

Classification of the Arthropoda

Phylum Arthropoda   Animals with externally jointed appendages and chitinous exoskeleton. Coelom much reduced, present only as the cavities of the gonads, and of certain excretory organs. Blood-filled body cavity, *hemocoel*, is present. Cilia are absent.

CLASS I. CHILIPODA. Single pair of long antennae, body divided into head and trunk, with one pair of legs per segment; poison jaws present; excretory structures are Malpighian tubules, and respiration by tracheae. Example: centipede.

CLASS II. DIPLOPODA. One pair of short antennae, body divided into head, thorax, and trunk, with two pairs of legs per double segment. Malpighian tubules for excretion, and tracheae for respiration. Example: millipede.

CLASS III. ARACHNOIDEA. Body divided into cephalothorax and abdomen, no antennae present, has poison jaws and four pairs of walking legs. Excretory organs derived from coelomic sacs; and with respiratory organs in the form of tracheae, gills, or book gills. Examples: spiders, mites, ticks.

CLASS IV. CRUSTACEA. Body divided into cephalothorax and abdomen. Two pairs of antennae; usually five pairs of walking legs. Excretory organs modified coelomic sacs, and usually gills for respiration; no Malpighian tubules. Examples: lobster, crayfish.

CLASS V. INSECTA (*Hexapoda*). Body divided into head, thorax, and abdomen. One pair of antennae present, and usually two pairs of wings. Three pairs of legs present on thorax. Malpighian tubules for excretion, and tracheae for respiration. Examples: grasshopper, fly, mosquito.

Certain classes of Arthropoda are omitted from the above classification. These classes are extremely important to the zoologist but are not of too great interest to the beginning student.

REFERENCES

BORRER, DONALD J., and DWIGHT M. DeLONG, *An Introduction to the Study of Insects.* Rinehart and Company, New York, 1954.

BROWN, F. A. (ed.), *Selected Invertebrate Types,* pp. 360–504. John Wiley and Sons, New York, 1950.

CARPENTER, G. H., *The Biology of Insects.* The Macmillan Company, New York, 1935.

EMANS, E. V., *About Spiders.* E. P. Dutton and Company, New York, 1940.

EVANS, HOWARD E., "Predatory Wasps," *Scientific American, 208,* April 1963, pp. 144–154.

FABRE, J. H., *The Life of the Spider.* Dodd, Mead and Company, New York, 1919.

GERTSCH, W. J., *American Spiders.* D. Van Nostrand Company, New York, 1949.

IMMS, A. D., *Social Behavior in Insects.* Methuen and Company, London, 1947.

JAQUES, H. E., *How to Know Insects.* Wm. C. Brown Company, Dubuque, Iowa, 1947.

LUTZ, F. E., *Field Book of Insects.* G. P. Putnam's Sons, New York, 1935.

MAETERLINCK, M., *The Life of the Bee.* Dodd, Mead and Company (Blue Ribbon Books), New York, 1901.

RIBBANDS, C. R., *The Behavior and Social Life of Honeybees.* Dover Publications, New York, 1964.

SCHNEIDERNEAU, HOWARD A., and LAWRENCE J. GILBERT, "Control of Growth and Development in Insects," *Science,* January 1964.

SNODGRASS, R. E., *Anatomy and Physiology of the Honeybee.* McGraw-Hill Book Company, New York, 1935.

SNODGRASS, R. E., *Principles of Insect Morphology.* McGraw-Hill Book Company, New York, 1935.

SNODGRASS, R. E., "Evolution of the Annelida, Onychophora, and Arthropoda," *Smithsonian Miscellaneous Collections,* Vol. 97, 1938, pp. 1–159.

SNODGRASS, R. E., *Comparative Studies on the Head of Mandibulate Arthropods.* Comstock Publishing Company, Ithaca, New York, 1951.

TURNER, C. DONNELL, *General Endocrinology,* 3rd ed. W. B. Saunders, Philadelphia, 1960, pp. 468–481.

VON FRISCH, K., *Bees.* Vail-Ballou Press, Binghamton, New York, 1950.

WHEELER, W. M., *Demons of the Dust.* W. W. Norton and Company, New York, 1930.

WHEELER, W. M., *The Social Insects.* Harcourt, Brace and Company, New York, 1938.

WIGGLESWORTH, V. B., *The Principles of Insect Physiology.* Methuen and Company, London, 1939.

WIGGLESWORTH, VINCENT B., *The Life of Insects.* World Publishing Company, Cleveland, Ohio, 1964.

WINNER, ADRIAN M., "Sound Communication in Honey Bees," *Scientific American, 210,* April 1964, pp. 116–125.

16

Hydraulics

Phylum

Echinodermata

●

It seems as if nature had essayed one after the other every manner of living and moving, as if she had taken advantage of every permission granted by matter and its laws.—Gide, quoted by Woodruff and Baitsell in Foundations of Biology

Phylum Echinodermata ("spiny-skinned" animals) is the most distinctive in the animal kingdom, with the possible exception of the sponges. They are exclusively marine, with unique features in the form of *five-part radial symmetry* and the development of a *hydraulic system* for locomotion. Body form and activity are variable, ranging from the almost wormlike sedentary sea cucumber and the stalked, flowerlike sea lily to the active serpent, or brittle, star with snakelike arms. Special organ systems are poorly developed in the echinoderms, and excretory organs are absent; the nervous system is also greatly reduced. These characteristics, in addition to the radial symmetry, were responsible for many years for the inclusion of the echinoderms and the coelenterates in a single group, no longer recognized, the Radiata. The actual relationship of the echinoderms to the coelenterates is remote, however; and they appear to be closer to the chordates than to the annelids, mollusks, or arthropods. The support for this conclusion is based on several lines of evidence: *first*, the radially symmetrical adult is derived from a bilaterally symmetrical larva; *second*, the structure of the larvae and the evidence of serological tests* suggest an affinity with the chordates; *third*, the lack of certain organ systems is

---

*Cell or tissue extracts of an animal are injected into the blood stream of a rabbit, producing *antibodies* against the specific chemical substances in the extracts. The antibodies will then precipitate other extracts, and theoretically, the closer the relationship, the greater should be the amount of precipitate. However, there are many technical difficulties which remain to be solved, and it is only one of several possible evidences for relationship. Serological tests will be discussed later.

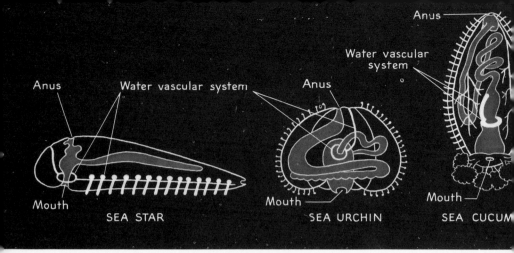

Figure 16.1.   Typical echinoderm body forms.

considered to be a secondary simplification; *fourth*, the blastopore, or blasto-pore region, of the embryo becomes the anal opening of the adult (instead of the mouth, as in most other invertebrates); furthermore, a new mouth is formed in the echinoderm embryo, and the mesoderm develops as in the chordates.

The economic importance of the echinoderms is relatively insignificant when compared with that of many other phyla.   Sea cucumbers are eaten by man in a few areas of the world, and the skeletons of other echinoderms may be used for fertilizer.   The sea stars, commonly called "starfishes," are a considerable nui-sance to oyster fisherman because of the fact that they may destroy profitable oyster beds by eating large numbers of these mollusks.   A single sea star, for example, may devour as many as 20 oysters in a single day.   The zoologist, on the other hand, has found the members of the group to be very helpful for bio-logical research, especially in the study of fertilization and embryonic develop-ment, because eggs and sperm are secured easily, and the embryonic stages can be observed readily.   Experimental modification of embryonic development has contributed to our understanding of the processes involved in the division of labor between cells and layers.   The echinoderms have a remarkable ability to regenerate large portions of the body; for example, an arm that is injured or broken off may be subsequently replaced by a new arm.   This process, as we have already noted (p. 264), is called *autotomy* and occurs in only a few other instances in the animal kingdom.   The selection of a type form to depict the features of the phylum Echinodermata is less difficult than in many other phyla; the sea star serves very well for this purpose, and an understanding of its struc-ture will provide us with a picture of the basic organization of the phylum. It should be emphasized, however, that the sea star is a greatly altered de-scendant of ancestors which probably were bilaterally symmetrical.   Their unique features as echinoderms should be considered as further evidence of the flexibility of structural design which can be expressed by protoplasm.

The Sea Star*

Body form

The living sea stars are colorful animals with variable hues, ranging from cream to orange or from pink to purple, but these colors disappear when the animals are preserved for study. The five *arms*, or rays, of the sea star are broadly joined to the *central disk;* however, there are sometimes fewer or more than five arms, but this variation in number is probably a result of autotomy and regeneration. The fleshy body of the animal is flexible but has calcified plates embedded in it which limit the freedom of movement. The surface of the sea star is ciliated and is armed with minute pincers, the *pedicellariae,* and with blunt *spines.* Membranous *skin gills* which can be protruded from the surface are important in respiration and excretion, although no special organ systems exist to carry out these two body functions. There is no trace of a head, and the animal is usually described as having *oral* (mouth) and *aboral* (opposite the mouth) sides, which recalls a similar condition in the coelenterates. The problem of symmetry is somewhat confusing, as it is for the squid; therefore, the terms *dorsal* and *ventral* will not be employed in describing the animal. A sieve plate, the *madreporite,* is present on the aboral surface, and minute pores open through it into the *stone canal,* to be described later. The oral side of each arm has a groove, the *ambulacral groove,* and each groove contains a

° *Asterias forbesi.*

Figure 16.2.   Four of the five classes of echinoderms are shown in Figures 16.2 and 16.3. The fossil sea lily has preserved the shape of its feathery tentacles, cuplike body, and stalk for nearly 200,000,000 years.   Though the serpent, or brittle, stars look so much like the starfishes, they actually belong to a separate class.   [(a) Courtesy Ward's Natural Science Establishment, Inc.; (b) copyright by Douglas P. Wilson, F.R.P.S. Marine Biological Laboratory, Plymouth, England.]

(a)   (b)

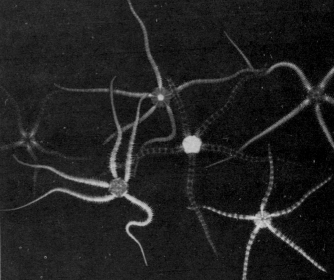

(a) **(b)**

Figure 16.3.   The sea urchin is a globular, spiny echinoderm with somewhat disguised five-part radial symmetry.   The unusual behavior of the sea cucumber is shown in (b); the animal, disturbed by handling, has everted its intestine.   In its normal habitat, however, this animal could grow a new set of "innards."   (Courtesy Clarence Flaten.)

double row of *tube feet*, which are the primary locomotor and feeding organs. A simple eyespot consisting of a pigmented area and light-sensitive cells is located on the tip of each arm.

It is convenient for a description of the internal anatomy to begin with the water vascular system.   The *stone canal* has a calcareous wall and runs from the madreporite to the *ring canal*, which encircles the mouth and sends the radial canal into each arm.   Numerous small passages, the *lateral canals*, arise at right angles to the radial canal, and each connects with a pair of bulbs, the *ampullae*, which are continuous with the tube feet.   The ampullae project into the body cavity, but the radial canal and tube feet are outside, in the groove.   Since the wall of an ampulla has circular muscle and the tube foot longitudinal muscle, the contraction of the muscles of the ampulla forces water into the foot, causing it to elongate and to attach by means of the sucker, or adhesive disk, located at its tip.   Relaxation of the ampulla muscles and contraction of the muscles of the tube foot will cause water to flow back into the ampulla and the foot to shorten.   Valves prevent the flow of the water back into the radial canal.   Each tube foot has been estimated to be able to pull up to 29 grams (one ounce), and the combined action of all the tube feet acting in concert can, therefore, exert a relatively great pull.   An oyster can withstand this pull for short periods, but the tube feet work alternately, and eventually the adductor muscle of the oyster tires and the shell opens.   This is an example of one of the advantages of the hydraulic system, because the actual energy expended by the tube feet in opening the oyster is slight.

The *mouth* connects by a narrow *esophagus* into a large *cardiac stomach*, which is partially separated from the smaller *pyloric stomach* by a constriction.

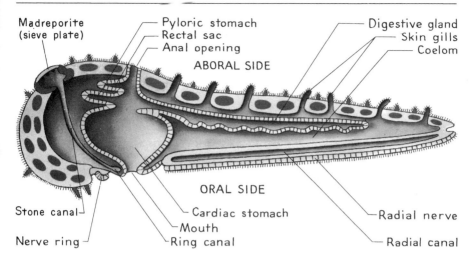

Madreporite (sieve plate)
Pyloric stomach
Rectal sac
Anal opening
ABORAL SIDE
Digestive gland
Skin gills
Coelom
Stone canal
Nerve ring
Cardiac stomach
Mouth
Ring canal
ORAL SIDE
Radial nerve
Radial canal

Figure 16.4.   This drawing shows the basic anatomy of the sea star.   Since the animal has five arms, a longitudinal section of this kind could cut through only a single arm.

Hollow, ciliated *digestive glands,* which have the ability to secrete great quantities of protein-splitting enzymes, are joined to the pyloric stomach.   A short *intestine* also connects the pyloric stomach with the *anus,* located in the aboral surface; and the *rectal sac,* a lateral pouch, branches from the intestine.   Many sea stars have the ability to turn the stomach inside out through the mouth, and by this means a sea star can digest an oyster or other bivalve while it is still in the shell.

Each arm of the sea star has an extensive coelom continuous with the coelom of the central disk; the coelom is lined with a ciliated epithelium which constantly circulates the coelomic fluid.   The paired digestive glands and the gonads project into this so-called perivisceral (about-the-viscera) coelom but are covered with peritoneum and supported by sheets of tissue, the *mesenteries.* Mature ovaries are orange-colored; testes are gray; and each gonad opens directly to the outside by a small *genital pore.*   Many thin-walled, fingerlike projections lined with peritoneum project from the coelom through the body wall to the outside; these are the skin gills, mentioned earlier.   An additional set of water tubes derived from the embryonic coelom is present in the sea stars; this is called the *hemal system.*   Its function is uncertain, however, and the term *hemal* is misleading, because the system does not correspond to the blood system of annelids or mollusks.   The nervous system is reduced to a nerve ring about the mouth and radial nerves in each arm.   Additional less important nerve complexes of a nerve-net type are found near the oral and aboral surfaces.

Nutrition

The echinoderms in general eat both plant and animal material, and although the chief food of the sea star is the oyster or clam, it will also capture small

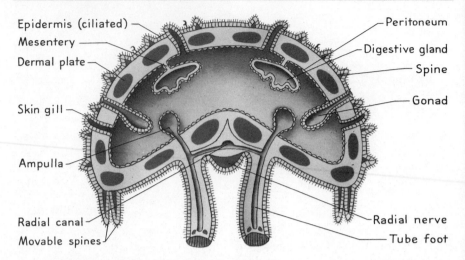

Epidermis (ciliated)
Mesentery
Dermal plate
Skin gill
Ampulla
Radial canal
Movable spines

Peritoneum
Digestive gland
Spine
Gonad
Radial nerve
Tube foot

Figure 16.5.   The structures of a sea-star arm are shown here in cross section.

organisms with its pedicellariae and tube feet.   The sea urchin feeds on both plants and animals, tearing them into small pieces by the chewing action of the teeth, which are part of an elaborate oral organ known as *Aristotle's lantern*. The sea cucumber, which lives on the bottom, often in soft mud, waves its tentacles about to capture small organisms on the surface, after which the food-laden tentacles are drawn into the mouth, the food scraped off, and sand or mud ejected.   Both intracellular and extracellular digestion take place in the echinoderms, and the walls of the digestive glands play an important part in both processes.   There are many amoebocytes moving about in the digestive tract, and these ingest and digest food in a manner like that previously described in the clam.   Animals such as the sea star, which partially digest the food outside the body, secrete copious amounts of the powerful protein-splitting enzyme formed in the large digestive glands.

Respiration

The large size of the fluid-filled coelom simplifies the respiratory problems of most of the echinoderms.   The simple skin gills, which are actually only

Figure 16.6.   A starfish is opening a mussel with its tube feet.   (Courtesy W. K. Fisher, Pacific Grove, California.)

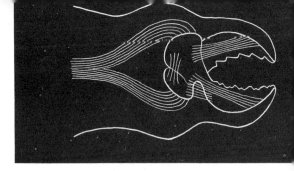

Figure 16.7. The pedicellariae are tiny jaws which protect the surface of the echinoderm, especially the skin gills. Food and debris will be caught and held in the jaws, which are opened and closed by muscle contractions.

thin-walled projections of the coelom, extend to the outside of the body. Since the cilia on the lining of the coelom and the cilia on the surface of the body create slow-moving currents of water, carbon dioxide can be eliminated and oxygen absorbed through the papillae as the water flows over the gills. It appears that the tube feet also are very important in respiration, and in the sea star about 50 per cent of the gaseous exchange is by way of these structures. The sea cucumbers have developed a remarkable respiratory system which is undoubtedly correlated with their life on the sea bottom, where the amount of available oxygen is low. The posterior part of the alimentary canal, the *cloaca*, in sea cucumbers becomes a water pump, by means of the alternate contraction and relaxation of the muscles attached to its wall. A much-branched *respiratory tree* projects from the cloaca into the coelom and makes possible the diffusion of the gases throughout the coelom; there are even red blood cells containing hemoglobin present in the sea cucumber. The animal, in spite of the fact that there may be only small quantities of oxygen present about it, is able to respire efficiently.

Excretion

The skin gills not only function for respiration but also aid in excretion. The waste materials in the coelomic fluid diffuse through the papillae into the sea

Figure 16.8. The aboral view of the starfish (a) shows its dermal spines. The oral view (b) shows the tube feet retracted and covered by movable spines. (Courtesy Clarence Flaten.)

(a) **(b)**

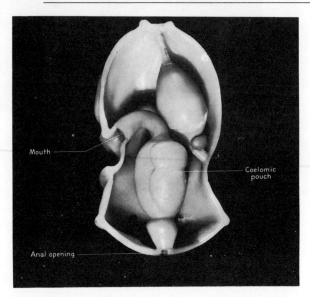

Mouth

Coelomic pouch

Anal opening

Figure 16.9.   A model of a tornaria larva.   It is obvious that this embryonic form is quite different from the trochophore larva of the annelids. (pp. 220, 239).   (Courtesy Clarence Flaten.)

water, and ammonia is reported to be the most common form of nitrogenous waste product; but there is also approximately 20 per cent of the nitrogenous waste excreted in the form of amino acids.   Amoebocytes may also ingest nitrogenous materials and help with excretion in this manner.   There is no special organ or structure designed to stablize the fluid content of the body, and it is not surprising, therefore, to discover that the coelomic fluid has a chemical composition almost identical with that of the sea water outside the animal.

Reproduction

The sexes are separate in the echinoderms, and the relationship of the reproductive organs to the coelom has already been described.   Perhaps the most important feature in reproduction is the development of a *tornaria larva*.   This type of barrel-shaped, free-swimming embryo with characteristic ciliated bands is found elsewhere only in some of the animals which are usually considered to be primitive chordates.   The mouth develops as a new structure in these larvae, and the blastopore region becomes an anus, a development in marked contrast to that which takes place in the *trochophore* larva which we discussed previously.   The development of the mesoderm also is different: instead of arising from mesodermal bands, as in the trochophore, it is formed from pouches which grow from the archenteron, as was described earlier in Chapter 12 on coelom development.   These embryonic processes have been emphasized by many zoologists, who consider that such evidence demonstrates a close relationship between the Echinodermata and the Chordata, because the embryos of some primitive chordates have the same features.   This conclusion, however, should be accepted with reservations at present.

Coordination

The nervous system is a combination of a nerve ring and radial nerves, with a nerve-net system in the oral and aboral surfaces. There is no indication of any structure which might even remotely resemble a brain. Transmission in the nerve net is diffuse and slow, comparable with that of the coelenterates; but some rapid-conducting nerve fibers do cut across the nerve nets. Coordinated movement of the arms is dependent on conduction through the nerve ring, and the tube feet are controlled primarily by the radial nerves. Studies which have been made of the behavior of the echinoderms have indicated that the sense organs are simple, and that adjustments to stimuli are a result of trial-and-error

Figure 16.10. The slow, methodical motion of the starfish in turning over is seen in this sequence. Note the flexibility and coordination of the animal's movements and the use of its tube feet. (Courtesy Ralph Buschbaum.)

(a) **(b)**

(c) **(d)**

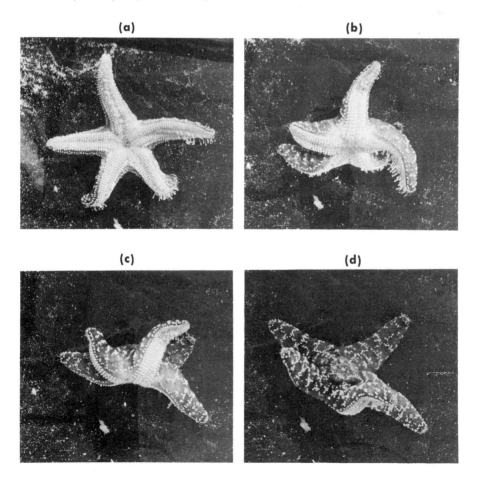

processes.   As might be expected, the echinoderms give very little evidence of being able to learn after being subjected to repeated trials.

General considerations

The unique hydraulic system and the interesting radial symmetry have not evoked the amount of intensive study of the Echinodermata that might have been expected.   Actually, very little is known about the physiological processes of the members of the phylum, and no detailed investigation has been made of any one form.   Our knowledge of the phylum at present represents a piece-meal collection of information from the study of various organisms.   The fact that there is considerable diversity in structure and habitat demands that we should be cautious in our attempts to explain the functional processes of the entire phylum from such incomplete evidence.

Classification of Echinodermata

Phylum Echinodermata   Five-part radial symmetry, nonsegmented, and with a well-developed water vascular system and coelom.   A spiny calcareous skeleton is present.

CLASS I. CRINOIDEA.   Sessile animals attached by a stalk and with branched arms having many small, lateral projections.   Example: sea lily.

CLASS II. ASTEROIDEA.   Usually five, or groups of five, arms which are not marked off from the central disk.   Many tube feet with adhesive disks are present on the oral surface.   Example: sea star.

CLASS III. OPHIUROIDEA.   The five arms are definitely marked off from the central disk.   Ambulacral groove is absent, tube feet without adhesive disks and modified as tentacles.   Examples: serpent star, or brittle star.

CLASS IV. ECHINOIDEA.   Arms are absent, and body form is spherical. Skeleton has calcareous plates which possess movable spines.   Example: sea urchin.

CLASS V. HOLOTHUROIDEA.   No arms are present, and the skeleton is reduced.   Body form is an elongated tube, with tentacles surrounding the mouth. Example: sea cucumber.

REFERENCES

BROWN, F. A. (ed.), *Selected Invertebrate Types,* pp. 515–546.   John Wiley & Sons, Inc., New York, 1950.

CLARK, A. H., "Sea Lilies and Feather Stars," *Smithsonian Miscellaneous Collections,* Vol. 72, No. 7, 1921.

HARVEY, ETHEL BROWNE, *The American Arbacia and Other Sea Urchins.* Princeton University Press, Princeton, N.J., 1956.

HYMAN, L., *The Invertebrates: Echinodermata,* Vol. IV. McGraw-Hill Book Company, Inc., New York, 1955.

LANKESTER, R. E. (ed.), *Treatise on Zoology,* Part 3. Adam and Charles Black, London, 1900.

MACGINITIE, G. E., N. MACGINITIE, *Natural History of Marine Animals,* pp. 221–251. McGraw-Hill Book Company, Inc., New York, 1949.

MEAD, A. D., *Natural History of the Starfish,* pp. 203–224. Bulletin, United States Fish Commission, Vol. 19, 1900.

17

How to
Live on Income

Parasitism

●

The difference between a carnivore and a parasite is simply the difference between living on capital and income, between the burglar and the blackmailer.
—Elton, 1935

A man who is able to live on income is usually greatly respected, especially by his banker, but the people who admire a thrifty man do not accord the same respect to that thrifty animal, the parasite. Biologically speaking, this aversion to parasitism is not justified, because a successful parasite is a very conservative organism which lives its adult life on another animal or plant, the *definitive host*, without destroying the life of that host. A carnivore, in contrast, is a highly wasteful animal, because it ruthlessly destroys the life of another organism in order to secure its food material. The distinction between a parasitic and a nonparasitic animal, however, is often difficult to make, because an animal which lives primarily as a carnivore may be essentially a parasite at certain times. A man, for example, when he drinks a glass of milk or eats honey, is partaking of food in a parasitic manner.

The economic aspects of parasitism are considerable, as far as human welfare is concerned. Not only is man victimized by parasites, but the domesticated animals and plants upon which he depends so largely for his food frequently are heavily parasitized. Parasitic infestations render many parts of the world almost uninhabitable. Malaria, caused by a protozoan, is one of the major causes of death in the world today, and in ancient times was one of the contributing factors to the downfall of the Roman Empire. Even today it has been estimated that 2,200,000,000 people are infested by worms, and in parts of Africa hundreds of thousands of people have died in the past 50 years as a result of the attacks of sleeping sickness, which is caused by another parasitic protozoan.

322

Figure 17.1. The cocoons of a wasp in (a) can be seen on the back of the tomato worm (hawk moth larva). The fatal results of this pickaback ride are apparent in (b). (Copyright by General Biological Supply House, Inc., Chicago.)

(a)   (b)

Areas of the world in which personal and group hygiene are practiced extensively are not immune from parasitism. Infestations with hookworm, with trichina, and with *Ascaris* are common in North America; and it has been estimated that 16 per cent of the population of the United States has suffered from trichinosis as a consequence of eating improperly prepared pork. Fortunately, most parasitic infections are not fatal, but their effects, though subtle, are important to man because parasitized persons often are unable to work efficiently, and thus millions of man-hours of productive labor are lost annually. The problem of parasitism has been emphasized in recent years because modern aircraft have had the effect of shrinking the size of the world. It is possible in a matter of a few hours to reach the metropolitan districts of the world from the most remote regions, and parasitic diseases originally confined to limited areas can now be transmitted to all parts of the world in a matter of only a few hours. Parasites which were read about in books, or were something which happened only to primitive people, now can be carried throughout the world, and anyone may be subjected suddenly and with no warning to their attack.

A parasite is often considered to be degenerate, but we should emphasize that parasites are highly specialized rather than degenerate. It is true that certain structures typical of free-living organisms are lost during the adaptation for parasitic existence; but as a compensation parasites develop other organs to a far greater extent than do free-living animals. Every gradation in the degree of parasitism and parasitic modification exists. Some animals, such as the leeches, exercise an option of being either parasites or carnivores; others, such as the mosquitoes, are occasional parasites, visiting the host only long enough to eat, and are parasitic only as adults. Conversely, many insects are parasitic in the larval stage but are free-living when adult. The most striking parasitic modifications are the *development of attachment organs*, such as hooks or suckers; the *degeneration of sense and locomotor organs;* and an astounding emphasis on the *production of reproductive cells* or *cysts.* Equally remarkable is the formation by many parasites of *special larval types*. Only in the larval stage do these types parasitize the animals in which they live, the *intermediate hosts;* and they may also reproduce while in the larval forms. The parasites as a group, therefore, constitute an unusual assemblage of highly adapted organisms, and the problem of their origin constitutes another biological mystery story.

Parasites undoubtedly developed from free-living organisms after a long period of adaptation, although there is no direct evidence for their origin in any one phylum. But, as in the case of the origin of the metazoans, indirect evidence is available concerning the manner by which free-living organisms could have become parasitic, and the facts are very suggestive. Many animals live as guests in or on other animals, a condition we noted previously in protozoans, sponges, and coelenterates. This association is termed *commensalism*, and it may transform into another relationship called *mutualism*, in which the organisms are helpful to each other. The protozoans which live in the alimentary canal of the termite are classic examples of mutualism, because these acellular animals break down the cellulose of ingested plant cells to simpler chemical substances that can be digested by the termite. The protozoans in turn are protected, and feed on materials in the termite alimentary canal. It has been shown that if the protozoans are killed by exposing the termite to pure oxygen, the latter starves, because its own enzymes are unable to digest cellulose. A somewhat similar situation exists in the digestive system of man, where millions of bacteria and Protozoa in the large intestine aid in the breakdown of partially digested food and thus prevent the formation of toxic substances. The number and kinds of these organisms actually varies with diet, and it is possible to distinguish between a vegetarian and a meat eater by examining the intestinal guests.

When one member of the pair of organisms in a mutual association ceases to perform its share of the work and begins to live entirely on materials supplied by the other partner, a condition of *parasitism* is created. One of the most interesting examples of this was mentioned in the discussion of the flatworms (p. 176). It will be recalled that the worm Acoela has a mutual arrangement with certain plant cells, which supply oxygen and use carbon dioxide in the

Figure 17.2. This "parasitic" wasp has paralyzed two locusts and dragged them to her underground nest. Then she deposits a single egg in one of the bodies. Note the developing Parasitic larva in (c). (Courtesy National Audubon Society; photos by Hal W. Harrison.)

(a)   **(b)**   **(c)**

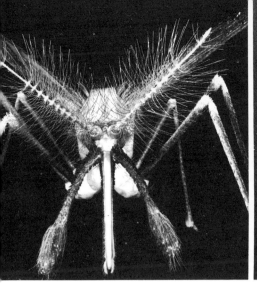

Figure 17.3. The heads of these two ectoparasites, the mosquito and the lamprey eel, show very different organs for feeding. The mosquito is an efficient parasite but may carry the malarial parasite, which frequently is inefficient. The lamprey often is inefficient. (Courtesy American Museum of Natural History.)

young worms. The adult Acoela, however, cease to feed but live entirely at the expense of the guest plant cells which, unfortunately, are unable to support both themselves and the acoel; as a result, both die. Some animals undoubtedly have become parasites as a result of having been accidentally ingested by another animal. When structures are present that could protect the ingested animal within the host, parasitism may develop. The nematode worms with their protective cuticle are well adapted to survive this kind of an accident, and it is not surprising, therefore, that there are many notable parasites in this group.

Kinds of Parasites

Parasites are usually classified according to their *position* and their *success*, or *efficiency*. Organisms which live on the surface are the *ectoparasites;* and those which live within the alimentary canal, blood, body cavities, organs, or tissues are the *endoparasites*. It is often difficult, however, to make a sharp distinction between the two groups, because certain external forms—for example, the leeches—occasionally may enter the mouth or nasal passages; and others, such as mites and ticks, may burrow below the superficial skin layers. Biologically speaking, the success of the parasite is more important than its position, and those forms which do not destroy the host are termed *efficient*, whereas those which kill the host are called *inefficient*. These designations give rise to further classification difficulty, because some parasites may live during their larval stages in intermediate hosts which they frequently kill, but if they do not kill the definitive host, these parasites are considered to be efficient. The most significant modifications of the parasites are superimposed upon the features of the various phyla, and these modifications, therefore, are more important for the description of parasites than are the characteristics of the specific phylum to which each belongs. We will for convenience or reference, however, organize our discussion according to phyla.

Protozoan parasites

The versatility of the protozoans is strikingly demonstrated by their parasitic forms, because there is hardly an animal which does not harbor at least one protozoan parasite especially adapted for it—and many animals have dozens. The protozoans even parasitize each other, as is illustrated by some large ciliates which provide food and transportation for at least a hundred parasitic amoebae. The Protozoa vary in their parasitic adaptations from the slight modifications we will observe in those called *kissing amoeba* to the development of complex reproductive stages in the malarial organisms, but it would be impossible to describe all the major features of parasitism merely by limiting our discussion to the protozoans.

AMOEBIC PARASITES • The kissing amoeba (*Entamoeba gingivalis*) and the dysentery amoeba (*Entamoeba histolytica*) are both parasites of man, and they are relatively unmodified. The kissing amoeba is found in about 50 per cent of the human population (estimated 75 per cent of those people over 40), and lives in the mouth cavity at the base of the teeth. It is not certain that this animal is the cause of the disease *pyorrhea*, but the amoeba is usually present when this pathological condition exists. The animals feed on white blood cells and occasionally on red blood cells, ingesting these cells as though feeding on other Protozoa. Aside from the obvious method of transmission implied by its name, this organism is transferred by careless cooks who cough into the soup or who do not wash their hands carefully before dishing up a hot dog or a hamburger.

The dysentery amoeba is somewhat more specialized in structure and restricted in its habits than is the kissing amoeba. It lives in the alimentary canal and often causes ulcers by eroding the wall of the intestine. Its food is ex-

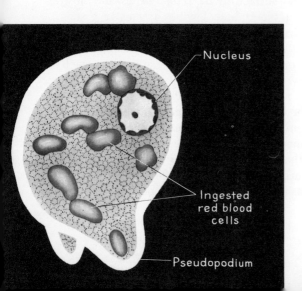

Nucleus

Ingested red blood cells

Pseudopodium

Figure 17.4. This amoeba is the cause of amoebic dysentery, the scourge of many tropical countries. It can form a resistant cyst and, in this stage, may be easily transferred from one person to another.

clusively red blood cells. These amoebae sometimes get into the blood stream instead of remaining in their usual haunt, the intestine, and are distributed about in the body. Serious complications result from such inadvertent migrations, because the amoebae settle down in such atypical habitats as the brain, liver, or other organs, where they can produce ulcers. Probably the most important specialization of the dysenteric amoebae is the formation of protective coats about themselves, and in this condition they are called *cysts*. These cysts may leave the body with the fecal material of the host and then exist for long periods of time even under adverse environmental conditions. Unfortunately for mankind they are resistant, while in the cyst stage, to the usual chemical methods employed in water purification; and polluted drinking water, therefore, is an important means of transfer from one person to another. The most serious outbreak of *amoebic dysentery* in recent years in the United States occurred at the Chicago Fair of 1933, where the drinking water in two hotels became contaminated by leaks from the sewers; 1000 cases of amoebic dysentery are known to have developed, from which 58 known deaths resulted. Amoebic dysentery is a major disease in the tropics, as many GI's discovered during World War II, but only 5 to 10 per cent of the population of the United States is infected.

FLAGELLATE PARASITES • Although astronomical numbers of flagellates live in mutual associations, it is fortunate that the parasitic forms of flagellates are relatively few in number. These live primarily in the intestine or in the blood stream of the definitive host; but some, such as those responsible for *oriental sore*, invade the superficial tissues of the body. The most deadly of all flagellates, the *trypanosomes*, are responsible for *African sleeping sickness*° and will serve to illustrate some modifications of the group. The versatile trypanosomes can live in deer, antelope, alligators, and even leeches, where they apparently are guests; it is only when they are in the blood stream of man or of domestic animals that they become killers. It was as late as 1909 before the methods of transmission and the life cycles of the trypanosomes were discovered, although their role as the causative agent for sleeping sickness was established earlier. The animals are carried from one host to another by the *tsetse fly*, which is the intermediate host, and some slight changes in body form occur while in the different hosts. Werc it not for the fact that the tsetse-fly carriers and the trypanosomes which cause the disease are confined to limited areas of Africa, sleeping sickness would undoubtedly be public enemy number one among human diseases. The death rate among children who contract the disease is from 80 to 90 per cent, and it is also very high among adults. The trypanosomes probably were introduced into the Uganda region of Africa by the Stanley Expedition of 1888; and in that area from 1901 to 1908 there were 200,000 deaths from sleeping sickness in a native population of 300,000! The sleeping

° Not to be confused with encephalitis, the "sleeping sickness" found in the United States, which is caused by a virus.

sickness trypanosomes are, of course, very inefficient parasites in man.   Another trypanosome causes *kala azar* disease in oriental countries, and it is also highly inefficient.   The intermediate host in this case is a *sand fly;* and until this fact and a means of control were discovered, as many as 95 per cent of the population of some villages died from kala azar.   The important adaptation possessed by the flagellates, which was not present in the amoebae, is the use of insects as an intermediate host.   The insects provide aerial transportation and greatly improve the chances for the parasites to be transmitted to new hosts.   The trypanosomes also possess remarkable adaptive abilities which enable them to develop strains resistant to the drugs used to kill them.   This development of resistance presents a major difficulty for the control of these parasites.

SPOROZOAN PARASITES • The class Sporozoa is exclusively parasitic, and as early as 1903 Lankester's *Treatise on Zoology* listed 27 pages of animals parasitized by sporozoans.   The sporozoans have evolved complex specializations which are especially noteworthy because of the formation of the *spores*, reproductive stages which give to the class the name *Sporozoa* (spore animals).   Well-known parasites among the Sporozoa are *Monocystis* in earthworms, and para-

Figure 17.5.   Malaria cycle.   The arrows show the progress of the malarial organisms and their relationship to the mosquito and the human host.

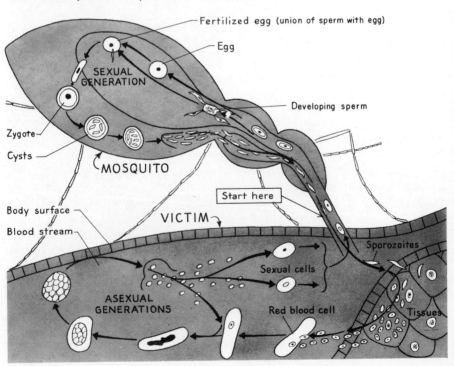

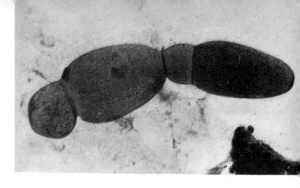

Figure 17.6. The sporozoans cause a great variety of diseases in many different organisms, being parasites of the body cavity and bloom stream. These two gregarine sporozoans are joined end-to-end as they were when removed from a cricket. (Copyright General Biological Supply House, Inc., Chicago.)

sites which cause *coccidiosis* in cattle and fowl, *pebrine* disease of silkworms, and *malaria* in birds and man. Malaria, because of its dreadful effect on man, probably has been studied more than any other disease and will be the subject of our discussion.

The malarial organism, *Plasmodium,* was discovered in 1880, and in 1898 Sir Ronald Ross proved experimentally that certain species of mosquitoes were necessary for the transmission of bird malaria from one host to another. Giovanni Grassi, almost simultaneously, worked out the details for the life cycle of human malaria. Although malaria ("bad air") has been known since ancient times, it remains the cause of more deaths annually than any other single disease. Chandler quotes data for 1943 listing 300,000,000 cases of malaria responsible for 3,000,000 deaths. India is probably the country most devastated by this disease. The control of malaria is relatively simple, cures can be effected at a moderate cost, and the disease undoubtedly could be completely eradicated if it were systematically attacked. The number of cases in the United States, for example, decreased from 4435 in 1935 to only 341 in 1946. The saving in hospital costs and man-hours of work and the improvement of general health more than compensated for the money expended in control.*

The two types of malaria most common in human beings are *benign (P. vivax)* and *malignant (P. falciparum)*, both characterized by chills and fever in 48-hour cycles. The parasites, after being introduced into the blood stream by the mosquito, disappear within a few minutes into the tissues, where they develop and multiply for several days before returning to the blood stream. The red blood corpuscles then are invaded by the parasites. Only about 1 per cent of the cells of the body of the host are attacked in benign malaria, but 10 per cent are parasitized in malignant malaria. The parasites undergo rapid divisions within the cells, after which they break free and invade other blood cells. This periodic destruction of blood cells for some unknown reason takes place at regular time intervals and is accompanied by the characteristic chills and fever.

The parasites begin a new type of development after going through several *asexual generations* in the corpuscles. The parasites' plasmodium grows more slowly, develops pigment, enlarges, and forms *sexual cells* of either sperm or egg

* In 1945 there were 411,600 malaria cases in Italy; in the first six months of 1951 there were only 392 cases.

type. These reproductive individuals, when sucked up from the blood stream of the host by a certain type of mosquito, unite to form a body which is comparable with a fertilized egg, and then begin a new cycle of development and specialization. A wormlike organism appears first, penetrates the stomach wall of the mosquito, and develops into a *cyst.* The contents of the cyst undergo repeated divisions until as many as 10,000 new individuals are formed within the cyst wall. Since each mosquito may have as many as 50 cysts, it is obvious that the reproductive potential is tremendous. The cyst finally ruptures, releasing new organisms into the mosquito body cavity, from which they migrate to the salivary glands and are discharged with the saliva into the blood stream of the persons bitten by the mosquito.

It is obvious from this account that the specialization for parasitism in *Plasmodium* involves not only the use of an intermediate host but also the development of sexual and asexual reproductive stages. The mosquito becomes a flying transport, and the fantastic numbers of new organisms produced within it improve the odds that at least a few individuals will be able to circumvent the body defenses of the host to establish a new generation.

Metazoan parasites

The metazoan parasites are generally better known than are the protozoan, although the diseases caused by protozoan parasites are familiar enough, as we have seen. Especially prominent among metazoan parasites are the parasitic worms. It was mentioned that there are approximately 2,000,000,000 worm infestations in man, but these are not equally distributed. Some individuals are completely free of worms, whereas others may play host to several different kinds. The chief offenders, in total numbers, among the parasitic worms are the *roundworms,* but the most vicious are the *flukes* and *tapeworms* of the phylum Platyhelminthes. These parasitic flatworms are also among the most highly specialized parasites and can be used to illustrate the lavish adaptations which can exist in parasites.

FLATWORM PARASITES • It will be recalled that the *liver fluke* is similar in its structure to the planarians, but it has a complicated life cycle, with asexual and sexual reproduction, which involves an intermediate host as well as a definitive host. The life cycle of the sheep-liver fluke is typical of that of many other flukes. The eggs may be produced at the rate of 10,000 to 25,000 per day and are deposited outside the body with the fecal material of the host, usually in a pasture with a marshy area. Each egg develops into a free-swimming ciliated larva, the *miracidium,* which resembles a protozoan. This larva swims about in a spiral path until it chances to encounter an aquatic snail (each species of fluke requires a special species of mollusk), into which it works its way by boring or by digesting away the surface tissues. The larva then migrates into the liver of the snail, where it produces a protective wall about itself to form a cyst, and begins to reproduce asexually to form a second larval type, the *redia.* This in

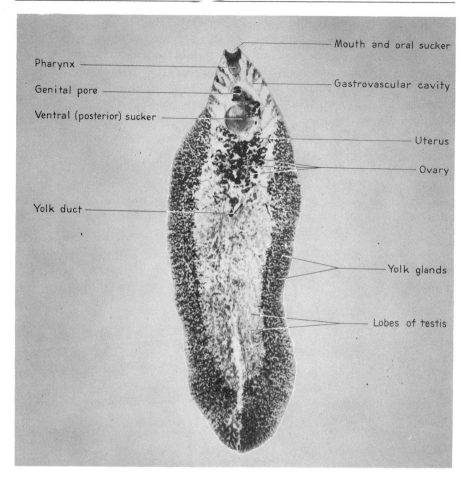

Mouth and oral sucker

Pharynx

Genital pore

Gastrovascular cavity

Ventral (posterior) sucker

Uterus

Ovary

Yolk duct

Yolk glands

Lobes of testis

Figure 17.7.   The structure of the liver fluke.   (Courtesy Clarence Flaten.)

turn gives birth asexually to second- and third-generation rediae.   Eventually there is formed a third larval type, the *cercaria*, which escapes from the snail and encysts on vegetation or, in the case of the human-liver fluke, becomes free-swimming.   The encysted larvae, when eaten by the definitive host, escape from the cyst and work their way to their final lodging in the lungs or liver.   The human-liver fluke is a very common parasite in the orient.   This parasite also has adopted a fish as an additional intermediate host.   The oriental custom of eating raw (or slightly heated) fish leads to a very high incidence of human infection, because the larval flukes are not killed except by thorough cooking.

The *blood flukes* rather than the liver flukes are the most serious flatworm parasites in human beings.   These worms in their adult stages live in the blood vessels and tend to select those in the region of the alimentary canal and the bladder. The blood flukes are especially deadly in Egypt, Japan, China, and the Philippines, where the percentage of infection is relatively high. They differ from most flukes in that the sexes are separate, and the females usually live most of their lives within a groove on the surface of the male. The reproductive potential is high, and a single miracidium may give rise to as many as 200,000 cercariae. Infection is caused by the cercariae boring through the skin, or through the membranes of the mouth if they have been taken in with polluted drinking water. They are destroyed when taken into the digestive tract. The

Figure 17.8.   The Chinese liver fluke (a), a human parasite transferred through raw or partially cooked fish.. The egg of a blood fluke (b). The characteristic shapes of different flukes' eggs, when studied in fecal matter, can be used to diagnose infection. A giant redia (c) through whose transparent body wall can be seen unborn cercariae. The cercaria of Fascicola (d) Cercaria of Echinostoma (e). These show the possible variation in shape of these larvae. (Courtesy General Biological Supply House, Inc., Chicago.)

(a)   **(b)**

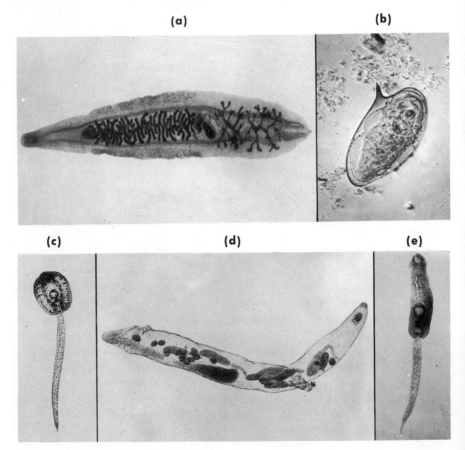

(c)   **(d)**   **(e)**

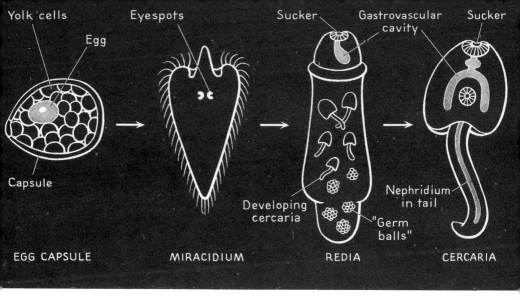

| Yolk cells | Eyespots | Sucker | Gastrovascular cavity | Sucker |

Egg

Capsule

Developing cercaria

Nephridium in tail

"Germ balls"

EGG CAPSULE   MIRACIDIUM   REDIA   CERCARIA

Figure 17.9. Though different in detail, in general structure the fluke larvae are uniform, and all pass through the development stages represented.

blood flukes are versatile and some can be cultivated in laboratory animals. Birds frequently are victims of these worms, and the cercariae of the *bird flukes* often are so numerous in the Great Lakes region that they produce the *swimmers' itch* when they attack human beings. Fortunately, an allergic reaction is about the only serious result.

TAPEWORMS • The tapeworms represent almost the acme in parasitic adaptations, and it may be said literally that they eat to reproduce. This was pointed out previously for the beef tapeworm, which in a 10-year period may lay as many as 2,500,000,000 eggs. It will be remembered that the tapeworms are flattened animals divided into a series of segments called *proglottids*, and a head region, the *scolex*, which possesses suckers and, in many cases, hooks for attachment. The tapeworms have undergone such extensive modifications that the sense organs and the gastrovascular cavity have been lost completely. These animals, therefore, depend entirely on food material digested for them by the host; and the food must be absorbed through the body wall of the worm. The surface of the tapeworm is protected by a cuticle which supports the animal and prevents the enzymes of the host from digesting the worm. Tapeworms not only have definitive hosts but also live in a surprising variety of intermediate hosts.

The *hog tapeworm*, the *dog tapeworm*, and the *broad tapeworm*—and to a more limited extent, the *beef tapeworm*—are especially important to man, and their extreme modifications do not obscure their flatworm characteristics. The structural features of the tapeworms, as well as their ability to develop new segments, were outlined in the discussion of the Platyhelminthes and will not be repeated here; but reproduction should be considered in more detail at this time.

The fertilized eggs are protected by a "shell" secreted about them by the shell gland and begin their embryonic development within the tapeworm's saclike uterus. The uterus acquires numerous branches as the embryos develop, and simultaneously the testes and the female reproductive organs degenerate. The greatly branched and distended uterus eventually fills the interior of the proglottid almost completely. The proglottid at this stage is *ripe* and is located at the end of the worm. This ripe proglottid will be broken from the worm and eliminated from the body of the host with the fecal matter. The multitude of embryos contained within the proglottid is freed and is confronted with the hazards of the world and the difficulty of infecting the intermediate host.

When the embryos have been eaten by the intermediate host—for example, the hog—and enter the alimentary canal, they are released from their protective coating and penetrate the intestinal walls; then they enter the blood vessels, in which they are carried throughout the body, finally lodging in skeletal muscle. The embryo develops into a *bladder worm* which produces an inverted scolex on its inner wall. There may be hundreds of these in a few ounces of pork and their presence gives a "measly" appearance to the pork.

Proper refrigeration at low temperatures for several weeks will destroy the bladder worms, as will thorough cooking. The practice of eating freshly-butchered pork or pork roasts which are not adequately cooked throughout is responsible for human infection. Many Europeans have a fondness for smoked sausages, and in some areas of Europe as many as 90 per cent of the population have been reported to be infected. The hog tapeworm is especially dangerous

Figure 17.10. The mature proglottid in (a) has well-developed testes, ovaries, and a duct system; that in (b) is in an advanced state of becoming a mere broodsac. (Courtesy Clarence Flaten.)

(a)   **(b)**

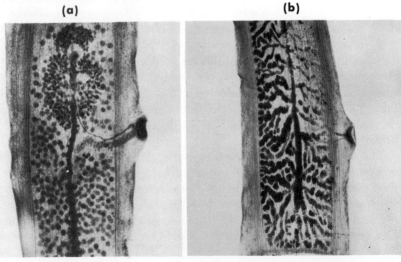

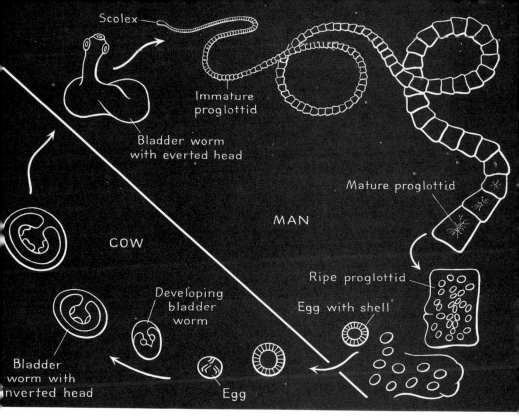

Figure 17.11. Tapeworm life cycle, showing the principal stages of development in each of the two necessary hosts.

to man, because occasionally a proglottid may rupture within the intestine and the bladder worms develop in the host, who of course becomes an intermediate host as well. If the bladder worms should develop within the brain or liver the results may soon be fatal.

The incidence of hog-tapeworm infection in the United States is on the decline, thanks to meat inspection at the packing houses. Unfortunately, the broad tapeworms and one of the small, dog tapeworms have become more serious menaces. The huge, broad tapeworm, which was introduced into the Great Lakes region after 1900 by European immigrants, has two intermediate hosts: a water flea and fishes, usually pike or pickerel. The eating of pickled or improperly cooked fish in which the bladder worms have not been killed is responsible for the transfer to human beings. This worm is now being spread widely to regions outside the Great Lakes area. The hyatid, a dog tapeworm, is very small and has man as the intermediate host! The bladder worm of the hyatid, however, may become two or more inches in diameter; and when lodged in the brain, liver, or abdomen, it produces death. The habit of letting the pet dog "kiss the baby" is not recommended in the best zoological circles.

ROUNDWORMS • The nematodes have been examined more thoroughly than any other of the phyla of worm parasites, because these ubiquitous creatures parasitize most species of vertebrates as well as many plants. They are of interest to the zoologist and parasitologist since they illustrate every degree of adaptation for parasitism: some have very little modification of structure or life cycle; others either have intermediate or definitive hosts; and a few have two intermediate hosts in addition to the definitive host. Nematode parasites, therefore, parallel closely the pattern of development of parasitism which we have observed in the Protozoa. It will be possible to consider only a few of the more notorious roundworms, and these will be chosen for the purpose of illustrating a few of the variations in adaptation.

Ascaris has been described by A. C. Chandler as "man's faithful and constant companion," and its association with man is recorded from ancient times. The hog ascaris and the human ascaris are almost indistinguishable, but probably are rarely, if ever, transferred from one to the other. The hog and man both are infected, however, through filthy living habits, for the eggs must be ingested in order for the host to be infected! Rural areas and the outskirts of some cities, where sanitation may be poor and where human excrement may be used for fertilizer or merely voided on the ground, are regions in which these parasites

Figure 17.12. The heads of these two dreaded endoparasites, the tapeworm and the hookworm, show with frightening clarity how each attaches to the living substance of its host. The head of the tapeworm (a) is photographed from above. The head of the hookworm (b) is shown in longitudinal section. [(a) Courtesy H. Walter Steffens, University of Idaho; (b) Armed Forces Institute of Pathology, neg. no. 33819.]

(a)   **(b)**

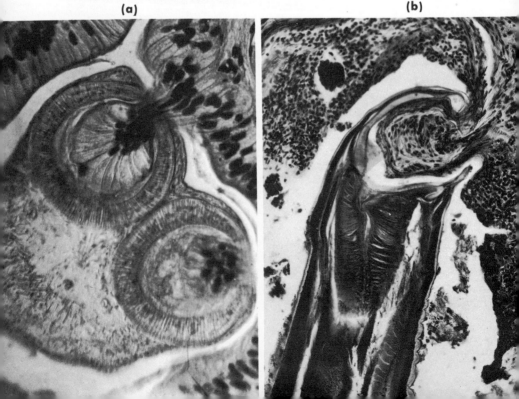

thrive. Ascaris eggs are protected by a "shell" which is very resistant, even to strong chemicals, and thus the developing embryo may survive very adverse conditions. The eggs hatch within the intestine of the host but do not remain in this region. The young animals take an extensive 10-day excursion throughout the body, during which time they increase in size about tenfold. The newly hatched worms enter the blood vessels and migrate to the lungs, where they leave the capillaries and enter the air passages, journey through the air passages to the throat, and are swallowed to return to the intestine.

Several hundred adult worms may be present in the intestine at any one time. The females vary in length from 8 to 14 inches and the males are 6 to 12 inches long. The adults live only about one year, and a person parasitized by *Ascaris* will be free of the worms at the end of this time, unless reinfected. The damage done by the ascaris is varied. They compete with the host for food, of course, because infection often involves several hundred of these sizable nematodes. The major harm, however, results indirectly from their activities: pneumonia and tuberculosis are common, and often fatal, because of the damage done to lung tissue by the parasites; there may be rather severe allergic reactions; and the intestine may be blocked completely if the worms are irritated (p. 338). Such blockage may be fatal unless the animals are removed surgically. Furthermore, the adult ascaris is an explorer and may migrate to such unusual dwelling places as the liver.

The reproductive ability of the female ascaris is stupendous. The worm at the height of the reproductive cycle may lay 100,000 eggs per day and during her one year of life she may ovulate 27,000,000 eggs. This gives some indication of the chances against any single egg infecting a new host—the odds must be millions to one.

The *hookworms* have been the most thoroughly studied of any single group of worms, and the reasons are obvious. These parasites have an insidious effect; they sap the energy of the host, which produces lethargy and shiftlessness and often stunts growth. They, like the ascaris, are transferred from one host to another by filthy habits. The use of human excrement for fertilizing gardens and the lack of sanitary facilities are the contributing factors, along with the common practice, in some areas of the world, of walking barefooted through the mixture of soil and fecal material. Infection takes place when the larvae penetrate the skin, usually of the hands or feet, and work their way into the blood vessels. The hookworms migrate in the same fashion as the ascaris worms, eventually reaching the air passages and being swallowed. The worms attach to the intestinal wall and suck blood and tissue debris. Severe anemia is the usual result, and pneumonia or tuberculosis frequently accompany a hookworm infection.

The adult female is 10 to 11 millimeters long, and may live five years, during which time she may lay 10,000 eggs per day. Control measures are simple, cheap, and very effective. The administration of carbon tetrachloride (cleaning fluid), or of tetrachloroethylene and epsom salts, costs only a penny or two and

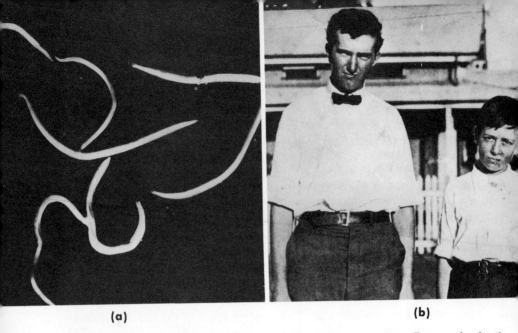

(a)   (b)

Figure 17.13. Hookworms are only about half an inch long, but their effects can be drastic. They feed on both blood and tissues and, when present in any number, cause severe anemia. In children this results in stunted growth. The two men are the same age, but the one on the right had hookworm. [(a) Courtesy, Armed Forces Institute of Pathology, neg. no. 47213; (b) Rockefeller Foundation.]

usually cures the patient. The major danger in the treatment arises from the fact that frequently ascaris worms are present along with the hookworms. Carbon tetrachloride merely irritates the ascaris, which may mass together into a squirming ball and block the intestine. Those who are interested in a most fascinating account of the world-wide crusade against the hookworms are referred to Dr. Victor Heiser's exciting story, *An American Doctor's Odyssey.* It will be seen that the ascaris worms have very few specializations for parasitism, and that the hookworm is only slightly more modified. The latter has a better method of access to the host and a more intimate relation to the host by attaching to the intestinal wall.

Trichinella and the *filarial worms* (genus *Wuchereria*) are still more specialized for parasitism. *Trichinella spiralis* has developed an association with several hosts in what is almost an intermediate-host relationship. Infestation by trichinella in man causes the disease *trichinosis.* The human being is infected by these worms as a result of eating pork which contains the larvae encysted in the muscle of the hog. A single ounce of pork may contain 100,000 larvae, which are freed when the pork is digested, attach to the intestinal wall, molt several times, and reach sexual maturity in about 40 hours. Approximately half the worms are females, and they are only three to four millimeters long; the males are smaller. Each female, after mating, may release as many as 1500 larvae into the blood. The larvae migrate through the body, and finally settle down in skeletal muscle. They are about one millimeter long at this time and wind themselves into a characteristic coil.   After a time, the host secretes a coating of calcium about the larva, and the encapsulated parasite eventually dies.   Hogs originally become infected by eating garbage containing pork scraps.   The practice of feeding garbage to stock is much more common than is usually known, because most large cities sell their garbage to contractors for feeding to hogs.   Human beings become infected by eating infested pork which has been improperly refrigerated and cooked.   The consumption of home-butchered meat or of meat from small slaughterhouses where meat inspection is not a regular or careful procedure is responsible for the spread of the disease. It is very disconcerting to discover that in such a supposedly sanitary country as the United States, at least 16 per cent of the population has or has had *trichinosis*.

The symptoms of trichinosis are varied, depending upon the degree of infection.   Muscular pains, intestinal disorder, and a general rundown feeling, often interpreted as an intestinal upset, may be the only symptoms.   A heavy infection, on the other hand, may be fatal in a very short time.   It has been estimated that death will follow if a man ingests five worms per gram of his body weight. Since a single pork chop may contain several hundred thousand worms, it is obvious that these minute animals are a real menace to man.   Trichinosis was undoubtedly the major factor which led to the Jewish ban on pork.

The *filariae* produce the most spectacular effect on many of any of the nematode worms.   These animals are widespread in the tropical regions of the world, where they are carried in an intermediate host, a mosquito.   Adult females are from 65 to 100 millimeters long, and the smaller males are about 40 millimeters in length.   They live in the blood or lymph vessels, where they may form tangles, the consequences of which we will discuss later.   The larvae, known as *microfilariae,* are released into the blood and live in the deeper tissues during the day but migrate to the capillaries of the skin during the night.   A mosquito feeding on an infected person sucks up some of the larvae with the blood which it ingests.   The microfilariae migrate to the thoracic muscles of the mosquito and grow for about two weeks, after which they move to the mouth and are spit

Figure 17.14.   Trichinosis, the disease caused by the infestation of Trichinella, usually comes from eating improperly cooked pork.   No damage is done in the cyst stage within the muscle, as shown here.   The harm is caused by the millions of larvae that tunnel through the intestinal wall and blood vessels to reach the muscles.   (Courtesy General Biological Supply House, Inc., Chicago.)

out by the mosquito when this flying transport feeds on a new host. What happens to the worms in the definitive host between the time they enter the body of the host and the adult stage remains a mystery.

The effects of the filariae depend upon the length of the infection and upon the number of reinfections. The obvious results usually are allergic reactions and a swelling in localized regions of the body. The tragic result of long-continued infections is the development of "elephant's disease," or *elephantiasis*. Blood and lymph vessels in various regions of the body are blocked by the tangling of the animals, and swelling follows as a result of fluid accumulation. The person so affected may become a grotesque caricature of a human being. A leg may weigh as much as 200 pounds or a scrotum 40 pounds in a person with elephantiasis (see Figure 17.15).

An interesting problem associated with the filariae is the question as to how the microfilariae know when it is nighttime, and therefore time for them to migrate to the surface vessels. This was further complicated by the additional discovery that some filariae in the South Pacific are carried by day-flying mosquitoes, and in this case the migration is the reverse of that usually observed. No satisfactory explanation has been advanced to date to account for this peculiar phenomenon.

Dracunculus probably is not the "fiery serpent" dramatically referred to in the Bible, but it has some unusual biological features. The larval stage of the animal lives in the water flea, *Cyclops;* and infection occurs when *Cyclops* is taken into the body with the drinking water. The adult worm migrates to the skin tissues and reaches a length of 24 to 36 inches! A blister is formed over the end of the animal, and an opening to the outside is created. When the parasitized person goes into the water, or water is poured over the opening, larvae are discharged to take up their abode in *Cyclops*.

The worm produces a marked reddening of the skin, hence the term *fiery serpent;* and it is estimated that as many as 48,000,000 people, chiefly in Oriental countries, are infected. Drinking water from open wells, especially the "step wells" where persons go down into the well to secure water, is primarily responsible for transmission. Control is relatively simple—do away with open wells, or treat the water with copper sulfate to kill *Cyclops*, and the parasites can be controlled. The perverseness of human nature is such, however, that there is resistance even to these simple procedures.

ARTHROPOD PARASITES • The arthropod parasites are numerous and varied, but in regard to their effects on human beings they are noted for their annoyance and as carriers of some very serious diseases. The *mites* and *ticks* in the class Arachnoidea and the *fleas, lice,* and *mosquitoes* of the class Insecta are the chief offenders. The most extreme case of parasitic adaptation in the animal kingdom is to be found in *Sacculina*, a very unusual crustacean.

Many common mites and ticks are annoying ectoparasites. Some live in the hair follicles, but most of them merely attach to the surface of the body, or burrow a short distance below the superficial layer of the skin. Most mites are

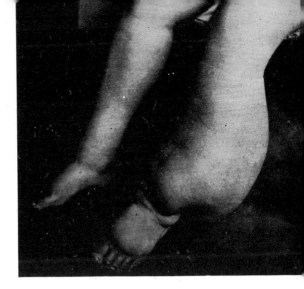

Figure 17.15. By blocking the circulation of their host, filarial worms cause swelling, especially of the arms and legs. "Elephantiasis" is a good description of the horribly misshapen results. (Courtesy Armed Forces Institute of Pathology, neg. no. 78873.)

very small and are noted primarily for the discomfort they cause. Itch mites, mange mites, and chiggers are the best known, and persons who are repeatedly attacked may develop a marked allergic reaction to them. Fortunately, others acquire an immunity. Some members of the chigger family transmit *scrub typhus*, which is an important disease in certain regions of the world. This, as well as several other diseases, may be carried in the egg of the arthropod and transmitted from generation to generation in this most unusual manner. Mites occasionally may invade the lungs, intestine, or bladder of animals, but this is not a disease problem with man.

The ticks are much larger than the mites, are notorious bloodsuckers, and transmit several serious diseases. Ticks, when present in large numbers, may cause anemia and death. *Texas fever, Rocky Mountain spotted fever, relapsing fever,* and *tularemia* are tick-borne diseases. Ticks may occasionally be responsible for paralysis, called the *tick paralysis,* which probably results from a poison present in the egg-laying females. The paralysis may be fatal, especially to domestic animals. Spotted fever is a particularly dangerous human disease, and tick transmission makes it a considerable threat throughout a large portion of the United States.

The prevalence of lice and fleas on human beings is famous in picture, song, and story. The advent of central heating, with more regular bathing, and the practice of shaving and of cutting hair have decreased the incidence of these pests in many parts of the world. It is not possible to be complacent on this subject, however, because in crowded areas of the large cities and whenever armies gather or disasters occur, fleas and lice rapidly increase and become pests. Adaptations in the form of claws, hooks, and spines are well illustrated by these arthropods. Fleas with their streamlined bodies and their surface spines are nicely adapted for creeping among the hairs and maintaining their position against the efforts of their mammalian hosts to dislodge them. Loss of blood to lice or fleas may be serious, but the most harmful effects are a result of the

Figure 17.16. Ticks feed on the blood of other animals and, if unmolested, will gorge on their prey until bloated to four or five times their normal size, as shown by these drawings. (From Gruenberg and Bingham, *Biology and Man*, Ginn and Co.)

diseases carried by the pests. The *plague* and *typhus* are two of the major human diseases so transmitted; during the Fourteenth century an estimated 25,000,000 people died in Europe of the flea-borne plague. Typhus has decimated armies several times in the history of the world, and, as recently as the beginning of World War I, was more effective than rifles and artillery because the disease completely stopped the advance of the Austrian army through Serbia.

The larval forms of many other insects are parasitic. The wasps and flies are noteworthy in this regard and are factors in the phenomenon called *biological balance*. Plagues of locusts are destroyed by parasitic insects which lay their eggs in the locust's body; the newly hatched larvae consume the host. Many domestic animals and wild mammals also are attacked by fly larvae, with a resultant economic loss because of the debility and ill health which follow.

The members of the genus *Sacculina* present one of the most remarkable achievements in parasitism to be found anywhere in the animal kingdom. These organisms are related to barnacles and begin life as free-swimming flealike larvae which look very much like the adult form of one of the water fleas, *Cypris*. This flealike stage attaches to a crab and undergoes a fantastic transformation. Most of the body tissues and organs are lost; only a small sac of skin containing

Figure 17.17. This diagram shows the three stages of Sacculina's development (A, B, C) and also how the organism attaches itself to its host, the crab (D). (From Gruenberg and Bingham, *Biology of Man*, Ginn and Co.)

342

Figure 17.18. From the smallest to the largest, all animals are prey to parasites and many unwillingly furnish "income" to unwelcome guests. The crustacea shown here live on whales and are known as whale lice. (Courtesy Clarence Flaten.)

reproductive cells and some rootlike processes remains. These invade the crab, and the "roots" branch profusely through the body of the host to sap nutrient from the host tissues. The sac eventually reaches a position on the ventral surface of the crab and proceeds to manufacture a superabundance of reproductive cells. The adult animals, therefore, have reduced all their body processes to a minimum and devote their full energies to the production of the next generation. This animal furnishes another illustration of the significance of a basic working knowledge of embryological development in our classification of organisms.

We may say in conclusion that the biologist looks upon parasitism as another *method of life*, to be neither condemned nor condoned. The evidences of parasitism are merely additional illustrations of the adaptability of protoplasm, both structurally and functionally. Certainly the life of a parasite is beset with many tribulations and is most difficult. The host constantly attempts to dislodge the parasite, and an inefficient parasite which kills the host commits suicide in the process. It should be re-emphasized that parasitic adaptations are independent of the characteristics of phyla. Loss of structures, development of attachment devices, and the acquisition of intermediate hosts are a few of the more obvious features which illustrate this independence.

REFERENCES

Alvarado, Carlos A., and L. J. Bruce-Chwatt, "Malaria," *Scientific American*, 206, May 1962, pp. 86–98.

Brown, F. A. (ed.), *Selected Invertebrate Types*, pp. 158–208. John Wiley and Sons, New York, 1950.

Cameron, Thomas W. M., *Parasites and Parasitism*. Methuen and Company, Ltd., London, 1956.

Carter, G. S., *A General Zoology of the Invertebrates*, pp. 459–468. The Macmillan Company, New York, 1940.

Chandler, A. C., *Introduction to Parasitology*. John Wiley and Sons, New York, 1949.

CHENG, THOMAS C., "Some Biochemical and Immunological Aspects of Host-Parasite Relationships," *New York Academy of Sciences, 113*, art. 1, 1963, pp. 1–510.

ELTON, C., *Animal Ecology.* Sidgwick and Jackson, Ltd., London, 1949.

HEGNER, R. W., F. M. ROOT, D. L. AUGUSTINE, and C. J. HUFF, *Parasitology.* D. Appleton-Century Company, New York, 1938.

HEISER, VICTOR G., *An American Doctor's Odyssey.* W. W. Norton and Company, New York, 1936.

HYMAN, L. H., *The Invertebrates: Platyhelminthes and Rhynchocoela,* Vol. II, pp. 219–417. McGraw-Hill Book Company, New York, 1951.

LAPAGE, GEOFFREY, *Parasitic Animals.* Cambridge University Press, London, 1951.
　　　　　　Animals Parasitic in Man. Penguin Books, Baltimore, 1957.

LENGER, WILLIAM L., "The Black Death," *Scientific American, 210,* February 1964, pp. 114–123.

MACFADYEN, AMYAN, *Animal Ecology.* Pitman, London, 1963.

WARDLE, R. A., and J. A. McLEOD, *The Zoology of Tapeworms.* University of Minnesota Press, Minneapolis, 1952.

ZINSSER, HANS, *Rats, Lice, and History.* Little, Brown and Company, Boston, 1935.
　　　　　　As I Remember Him. Little, Brown and Company, Boston, 1935.

18

Accent on Brains

Phylum
Chordata,
Subphylum
Vertebrata

●

The brain itself, at first devoted to the details of sensory and motor function, comes increasingly to preside over all the body functions, and to give to the vertebrates that "drive" which is one of their most characteristic functions. —J. Z. Young, 1950

The members of the phylum Chordata constitute the *nouveau riche* of the animal kingdom. They have been able to establish themselves as one of the dominant groups in biological competition, in spite of the fact that they are innovations, with a relatively short existence of probably not more than 500,000,000 years. Architecturally, the body of the chordates is a new type of construction and is the antithesis of the body form of their major competitors, the Arthropoda. Our interest in the phylum also rests upon several other considerations. Three well-known groups—the reptiles, the birds, and the mammals—have emerged from the water to live successfully on land in an air environment; and in spite of a paucity of numbers of species and individuals, they are able to compete in both air and water with the multitudes of arthropods. The chordate nervous system has been developed to a high degree of efficiency; and rapid, complex adjustments to diverse stimuli are possible. Finally, the animal in which we have our greatest interest, *man*—the textbook-writing animal—is a member of the phylum Chordata.

All chordates at some stage of their existence possess three unique structural features. *First* is a flexible truss, the *notochord*, which usually extends nearly the full length of the body. The notochord is composed of a tough sheath filled with a jellylike material, and it serves as the skeletal axis because of its position ventral to the nerve cord and dorsal to the alimentary canal. The length and flexibility of the notochord make possible the characteristic lashing or

345

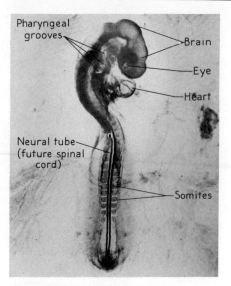

Figure 18.1. Segmentation is obscured in adult vertebrates, but it is apparent in embryonic vertebrates. The somites of the developing chick here are shown clearly. The pharyngeal grooves of the chick are comparable to the gill slits of the ammocoete larva. (Courtesy Clarence Flaten.)

undulatory movements of the chordates' body. Without the internal resistance of the notochord, contraction of the body muscles would result in a shortening, or telescoping, of the animal and a creeping, wormlike type of locomotion. The notochord may serve also as a fulcrum against which the muscles can pull.

The *second* diagnostic characteristic of the chordata is the presence of *pharyngeal grooves,* which are usually spoken of as the *gill slits* (although, as we will note later, in many chordates actual gill-slit openings into the pharynx may not develop). Water can be taken in through the mouth and expelled through the pharyngeal slits, and this serves as an excellent respiratory mechanism for aquatic forms. Also, small food particles can be strained from the water as it passes through the pharyngeal slits, which provides an important filter-feeding mechanism in many chordates.

The *third* diagnostic characteristic of the Chordata is the *dorsal tubular nervous system.* This system is in marked contrast with that observed in the nonchordate phyla because, with rare exceptions, the nervous systems of other phyla are ventral or lateral and are solid cords of cells, while in the Chordata the anterior portion of the nerve cord is developed into a complex coordinating center, the *brain,* and the posterior part into the *spinal cord.* Pairs of nerves emerge from the spinal cord and extend to the internal organs and to bundles of segmentally arranged muscles. Coordination in most chordates is supplemented by a copious secretion of chemical substances, the *hormones,* which are released directly into the blood stream. These hormones modify the activity of distant parts of the body and make it possible for chordates to adjust to stimuli of long duration. Chemical coordination is more elaborate in the Chordata than any found elsewhere in the animal kingdom.

Several other structural features emphasize the differences between chordates and nonchordates, especially between chordates and the arthropods. These features in chordates include an *internal skeleton*, a well-developed *coelom*, and a *closed circulatory system*. A *tail* (postanal continuation of the body) and a well-developed *head* are also prominent characteristics. The latter two features are especially noteworthy in the major group of the chordates, the *vertebrates*. The chordates are *segmented* animals with *bilateral symmetry*.

The chordates are a motley assemblage of animals which range from minute, sessile, colonial tunicates to gigantic seagoing mammals weighing 80 to 100 tons. This marked disparity in structure and habitat has led to the subdivision of the phylum into four subphyla for convenience in classification and for the purpose of demonstrating relationships. Only one subphylum, the Vertebrata, is of major importance, and most of our discussion will be limited to this group. The theoretical significance of the other three subphyla will be considered briefly.

The Acorn Worms[*]

The *acorn worms* and their relatives are usually considered to be chordates. Even though this relationship has been seriously questioned in recent years, *Balanoglossus* is often used to illustrate the characteristics of the group. These wormlike animals range in length from two centimeters to two meters and have an egg-shaped anterior *proboscis* which fits into an encircling *collar*. The appearance of this anterior region is much like that of an acorn in its cup, hence the name of the worms. The animals employ a hydraulic system for burrowing their way through the sand. The hollow proboscis and the collar can be

[*] Subphylum Hemichordata.

Figure 18.2. Model showing the external features of the acorn worm.

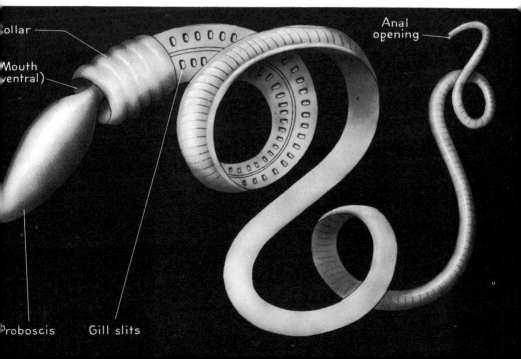

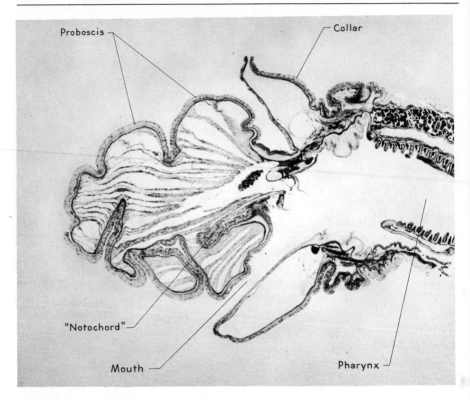

Figure 18.3.   Longitudinal section of the anterior end of an acorn worm.   (Courtesy Clarence Flaten.)

distended by water entering through the two *water pores* in the collar and a single pore in the proboscis.   The extended proboscis and the collar are forced forward through the sand, and a subsequent distention of the collar anchors the animal so that a contraction of the body muscles pulls the trunk of the worm forward.   The proboscis and collar can be emptied of water through their respective water pores and the procedure repeated.   The presence of the hydraulic system as an aid to locomotion is reminiscent of the echinoderms rather than typical of the chordates.

The mouth, which is covered by the collar, is permanently open and is located on the ventral side of the proboscis.   Sand containing organic debris is ingested, and the organic matter is digested during its passage through the alimentary canal.   The feeding mechanism is comparable, therefore, to that previously observed in earthworms and is not a filter-feeding process utilizing the pharyngeal clefts, or grooves, as in most chordates.   The *gill slits,* however, are the most typical chordate structure present in acorn worms.   Numerous gill slits are located on the anterior part of the body, directly behind the collar, and open from the pharynx to the outside through the dorsal body wall.   Water enters the mouth, circulates through the pharynx, and emerges through the gill slits.

The presence of a notochord and a dorsal tubular nervous system in the acorn worms must be questioned seriously.   There are concentrations of nerve cells in the form of nerve cords immediately below the epidermis on both the dorsal and ventral sides of the trunk, and an even greater number of nerve cells is present in the dorsal area of the collar.   This area may be grooved or may fold to form a short tube which is open at each end.   It is very doubtful, however, whether this is sufficient justification for deciding "that a dorsal tubular nervous system exists" in the acorn worms.   The ventral nerve cord is unique and is unknown in other chordates.   A short strand of cells extends from the dorsal region of the pharynx into the proboscis.   This is the alleged "notochord"; but it must be recognized that it does not extend posteriorly beneath the dorsal nerve trunk as a typical notochord should.

There is considerable reluctance to exclude the acorn worms from the chordates, because of the fact that their larval forms furnish a clue to a possible relationship with the echinoderms.   The tornaria larva of *Balanoglossus* is so similar to some larvae of the Echinodermata that for many years it was thought to be a member of that phylum.   The development of the mesoderm is similar (enterocoelic), and the water cavities in the anterior end are reminiscent of the water-vascular spaces of the echinoderms.   Perhaps the acorn worms and their relatives should be placed in a separate phylum, recognized as closely related to echinoderms and chordates, or should be considered "degenerate" chordates.

The Tunicates*

A few of the *tunicates* are free-swimming animals, but the majority of the members of this subphylum are bulbous, sessile organisms.   They are worldwide in distribution but lead a retiring existence on the ocean bottom, attached to rocks or sea plants.   The body wall is a tough, leathery *tunic*, lined by a single layer of epidermal cells.   The tunic itself has only a few cells, which are mesodermal in origin and migrate to their position in the tunic.   The greater portion of the body of the tunicate is composed of an expanded barrel-like pharynx, and laterally and dorsally the pharynx is surrounded by a large space, the *atrium*. The immense pharynx is perforated by a large number of *pharyngeal slits*, the margins of which are covered with cilia.   The tunicates possess two dorsal openings: a terminal *mouth*, which is an entrance into the *pharynx;* and the *atrial opening* from the atrium to the outside.   A strong contraction of the well-developed muscles of the body wall will squirt water forcibly from the two openings, a fact which gives the animals their popular name of *sea squirts*.   The two openings, when located at opposite ends of the body, enable some animals to swim by jet propulsion.

The pharynx connects with a short alimentary canal composed of a *stomach,*

* Subphylum Urochordata.

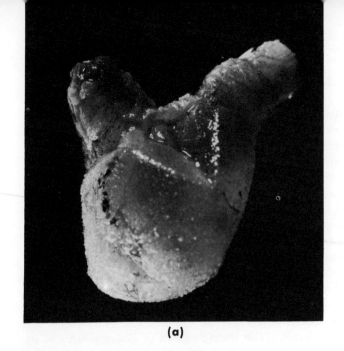

(a)

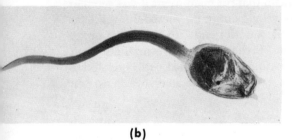

(b)

Figure 18.4. In (a) is shown a sea squirt, a typical tunicate; in (b), a tadpole-like larva of a tunicate. [(a) Courtesy Clarence Flaten; (b) copyright by General Biological Supply House, Inc., Chicago.]

an *intestine*, and an *anus* which opens into the atrium. Feeding and respiration are accomplished simultaneously as a result of the circulation of water through the animal. The cilia on the pharynx create a current of water which enters the mouth, passes through the pharyngeal slits into the atrium, and flows out by way of the atrial opening. Food particles are trapped during the passage of the water through the pharynx, and gaseous exchange occurs at the same time. It has been estimated that an average-size tunicate can circulate approximately 180 quarts of water in a 24-hour period. The animals obviously are very effective filter-feeders.

The tunicates have a *heart* located below the pharynx, and a series of irregular *blood spaces*, some with an epithelial lining, are extensively scattered throughout the body. The pharynx and the stomach, as we might anticipate, are well supplied by branches of the major vessels. A peculiar feature of heart action is the fact that the direction of the beat is reversed regularly, blood being pumped with facility in either direction.

The nervous system is simple, consisting of a "brain," located above the

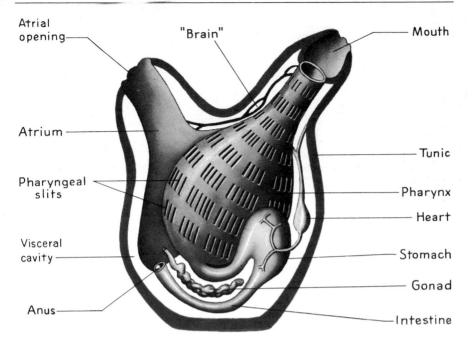

Figure 18.5.   The anatomy of the sea squirt.

pharynx, and the *nerves*, which extend to the major organs of the body.   The reactions of the tunicates are not elaborate, and this simple communication system is able to supply necessary pathways for the uncomplicated reflexes.

The animals are hermaphroditic, and the gonads lie near the intestine. Sperm and eggs are discharged into the atrium and leave the body through the atrial opening.   The egg develops into a free-swimming, tadpolelike larva which is of considerable theoretical interest because it has pronounced chordate characteristics.

The larva has a well-developed *dorsal tubular nerve cord* with an expanded *cerebral region* and a *notochord* that extends to the tip of an elongated tail.   The latter condition is the basis for the subphylum name, *Urochordata* (tail cord). The oval-shaped "head" contains the pharynx, the heart, and the alimentary canal.   The larva, however, does not feed and swims about for only a few days before attaching to the ocean bottom by means of a sucker on the anterior end. Radical transformation occurs after attachment: the tail disappears; the pharynx expands; the tunic develops; the sucker becomes the base, or stalk; and the adult body form is established.   The larva is obviously superior to the adult form as a chordate and is yet another excellent illustration of the way in which embryonic forms may be used to determine the relationships of adult animals.

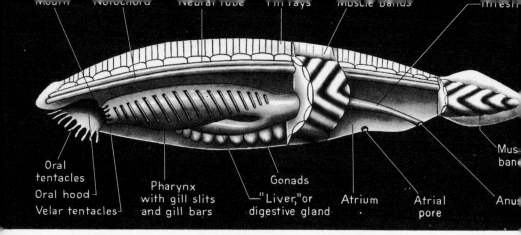

Oral
tentacles

Oral hood

Velar tentacles

Pharynx
with gill slits
and gill bars

Gonads

—"Liver,"or
digestive gland

Atrium

Atrial
pore

Mus
ban

Anu

Figure 18.6.   The anatomy of Amphioxus.

Amphioxus*

The lancelet, Amphioxus, has been one of the most thoroughly studied organisms in the animal kingdom. Its popularity is due to the almost diagrammatic way in which it illustrates some of the chordate characteristics, but it should be emphasized that the simplicity of structure of Amphioxus is correlated with its burrowing habits and is not a primitive condition. The animals spend most of their time buried in the sand, with only the anterior end protruding; they can and do swim about actively, however, with a characteristic undulating movement of the body. A notochord extends the length of the animal, and a tubular nervous system lies dorsal to the notochord. The brain, in marked contrast with that in most chordates, is poorly developed. This fact has led zoologists to consider the Amphioxus to be headless, or *acephalic.* Paired spinal nerves emerge from both the dorsal and ventral sides of the nerve cord, but contrary to the situation in the vertebrates, these roots do not unite to form a single spinal nerve. The *pharynx,* as in the tunicates, is enormous and is perforated by 50 to 60 pairs of *gill slits.* The walls of the pharynx are strengthened by the presence of *gill bars* on either side of the gill slits. The gill bars are profusely covered with cilia on their inner and lateral edges, and the beating of the cilia is responsible for the flow of water through the pharynx and for the movement of food materials. The pharynx is not visible externally, because two body folds develop in the embryo and grow over the pharynx to fuse in the mid-ventral line. The enclosed space formed by this overgrowth is the *atrium;* it opens externally by a ventral *atrial pore* anterior to the anus. The relationship of atrium and pharynx is similar to that of the tunicates. The *mouth* is at the base of a funnel, the *oral hood;* the outer edge of the funnel is encircled by the *oral tentacles;* the mouth itself is guarded by the *velar tentacles.*

Segmentation in Amphioxus is apparent in the musculature, the gonads, and

* Subphylum Cephalochordata

the excretory organs. The muscles are arranged in V-shaped bands, separated by connective tissue. The reproductive organs occur in the form of 26 pairs of hollow sacs located at the base of the muscle bundles in the pharyngeal region. Sexes are separate, and the reproductive cells are discharged directly into the atrium by a rupture of the wall of the gonad. The union of sperm and egg and subsequent embryonic development occurs in the water outside the animal. The excretory organs are unique and do not compare with those of other chordates. Associated with each gill bar is a *vesicle,* or cavity, which opens into the atrium, and each vesicle is equipped with numerous *flame bulbs.* The vesicle and its flame cells are often referred to as *nephridia,* and indeed they are comparable to the excretory organs of flatworms and annelids. There is little doubt that their embryonic origin is from the ectoderm, and that they differ fundamentally from the kidneys of the vertebrates.

The Ammocoete Larva

Much attention has been directed toward Amphioxus as a primitive form comparable to the immediate ancestors of the vertebrates. We noted in the initial remarks on Amphioxus, however, that much of the simplicity of structure is a result of degenerative changes correlated with the burrowing habits of the animals. The acephalic anterior end, the nephridia, and the elaborate atrium are not typical vertebrate structures. Interest has developed in recent years in another organism as more representative of an ancestral form. This is the larva of the lamprey eel, called the *ammocoete larva.* The lampreys are primitive living vertebrates, and the larva is an even more generalized chordate than Amphioxus. The ammocoete exists for several years in the larval stage before transforming into an adult animal. Its brain is complete, the atrium is less extensive, the number of gill slits is only seven, as in sharks, and they can be

Figure 18.7.   A structure of an ammocoete larva.   (Courtesy Clarence Flaten.)

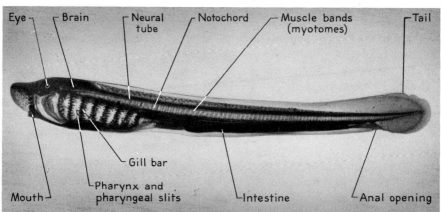

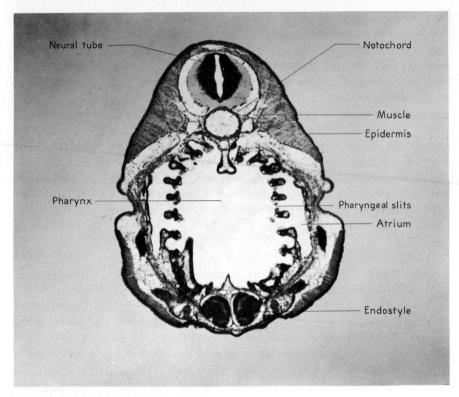

Figure 18.8.   A cross section of the ammocoete larva.   (Courtesy Clarence Flaten.)

compared directly to those of the sharks.   Finally, the cranial nerves are remark-ably similar to those of some of the fossil fishes, the Ostracoderms, which generally are recognized as being directly related to modern vertebrates.

The Frog:* An "Average Vertebrate"

The annelids were referred to earlier as "average animals," and in a similar fashion it is often customary to call the frog an "average vertebrate."   Several resons may be given for this designation.   There are seven classes of modern vertebrates, and the class Amphibia to which the frog belongs is the middle class.   Three of the classes are aquatic, three are air dwelling, and the Amphibia are both aquatic and air dwelling.   Finally, except for a few minor specializa-tions, the frog illustrates the typical vertebrate characteristics in an almost diagrammatic way.

The Amphibia had their peak of importance in the geologic past, yet in a

* Subphylum Vertebrata. Descriptions that follow pertain primarily to *Rana pipiens*.

quiet fashion they maintain themselves successfully today. They are world-wide in distribution, but present-day amphibians are limited to the vicinity of fresh water. Most amphibians lay their eggs in pools, and their early life is passed as a *tadpole*, a typical aquatic vertebrate. Limbs and lungs do not develop until the tadpole transforms into an adult, at which time the animal becomes truly amphibious.

It is advantageous to enumerate the features which distinguish the Vertebrata from the other chordate subphyla before discussing the frog in detail. The structures which are responsible for the name of the subphylum are the *vertebrae*. These are a chain of cartilaginous and bony units which surround the neural tube and notochord to form a *backbone*. The segmental arrangement of the vertebrae adds greater strength to the central skeletal axis and makes the backbone much more efficient than the unsupported notochord. Nearly all the vertebrates possess *two*, but only two, *pairs of limbs*, and these may be either *fins* or *legs*. All vertebrates have an elaborate brain, which has its maximum development in man and his close relatives. The brain of the vertebrates is encased in a *skull* of cartilage and bone, and this combination of skull and brain gives the vertebrates the most pronounced *head* to be found anywhere in the animal kingdom. A *closed circulatory system* is extensively developed, and a ventrally located *heart* provides the propulsive force for the circulation of the blood, which flows forward on the ventral side and backward on the dorsal side. This is the reverse of the direction of flow in nonchordates such as the earthworm and clamworm. The exact relationship of the vertebrate structures will become more obvious when specifically observed in the frog.

Figure 18.9. The skeletons of a frog and a bird, though they obviously differ in many respects, nevertheless share a basic similarity of structure. (Courtesy Clarence Flaten.)

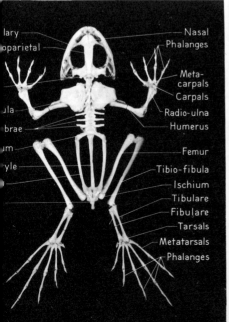
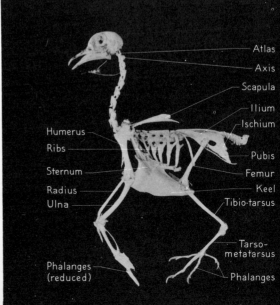

Body form

The body of the frog is divided into the three basic regions which are recognizable in most vertebrates. These regions are the *head,* the *neck,* and the *trunk.* The neck region of the frog, however, is reduced, so that upon a merely superficial examination the head appears to be firmly attached to the trunk. Some free movement of the head is possible as a result of the fact that the head is joined to the trunk by a supporting vertebra, aptly named the *atlas.* This is the only trace of a neck which is present in the frog. The trunk region of the frog is also reduced, and the tail exists only as a small stub which can be identified only by careful dissection of the skeleton. The most obvious external vertebrate feature of the frog is the two pairs of appendages: the *forelegs,* or arms; and the *hind legs.* The legs are modified for the swimming and jumping which are so characteristic of the frog. Except for the human being and the kangaroo, few living vertebrates have such relatively large hind legs. The head is better developed than in the fishes, a result of the fact that the *eyes,* the *external nares,* or *nostrils,* the external openings to the *ears,* as well as the en-

Figure 18.10.　Dorsal and ventral views of the major muscles of the frog.

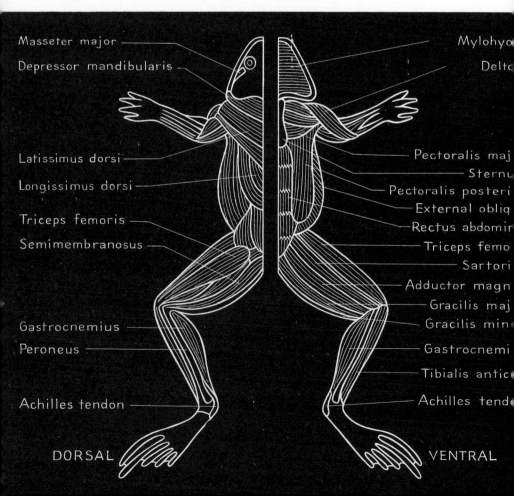

Masseter major

Depressor mandibularis

Mylohyo

Delt

Latissimus dorsi

Longissimus dorsi

Triceps femoris

Semimembranosus

Pectoralis maj

Sternu

Pectoralis posteri

External obliq

Rectus abdomir

Triceps femo

Sartori

Adductor magn

Gracilis maj

Gracilis min

Gastrocnemius

Peroneus

Gastrocnemi

Tibialis antic

Achilles tendon

Achilles tend

DORSAL

VENTRAL

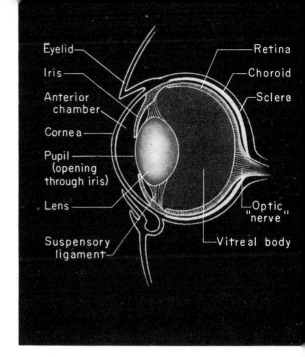

Figure 18.11. The structures of the typical vertebrate organ of vision. Compare with drawing of the human eye on page 461.

Labels in figure: Eyelid, Iris, Anterior chamber, Cornea, Pupil (opening through iris), Lens, Suspensory ligament, Retina, Choroid, Sclera, Optic "nerve", Vitreal body

larged *brain* are located in the head region. The lack of gills in the adult frog has resulted in a decrease in the size of the pharyngeal region and a reduction in the bone and cartilage of that area.

A better understanding of the architectural design of the frog can be gained by referring to the skeleton of the animal. We can observe upon dissection that the skeleton can be divided into two major portions: the *axial skeleton*, and the *appendicular skeleton* which is part of the *limb structure*. The axial skeleton is composed of the skull and vertebral column; whereas the appendicular skeleton is constructed of the leg bones together with the bones and cartilages which join the legs to the axial skeleton, called the *girdles*. The girdle in the fore region of the animal is the *shoulder*, or *pectoral girdle;* that in the posterior region of the animal is the *pelvic girdle*. The foreleg consists of an *upper arm*, a *forearm*, a *wrist*, and a *hand*. The hand possesses four *fingers*, or digits, and the *thumb* is reduced. A large swelling, or *thumb pad*, is especially prominent in the male during the breeding season. The hind limb is made up of *thigh*, *shank*, elongated *ankle region*, and *foot*. The foot possesses five *toes*, between which are prominent *webs*. Even a casual examination of the frog will reveal the remarkable adaptations of the hind limbs for jumping and swimming. The posterior part of the vertebral column is modified into the *urostyle*, which serves as an effective lever for transmitting leg action to body movement.

The head of the frog has well-developed sense organs and prominent openings. At the tip of the head are the entrances into the nasal passages, the nostrils or external nares. The mouth is a much enlarged aperture closed by a flaplike lower jaw. The eyes, prominent structures in the head region, are protected by *eyelids.* A notable feature of these eyelids is the presence of the *nictitating membrane,* a thin, filmlike third lid which can be drawn over the eye for protection. This thin fold is prominent in birds, and traces of it can be observed at the corner of the human eye. Immediately behind the eyes are the circular *tympanic membranes,* which cover the ears and act as drumheads to pick up sound waves and transfer the vibrations to the middle and inner ears.

Nutrition

The digestive functions of the vertebrates have been studied more intensively than those of any other phylum, and fortunately the frog nutrition is typical. Frogs are not selective in their menu, and their varied appetite has undoubtedly been to their advantage in making it possible for them to survive in widely different situations. The tadpole is *herbivorous,* living on plant food; but the adult is *carnivorous,* living on a meat diet composed chiefly of worms and insects. This fact affords an opportunity to observe some of the vertebrate modifications that are correlated with the type of diet.

The *mouth* of the frog is large, but the *teeth* are much reduced and are used merely for holding prey, not for chewing. Food is captured by means of the tongue, which is attached at the front of the mouth and which can be flicked forward rapidly by the contraction of its muscles. The mouth is lubricated and the tongue made sticky by the secretions of the *mucous glands.* A short *esophagus* connects the mouth with the *stomach* and is a chute for the passage of food. The stomach, a relatively simple organ, has well-developed musculature

Figure 18.12.   Food is pushed along the alimentary canal by alternating waves of contraction and relaxation, as shown in this model.

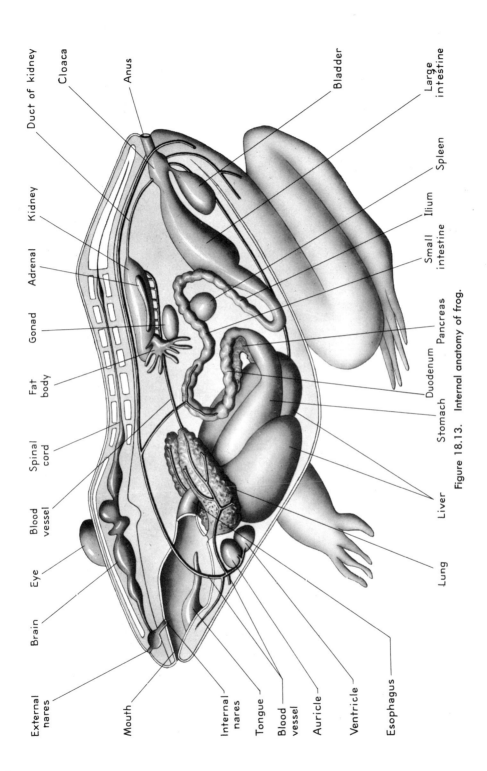

Figure 18.13. Internal anatomy of frog.

External nares

Brain

Eye

Blood vessel

Spinal cord

Fat body

Gonad

Adrenal

Kidney

Duct of kidney

Cloaca

Anus

Bladder

Large intestine

Spleen

Ilium

Small intestine

Pancreas

Duodenum

Stomach

Liver

Lung

Esophagus

Ventricle

Auricle

Blood vessel

Tongue

Internal nares

Mouth

and a glandular lining. It is in the stomach that food is fragmented and partially digested. The cells of the stomach secrete *hydrochloric acid* and the digestive enzyme *pepsin* which, in the presence of the hydrochloric acid, partially digests and speeds the distintegration of the food particles.

Digestion and absorption of food is accomplished chiefly in the *small intestine,* which is separated from the stomach by the *pyloric constriction;* this functions as a valve to control the exit of food from the stomach. There are two divisions of the small intestine: the *duodenum* and the *ileum.* The duodenum curves forward over the *liver,* and the *pancreas,* a digestive gland, is located in the loop formed by the duodenum. The *liver,* a multilobed gland, is the largest organ in the body; it is an important storehouse of carbohydrates and also has a prominent role in digestion. *Bile* is secreted by the liver and is emptied by the *bile duct* into the duodenum; it serves to neutralize the acid which enters the intestine from the stomach. Bile also helps to emulsify the fats, so that they may be acted upon more readily by the enzymes. The pancreas secretes enzymes which digest fat, protein, starch, and sugar, and since the pancreatic enzymes cannot act in an acid medium, the importance of the neutralizing action of the bile is obvious. The small intestine makes a second bend posterior to the duodenum, and this posterior portion is the ileum. Most of the digestion and absorption of food takes place in these two parts of the small intestine.

The ileum continues posteriorly to join with the expanded *large intestine,* which gradually tapers to become the *cloaca* (sewer). The noteworthy functional feature of the large intestine is the reabsorption of water through its walls. The various digestive secretions deposit considerable amounts of fluid in the alimentary canal, and if it were not for the reabsorption of water in the large intestine, the animal would be greatly dehydrated.

The cloaca, the most posterior part of the alimentary canal, opens externally through the *anus* and receives the ducts from the *kidneys* and the *reproductive organs.* It serves, therefore, as the receptacle for eggs or sperm, for the urine, and for the fecal material. The ventral wall of the cloaca has an opening into the large, thin-walled, *bilobed bladder.* The bladder serves as a reservoir for urine, and water also may be absorbed from it as an additional aid in preventing desiccation, or dehydration.

It is interesting to note that the tadpole, which is a vegetarian, has an alimentary canal that is many times longer than that of the adult animal, which is a carnivore. The greater length of the alimentary canal results from the coiling of the intestine, and this correlation of a longer alimentary canal with a diet of plant food is relatively common among the vertebrates. It is probable that the plant food, with a high water content and a large amount of indigestible cellulose, does not afford the same amount of nutrient material as does an equivalent weight of animal food. A longer intestine, therefore, provides for a greater period of time for digestion and absorption and, by this means, increases the efficiency of the digestive tract.

Movement of food through the alimentary canal is made possible by the contractions of the muscular walls. These contractions can be observed in the small intestine of an anesthetized animal, appearing as a series of contractions of the entire digestive tract. Each wave of contraction is preceded by a wave of relaxation, so that the effect of the combined waves is to "squeeze" the food posteriorly. The series of waves is termed *peristalsis*. *Reverse peristalsis*, in which food is directed anteriorly instead of posteriorly, can also occur.

Respiration

The problem of respiration in the air-dwelling vertebrates is comparable to that encountered by the terrestrial arthropods. Respiration is oxybiotic, and the situation in both cases requires that oxygen be available to all cells of the body but also requires that dehydration must be prevented. Gaseous exchange in either an aquatic arthropod or an aquatic vertebrate is accompanied by a flow of water over the gills or a comparable respiratory structure. This flow of water assures that there will be no dehydration, because the membranes and surfaces are kept moist during the exchange of oxygen and carbon dioxide. A current of air, on the other hand, although very high in oxygen, will remove moisture from the surfaces over which it passes. The manner by which the frog solves this problem of gaseous exchange with minimum dehydration will illustrate the way the air-dwelling vertebrates respire.

There are three respiratory surfaces in adult frogs: the *lungs*, the *skin*, and the *lining* of the *mouth cavity*. It is necessary that all three of these areas remain moist, because oxygen can be absorbed from the air only when it enters into solution. The surface of the skin is moistened by skin secretions, forming an efficient respiratory organ, especially when the frog is submerged in cold water. The skin has an excellent capillary blood supply, and it has been estimated that in an hour the skin will pick up one and a half cubic centimeters of oxygen per $\frac{1}{100}$ square meter of skin surface. The lungs, by comparison, can absorb about three or four times as much oxygen, but it is apparent that the skin makes an important contribution to respiration. The exchange of carbon dioxide between the frog and its environment is, of course, a fundamental part of respiration as well as of excretion, and the skin seems to be even more effective in the elimination of carbon dioxide than the lungs. It has been estimated that in an hour as much as three cubic centimeters of carbon dioxide per $\frac{1}{100}$ square meter of surface will be eliminated through the skin. The moist mouth cavity of the frog is well supplied with capillaries, and it also serves as an effective area for gaseous exchange.

The exchange of oxygen and carbon dioxide between the respiratory organs and the environment is termed *external respiration*, and a distinction should be made between *breathing* and external respiration. Breathing may be defined as bringing the air in contact with the respiratory surfaces (inhaling) and the elimination of carbon dioxide after it has been released from the respiratory surfaces

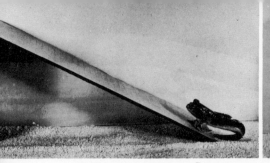

Figure 18.14. This acrobatic mud skipper is equipped to live out of water for long periods of time. His respiratory organs are adapted for breathing; his thick skin prevents evaporation of water; and his powerful fins enable him to walk about and even climb trees. He can swim or he can move along tidal mud flats as fast as a man can run. (Courtesy Three Lions, Inc.)

(exhaling). The frog affords a good illustration of a simple breathing mechanism. The respiratory surfaces involved in breathing in the frog are the mouth and the lungs. The air must first of all be drawn into the mouth and subsequently forced into the lungs. The mouth cavity is closed during inhalation, the nostrils are open, and the floor of the mouth is depressed. The mouth acts as a bellows, and the depression of its floor draws air into the mouth cavity through the nostrils. The nostrils are then closed, and the floor of the mouth is elevated to force the air through a vent, the *glottis*, into the respiratory passages and the lungs. Exhalation is accomplished by a forceful contraction of the muscles of the body wall, which exerts pressure on the lungs to force the air into the mouth and out the nostrils. This mechanism of filling and emptying the lungs operates at intervals but is not necessarily carried out in full each time the floor of the mouth is lowered or raised. Numerous small fluctuations in respiration can be associated with a gentle pumping of the air back and forth between the lungs and the mouth only. Oxygen may be thoroughly extracted from the air by this means without any considerable dehydration, because one sample of air is used over and over again until the oxygen supply is almost exhausted. Likewise, the gentle movements of the floor of the mouth may draw air through the nostrils into the moist mouth cavity where gaseous exchange can occur. If the animal is inactive and in a cool environment, metabolism will be low and the oxygen exchange through the skin and through the lining of the mouth may be sufficient to supply the needs of the animal.

The distribution of oxygen and carbon dioxide throughout the organism is accomplished by means of the *circulatory system*. Oxygen is taken up by the blood and is transported by the respiratory pigment, *hemoglobin*, which is found in the red blood cells of the frog. Most of the oxygen is carried in chemical combination as *oxyhemoglobin*. Some oxygen, however, will be transported in solution in the *plasma*, but this is a small percentage of the total oxygen supply transported. The transportation of carbon dioxide is much more complex; 10 per cent of the carbon dioxide can be carried in chemical combination with hemoglobin, but most of the carbon dioxide will be transported in the form of carbonic acid and as bicarbonate.

The exchange of gases between the blood and the body fluids and cells is termed *internal respiration.* This exchange is accomplished by a process of diffusion from greater to lower concentration of the gases. The oxygen concentration in the region of the cells is very low, whereas the amount of oxygen in the blood is high. The movement of the molecules of oxygen, therefore, will be from the blood into the body fluid and the cells. Since the carbon dioxide concentration in the region of the cells is high, whereas the amount of carbon dioxide in the blood is low, the movement of carbon dioxide will be from the cells and fluids into the blood stream.

It should be remembered that the tadpole is an aquatic vertebrate and that respiration in the tadpole is accomplished by means of gills. During the transformation of the tadpole to the adult, the gills disappear and the lungs are formed. The lungs of the frog are relatively simple sacs but are very vascular and are folded internally to increase the surface area. The adult frog is truly amphibious and can survive in both air and water. It should be pointed out, however, that in very warm water the oxygen concentration is low, and if the metabolic activity of the frog is high, the animal cannot survive if kept submerged. This means that the skin is an inadequate respiratory organ under these conditions. When the water is cool, the amount of oxygen in the water is high, and if the frog's metabolic activity is low, the frog can remain submerged indefinitely. It is possible under these conditions to secure enough oxygen through the skin to maintain life. This explains the fact that a frog can bury itself in the mud on the bottom of a pond or stream and survive the winter months. Some of the amphibians are able to exist in mountain streams without ever coming to the surface, and other amphibians have no lungs in the adult stage; but the combination of ample oxygen supply and low metabolic rate is always necessary for the maintenance of these animals. The skin is able to provide for ample gaseous exchange, as we mentioned previously.

Circulatory system

Most of the functions of a circulatory system in nutrition, respiration, excretion, chemical coordination, and body defense, and as a supplier of fluid medium for the cells, have been discussed previously. The closed blood-vascular system of the vertebrates is the most elaborate and efficient in the animal kingdom. The vertebrates have developed an effective pump, the *heart,* and tubes to carry the blood throughout the body. Certain of these tubes, the *arteries*, carry blood from the heart; others, the *veins*, deliver blood to the heart; and the microscopic *capillaries* connect the arteries to the veins. The vertebrates also possess a second vascular system, composed of the *lymph vessels*, which drain fluid from the tissue spaces back into the blood vascular system. The features of the circulatory system can not be described adequately without reference to the pioneering work of William Harvey, who in 1616 first reported his experiments on the movement of the blood. Harvey has been justly named as the originator of the experimental method in biology on the basis of this work. A brief account of the ideas on circulation which were prevalent previous to Harvey's work will serve to emphasize his contribution.

Galen, an ancient Greek physician (130–200? A.D.) who lived in Rome, postulated on the basis of anatomical studies that venous blood was being formed constantly in the liver, mixed with "spirit," and distributed through the veins to the entire body. He also believed that blood oozed through "pores" from one side of the heart to the other and thus might be found in the arteries. Vesalius in 1555 proved that such heart pores did not exist. Colombo shortly afterward demonstrated that blood flowed from the heart to the lungs and returned, and Fabricius observed that valves were present in veins, but he did not understand their function. It was the presence of these venous valves that gave Harvey his initial clue for understanding the mechanism of circulation.

Harvey, by a direct observation, demonstrated that the blood in the veins of the arm flowed only in the direction of the heart, and that the valves observed by Fabricius prevented any venous flow away from the heart. He noted that

Figure 18.15. These diagrams illustrate the arrangement of auricles and ventricles in representative vertebrate hearts. The reptile heart contains two auricles and two ventricles. But the two ventricles are not always completely separated from each other as shown in the sketch, where separated, they are divided by only a perforated membrane.

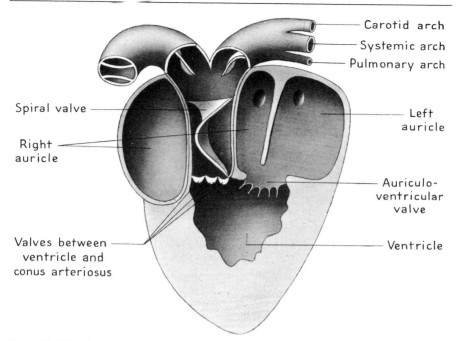

Figure 18.16.   The three-chambered heart of the frog is an amphibian modification and is not typical of vertebrates in general.

when he put enough pressure on an artery to stop the flow of blood, the flow also ceased in the corresponding vein. This simple experiment demonstrated the relationship between arteries and veins, and although he did not know of the existence of capillaries, he realized that connections between the major vessels must exist. It remained for our old friend Leeuwenhoek and for the Italian microscopist, Marcello Malpighi, to demonstrate the existence of the capillaries. Harvey's determination of the rate of blood flow proved to be the key which unlocked the puzzle of the mechanism of blood circulation. Although he made several gross errors in his actual calculations, the general conclusions that he reached were irrefutable. Furthermore, his work provided the impetus for the extension of the experimental method to other biological problems and aroused an interest in the study of living, as opposed to preserved, organisms. The simplicity of his experiments and the logic of his deductions established a pattern for investigators that became most influential.

Many features of the frog's circulatory system are comparable with those of other vertebrates, and although some peculiarities exist, those do not alter the basic relationships. The number of chambers in vertebrate hearts varies, as the diagrams show (Figures 18.15, 18.16). The shark heart, for example, has only two chambers: an *auricle*, or receiving chamber, and a *ventricle*, or pumping

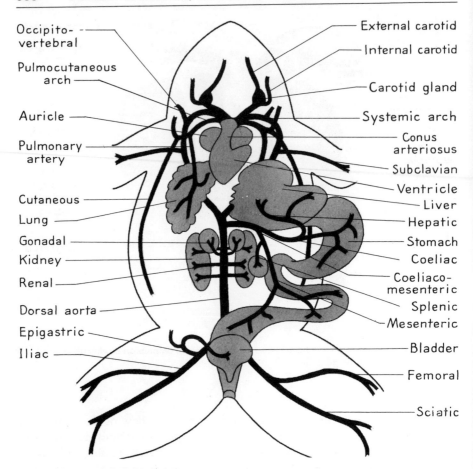

Figure 18.17.   The arterial circulation of the frog.

chamber. The hearts of birds and mammals possess four chambers: *two auricles* and *two ventricles*. The frog heart is intermediate in structure and has only three divisions: two auricles and a single ventricle.

The circulation of blood through the frog heart has remained a puzzle for many years. Zoologists have been reluctant to accept the idea that pulmonary blood from the left auricle and systemic blood from the right auricle are mixed in the ventricle, and many attempts have been made to prove that the blood is not mixed. Recent work, however, which uses the injection of India ink into blood vessels to trace flow and X-ray motion-picture photographs to show the movement of materials through the heart, demonstrates that complete mixing does take place. This does not impress one as being efficient, but we must remember that mechanical efficiency and biological efficiency do not always correspond. Certainly the frog and other amphibians have a circulatory sys-

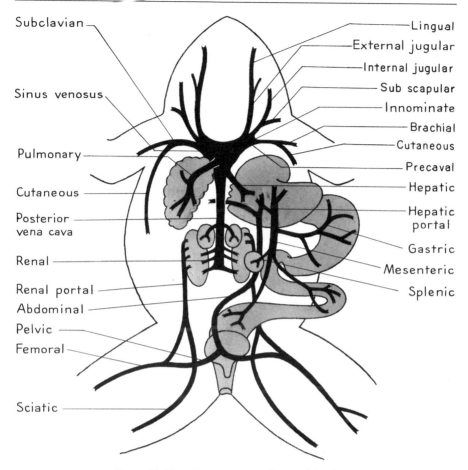

Figure 18.18.   The venous circulation of the frog.

tem adequate for their needs, in spite of this mixing of "pure" and "impure" blood.

The details of the arterial and venous blood vessels may be gathered from the circulation diagrams, but we should say a word about the lymphatic system previously mentioned. Fluid filters through the capillary walls into the tissue spaces of the body to provide a fluid medium for the cells, and not all this fluid can drain back into the capillaries, partly because of the slight pressure in the vessels, against which it would have to move. This material bathing the cells is the *lymph*, a colorless fluid which contains variable numbers of white blood cells. A series of irregular vessels, the *lymph capillaries*, opens into the tissue spaces and drains the lymph through *lymph vessels* into the venous system. Frequently present are pulsating areas, the *lymph hearts*; and these, coupled with valves which permit lymph to flow only toward the veins, are responsible for the return of the lymph to the blood-vascular system. There are large lymph sacs in the frog where lymph accumulates, and two pairs of lymph hearts pump the fluid into the iliac veins in the trunk and the jugular veins in the neck.

Excretory system

There is such an intimate structural and functional relationship between the excretory and reproductive systems of the vertebrates that the two systems are usually considered together as the *urogenital system*. It may be recalled that there are two types of tubular excretory systems in the animal kingdom. The first of these is the *nephridial system* in which tubules with ciliated funnels drain the coelomic cavity. The tubules are derived from the ectoderm, and we saw this system in the annelids. The second type of excretory system is derived from the coelom. The coelomic sacs of the crustaceans illustrate this condition. The excretory tubules which develop from the coelom are sometimes referred to as a *coelomoduct system*.

THE VERTEBRATE KIDNEY • The functional unit of the vertebrate kidney is called a *nephron*, and the kidney is composed of an aggregation of thousands or even hundreds of thousands of these functional units. It has been traditional to recognize three stages in the development of the vertebrate kidney: the *pronephric*, the *mesonephric*, and the *metanephric* stages. Unfortunately, these stages have often been considered to be three separate kidneys which sequentially assume functional activity in the vertebrate. Recent concepts of kidney structure and function suggest, however, that it is much more accurate to conclude that the vertebrates possess a single kidney with three variations in the degree of its development. It is important to recognize in this connection that there is a significant difference in the development of the kidneys of the lower vertebrates and those of the higher vertebrates, but in both groups it is advantageous to think of the kidney as an entire structural unit, the *holonephros*.

Two regions of the holonephros can be recognized in the sharks, fishes, and amphibians. These regions are the *pronephros*, "head kidney," and the *opistonephros*, "black kidney." The pronephros is a temporary structure functioning in the embryonic stage or larval stage of these animals. The nephrons of the pronephros often possess an opening, the *peritoneal funnel*, which connects with the coelomic cavity. This arrangement is shown in Figure 18.19. The pronephros functions in the embryo or larva of the lower vertebrates, but, when the adult stage is reached, the opistonephros becomes the functional unit of the kidney and the pronephros degenerates.

The development of the kidney in the reptiles, birds, and mammals is somewhat more complex. It has been traditional, as was observed earlier, to think of the kidney of the higher vertebrates as a tripartite kidney and to designate three distinct stages. We should note, however, that the pronephros may be absent or may be a very minute portion of the kidney of higher vertebrates. The middle region of the kidney, which would correspond to the anterior part of the opistonephros of the lower vertebrates, becomes a functional kidney of the embryo or larval stage. This region is often called the *mesonephros,* or "middle kidney." During embryonic development a more posterior portion of the holonephric kidney develops, and this region becomes the functional kidney of the adult. This is the *metanephros,* or "last kidney." The mesonephros ceases to function when the embryo enters the postembryonic state and the metanephros becomes the functional adult kidney. We will notice shortly that the mesonephric portion of the kidney does not degenerate completely but becomes involved with the development of the reproductive system.

Each *nephron* is composed of a coil of arterial capillaries, the *glomerulus* (plural, *glomeruli*), surrounded by a cup formed by the end of the kidney tubule. This cup, *Bowman's capsule,* and the glomerulus constitute a *renal corpuscle.*

Figure 18.19. The drawing of a generalized tubule, or nephron, of a frog kidney indicates the complex structure required to accomplish the functions that are performed by this organ. Compare with the drawing of the human kidney tubule in Figure 19.14.

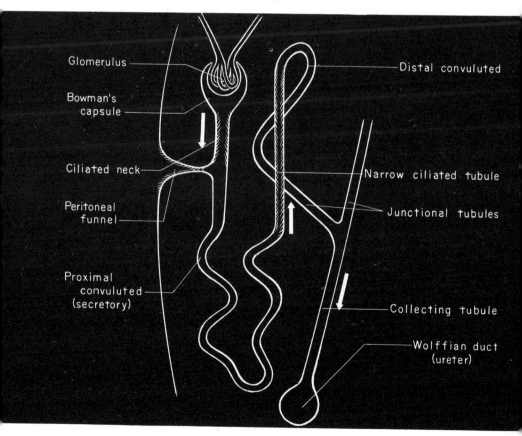

There are thousands of renal corpuscles in each kidney, and each one is continuous with a coiled tubule to form the excretory unit which we have designated as the nephron.   The kidney in the amphibia consists of the two stages: the *pronephric stage*, which functions during early embryonic development; and a portion of the opisthonephros, the *mesonephros*, which functions during later embryonic stages and in the adult.   One structural oddity of the frog kidney is the presence of ciliated funnels which open at one end into the coelom and at the other end into capillaries in the kidney to drain coelomic fluid into the blood stream.   Funnels of this type in certain other vertebrates also may connect with the nephrons instead of with the capillaries, and because of their relationship to the abdominal coelom, they are referred to as *peritoneal funnels*.

This second, or mesonephric, stage of the kidney usually has nephrons which typically do not have openings into the coelom, and there are several nephrons in each body segment.   Furthermore, these nephrons are much more elongated and coiled than are the more anterior ones which preceded them.   Some of the most fundamental work on vertebrate kidney function was done on these tubules by A. N. Richards, who in 1922 was able by micromanipulation to withdraw samples of fluid from various portions of the nephron and to analyze these samples chemically.   Richards' researches supplemented the observations on kidney function which were being made by many other investigators and helped establish the importance of the filtration of fluid through the capillaries of the glomerulus into the tubules.   More important, he was able to demonstrate that both usable and waste materials were filtered, that the cells of the tubule wall must concentrate the urine by reabsorbing the usable materials, and that the cells also might secrete additional waste materials into the tubule.   The mechanism of excretion has been studied in great detail since Richards's original investigations, and the more recent observations are in close agreement with his studies.   We will note later that the basic phenomena of function observed in the frog kidney are duplicated in man (p. 432).

A few fishes, as well as some amphibians and mammals, have nephrons which lack glomeruli and in which only tubular excretion can occur; filtration thus is at a minimum in such nephrons.   Kidneys without glomeruli are found in vertebrate animals that have a major problem of water conservation, such as fish that live in very salty water and certain animals that live in desert areas.

The posterior region of the holonephros develops to a marked degree only in the reptiles, birds, and mammals.   There may be little or no development of the pronephric regions in these classes (as man illustrates).   The mesonephric region of the kidney, which functions in the adult fishes and amphibia, serves as the functional kidney of the embryo only in reptiles, birds, and mammals, and is supplanted in the adult by the last, or *metanephric, stage* of the kidney. There are several important differences between the structure of the metanephric kidney and that of the mesonephros.   The tubules in the metanephros are not segmentally arranged and are even more coiled and elongated than those in the mesonephros; also, peritoneal funnels are never present in the metanephros.

Figure 18.20.   Most amphibian vertebrates lay their eggs in the water, and these eggs usually pass through a free-living tadpole stage.   The "obstetrical" toad above, however, carries the eggs in a pouch, and these eggs develop right through the tadpole stage, finally popping out as fully formed little toads!   (Copyright by Duell, Sloan & Pearce, Inc.; photo by William Beebe.)

The function of the metanephric stage of the kidney is somewhat more elaborate than that of the more anterior regions of the kidney.   Since this portion of the kidney develops only in adult air-breathing vertebrates, its importance in water conservation is particularly significant.

The way the kidney functions in excretion is a result of three processes: *first,* the filtration of fluid from the blood into the tubules of the kidney; *second,* the secretion, by cells of the tubule wall, of waste material into the cavity of the tubules; and *third,* the selective reabsorption and return to the blood, by the cells of the tubule wall, of the usable materials which were originally filtered from the blood.   A urine which is high in nitrogenous waste is produced by this filtration, secretion, and selective reabsorption.   Filtration occurs at the glomerulus, where the pressure of the blood in the capillaries causes fluid to ooze through the thin capillary walls and enter the tubule through the cuplike Bowman's capsule, which acts as a funnel to collect the fluid from the glomerulus. The composition of the filtrate in Bowman's capsule is the same as the fluid of the blood minus proteins, so it contains dissolved food substances and salts as well as waste material.   Additional nitrogenous waste material in the form of urea or uric acid is secreted into the fluid as it traverses the tubule toward the excretory duct.   The tubule cells simultaneously reabsorb dissolved foods, salts, and water.   The end result, therefore, is the production of urine with a high concentration of waste but with a small amount of usable material.

The total number of glomeruli in the frog kidney has been estimated at approximately 2000.   These units may not all function at the same time, however; and this fact can be demonstrated by direct observation of the kidney function in the living frog.   The amount of urine excreted by the frog in a 24-hour period may equal one third of the total body weight of the animal.   Since much more fluid is filtered through the glomeruli than is excreted, this figure will give an idea of the amount of work done by the kidney, and it is obvious why frogs and other amphibians must remain submerged or in very moist surroundings if they are to avoid dehydration.   It is interesting to note in this connection that some of the amphibians that live in desert regions have lost the glomeruli.   This adaptation prevents excessive loss of water through the kidney tubules, but excretion can still be accomplished by the tubules themselves, which are highly selective in such instances.

Reproductive system

The gonads of the frog first appear as thickenings on the wall of the embryonic coelom and are suspended from the body wall by mesenteries. The testes are connected to the anterior end of the opisthonephros by a series of very fine tubules, the *vasa efferentia.* Sperm pass through the vasa efferentia to the tubules of the kidney, and thence to the cloaca by way of the mesonephric duct. The mesonephric duct of the male frog, therefore, is both an excretory and reproductive duct, and therefore is a true *urogenital duct.* In the female, however, the eggs are transported to the cloaca by way of a second duct, the *oviduct.* The oviduct of the frog develops from the wall of the coelom, and first appears as a groove, which later folds and closes to form a tube. The oviduct begins anteriorly as a ciliated funnel which opens into the abdominal cavity; it is coiled, and shows some regional specialization. The ovaries are attached near the kidneys, and eggs are discharged directly into the body cavity, from which they are carried into the oviduct by ciliary action. A gelatinous material is secreted about the eggs by the upper part of the oviduct. The lower part of the duct may serve as a temporary storage place for them. The portion of the oviduct which serves to retain the eggs is frequently designated as the *uterus.* The eggs move

Figure 18.21.   The urogenital system of male and female frogs.

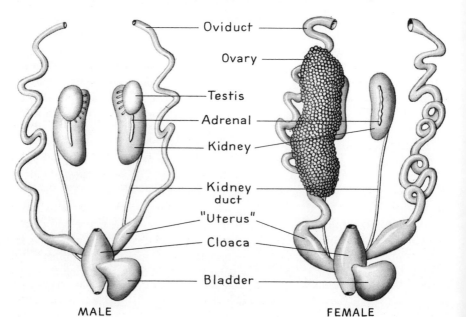

MALE   FEMALE

through the oviduct into the cloaca by the ciliary action of the walls of the oviduct. This appears to be a haphazard method for ensuring that eggs will be carried to the outside of the body; but the method, contrary to appearances, works very efficiently. A similar structural relationship exists in mammals, including man.

The yellow *fat body* which can be observed adjacent to the gonad has no reproductive function. These fat bodies provide the animal with a reserve of food because of the high caloric value of the fat of which they are composed.

The frog *Rana pipiens* is a convenient animal to use to illustrate the reproductive system of the Amphibia. A well-developed oviduct is present in the male as well as the female, and although the oviduct is not functional in the male, it is relatively large. It is important to note that during development the gonads go through a sexually *indifferent stage*, in which an outer layer, the *cortex*, and a middle region, the *medulla*, develop. If the cortex continues to develop and the medulla is reduced in size, the animal becomes a female; conversely, if the medulla grows and the cortex regresses, the animal becomes a male. Since both cortex and medulla are present in the sexually indifferent stage, and since both oviduct and sperm ducts are present, the animals may be said to be *bisexual* at this time. That the animals are truly bisexual can be demonstrated experimentally even in some adult amphibia. The cortical portion of the gonad in the adult male toad is confined to a limited area at the anterior end of the testes, the *Bidder's organ*. If the testicular portion of the gonad is removed, Bidder's organ, the cortical portion, will enlarge, and, since it is cortical material, an ovary will be developed. After a lapse of a year or two the animal will be a functional female; thus the sex has been completely reversed. Such experiments are advantageous when interpreting the rare cases of sex reversal which appear in other vertebrates, such as birds and mammals. The phenomenon is also important for an understanding of the occasional cases of a false hermaphroditism which occur in human beings.

Nervous coordination

The impressive success of the vertebrates lies not so much in the unique architecture of the body as in the development of elaborate coordinating mechanisms. It is questionable, as a matter of fact, whether the vertebrates are mechanically as efficient as the arthropods; but their coordinating mechanisms have made it possible for them to adjust with great rapidity to very complex environmental influences. The topography and function of the frog brain, spinal cord, and sense organs are similar to those of other vertebrates, including man. There are, of course, some features of the frog nervous system which are not typical of the vertebrates, among the differences being a shortened spinal cord and the lack of a complete set of nerves associated with the brain. The parts of the frog brain, however, are the same as those found in the mammals, and the spinal cord has an arrangement of spinal nerves typical of other vertebrates. Structurally, the nervous system has two major divisions: the *central* nervous system, and the *peripheral* nervous system.   The *brain* and *spinal cord* constitute the first, whereas the *paired nerves* which extend from the brain and spinal cord and the numerous *ganglia* of the body comprise the peripheral system.

The frog brain is divided into five major regions.   The most anterior of these regions is the *cerebrum*, which is followed by the *diencephalon*, a small area of the brain, with a thin-walled roof.   Posterior to the diencephalon are two obvious enlargements of the brain which are the *optic lobes* of the *mid-brain*.   Immediately behind the mid-brain is the *cerebellum*, which is much less prominent in the frog than in most other vertebrates; and posterior to the cerebellum is the *medulla oblongata*, which tapers gradually to join with the spinal cord.   Because of this tapering, the exact limits of the medulla oblongata cannot be easily determined.   The cerebrum is bilobed, and each half possesses an *olfactory lobe* from which delicate *olfactory nerves* extend to the nasal region.   The diencephalon is notable because of two structures that are associated with it.   On the dorsal surface is a tubular structure, the *pineal gland;* and on the ventral surface a projection, the *infundibular process*.   This is joined by a growth from the anterior part of the mouth cavity to form the *pituitary gland*.   The process from the diencephalon forms the posterior lobe of the pituitary gland, and the growth from the mouth cavity becomes the anterior lobe of the pituitary gland.

Figure 18.22.   The brain of a frog and the brain of a man.

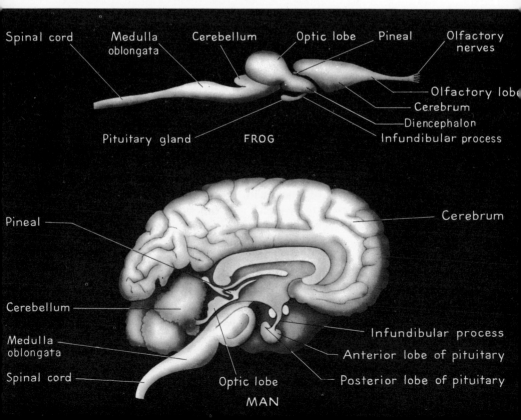

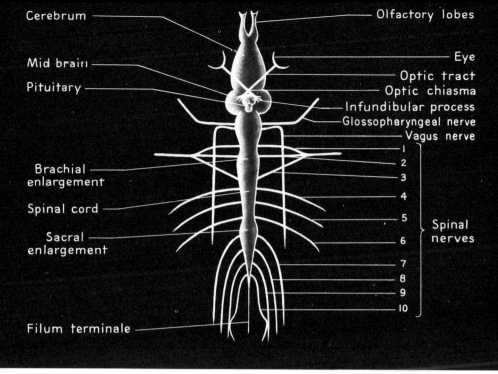

Figure 18.23.   The central nervous system of the frog.

The optic lobes are the most prominent portion of the brain of the frog, and it is in the optic lobes that the *optic nerves* terminate.   The lobes are, therefore, the visual centers.   This relationship is not true for all vertebrates; for example, in man the optic nerves terminate in the cerebrum.   The prominent *optic tracts* can be observed on the ventral surface of the brain, and these tracts cross in front of the infundibular process to form a characteristic landmark, the *optic chiasma,* on the ventral surface of the brain of all of the vertebrates.

The brain is hollow, and the spaces within the lateral lobes of the cerebrum are the *ventricles.*   The two ventricles of the cerebrum are connected by a narrow canal to the third ventricle, which lies in the mid-brain.   The third ventricle in turn connects with the fourth ventricle in the medulla oblongata.

The nerves associated with the brain are designated as the *cranial nerves.* There are 12 cranial nerves in the mammals, reptiles, and birds but only 10 in the frog.   The two most posterior nerves, the *spinal accessory* and the *hypoglossal,* are lacking in amphibians.   The cranial nerves of the frog are listed in tabular form in the accompanying chart (p. 376).   We note that some nerves are sensory, some motor, and others both sensory and motor in their function.

As we might expect, the frog brain is not as complicated in its functions as that of man; moreover, the ratio of the brain to the spinal cord is less than 1.0 in the frog.   The mammals often have a brain-cord ratio of 4.0; and in man this ratio is much greater (p. 445).   The frog cerebrum is only slightly enlarged and

		Cranial Nerves of the Frog	
No.	Name	Type of fibers	Region of body
1	Olfactory	Sensory	Nasal epithelium
2	Optic tract (not a true nerve)	Sensory	Retina of eye
3	Oculomotor	Motor	Four eye muscles
4	Trochlear	Motor	One eye muscle
5	Trigeminal	Sensory and motor	Upper and lower jaws
6	Abducens	Motor	One eye muscle
7	Facial	Sensory and motor	Tongue, muscles of "face and neck"
8	Auditory	Sensory	Inner ear
9	Glossopharyngeal	Sensory and motor	Tongue, muscles of pharynx
10	Vagus	Sensory and motor	Pharynx, lungs, heart, and viscera

is concerned almost exclusively with the sense of smell. The frog gets along about as well after the surgical removal of the cerebrum as it does with the cerebrum present. The diencephalon in the frog, as in most of the vertebrates, serves chiefly as a connection between the cerebrum and the more posterior regions of the brain. The optic lobes, as we noted previously, are concerned with vision. The relatively small cerebellum serves as the center for automatic control, particularly with respect to muscular coordination. The movements of the frog are not as complex as those of some of the other vertebrates, and the

Figure 18.24.   A simplified cross section of a vertebrate spinal cord.

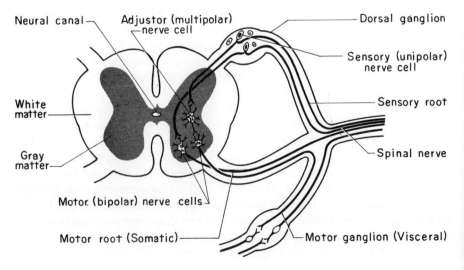

Figure 18.25. A frog with the cerebrum removed will still respond to many stimuli. The leap of this frog in response to a pin prick is typical of such reflex actions. (Courtesy Dr. A. M. Winchester, Stetson University.)

cerebellum is not called upon to perform elaborate integrations. The medulla oblongata is primarily a bridge connecting the spinal cord to the brain. The cerebrum of reptiles, birds, and mammals, in contrast with that of the frog, undergoes great enlargement. The enlargement is especially noticeable in the mammals and is due to extensive growth of the dorsal part of the cerebrum. The ability of a vertebrate to make complex adjustments is largely controlled through the cerebrum, which is the center for intelligence. The frog is essentially an automaton, and the primary responses are *reflex* reactions. The transmission of impulses in the frog is rapid, however, and although the speed is not equal to that in the birds and mammals, nervous conduction is much faster than in the average invertebrate. This is one of the important factors which has enabled the frog to live successfully.

The spinal cord is tubular, but it is small. Two enlargements of the spinal cord can be seen. These are the *brachial enlargement* in the region of the forelimbs, and the *sacral enlargement* in the area of the hind limbs. These enlargements indicate the presence of the large number of nerve cells and processes which are associated with the movement of the limbs. A series of 10 spinal nerves arises from the spinal cord, representing spinal nerves 2 to 11 of the typical vertebrate, the first spinal nerve having been lost. The tadpole possesses 20 or more spinal nerves, depending on the species of frog, but the more posterior spinal nerves disappear when the tail is reabsorbed. The posterior portion of the spinal cord of the adult frog, therefore, is highly modified. We can observe that a very fine process of the spinal cord, the *filum terminale,* continues into the tip of the vertebral column, the *urostyle.*

A typical spinal nerve is composed of two parts: a dorsal branch and a ventral branch; these join laterally to the cord to form a single spinal nerve. The nerve, therefore, is composed of fibers which are contributed by both the dorsal and ventral branches. The cell bodies of the dorsal branch of each spinal nerve can be found in an enlargement, the *spinal ganglion,* which is located dorsal and lateral to the cord. The nerve cell bodies of the ventral branch, however, are found in the spinal cord. More than a century ago Sir Charles Bell and François Magendie showed that the dorsal branch of the spinal nerve contains *sensory fibers,* whereas the ventral branch is made up of *motor fibers.*

Another set of nerves is also associated with the brain and spinal cord. These are the nerves of the *autonomic nervous system.* The autonomic nervous system begins in the brain region; and the autonomic nerve trunks run posteriorly, parallel to the spinal cord. A series of ganglia is associated with the autonomic nerve trunks at points where the trunks receive branches from the spinal nerves. The number of ganglia in the autonomic nervous system is comparable to the number of dorsal ganglia; however, there is some variation in the number, especially in the posterior region, where a variable amount of fusion occurs. The autonomic nervous system is a *motor system,* and the ganglia are of two types: the *sympathetic ganglia,* which are located near the spinal cord; and the *parasympathetic ganglia,* which are located a considerable distance from the spinal cord. The parasympathetic ganglia are usually embedded in the structures which they innervate. We can observe, for example, that there are ganglia of the parasympathetic system embedded in the walls of the heart, the alimentary canal, and the bladder.

The functional unit of the nervous system is the *spinal reflex.* A stimulus affects a receptor—such as pain, touch, taste, or sight—and an impulse is relayed over a spinal nerve to the *dorsal portion* of the spinal cord. The message is then shunted to the *ventral part* of the cord, where it is picked up by motor nerve cells and carried out on the ventral branch of the spinal nerve to a region which will respond. A simple reflex may involve only one side and one level of the body. Thus the pinching of the leg of the frog will result in the withdrawal of the leg. The message, however, can be shunted to the opposite side of the cord, so that if a leg is pinched and held so that it cannot be withdrawn, the leg on the opposite side will kick. Reflexes, however, may become much more complex, and messages can be directed along the spinal cord to the other levels or regions of the body. The pinching of a hind leg may result in the movement of an arm on the same or the opposite side, and the message will also be relayed to the brain, where the entire complex coordinating action of the brain may be called into action. Since many stimuli are being received, countless impulses result, and these impulses are sent over the reflex circuits to the brain. This sequence is responsible for complex adjustments on the part of the animal.

Chemical coordination

We customarily think of coordination in terms of responses mediated through the nervous system, and this is especially true in the vertebrates, where nervous reactions are remarkably rapid and efficient. We have already noted that elsewhere in the animal kingdom there are chemical substances that have important effects on the body and serve to coordinate activities. There are tissues and glands in many animals which secrete into the blood and body fluids specific chemical substances which can alter the function, and even the growth, of cells, tissues, and organs. We noted previously that these chemical principles are the *hormones.* Since the hormones are secreted internally into the blood or body fluids, they are called *endocrine* (internal) *secretions,* and the glands which secrete hormones are therefore called *endocrine glands.*

The term *hormone* derives from a Greek word meaning "to excite" or "to stimulate" and was first used by Bayliss and Starling at the turn of the century, but we have since learned that hormones can inhibit as well as stimulate. As a matter of fact, a hormone may simultaneously stimulate one part of the body and inhibit another. Nevertheless, the term *hormone*, in spite of the ineptitude of its literal meaning, continues to be used for those chemical messengers secreted by the endocrine glands and tissues.

Products of cellular metabolism, such as carbon dioxide, urea, lactic acid, and glucose, also are being released constantly; and as they circulate or diffuse throughout the body, they stimulate or inhibit cellular reactions distant from their source of origin. These metabolic materials are universal *chemical coordinators* and are often designated *parahormones*.

The significance of the hormones and parahormones in coordination can be understood best by considering briefly their role in body function. It may be stated, by way of introduction, that the chemical coordinators supplement the vertebrate nervous system in two important respects: transmission speed, and duration. Whereas nerve impulses are transmitted in the smallest fractions of a second, hormones require many seconds or even minutes for their transportation. The response to nervous stimulation is very short lived, and, unless repeated, may last for only a fraction of a second—for example, a single muscle twitch. Conversely, the responses to hormones may continue for minutes, hours, or days. The reaction of a person to an unexpected loud sound will illustrate the way in which the two actions of nervous and chemical coordination may cooperate. The sound causes the person to "jump," the heart rate and blood pressure to increase, the pupils of the eyes to dilate, the air passages of the lungs to enlarge, and the amount of sugar in the blood to increase. The responses at first are primarily a result of the stimulation of the sympathetic nervous system and would disappear quickly if it were not for the fact that the adrenal gland is also stimulated to release *epinephrine*, a hormone, into the blood. Epinephrine produces effects that usually are similar to those which follow nervous stimulation, but the action of epinephrine will continue for many minutes. One may, therefore, have an elevated heart rate and blood pressure long after the sudden noise has been recognized as a harmless sound, and after sympathetic nervous stimulation has ceased.

The frog possesses a full complement of endocrine glands. Unfortunately, these glands have been studied less intensively in the frog than in some of the other vertebrates. The hormones apparently are the same, or at least similar to, those which are found in man; but since their action has not been fully determined, information concerning chemical coordination in the frog must be obtained by comparing it with what we know about other vertebrates.

THE PITUITARY GLAND • This gland, which we have already described as being located on the ventral floor of the brain, is a dual structure. One part of the gland develops as an evagination, or outpocketing, from the floor of the brain, and the other part arises as a forward-growing pouch from the embryonic

Figure 18.26.   This tadpole, performing his barrel-roll, gives us a fine view of an early stage in the life of an aquatic vertebrate.   Not yet amphibious, breathing by means of gills, with rudimentary limbs just beginning to develop, this tadpole's metamorphosis to true vertebrate form and function depends on the action of hormones and enzymes.   (Courtesy Clarence Flaten.)

mouth cavity.   These two separate regions lie close together in the adult and frequently with one part partially folded around the other.   As a result of differential growth in the mammals and some of the other vertebrates, the portion which arises from the mouth cavity comes to lie anterior to that part which develops from the brain.   The two parts of the pituitary gland, for this reason, are usually spoken of as the *anterior lobe* and the *posterior lobe.*   The functions of the two lobes of the pituitary gland are entirely different, and the anterior lobe has the greater endocrine significance.   The importance of the anterior lobe may be gauged by the fact that it frequently is spoken of as the "master gland" of the body.   This is a case of overemphasis, however, because the pituitary gland is influenced by the action of the other glands, just as it in turn has important effects on other parts of the body.

The secretions of the anterior lobe influence the development of the reproductive system, growth, and general metabolism.   It has been demonstrated experimentally that the anterior lobe secretes *gonadotropins,* hormones which stimulate the development of the gonads, and there are at least two of these hormones.   The administration of the gonadotropic hormones will cause precocious sexual maturity in laboratory animals and also an increase in the number of young in a litter.   The interest in the frog as an experimental animal has led to a need for frog tadpoles at all times of the year.   The frog breeds only in the spring, but this difficulty has been overcome by the administration of an anterior pituitary hormone that will cause the frog to lay eggs at any season, and thus the experimenter can have tadpoles available for his investigations whenever he desires them.   It has also been demonstrated that the anterior lobe of the gland secretes another substance, *prolactin,* which has a marked influence on maternal behavior and on the secretory activity of the mammary glands.   This substance, when injected into roosters, may cause them to set on eggs and to "mother" baby chicks.   The anterior lobe also secretes other tropic hormones that stimulate both the thyroid gland and the adrenal cortex.   These hormones are known respectively as the *thyroid stimulating hormone* (TSH) and the *adrenocorticotropic hormone* (ACTH).   It is obvious that the anterior lobe is a very important gland in coordinating reproductive functions and general metabolic activities.

One of the most striking effects produced by the anterior lobe is a result of the secretion of the *growth hormone*. An inadequate amount of this hormone results in a failure of the long bones to grow properly, and an animal which suffers from the lack of this hormone will be a dwarf. Conversely, an over-secretion of the growth hormone stimulates cell activity and causes an elongation of the bones; this overgrowth can result in gigantism. The increase in the amount of growth hormone secreted may, unfortunately, occur after an animal has reached maturity. As such a time, the long bones of the body cannot grow, and only the bones at the joints and certain other regions of the body may increase in size. It is probable that many of the size differences which are observed among the various vertebrates are due to a variation in the amount of growth hormone which is released; for example, the giant dinosaurs of prehistoric times undoubtedly had an overabundance of anterior pituitary growth hormones, whereas dwarf mice have a scarcity.

The posterior lobe, in contrast to the anterior lobe, is of much less physiological importance. It secretes chemical messengers that influence the contraction of certain smooth muscles of the body, especially those of the uterus, and that regulate water balance. It has now been definitely determined that these two hormones are secreted elsewhere.

The intimate structural relationship that exists between the anterior and posterior lobes of the pituitary sometimes makes it difficult to distinguish the exact limits of the two lobes. The cells in the region of junction, however, are known to secrete a hormone, *intermedin*, so named because it comes from the "intermediate region" of the pituitary gland. The hormone is probably secreted by cells that originally developed in the anterior lobe of the pituitary. This hormone affects pigmentation in animals and, when injected into frogs, will disperse the pigment of color cells and cause a darkening of the skin.

THE THYROID GLAND • This is a well-known endocrine gland, and its function in the frog has been studied in considerable detail. The thyroid is located in the throat region; and in the vertebrates there may be two separate glands either located on either side of the mid-line, or fused into a single median bilobed structure. The secretion of the thyroid gland has a marked influence on the maturation of the frog tadpole. The presence of excess thyroid hormone in many vertebrates, especially birds and mammals, also greatly increases the rate of cellular oxidation. Conversely, if there is an inadequate amount of thyroid hormone, or if the thyroid gland is removed, the rate of oxidation will be greatly depressed.

The importance of oxidation in the functioning of all cells of the body is apparent, and a cell which does not carry on active metabolism will not grow nor function properly. An animal, therefore, with an inadequate amount of thyroid hormone may be a dwarf, but these dwarfs should not be confused with pituitary dwarfs, because in the thyroid dwarf the body proportions and body functions are abnormal. The studies of the frog have been helpful in understanding proper functioning of the thyroid gland in man. The secretion of thyroid hormone

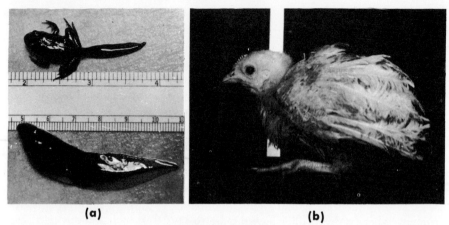

(a)   **(b)**

Figure 18.27.   The thyroid gland plays a major part in metamorphosis.   The upper tadpole in (a) has not been tampered with and is developing limbs in a normal fashion.   The lower tadpole has been given a drug to prevent his thyroid from functioning.   As a result, there has been no metamorphosis, and the tadpole has grown to an unnatural size.   The chicken in (b) had his thyroid removed.   His growth is stunted and his feathers are scraggly and forlorn.   Lack of thyroid secretion also has caused a lack of the male hormone, and this in turn has resulted in minute comb and wattles.   (Courtesy Charles H. Steinmetz.)

begins during the tadpole stage, and if the thyroid gland is removed, or if the formation of the thyroid hormone is prevented, the animals do not transform into adult frogs.   The tadpole, however, will continue to grow at a slow rate and may become a giant tadpole.   Conversely, the administration of extra thyroid hormone to tadpoles will speed their transformation into an adult, and the tadpoles may transform at an early age into miniature adult frogs.   The fact that the bullfrog exists in the tadpole stage for two to three years, whereas the common grass frog or leopard frog remains in the tadpole stage for only a few months, may be a result of the relative amounts of thyroid hormone which are present in these species.

THE PARATHYROID GLANDS • These glands are located near the thyroid and, in some forms, may be embedded in the thyroid gland.   Their origin in the embryo is entirely different from that of the thyroid and, although little is known of their function in the frog, what they do in other vertebrates is well understood.   The parathyroid glands secrete a substance which is important in maintaining the proper balance of calcium and phosphorus in the body.   If the parathyroid glands are removed surgically, or damaged so that the amount of their secretion is decreased or is absent entirely, the animal suffers from a condition called *tetany*.   The muscles contract forcibly, and the animal becomes rigid.   The adverse effects of the lack of parathyroid secretion are due to alterations in the amount of calcium in the blood.   It appears that the parathyroid glands are endocrine glands which are almost absolutely necessary for the maintenance of life. It is possible for an animal to survive removal of the other endocrines, but it cannot survive removal of the parathyroids unless very careful substitution therapy is practiced.

THE PANCREAS • The pancreas secretes digestive enzymes through ducts into the alimentary canal, but it is also an endocrine gland, releasing a hormone, *insulin*, directly into the blood stream. The hormone is secreted by clumps, or islands, of cells which are scattered throughout the gland. These are called the *islets of Langerhans*. The story of the identification and the purification of insulin is one of the fine examples of teamwork in biological research.

THE ADRENAL GLAND • This gland also has a dual structure, comparable in this respect to the pituitary; but the two parts of the adrenal gland are closely interrelated and exist as interlacing cords of cells in most of the vertebrates. The relationship of the adrenal gland in the mammals is such that one part is arranged as a covering *cortex* which surrounds a central *medulla*. It is convenient for this reason to consider the two parts of the adrenal gland as the *cortex* and the *medulla*. The two regions of the adrenal gland have very different origins. The medullary portion is derived from embryonic nerve cells which originate from the area between the spinal cord and the superficial ectoderm of the embryo and migrate ventrally into the region of the gland. The medullary portion, therefore, is of ectodermal origin. The cortical portion of the gland

Endocrine Glands of Frog	
GLAND	ACTION ON
Pituitary:	
Anterior lobe	Reproductive system
	Growth
	Thyroid
	Adrenal cortex
Posterior lobe	Smooth-muscle contraction
	Water balance
Intermediate region	Pigmentation
Thyroid	Metabolic rate of cells
	Maturation
Parathyroid	Calcium and phosphorus balance
Pancreas (islets of Langerhans)	Carbohydrate metabolism
Adrenal:	
Cortex	Sodium and potassium balance
	Carbohydrate metabolism
Medulla	"Emergency" reactions
Gonads	
(ovaries and testes)	Secondary sex characters

develops from coelomic epithelium in the embryo and is, of course, meso-dermal. The cortical and medullary portions of the gland in most of the amphibians, the reptiles, and the birds are arranged in the form of interlacing cords of cells. The two parts of the gland are separated in fishes and in some of the amphibians and consist of two separate masses of cells.

The medullary portion of the adrenal gland secretes the hormone *epinephrine*, or *adrenalin*. This substance, when released into the circulatory system, produces the same effect as that of the stimulation of the sympathetic nervous system, an effect which is quite striking. As we mentioned previously, the heart rate increases, the blood pressure is elevated, the amount of sugar in the blood is increased, the pupils of the eyes dilate, the blood clots more rapidly, and the air passages to the lungs are enlarged.

The function of the adrenal cortex is entirely different from that of the adrenal medulla. Although it is not certain that two distinct hormones are secreted by the cortex, it is possible to isolate two chemicals from the gland. One of these substances controls the sodium and potassium balance and the other controls carbohydrate metabolism. The first substance is therefore sometimes spoken of as the *salt principle*, and the second as the *sugar principle*.

Little is actually known about the function of the adrenal gland in the frog, but it is assumed, on the basis of the information which we have concerning the function of the adrenal cortex in mammals and other vertebrates, that this gland probably functions in much the same manner in the frog.

THE GONADS • The gonads, like the pancreas, fulfill a dual purpose—that is, the testes and the ovaries are cell-producing, or *cytogenic*, glands, as well as endocrine glands. As cytogenic glands, the gonads form eggs or sperm; and as endocrine glands, they release male and female sex hormones into the blood. The hormone of the testis, *testosterone*, influences the development of the male characteristics. The enlarged thumb pad in the frog at breeding time is a result of the secretion of testosterone, and this hormone also has pronounced effects in other vertebrates. The large comb in the fowl, certain of the feather-pigment patterns in birds, the difference in the voice between male and female, and even the growth of the skeleton are influenced by the male sex hormone. Characteristics such as the voice, comb, thumb pad, and other features which are influ-

Figure 18.28. These cockerels are all the same age. But the one in (c) has been caponized (testes removed) and hence has almost no comb. The bird in (b) is quite normal in all respects. The one in (a) was given an extra supply of the male hormone and has piled glory on glory and developed a tremendous comb and wattles. (Courtesy W. R. Breneman.)

(a)   **(b)**   **(c)**

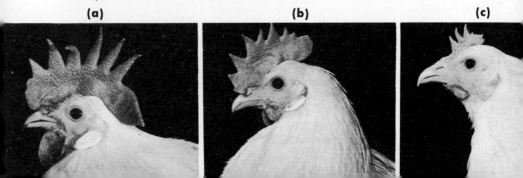

enced by sex hormones are said to be *secondary sex characters*, in contrast to the *primary sex characters*, which are the gonads. The female sex hormone, *estradiol*, also modifies secondary sex characters. The growth of the oviduct and its secretory activity are profoundly influenced by the secretions of the ovary.

Much remains to be learned concerning the actual method by which the hormones act in the vertebrates. These substances are chemical coordinators, of course, but they appear to act as enzymes or to function in cooperation with the enzymes. As a matter of fact, the hormones, like the enzymes, are consumed only in very small amounts in cellular chemical reactions. It can be demonstrated, for example, that the diabetogenic hormone of the anterior pituitary and insulin from the pancreas interact with the enzyme, *hexokinase*, and modify its activity in the transformation of glucose to glycogen. It can also be shown that the ovarian hormones, progesterone and estradiol, are involved in the production, or the inhibition of the production, of oxidative enzymes in the cells. One of the most exciting fields of biochemical research at the present time is that related to the action of the hormones and their effects within the individual cells of the body.

Classes of Vertebrates

There are seven classes of present-day vertebrates, six of which have representatives well known to everyone. Less well known, perhaps, is the class which is represented by the lamprey eels and ammocoete larvae, of which we spoke earlier. The classes of vertebrates can be subdivided into two major divisions: those without jaws, and those with jaws. The jawless vertebrates are represented by a single class, which includes the lamprey and its ammocoete larva. The six classes of vertebrates with jaws can be further subdivided into two distinct groups. One of these groups possesses embryos which develop within a fluid-filled covering membrane, the *amnion*, or *amniotic sac*. The embryos of the other three classes do not develop within such a sac, and the eggs must be laid in water. Those classes of vertebrates in which the embryos develop within the amniotic sac are called the *amniotes*, and the groups without an amnion are spoken of as the *anamniotes*.

The lampreys°

These animals are common in marine and fresh waters. Lampreys have a characteristic circular mouth, without upper or lower jaws. A tongue, which is well equipped with rasping teeth, is located in the center of the mouth. The body is without scales and does not possess paired fins; but there are well-developed dorsal fins and a tail fin. The lampreys have from 6 to 14 gill slits, although 7 are found in the typical lamprey. The eels attach to the bony fishes

---

° Class Agnatha, frequently referred to as cyclostomes (round mouth).

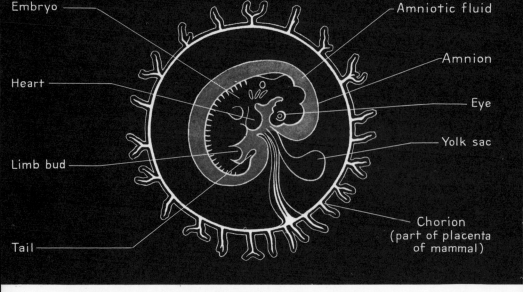

Embryo — Amniotic fluid

Amnion

Heart — Eye

Yolk sac

Limb bud —

Chorion
(part of placenta
Tail — of mammal)

Figure 18.29. The embryos of reptiles, birds, and mammals develop within a fluid-filled sac called the amnion; at this stage of their lives they are truly aquatic.

by means of the circular mouth and, using the tongue as a rasp, cut holes in the tissues of the animal which is attacked. The group is not only an economically important one but is also very interesting biologically. Although most animals must live permanently in either a salt-water environment or in a fresh-water environment, these versatile animals have been able to invade the fresh water from the sea and to thrive in that new environment. The lampreys have migrated into the Great Lakes and have become a distinct threat to the fishing industry of that area. They, more than any other single factor, have reduced the lake-trout fishing there from a very profitable industry to one which is barely surviving. We discussed the biological significance of the ammocoete larva of the lamprey earlier. This larva, we recall, is a primitive animal, similar to the probable ancestral type of vertebrate.

The cartilaginous fishes[*]

This group of fishes is perhaps the best known, because it includes the sharks and sharklike forms. There are many representative forms that are well known to everyone, some of them reaching gigantic proportions. The cartilaginous fishes differ from the lampreys in that they possess jaws, paired fins, and scales. There are seven external gill slits present, but the first gill slit is modified as a simple pore. The sharks do not possess the air bladder found in the bony fishes, and the skeleton is of cartilage. This cartilaginous material, however, has apparently *replaced* bone, which was undoubtedly the original skeletal material in this group of animals.

[*] Class Chondrichthyes

The bony fishes*

This class of fishes embraces the well-known forms of game fishes and other true fishes. These can be distinguished easily from the sharks by their bony skeleton, and by the lack of gills on the external surface. This is because the gills are covered by the *gill cover*, or *operculum*. The bony fishes possess an air bladder which is located inside the body, dorsal to the alimentary canal in many forms. This air bladder is used for two important functions in the fishes, the *first* of which is that gas can be secreted into the bladder and a considerable internal pressure can be developed. The animals can thus descend to great depths and are able to withstand the terrific pressures exerted by the water in the ocean depths or in very deep lakes. The air pressure within the air bladder also can be decreased, which enables the animal to adapt itself to varying depths in the water. The *second* function of the air bladder is illustrated in the lungfishes and the lobe-finned fishes. The air bladder serves as a lung in these animals, into which they are able to gulp air at the surface. This mechanism enables them to survive in stagnant water. A fascinating account of lungfishes is given by Smith in his book, *Komongo*, in which he describes his experiences in collecting these unusual fishes. He found, much to his amazement, that unless the lungfishes could get their heads out of water in the tubs in which he carried them, they would drown. The animals have become almost completely dependent on the air bladder for respiration.

The amphibians†

The frog demonstrates the salient features of the amphibians. It is probable, however, that the salamander should be considered as a more typical representative of the class. The modern amphibians have lungs, and some, in addition, have gills. Many of them respire by means of gills in the tadpole stage. The animals are adapted for both aquatic and terrestrial habitats, as the name *Amphibia* implies. The class has not been entirely successful in freeing itself from a water environment, however, because most amphibians lay their eggs in water. The amphibians represent the last class of anamniote vertebrates.

The reptiles‡

This class is well known because the snakes are members of it. Snakes, however, are not the best representatives, because the loss of legs is a specialization which is not typical of most of the reptiles. The lizards are a better example. Most of the reptiles are scaly, although they may be armored, as is the

* Class Osteichthyes
† Class Amphibia
‡ Class Reptilia

Figure 18.30.   Six of the seven classes of vertebrates are shown here: (a) cyclostomes; (b) cartilaginous fishes (shark); (c) bony fishes (archer fish); (d) reptiles (lizard); (e) amphibians (tree frog); (f) birds (trumpeter swan).   Mammals, the last class of vertebrates, are shown on page 390.

turtle. They respire exclusively by lungs, and the gills are reduced to gill slits or gill pouches in the embryo. The circulatory system is more advanced in its deveopment than in amphibians. The heart contains three chambers, two auricles and a ventricle, and the ventricle is almost completely divided by a partition, so that some of the reptiles may be considered to have essentially a four-chambered heart. Eggs may develop within the female, or they may be deposited in a nest. In either case, a double fold encloses the embryo in a two-walled sac during embryonic development. This sac is the *amnion*, and it is filled with fluid. An embryo of a reptile is literally in an aquatic environment, but the condition is a result of the secretion of fluid into the enclosed amniotic sac. This sac is found in all the remaining classes of vertebrates, and is is well known in the human being where the tearing of the sac at the time of the birth is commonly called the "rupture of the sac of waters." The reptiles, as well as the other two remaining classes of vertebrates, have thus become independent of an external water environment for embryonic development, because the embryos develop in their own fluid medium.

The birds°

The members of this class are animals which are recognized by everyone. Birds have feathers as the important distinguishing characteristic. Most of these animals can fly, but some have adapted secondarily to terrestrial life. The ostrich is a good example of a bird which has lost the power of flight. The heart of birds has developed even further than that of the reptiles, and four distinct chambers are present, two auricles and two ventricles. The class was once more numerous and important in the biological world than it is at present.

The mammals†

The best-known vertebrates are the mammals, because man belongs to this group. These animals possess hair and mammary glands. The mammary glands are structures which secrete milk for the young. The body cavity is divided by a diaphragm, which separates the lung cavity from the abdominal cavity, and aids in breathing. Most of the mammals give birth to young which are in a very advanced state of development. Embryonic development in most mammals continues in the uterus for many months, and most young mammals are capable of taking care of themselves at the time of birth. *Intra-uterine development* is a special adaptation which permits the young to be born in this advanced state. A few members of the Mammalia lay eggs, an example being the duck-billed platypus of Australia. This animal is reptilian in some of its characteristics, and its egg is a reptilelike egg. The mammary glands are rather

°Class Aves
†Class Mammalia

Figure 18.31.   The mammals are an odd lot.   The opossum (a) is a marsupial whose ancestors lived nearly 70,000,000 years ago.   Giant armadillos (b) once grew to be 8 ft. long.   Some mammals such as the dolphin (c) and the walrus (d) have adapted themselves to new environments.   Among the higher mammals, primates, are the tarsier (e) and the rhesus monkey (f).

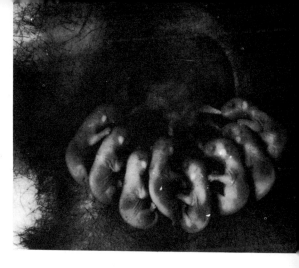

Figure 18.32. During a brief portion of their development, marsupial mammals live within the amnion. But early in the embryonic stage the embryos migrate from the uterus to the brood pouch, where they fasten to the nipples of the mammary glands and complete their development. This picture shows baby opposums in the pouch. (Copyright General Biological Supply House, Inc., Chicago.)

diffuse structures on the lower surface of the body, and the animals almost "sweat" milk, which the young lick from the fur of the mother. These unique animals indicate the relationship which exists between reptiles and mammals.

Classification of Chordates

Phylum Chordata Bilaterally symmetrical, segmented animals with a notochord, a dorsal tubular nervous system, and pharyngeal gill slits at some stage in deveopment. A closed circulatory system is present.

Subphylum Hemichordata. Wormlike animals with proboscis, dorsal and ventral nerve trunks, and numerous gill slits. A "notochord" extends into the proboscis. Example: acorn worm (*Balanoglossus*).

Subphylum Urochordata. Some are free-swimming, but most are sessile colonial animals. A tunic covers the body, and an enlarged atrium surrounds the pharynx. Larval stage is tadpolelike, and is a typical chordate. Example: sea squirt (*Molgula*).

Subphylum Cepalochordata. Notochord extends into the region of the brain, and the head is reduced. Atrium and many gill slits are present. A dorsal fin and ventral lateral folds also are present. Example: lancelet (Amphioxus).

Subphylum Vertebrata. Notochord and neural tube surrounded by cartilaginous or bony vertebrae. Two pairs of paired appendages are present, and basically not more than seven pairs of gill slits. Example: shark (*Squalus*).

CLASS I. AGNATHA. Possesses round mouth without jaws, semiparastic, has 6 to 14 pairs of gill slits. Example: lamprey eel (*Petromyzon*).

CLASS II. CHONDRICHTHYES. The cartilaginous fishes, with seven pairs of external gill slits. Pectoral and pelvic fins are present. Body is covered with scales. Example: dogfish shark (*Squalus acanthias*).

CLASS III. OSTEICHTHYES. The bony fishes, with gills covered by a gill plate; an air bladder is present. Body is covered with scales. Example: perch (*Perca*).

CLASS IV. AMPHIBIA. Respiration by gills and lungs. Fore and hind limbs are present, but no scales. Must lay eggs in water. Example: salamander (*Ambystoma*).

CLASS V. REPTILIA. Respiration by lungs. Fore and hind limbs present in most members of class, body is covered by scales. Embryo develops within amnion. Example: lizard (American "chameleon," *Anolis*).

CLASS VI. AVES. Respiration by lungs. Body covered with feathers; possess wings and legs; embryos develop within amnion. Example: sparrow (*Passer domesticus*).

CLASS VII. MAMMALIA. Respiration by lungs. Body covered with hair; fore and hind legs are present (forearms in some). Young develop within amnion. Example: rat (*Rattus*).

REFERENCES

AUDUBON, J. J., *The Birds of America*. The Macmillan Company, New York, 1937.

BEDDARD, F. E., "Mammalia", *Cambridge Natural History*, Vol. 10, Macmillian and Company, London, 1902.

CARROLL, P. L., and W. F. HOMER, *An Atlas of the Frog*. The C. V. Mosby Company, St. Louis, 1940.

DICKERSON, MARY C., *The Frog Book*. Doubleday, Doran and Company, New York, 1931.

DITMARS, R. L., *The Reptiles of the World*. Doubleday, Doran and Company, New York, 1928.

GORBMAN, A., and C. W. CREASER, "Accumulation of Radioactive Iodine by the Endostyle of Larval Lamprey and the Problem of Homology of the Thyroid," *Journal of Experimental Zoology*, 89, 1942.

HALL, PETER F., *Functions of the Endocrine Glands*. W. B. Saunders Company, Philadelphia, 1959.

HEGNER, R., *Parade of the Animal Kingdom*. The Macmillan Company, New York, 1944.

HOLMES, S. J., *The Biology of the Frog*. The Macmillan Company, New York, 1927.

HUBBS, C. L., "The Life Cycle and Growth of Lampreys," *Papers of Michigan Academy of Science*, Vol. 4, 1924.

HUGHES, G. M., *Comparative Physiology of Vertebrate Respiration*. Harvard University Press, Cambridge, Mass., 1963.

MOORE, JOHN A., *Physiology of the Amphibia*. Academic Press, New York, 1964.

NOBLE, G. K., *Biology of the Amphibia*. McGraw-Hill Book Company, New York, 1954.

PETERSON, R. T., *A Field Guide to Birds*. Houghton Mifflin Company, Boston, 1947.

ROMER, A. S., *Man and the Vertebrates*. University of Chicago Press, 1941.

ROMER, A. S., *Vertebrate Paleontology*. University of Chicago Press, 1945.

ROMER, A. S., *The Vertebrate Body*. W. B. Saunders Company, Philadelphia, 1949.

ROWAN, W., *The Riddle of Migration*. The Williams and Wilkins Company, Baltimore, 1932.

TORREY, T. W., *The Early Development of the Human Nephros*. Carnegie Institution Publication, Vol. XXXV, 1954. pp. 175–197.

WILLEY, A., *Amphioxus and the Ancestry of the Vertebrates*. Columbia University Press, 1894.

YOUNG, J. Z., *The Life of Vertebrates*. Clarendon Press, Oxford, 1950.

19

Man | The

Human

Organism

●

When it is said that the human race
is of far greater dignity than were any pre-existing beings
on earth, it is the intellectual and moral attributes only
of our race, not the animal, which are considered;

and it is by no means clear that the organization
of man is such as would confer a decided pre-eminence
upon him, if in place of his reasoning powers,
he was merely provided with such instincts as are
possessed by the lower animals.—Sir Charles Lyell, 1837

Man is best understood when it is recognized that all the properties of protoplasm and all the functions of organisms have their counterparts in him, and that he is but one of the myriads of organisms on earth. It may seem excessive to devote an entire chapter to a single species, *Homo sapiens*, when there are millions of species of plants and animals which we have treated only in a collective fashion. The biology of man, however, is the phase of biological science which is of the greatest interest to most of us. Our own well-being and our success as a species can be enhanced by a better understanding of man's position in the biological world and of his relationship to other organisms. The mere fact that a single species such as *Homo sapiens* has assumed such a dominant position on the earth is sufficient in itself to warrant extravagant treatment.

Since our primary concern in this discussion is with the biological features of man, and not with the sociological or psychological aspects of his being, we will consider human beings as we have studied other organisms. The construction of the human body, its cellular organization, and the functioning of its

393

diverse parts follow the biological rules which govern protoplasm; therefore, *body form, nutrition, respiration,* and the other facets of form and function will be analyzed as they pertain specifically to mankind.   It actually is quite an advantage to be able to contemplate man in this somewhat detached manner. Human potentialities and limitations appear in better perspective and can be evaluated more objectively.   It is important that we learn to expect neither too much nor too little of mankind in relation to the rest of the living world.

Body form

The human being is a typical chordate, possessing in early development a *notochord* and *pharyngeal pouches* or *grooves* (p. 346).   Neither, however, is as extensively developed as in most other chordates.   A *dorsal tubular nervous system* with a very much enlarged anterior *brain* is, of course, a prominent diagnostic feature of *Homo sapiens.*   Man also is *triploblastic, coelomate,* and *segmented.*   The coelom is partitioned into major subdivisions; the *pleural, pericardial,* and *peritoneal* cavities.   Although segmentation is obscured in the adult, the arrangement of the spinal nerves and of the vertebrae serves to indicate segmentation even in the adult form.

The vertebrate characteristics of man also are obvious.   The *vertebral column* with its string of bony vertebrae is evident, as are the *two pairs of appendages,* the arms and the legs.   *Gill slits* as such are not present, but pharyngeal pouches related to them are easily identified in the human embryo.   Also, a *tail* is not obvious, but the *coccyx* at the tip of the vertebral column is a rudiment of it.

Finally, the presence of *hair* and *mammary glands* places man in the class *Mammalia;* and the very large *brain,* the *eyes directed forward,* and *nails* (rather than claws) on the digits assign man to the order *Primates.*

Skin

It should be emphasized that man, along with the reptiles, birds, and other mammals, is an air-dwelling organism which has been able to adapt successfully

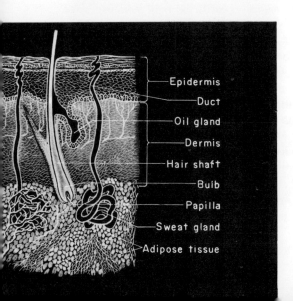

Epidermis

Duct

Oil gland

Dermis

Hair shaft

Bulb

Papilla

Sweat gland

Adipose tissue

Figure 19.1.   This diagrammatic drawing of human skin in cross section shows the tissues and other structures which make it possible for the skin to perform the respiratory function as well as to serve as a protective device.

to this rigorous, changeable environment. It is important in relation to this adaptation to note the nature of the skin, which provides an *airtight, chemically resistant,* and relatively *impervious cover* for the body. The outer portion of the skin is the *epidermis,* immediately below which is the vascular *dermis.* The latter, because of its network of connective tissues, holds the epidermis to the underlying loose connective tissue, the musculature, and the endoskeleton with a firm but pliable bondage.

The epidermis of man is stratified squamous epithelium (pp. 120, 122), the cellular structure of which is comparable to that of other vertebrates. The most significant difference is to be found in the presence of a greater number of flattened (squamous) cells at the surface. These are dead cells and have become hornified—that is, they contain a chemical substance, *keratin,* which is affected only by the action of relatively strong acids and alkalies. The thickness of this keratinized layer varies greatly on the different surfaces of the body; it may attain a thickness of more than 1000 microns on the soles of the feet, or of 700 microns on parts of the body not subjected to constant pressure or rubbing. Local thickenings such as callouses also are formed at friction points, as anyone who has spaded a garden or hoed weeds will know.

The advantage to man of the superficial layers of chemically inert cells lies not only in protection against external mechanical strains but also in the barrier provided by these layers against dehydration and bacterial invasion. Tissue fluids are effectively sealed within the body and evaporation into the dry air is minimized. The multitudes of bacteria which constantly impinge upon the surface of the body are denied admission as long as the epidermis remains intact. Only when a portion of the surface has been torn or eroded away can disease organisms gain entrance through the skin.

Closely correlated with the function of the epidermis in preventing dehydration is its role in the temperature control of the human body. Although the epidermis itself is nonvascular, the underlying dermis is well supplied with blood vessels. The epidermis, therefore, provides extensive surface area for the loss of heat by radiation and convection. Furthermore, the human skin is provided with more than 2,000,000 *sweat glands* which pour their watery secretion over the surface of the epidermis. The evaporation of this sweat is a very efficient method for cooling. The human being, accordingly, has a much better temperature control than do the warm-blooded birds and the mammals that do not posses sweat glands. The skin is an efficient thermostat.

It might appear, since the skin is such an effective barrier, that it would also insulate the body from external stimuli and thus prohibit an awareness of the environment. Your experiences minute by minute are a constant proof, however, that the opposite is true. There are countless sensory nerve endings in the skin which are *pain receptors.* The numerous *touch receptors* and the deep *pressure receptors* of the skin inform us of varying degrees and kinds of contact and pressure. There are also *receptors for heat and for cold.* Collectively, these sensory structures make the skin an elaborate sense organ which incessantly furnishes various kinds of information to the body about the external environment.

Skeleton

The skeleton of man is an *endoskeleton,* composed in the adult of slightly more than 200 separate bones. The exact number of bones changes with age, being greater in children than in adults because certain of the bones fuse as the individual matures. It is convenient to designate two major skeletal regions: the *axial skeleton,* composed of the bony elements in the mid-line of the body, and the *appendicular skeleton,* consisting of the bones of the appendages. The function of the skeleton in man, as in other animals, is to provide a partial support for the internal organs, a limited amount of protection, and a system of levers and joints for movement and locomotion. The appendicular skeleton is chiefly concerned with the lever systems, whereas the axial skeleton is primarily involved with support and protection.

The erect carriage of the body of man is a radical departure from the horizontal position of the body of most other mammals. The alterations in the skeleton of man which enable him to assume this erect carriage, however, actually are relatively minor and are even less drastic than the skeletal modifications which can be observed in certain other vertebrates; for example, the development of a urostyle in the frog as an aid in jumping (p. 357), or the adaptations of the bat skeleton which facilitate flying (Figure 22.14). The relatively minor modifications of the skeleton of man, therefore, will be mentioned only incidentally as we discuss the details of the skeleton.

The key structure in the axial skeleton is the backbone, or *vertebral column.* This serves as a pliable truss and, by reason of the 33 separate vertebrae of which it is composed, permits great flexibility in body movement. Furthermore, the elongated double curvature of the backbone provides a shock-absorbing action without which each step taken would transmit a pronounced jolt to the entire body. The backbone is made up of 7 *cervical vertebrae* in the neck region, 12 *thoracic vertebrae* in the trunk region, and 5 *lumbar vertebrae* in the small of the back. In addition, 5 vertebrae have fused to compose the broad *sacrum,* and 4 other vertebrae have merged to form the *coccyx,* the rudimentary tail which we mentioned previously. The protection provided the spinal cord by the vertebrae is of great significance. The spinal cord traverses the vertebral column through a small *neural canal* formed by the *dorsal spines* of the vertebrae. The cord is protected ventrally by the broad, heavy *body* of each vertebra.

The second major portion of the axial skeleton is the *rib cage,* or *basket,* composed of 12 pairs of flat bones which support and protect the wall of the chest. (Note that modern-day Adam and Eve have exactly the same number of ribs.) The first 7 pairs of ribs are attached ventrally to the breastbone, or *sternum.* The next 3 pairs of ribs are also fastened to the breastbone, but by means of elastic cartilage. The remaining 2 pairs of ribs are the short "floating ribs," and

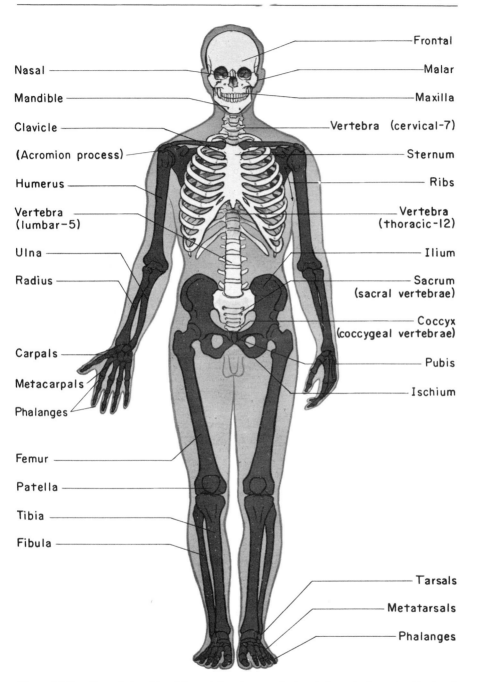

Nasal

Mandible

Clavicle

(Acromion process)

Humerus

Vertebra
(lumbar-5)

Ulna

Radius

Carpals

Metacarpals

Phalanges

Femur

Patella

Tibia

Fibula

Frontal

Malar

Maxilla

Vertebra (cervical-7)

Sternum

Ribs

Vertebra
(thoracic-12)

Ilium

Sacrum
(sacral vertebrae)

Coccyx
(coccygeal vertebrae)

Pubis

Ischium

Tarsals

Metatarsals

Phalanges

Figure 19.2.   The relationship of the axial and appendicular skeleton is shown in this sketch.
The bones of the axial skeleton are dark and those of the appendicular skeleton are light.   The
chart on page 399 lists the bones of these two divisions of the skeleton.

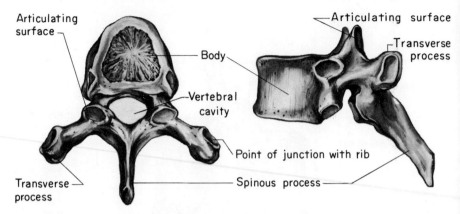

Figure 19.3.   These dorsal and lateral views of a thoracic vertebra demonstrate graphically the varied functions performed by vertebrae.   They serve not only as a central axis but also as a central canal and a protection for the spinal cord.   In addition, they provide rib attachments.

are not attached ventrally.   The rib cage plays a very important role in breathing in man, and the flexible attachment of the ribs to the vertebrae makes it possible to increase or decrease the chest size.   This function will be considered later.   The heavy bladelike sternum not only serves as the ventral attachment for the ribs but also provides a shield for the organs in the mid-line of the body, especially for the heart, which lies immediately underneath it.

Skull

Perched on the backbone and rotating on the top of the first vertebra is the *skull*.   This massive box is constructed of two portions: a brain case, or *cranium;* and a series of facial and jaw bones comprising the *face*.   The cranium in man is relatively larger and the face is relatively smaller than in most other vertebrates.   These size alterations reflect the large size of the brain encased within the cranium, and the reduced size of the jaws, which do not serve man as a weapon of defense or offense as they do in many other mammals.   It is of physiological interest that some of the bones of the jaw apparatus have actually been modified to such an extent that they have become ear bones.

Eight bones make up the brain case, and from front to back these are: the *frontal*, the two *parietals*, the two *temporals* (in the ear region), the *sphenoid* and the *ethmoid* (which form the anterior floor of the brain case), and the *occipital*.   A large opening in the occipital bone, the *foramen magnum*, enables the spinal cord to extend from its connections with the brain to the neural canal of the vertebral column.

The occipital bone rests on the modified, first cervical vertebra, the *atlas;* and the nodding of the head back and forth is made possible by special articulating surfaces, the *occipital condyles*.   The second cervical vertebra, the *axis*,

MAJOR BONES OF HUMAN SKELETON

Axial Skeleton			Appendicular Skeleton			
			Girdles		Appendages	
Skull	Vertebral Column					
	Vertebrae	Rib Cage	Pectoral (shoulders)	Pelvic (hips)	Forelimb (arm and hand)	Hind limb (leg and foot)
Cranium	Vertebrae	Ribs	Scapula	Ilium	Humerus	Femur
	Cervical	Sternum	Clavicle	Ischium	Radius	Tibia
Frontal	Thoracic			Pubis	Ulna	Fibula
Parietals	Lumbar				Carpals	Tarsals
Temporals	Sacrum				Metacarpals	Metatarsals
Sphenoid	Coccyx				Phalanges (fingers)	Phalanges (toes)
Ethmoid						
Occipital						

Face

Upper jaw (maxilla)
Lower jaw (mandible)
Cheekbone, or zygomatic (malar)
Nasal
Ear bones (malleus, incus, stapes)
Hyoid apparatus

This chart presents in tabular arrangement the major bones of the human skeleton. Reference to the drawing on page 397 will clarify the structural relationships of the skeleton. Compare the human skeletal structure with that of the frog, shown on page 355, and note the significant similarities.

also is altered in structure by having a special pivot which extends through the atlas to provide a means for the rotating movements of the head.

An arrangement of two girdles with the four limbs comprises the appendicular skeleton. This consists of the *pectoral girdle* (the shoulder), with the *arms;* and the *pelvic girdle* (the hips), with the *legs.* Modifications of the human skeleton associated with the erect carriage of the body are more apparent in the appendicular than in the axial skeleton. The arms, which correspond to the forelegs of terrestrial vertebrates, are relieved of the necessity of supporting the body of man, and the development of the hand with ability to grasp, to hold, and to manipulate is without counterpart in the animal kingdom. The legs, however, are relatively generalized, permitting man to run rather rapidly, to jump moderate distances, and to walk with reasonable ease. Man often is exceeded by other mammals in the efficiency of any of these activities—for example, by deer or kangaroo—but in over-all effectiveness for the services they render, the legs of man are better than average appendages.

The pectoral girdle is constructed of two bones on each side of the body. The first is a broad, flat shoulder blade, the *scapula*, which is located on the dorsal side. This bone is not joined to the axial skeleton but is held in position by the attachment of powerful muscles of the arm, shoulder, and back, and by its junction laterally with the collar bone, or *clavicle*, which is the second bone of the girdle. A large depression in the scapula, the *glenoid fossa*, receives the head of the bone of the upper arm, the *humerus*, and in this manner forms the ball-and-socket *shoulder joint*. The humerus is hinged at the *elbow* to the two bones of the forearm, the *ulna* and the *radius;* and these two in turn attach at the wrist of the 8 wrist bones, the *carpals*. The hand, perhaps man's most distinctive characteristic, has a total of 19 bones: 5 of these are the metacarpals, composing the undivided part of the hand and joining the *phalanges*, or *digits* (fingers and thumb). The digits contain 14 *phalanges*. Each of the digits except the thumb has 3 phalanges; in the thumb only 2 are present. The thumb also has a ball-and-socket joint at its base which enables it to be rotated to a position opposite the fingers. This mechanical arrangement gives the human hand its remarkable dexterity in the use of tools and the manipulation of objects.

Several interesting rearrangements and modifications have been made in the bones of the hip and leg, but for the most part the bones are comparable to those of the forelimb in other vertebrates. The pelvic girdle is composed of three fused bones on each side: the *ilium, ischium*, and *pubis*, which are firmly joined to the base of the vertebral column, the coccyx. The junction of the sacrum with the illium forms the *sacroiliac* joint, which is the point through which the weight of the body is transferred to the pelvis and legs. This is essentially a keystone-arch arrangement; and in spite of the "sacroiliac pains" which sometimes appear with age, this is a remarkable suspension system. The pelvic region has two other important functions: (1) the pelvic bones serve as a bony basket to partially contain the abdominal viscera; and (2) the *acetabulum*, a large depression on each side of the pelvis, receives the head of the thigh bone,

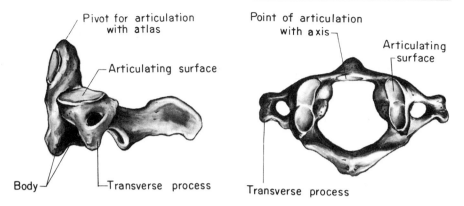

Figure 19.4.   The two vertebrae, the atlas and the axis, are important for the various movements of the head since they allow rotation and nodding to occur freely.   The broad articulating surfaces of the atlas show how it serves to support the skull, and the heavy process of the axis clearly is an excellent pivot about which the head can rotate.

the *femur*, to form the ball-and-socket *hip joint*.   This arrangement is comparable to that of the shoulder joint.   The other bones of the leg and foot are similar to those of the arm and hand, except for the heel bone, or *calcaneum*. The *tibia* and *fibula* correspond respectively to the radius and ulna; the *tarsals* and *metatarsals* of the foot, to the carpals and metacarpals; and the *phalanges*, or toes, to the fingers.

Musculature

Consideration of the body form of man would be incomplete without a brief discussion of the muscles associated with the skeleton.   These are the *voluntary*, or *skeletal, muscles* (p. 124), which in man are comparable in their arrangement to the muscles of most other mammals.   Indeed, there is even a striking similarity between the major muscles of man and those of the frog (Figure 18.10). The skeletal muscles operate with the bones of the skeleton to provide controlled movement and locomotion of the body.   Associated with various bones, the muscles supply the force for the lever systems involved in bending or straightening the appendages and for lifting weight—either the weight of the body itself or of objects handled by man.   The muscles of the abdominal wall, in addition, are subjected to considerable pressure from the viscera within the body cavity. This pressure is a result of man's erect position, and the abdominal muscles, therefore, must be strong enough to contain the viscera within the abdomen. Occasionally, the muscles may weaken and a partial protrusion of the viscera may occur.   This condition is spoken of as *abdominal hernia;* it may exist in the very young as an abnormality and often occurs in middle-aged or sedentary persons as a result of excessive physical exertion.

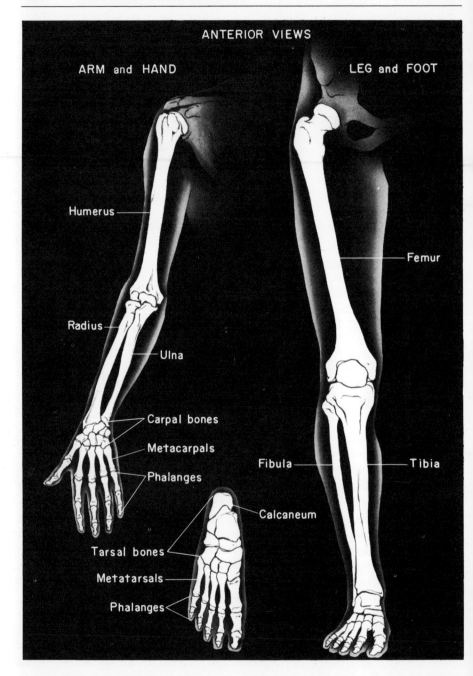

Figure 19.5.   The similarity between the human arm and leg is not obvious if one merely observes these appendages externally.   This drawing, however, shows the arrangement of the bones and emphasizes the similarity in the basic skeletal organization of the arm and leg.

The different muscles of the body will not be discussed separately, but if we refer to the illustration of the major muscles and to the chart on page 000, which tabulates the muscles, their origins and basic relationships to the bones, together with their chief functions, this should prove helpful in understanding muscular action. First, however, a few terms are necessary in order to comprehend the relationship of the muscles to the bones. These terms are also applicable to the muscles of other vertebrates.

Skeletal muscles have one end attached to a movable part and the other end attached to a stationary part. The movable end of a muscle is spoken of as its *insertion* and the immovable end as its *origin*. The *masseter* muscle of the jaw, for example, has its insertion on the lower jaw and its origin on the cheekbone. When the masseter contracts, the movable jaw is pulled toward the skull into contact with the upper jaw to close the mouth. When the contraction of a muscle results in the bending of a part (for example, the arm) it is said to *flex*, and the muscle is called a *flexor* muscle. When a muscle results in the straightening of a part, it *extends* and is called an *extensor* muscle. A muscle *adducts* when it pulls a part toward the mid-line of the body, and it *abducts* when it pulls a part away from the mid-line.

It should be emphasized, by way of summary, that the body form of man is relatively generalized. This is a distinct advantage to human beings in maintaining their dominant biological position, because they are able to adjust readily to a variety of environmental conditions. Although men cannot swim as well as the aquatic mammals, such as otters or seals, man can move rapidly through the water when he has trained himself in swimming. Likewise, man cannot run as fast as the hoofed mammals, such as the antelopes or zebras, but he can train himself to run rapidly and for long distances. Moreover, man, with his intelligence and dexterity, has been able to build machines to supplement his physical limitations, and as a result, he can surpass all other organisms in locomotion in the water, on land, and in the air.

The structural specializations in man which make possible his erect position are a mixed biological blessing. Somewhat greater mobility and a better opportunity to survey his surroundings are the advantages of standing upright; on the other hand, backaches, sacrolumbar discomforts, slipped vertebral disks, and abdominal hernias are the penalties which often must be paid for it. Man's second specialization, the forearm and hand, is strictly advantageous. Actually, the specialization represented by an opposable thumb provides for a greater variety of uses for the forelimb, and hence the arm and hand are biologically more adaptable. A unique situation exists, therefore, in which a structural specialization endows an organism with greater adaptability instead of limiting its ability to adapt.

Nutrition

The nutrition of man also reflects the generalized nature of the human form and its function. The normal diet of man is an omnivorous one; both animal

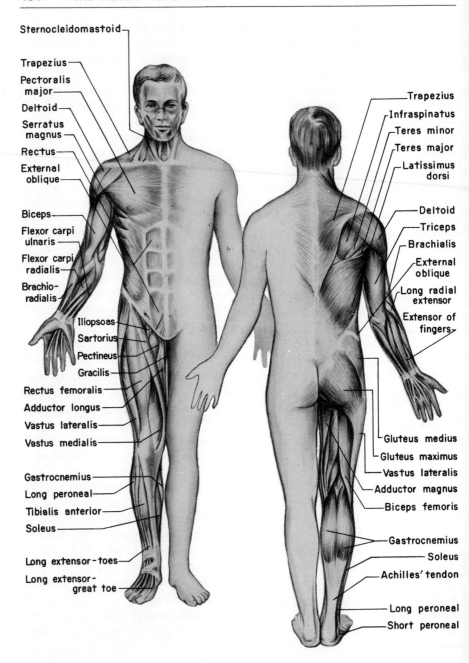

Sternocleidomastoid

Trapezius

Pectoralis
 major

Deltoid

Serratus
 magnus

Rectus

External
 oblique

Biceps

Flexor carpi
 ulnaris

Flexor carpi
 radialis

Brachio-
 radialis

Iliopsoas

Sartorius

Pectineus

Gracilis

Rectus femoralis

Adductor longus

Vastus lateralis

Vastus medialis

Gastrocnemius

Long peroneal

Tibialis anterior

Soleus

Long extensor-toes

Long extensor-
 great toe

Trapezius

Infraspinatus

Teres minor

Teres major

Latissimus
 dorsi

Deltoid

Triceps

Brachialis

External
 oblique

Long radial
 extensor

Extensor of
 fingers

Gluteus medius

Gluteus maximus

Vastus lateralis

Adductor magnus

Biceps femoris

Gastrocnemius

Soleus

Achilles' tendon

Long peroneal

Short peroneal

Figure 19.6.   The major muscles of the human body are shown in this drawing.   As with many
other structures, obvious similarities exist between the muscles in man and those in the frog
(see Figure 18.10, page 356).

RELATIONSHIPS AND FUNCTIONS OF MAJOR MUSCLES OF HUMAN BODY

Muscle	Origin	Insertion	Function
Trunk			
Pectoral	Clavicle and sternum	Humerus	Adductor and flexor of arm, also twists arm
Rectus muscles of abdomen	Ribs and sternum	Pubic bone	Flex (bend) trunk
External oblique muscles of abdomen	Lower 8 ribs	Mid-line of abdomen	Contract abdomen
Appendages			
Arm			
Deltoid	Scapula and clavicle	Humerus	Abductor of arm
Biceps of arm	Scapula	Radius	Flexes arm, also rotates hand
Triceps	Scapula and humerus	Ulna	Extends forearm
Flexor of hand	Humerus	Metacarpals	Flexes hand and wrist
Extensors of fingers	Humerus	Fingers	Extend fingers
Leg			
Semitendinosus	Ischium	Tibia	Flexor of leg and adductor of thigh
Biceps of leg	Ischium and femur	Tibia and fibula	Flexor of leg and adductor of thigh
Vastus and rectus femorus	Ilium and femur	Tibia	Extend lower leg
Gastrocnemius	Femur	Calcaneum (heel bone)	Extends foot
Peroneus	Fibula and tibia	Base of metatarsals and sole of foot	Extends and rotates foot
Anterior tibial	Tibia	First metacarpal (of big toe)	Flexor of foot
Extensors of toes	Tibia and fibula	Toes	Elevate toes
Head and Neck			
Masseter	Zygomatic (cheekbone)	Posterior part of lower jaw	Closes mouth
Temporal	Temporal bone	Upper angle of lower jaw	Closes mouth
Digastric	Temporal bone	Anterior part of jaw	Opens mouth
Sternocleidomastoid	Clavicle and sternum	Temporal and occipital bones	Bends and rotates head
Trapezius	Cervical and thoracic vertebrae	Scapula	Moves scapula

and plant products are consumed.   Man can, however, live on a carnivorous diet if the need arises or if he so desires.   Likewise, many human beings are vegetarians by choice and adhere to an herbivorous diet.   A man can be healthy by intelligently choosing his food, whether his nutrition is omnivorous, carnivorous, or herbivorous.

The digestive tract

The details of the structure of the human alimentary canal, or digestive tract, and its associated organs are strikingly similar to those of other mammals and are actually more typical of the vertebrates than are those of the frog (Figure 18.13).   The human digestive tract consists of a *mouth*, equipped with *teeth* and a *tongue*, an *esophagus*, a *stomach*, a *small intestine*, a *large intestine*, the *rectum*, and an *anus*.   The cloaca, which is typical of most vertebrates, is absent in the adult human being as it is in the other higher mammals.   A cloaca is present, however, during embryonic development, and we will discuss its significance in the development of the reproductive and excretory systems later (p. 443).   Associated with the digestive tract are the *salivary glands* in the mouth, which secrete digestive enzymes and lubricate the food; the *pancreas*, which contributes to the small intestine some of the most important digestive enzymes, and also is an endocrine gland; and finally, the *liver*, which secretes bile into the small intestine.   The liver also serves as a great reservoir of stored food in the form of the carbohydrate, *glycogen* (animal starch).

A brief description of the various parts of the digestive tract, beginning with the mouth, will illustrate the versatility of this organ system in man.   The teeth are of conservative construction.   The *incisors* have good cutting surfaces, but in this respect are inferior to those of the rodents.   The *canine* and *premolar* teeth are adequate for "tearing into a steak" but are neither so efficient nor so well developed as are those of the carnivores, such as the wolves.   Also, the *molars* have relatively broad grinding faces, but they are puny when compared with the huge milling surfaces observed in herbivores like cows or elephants. The human tongue as a nutritive aid is little more than a pushing device to hold food against the teeth and to push the chewed food to the back of the mouth and into the esophagus to be swallowed.

Three pairs of salivary glands empty their secretions into the mouth cavity. These glands are: the *submaxillaries*, the *sublinguals*, and the *parotids*.   The salivary glands have two functions of considerable importance: *first*, they secrete *mucin*, a watery, mucous fluid which lubricates the food as it is being chewed and enables it to be molded into a moist ball that can be swallowed readily; *second*, these glands also secrete a digestive enzyme, *ptyalin*, which can act in a neutral medium to convert (digest) starch into sugar.   The initial phase of digestion begins in the mouth and is continued until the acid secretions of the stomach acidify the food and halt the process.

The *esophagus* of man is little more than a chute connecting the mouth and the stomach.   It is not modified as in certain other vertebrates and, as a matter of fact, has only involuntary muscle in its wall.   Food moves along the esophagus to the stomach by means of gravity and *peristalsis* (p. 358).   The peristaltic movement of food is made possible by the circular and longitudinal muscle layers of the walls of all parts of the digestive tract.   The direction of peristaltic waves normally is from the mouth to the stomach, but in nausea *reverse peristalsis* (vomiting) can occur.   The opening between the esophagus and the stomach is guarded by a valve which opens as the peristaltic wave reaches it and permits the passage of food into the stomach.

The *stomach*, which has a capacity of one and a half to two quarts, is the "big mixer" of the digestive tract.   The mixing action of the stomach is aided by the presence of an extra layer of muscles in the stomach wall, the *oblique muscles*. The food is thoroughly churned within the stomach and is mixed with the secretions from the *gastric glands* in the lining of its walls.   These glands are estimated to number about 35,000,000, and their secretions are very acid because of the high concentration of hydrochloric acid; they have a *p*H of about 1.0. The gastric secretions also contain two enzymes: *pepsin*, which partially digests proteins; and *rennin*, which curdles milk.

Figure 19.7.   Three types of teeth are illustrated in this sketch.   The incisors are specialized for slicing, canines for tearing, and molars for grinding.   It is clear that the teeth are structurally comparable even though relative proportions are changed.   The similarity is especially obvious when sections of teeth are compared.

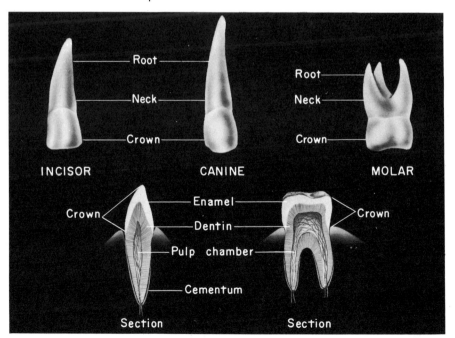

Although the strongly acid secretion of the gastric glands is remarkable and the amount of pepsin secreted is copious, the most important function of the human stomach probably is its mixing action. The contents of the stomach become thoroughly liquefied and reduced to particles of small size in the mixing process. The resulting rather homogeneous semifluid mass, called *chyme*, is funneled to the smaller *pyloric region* (pylorus) of the stomach; then the *pyloric valve* opens and the chyme is discharged into the small intestine. The relative unimportance of the stomach in the digestive process is evidenced by the frequency of operations in which the stomach is removed because of malignancy or ulcer. Such patients are able, with reasonable dietary care, to lead normal lives.

It had been known for many years that the muscles of an empty stomach contract rhythmically and with varying degrees of intensity, but the significance of these contractions was not understood until Walter Cannon and A. Washburn demonstrated in 1912 that the contractions are associated with hunger pangs. In their relatively simple experiment a human subject would swallow a small uninflated balloon which was connected to one end of a tube. The balloon was inflated within the stomach, and the tube connected to a lever that would deflect (that is, move up or down) as a result of pressure changes produced within the balloon by the contractions of the stomach muscles. The deflections of the lever were recorded on smoked paper on the surface of a continuously revolving drum. The subject in this experiment was not permitted to see the recording process but was asked to press a key whenever hunger pangs were felt. The depressing of the key also caused a mark to be made on the recording paper. It was found during the course of many experiments that the marks which denoted hunger pangs almost invariably corresponded with the lever deflections which indicated the peak of the stomach muscle contractions.

It should not be concluded, however, that the contraction, or spasm, of the stomach muscles is the only factor which produces a feeling of hunger, because persons who have had the stomach removed surgically can experience this primitive sensation. It appears that the amount of glucose (sugar) in the blood also plays a significant role in producing hunger pangs. When the level of blood sugar decreases appreciably, hunger will be experienced, even in the absence of a stomach.

The length of time that the food remains in the alimentary canal varies from 12 to 24 hours, but usually, about 20 minutes after food is eaten, the pyloric valve of the stomach opens to allow the first discharge of chyme into the *small intestine*. The small intestine probably averages slightly less than 20 feet in length and may vary from slightly less to slightly more than one inch in diameter. There are three distinct regions of the small intestine: the *duodenum*, the *jejunum*, and the *ileum*. The duodenum and jejunum comprise approximately two fifths and the ileum three fifths of the length of the small intestine. The duodenum, which is about 10 to 12 inches long, receives not only the food from the stomach, but also digestive juices from the pancreas and bile from the liver

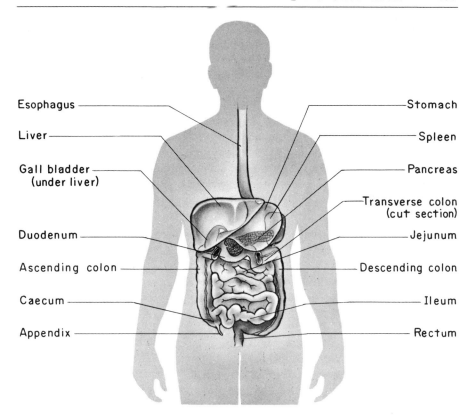

Esophagus

Liver

Gall bladder
(under liver)

Duodenum

Ascending colon

Caecum

Appendix

Stomach

Spleen

Pancreas

Transverse colon
(cut section)

Jejunum

Descending colon

Ileum

Rectum

Figure 19.8. Digestive system. The major divisions of the human alimentary canal and their positions relative to other vital organs are shown in this diagram. Note the similarity of the various regions of the digestive tract to those of the frog (Figure 18.13).

and gall bladder. As the food is moved slowly along the small intestine, the secretions of the *intestinal glands* are added to it. One of these secretions is *enterokinase,* which converts inactive *trypsinogin,* from the pancreas, to the active enzyme, *trypsin.* The movement of the food is accomplished by peristalsis, and the mixing of the food with the digestive fluids is facilitated by additional *segmental contractions* of the small intestine. These contractions are often spoken of as providing a "churning effect," because they do not move the food through the intestine but only churn the intestinal contents.

Most of the digestion and absorption of food occurs in the small intestine. The accompanying table shows the numerous digestive enzymes which act in the small intestine, their origins, the foods upon which they act, and the end products of their action. It should be evident that insoluble and chemically complex proteins, fats, and carbohydrates are converted (digested) into soluble and chemically more simple by-products which can pass into the capillaries and lymph vessels of the intestinal wall for subsequent distribution throughout the body.

It is important here to consider briefly the function of bile in the digestive process. Bile does not contain digestive enzymes, but it has an important role in neutralizing the acid chyme and in emulsifying fats. Bile is secreted constantly by the liver of man but is stored in the gall bladder until the entrance of food into the intestine stimulates the secretion of a hormone, *cholecystokinin*, into the blood. When the cholecystokinin reaches the gall bladder, it causes a contraction of the gall bladder, with a consequent rapid discharge of bile into the small intestine. This ensures that the maximum amount of bile will be available when food is present in the small intestine.

The absorption of food from the small intestine is aided by the large surface area of this portion of the digestive tract. Not only is the small intestine coiled, but its inner wall is folded; and many tiny fingerlike processes, the *villi*, are present. The villi and the folds increase the surface area of the small intestine approximately ten times and also serve to slow the passage of food, thus permitting the digestive enzymes to act for considerably longer periods of time.

The absorption of food from the small intestine into the lymph and blood vessels of the intestine is a rather constant process. This absorption is partly a result of osmosis, but additional factors are involved, as can be demonstrated by the fact that salts will enter the blood stream from the intestine against a greater concentration of salts within the blood itself. Similarly, the absorption of glucose from the intestine during the late stages of digestion is rapid, even though the concentration of glucose in the blood may be relatively high. These facts indicate that a secretory process actually is involved in intestinal absorption, and this emphasizes the great versatility of the cells which line the cavity of the intestine. They not only release digestive enzymes into the intestine, but also transport the digested food materials into the blood stream.

Food remains in the small intestine for a greater period of time than it does in any other portion of the digestive tract, usually a matter of several hours. Eventually, however, the material leaves the small intestine and enters the *large intestine*. The small intestine joins the large intestine about two and one half inches from the end of the latter. This lateral junction creates a small blind sac in the large intestine; this is called the *caecum*. It is from the caecum in man that a fingerlike process, the *vermiform appendix*, extends. This structure is well known because its inflammation results in appendicitis, which often leads to appendectomy.

The large intestine is approximately five and one half feet in length and is composed of several distinct regions. The first portion following the junction with the small intestine is the *ascending colon* which, as the name implies, proceeds "upward" toward the stomach on the right side of the body. The large intestine continues laterally as the *transverse colon* which crosses the body and becomes the *descending colon*. This passes "downward" on the left side of the body to connect with the *rectum*, from which the undigested fecal material passes from the body through an anal opening, the *anus*. The musculature of the large intestine is not as well developed as that of the small intestine, and the movement of materials in the large intestine is slower and less forceful than in the small intestine. There are, however, peristaltic waves and weak churning movements.

Digestion has not been entirely completed by the time food enters the large intestine, and the digestive enzymes which were added in the small intestine will continue their activity. This is especially true for the digestion of carbohydrates. It is also a rather startling fact that even the "purest" of human beings have billions of other organisms living and working within their large intestines. These micro-organisms, bacteria and protozoa, are especially important in the final breakdown of food materials by putrefactive and fermentative processes. It has been estimated that one milligram of fecal material in the large intestine may contain more than 100,000,000 micro-organisms. The kinds of bacteria and protozoa vary with the type of diet. Apparently, the more beneficial kinds of micro-organisms are to be found in individuals who have a varied diet and one which is relatively high in animal protein. Certain of the bacteria synthesize some of the vitamins which are needed by man, and in so doing they perform a service of further benefit to man, in return for their own "board and keep."

More important, however, than the residual digestion, food breakdown, and vitamin synthesis in the large intestine is the role which this part of the alimentary canal plays in the over-all water economy of the body. It is important in man, as in other air-dwelling forms (p. 278), that water conservation be effected. Especially important in this regard is the resorption of water from the contents of the large intestine. The chyme which enters the large intestine is very fluid because of the additions of the secretions from the salivary glands,

CALORIC REQUIREMENT OF HUMAN BEINGS (Average body weights)		
Adults	**Moderately active**	**Very active**
Young adult male	3200	5000 +
Young adult female	2300	3000 +
Woman in pregnancy	2800	——
Nursing mother	3800	——
Children		
4 to 6 years of age	1600	——
10 to 12 years of age	2500	——
Boys 13 to 15 years of age	3200	——
Girls 13 to 15 years of age	2600	——

the pancreas, the liver, and the intestinal glands. If, therefore, the contents of the large intestine were to pass unaltered from the body, very severe dehydration of the tissues would occur after each meal. Such dehydration, however, is prevented by the very efficient resorption of water by the large intestine.

We recall (p. 37) that food is necessary to supply the energy for metabolism, to build new protoplasm, and to maintain the proper physical and chemical conditions in the protoplasm. The demands of the human body with respect to these nutritional needs have been investigated more comprehensively than have those of any other organism. The energy requirements expressed in terms of *calories*° have been determined for men and for women, for children, for pregnant women and nursing mothers, for persons who lead sedentary lives, and for persons engaged in physical activity. Some of these are shown in the table below. The proportionate amounts of *proteins, carbohydrates,* and *fats* that are needed for growth and replacement of protoplasm have been ascertained; and the amounts of *vitamins* and *minerals* which are necessary for normal metabolism have been determined.

Since detailed information relative to the problems of nutrition fill many volumes of special reports, the subject obviously cannot be discussed at length here. It is possible, however, to consider briefly the essential requirements of human beings in terms of calories and of vitamins and minerals needed for day-to-day activity.

Proportion of Proteins, Carbohydrates, and Fats in Average Normal Diet†			
	Grams	Calories	% of Total Calories
Proteins	100	410	12
Fats	100	930	27
Carbohydrates	500	2050	61

†After Houssay, 1955.

Carbohydrate, fat, or protein may be used for fuel by the body. Carbohydrate is the most readily available and usable of the three. Carbohydrates actually contribute solely to the caloric demands of the protoplasm, and as much as 70 percent of the fuel needs of a man may be supplied efficiently by such foods. Fats also are excellent fuel and per unit of weight are more than twice as high in calories as are the carbohydrates or proteins (9.3 kg-cal per gram for fats, in contrast with 4.1 kg-cal per gram for carbohydrates). Certain fats, in addition, supply essential fatty acids and fat-soluble vitamins. Man cannot, however, live on fat or carbohydrate alone, for these foods do not supply the

---

° A large Calorie (Cal.), or kilogram-calorie (kg-cal), is equivalent to the amount of heat necessary to raise the temperature of 1 kilogram of water 1° C (from 14.5° C to 15.5° C) at atmospheric pressure.

neccssary chemical ingredients for the building of new protoplasm. Furthermore, an excess of fat cannot be completely burned in the body, with the result that it may be stored in the tissues and lead to obesity or to disturbed metabolism. The most versatile of the three major foods is protein. As an energy source, it may have nitrogen removed from its molecule (deaminization) and then be utilized for fuel; it may be converted to carbohydrate and burned; or it may even be converted subsequently to fat and stored as reserve energy. Both animal and plant proteins can be utilized efficiently for energy by the human body.

VITAMINS IMPORTANT IN HUMAN NUTRITION		
Vitamins	**Common Sources**	**Action**

A Complex
 	
A
A_1
A_2
	Liver, egg yolk,
	  butter, milk, cheese
	Conversion of provitamin
	  (color pigment) in green
	  and yellow vegetables
		Maintains epithelia in normal
		  condition
		Increases resistance to infec-
		  tions
		Prevents night blindness

B Complex
 	
B_1: thiamine
B_2: riboflavin
B_6: pyridoxin
B_{12}: antianemic factor
Folic acid
Nicotinic acid
	Brewer's yeast
	Liver, egg yolk
	Peas and beans
	Whole-wheat flour
	Cereals
		Normal carbohydrate metab-
		  olism
		Prevents beriberi disease
		Antianemic
		Prevents pellagra (black
		  tongue in dogs)

C (Ascorbic acid)	Citrus fruits Pineapple, tomatoes Fresh vegetables	Prevents scurvy Probably acts in oxidation- reduction reactions in body
D Complex D_2: calciferol D_3: cholecalciferol	Provitamin in yeast Fish liver oils Egg yolk	Normal bone growth Normal calcium metabolism
E (Tocopherols)	Wheat germ oil, lettuce, peas Egg yolk Vegetable oils	Antisterility (questionable if needed by man)

K Complex
 	
K_1
K_2
	Alfalfa, spinach, cauliflower,
	  cabbage
	(synthesized by intestinal
	  bacteria)
		Antihemorrhagic
		Coagulation of blood is
		  speeded

P (Citrin or hisperidin)	Citrus fruits	Maintains normal permeabil- ity of capillary walls

Nitrogen compounds in the form of *amino acids* derived from the proteins are essential for the manufacture of new protoplasm. Human beings cannot synthesize amino acids but must secure them by digesting proteins. Since neither carbohydrates nor fats contain amino acids, it is obvious that human beings must have protein in the diet if protoplasm, and therefore life, is to be maintained. The dependence of the body on certain of the amino acids for the synthesis of protoplasm is reflected in the term *esseitial amino acids,* by which they are designated.

Although the need for proteins in the diet seems self-evident, there are human populations on earth today that, because of economic or religious and social restrictions, are suffering from inadequate amounts of protein foods. Such populations are confronted daily, therefore, by the specter of starvation, not alone from the lack of calories, but even more important, from the lack of the essential amino acids. The biologist in modern society must cooperate with economists and sociologists in the solution of this vital bio-economic problem. The broader aspects of this problem will be considered in more detail in the final chapter.

Respiration

Respiration in man is primarily oxybiotic. Oxygen is necessary for the release of energy and for the chemical reactions involved in the oxidation of proteins, carbohydrates, and fats. These are the same oxidation reactions which were considered in Chapter 3 in the discussion of how work is done. We recall that the oxidation of organic materials also produces waste materials in the form of carbon dioxide and water, which are by-products of the reactions. The respiratory process in man, therefore, performs an important excretory function because it has come to be considered not only with the supplying of oxygen to the body but also with the elimination of carbon dioxide and water.

Man is enclosed within an airtight envelope provided by the squamous layers of the skin, and therefore the human skin is unable to serve as a respiratory surface as does the thin permeable skin of the frog. The difficulty in supplying oxygen to the cells lying deep within the body has been circumvented by man and other mammals, and also by the birds and the reptiles, by the efficiency with which the air passages and the lungs are able to deliver oxygen to the bloodstream for subsequent distribution throughout the body.

Oxygen utilization is an intricate process in human beings, and it is important to differentiate clearly between the various phases of this process. Four phases are involved in the functions which are associated with the respiratory process: (1) *breathing,* (2) *external respiration,* (3) *internal respiration,* and (4) *transportation of gases* (the carrying of oxygen to the tissues and of carbon dioxide from the tissues). Breathing involves only the mechanical problem of bringing oxygen-rich air into the lungs from the air at *inspiration,* and of discharging oxygen-poor air from the lungs into the air at *expiration.* Relatively more complex physical and chemical operations, however, are involved in external respiration, internal respiration, and transportation of gases.

The respiratory system

Any discussion of the respiratory function should be prefaced by a description of the structure of the human respiratory system and its relationship to the external environment and to the blood-vascular system. The respiratory system, structurally and functionally, actually is composed of two distinct regions: the first is purely conductive; only the second is actually respiratory. The conductive portion includes the various air passages, whereas the respiratory region is confined to the air sacs, or *alveoli* (singular, *alveolus*) of the lungs.

We will consider the *conductive portion* first. Air enters the *nasal cavity* at inspiration through the paired openings of the nose, the *external nares*. The epithelium surrounding the opening of the nares is comparable to that of the surface of the skin and has numerous hairs growing from it, which act as filters to prevent dust particles and other foreign matter from entering the nasal passages. The nasal cavity itself is short, usually only a few inches long, but a series of irregular channels formed by the protrusion of the *turbinate bones* into it causes the air to be swirled about turbulently, and therefore, to traverse a greater distance.

A ciliated columnar epithelium lines the nasal cavity, and mucus is secreted by goblet cells of this epithelium, with the result that a moist surface is provided which humidifies the inspired air. The mucus provides a further advantage because bacteria and small foreign particles which may have evaded the hairs guarding the external nares adhere to it. The epithelium of the nasal cavity is kept warm by the elaborate supply of blood vessels, and thus air is warmed as it passes over the nasal epithelium. Although the nasal cavity is small, it is obvious that it serves as an excellent air-conditioning device to filter, humidify, and warm the air before it passes to the remaining parts of the respiratory system.

Posteriorly, the nasal cavity is continuous with the *pharynx*. The mouth also joins this part of the respiratory tract, which serves as a common passageway for foods, fluids, and air. The connection of the mouth with the pharynx is advantageous because it permits "mouth breathing," which is necessary when the nasal passages are blocked. The protection of "air conditioning" is lost, however, when the nasal cavity is bypassed during mouth breathing. The lower part of the pharynx opens through the glottis into the *trachea* (the windpipe), the first and largest part of which is the *larynx*, or *voice box*. This region is in the *neck* and has a framework constructed of several well-developed cartilages. It contains the *vocal cords*, which are composed of bands of elastic tissue covered by a thin layer of stratified squamous epithelium. The walls of the larynx are well supplied with muscles and with cartilages to which the muscles are also attached. Contractions of the laryngeal muscles produce changes in

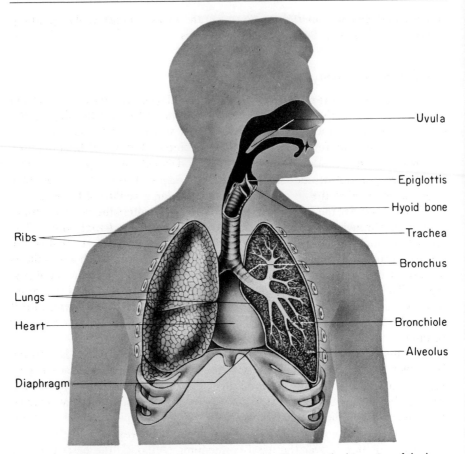

Figure 19.9. This frontal view of the respiratory system illustrates the large size of the lungs and the elaborate branching of the bronchioles. Considered collectively, the surfaces of the minute air sacs (alveoli) exceed the surface of the body many times.

the shape of the larynx and alter the tension on the vocal cords. The forced movement of air over the vocal cords causes them to vibrate, and this, in conjunction with the alteration in the shape of the voice box, produces *phonation*— that is, it provides man with his voice. Externally, the voice box is recognized as the Adam's apple and usually is more obvious in men than in women.

Since both food and air enter the pharynx from the mouth and nasal passages respectively, it is obvious that some protective device is needed to prevent food from entering the trachea through the glottis and producing strangulation. A flap, the *epiglottis*, projects over the opening of the trachea to prevent the entrance of food into the windpipe during swallowing, and this action is supplemcnted by other mechanisms which aid in closing the glottis. X-ray motion pictures of swallowing have demonstrated that the larynx also is brought upward toward the base of the tongue and that the vocal cords contract to narrow the cavity of the larynx. These actions occur simultaneously to produce an effective closure of the opening into the trachea. The importance of the laryngeal movements is further supported by the observation that when a portion of the epiglottis must be removed surgically, no serious disturbance of the swallowing mechanism occurs.

The trachea is a tube with a flexible framework constructed of from 16 to 20 C- or Y-shaped cartilages. The opening of the C or the Y is posterior, and the gap in each cartilage is filled by transverse bands of smooth muscle. The cartilages of the trachea do not calcify with age but remain flexible. Their important function is to ensure that the trachea will not collapse but will remain open under varying atmospheric pressures or when there is a forced inspiration. The lining of the trachea, like that of the nasal cavity, is a ciliated columnar epithelium which is also glandular. The secretion of mucus by the gland cells of the epithelium serves to trap very fine particles of foreign matter and bacteria which may have escaped the filters of the upper part of the conductive system. The cilia, furthermore, move rhythmically to sweep the mucus away from the lungs toward the mouth where it can be eliminated by coughing or by swallowing. This is another of the defensive mechanisms that protect the lungs from the invasion of foreign matter which otherwise would soon fill the lung cavities or produce serious infection.

The trachea continues from the neck into the thoracic cavity where, at about the level of the fifth rib, it *bifurcates* (divides) into two *bronchi* which enter the right and left lungs. The bronchi also have cartilaginous rings which keep them open. The bronchi, in turn, subdivide into smaller branches, the *bronchioles,* and these continue to branch into successively smaller tubules. The cartilage gradually disappears as the bronchioles decrease in diameter, and the epithelium also becomes thinner. The bronchioles are the smallest unit of the conductive portion and finally terminate in the alveoli.

The *alveoli* are tiny, saclike structures which comprise the *respiratory portion* of the respiratory system. An individual alveolus of the lung is extremely small, but since there are from 750 million to one billion of them in the two lungs, the total surface area of all the alveoli is immense, ranging from 80 to 100 square meters, or approximately 50 times the skin surface of the individual. The lining of the alveoli is a very thin squamous epithelium; and even this epithelium is lacking in certain alveolar areas, so that air is brought in direct contact with the thin-walled capillaries of the lungs. The structure of the alveoli thus provides for a minimum of interference for the passage of gases from the lungs into the blood stream or from the blood stream into the lungs. When we consider this fact in conjunction with the very large surface area which is represented by the alveolar lining, we can appreciate that the lungs provide an efficient device for gaseous exchange in the human being.

Breathing

A molecule of oxygen entering the nasal chamber must traverse nearly 20 inches of conductive passages before it reaches an alveolus. A molecule could travel this distance by diffusion but as a means of supplying oxygen to the blood, the method would be so woefully slow that a human being would be dead before oxygen could reach even the pharynx. A special mechanism for rapidly aerating the lungs is necessary, and this ventilation is provided by the inspiratory and expiratory phases of breathing. We will consider only the most obvious mechanical features of the breathing process, but first it is essential for us to understand the relationship of the lungs to the thoracic cavity.

The lungs lie in the *pleural cavity,* which is a portion of the coelom and has the same type of epithelium as that which lines the abdominal cavity. This epithelium, the *pleura,* not only lines the cavity but is reflected over the lungs, completely covering them. The lungs, therefore, actually rest in a double-walled cavity lined by *pleura,* and when competely inflated the lungs fill this cavity. If, however, the lungs are only partially inflated a sizable space is present. An infection of the lining of this cavity, incidentally, is known as *pleurisy.*

The pleural cavity is limited dorsally and laterally by the thoracic wall, and the floor of the pleural cavity is formed by a heavy sheet of muscle, the *diaphragm.* Since the diaphragm at expiration is dome-shaped, with the curve of the dome projecting into the pleural cavity, it also can be thought of as a muscular cap over the viscera of the abdomen. You will recall from the discussion of the skeletal system that the rib cage is a prominent feature of the thorax and that the ribs pivot on the vertebrae. They are attached firmly, however, to the sternum on the ventral side of the thorax. As a consequence of these attachments, when the *intercostal muscles* between the ribs contract at inspiration, the ribs are pulled forward and upward, increasing the size of the pleural cavity. Simultaneously, the diaphragm is flattened at inspiration by the con-

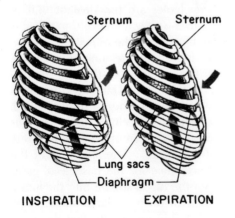

Sternum   Sternum

Lung sacs

Diaphragm

INSPIRATION   EXPIRATION

Figure 19.10. Inspiration and expiration. The space about the lungs is increased or decreased by changes in the position of the diaphragm and of the ribs. When the ribs are raised and the diaphragm is depressed, the chest cavity increases in size and air rushes into the lungs (inspiration). Depression of the ribs, accompanied by an elevation of the diaphragm, decreases the size of the chest cavity and forces air from the lungs (expiration).

traction of its muscle fibers, and it presses downward against the viscera. This change in the shape and position of the diaphragm produces a marked enlargement of the pleural cavity below the lungs. The pleural cavity is an airtight sac, and when it is expanded (as at inspiration) a partial vacuum is created within it. It is actually more precise to say that the pressure within the pleural cavity drops considerably below the pressure of the air surrounding the body. The greater pressure outside the body now causes air to flow rapidly into the air passages, and the lungs are inflated to the capacity of the pleural cavity. The lungs, therefore, are not filled by suction, but by the movement of air from a region of greater pressure to one of lesser pressure—that is, from the outside of the body into the lungs.

The process of expiration is simpler than that of inspiration and is due almost entirely to the relaxation of the intercostal and diaphragm muscles. The ribs drop downward and backward of their own weight when the intercostal muscles relax. In a similar manner the relaxation of the muscles of the diaphragm causes its dome shape to be restored, primarily as a result of the pressure of abdominal viscera against it. These changes in the position of the ribs and diaphragm reduce the size of the pleural cavity, and the pressure exerted by the thoracic wall and diaphragm, in addition to the natural elastic recoil of the lungs, forces air to be exhaled. During exercise or at any time when heavy or labored breathing occurs, the other muscles of the thorax and abdomen can be called into play for more forceful expansion of the chest and depression of the diaphragm. Exhalation also may be forced, and at such times will be accompanied by strong contractions of the abdominal muscles which press the viscera violently against the diaphragm.

The capacity of the lungs is approximately 4500 to 5000 cubic centimeters, and most people are surprised to learn that the volume of air exchanged during a normal respiratory cycle of inspiration and expiration is only about 500 cubic centimeters. This small volume of air which moves into and out of the lungs in a single respiratory cycle is called the *tidal volume.* Forced breathing may increase the amount of inspired air to a volume of 2000 cubic centimeters, and This is designated as the *inspiratory reserve volume.* Likewise, forced expiration may discharge from the lungs an amount of air which may reach a volume of 2000 cubic centimeters, and this is spoken of as the *expiratory reserve vol-tune.** The *vital capacity* of the lungs is equal to the sum of the inspiratory and expiratory reserve volumes, and a simple subtraction of this volume from that of the total volume of the lungs indicates that there remains approximately 1000 cubic centimeters, which is the *residual volume.* This represents the amount of air which is not exchanged during a respiratory cycle.

---

*The terms used here are not synonymous with the older terms *supplemental* and *complemental* since these do not include the amount of air equivalent to the tidal volume.

It is also significant that approximately 150 cubic centimeters of the tidal volume are trapped in the "dead air" spaces of the conductive portion of the respiratory system. This is the volume of air that, at the end of inspiration and before expiration, does not reach the alveoli but remains in the respiratory passages. The volume of new air which reaches the alveoli, therefore, is reduced to about 350 cubic centimeters. It is of physiological interest that human life can be maintained by the contact of less than one pint of fresh air with the alveoli at each inspiration. It should also be apparent, from the simple mathematical calculations which have been used to describe lung capacity, that the air reserve of the lungs greatly exceeds the normal respiratory demands of the human body. This explains why it is possible for persons to lead essentially normal lives after the removal of one lung.

The various movements associated with breathing are coordinated by the nervous system, and the control of breathing is both involuntary and voluntary. Breathing usually proceeds without any conscious control on the part of the individual, but the rate and depth of breathing can be altered voluntarily within certain limits. It is possible, for example, to cease breathing for a short period of time, but voluntary control is lost as soon as the amount of carbon dioxide in the blood increases appreciably, or if unconsciousness occurs. At such times breathing is resumed irrespective of the wish of the individual.

In 1824 almost a century and a half ago, Legallois discovered that there exists in the brain stem a center which controls respiration. This *respiratory center* has since been precisely located in the *medulla,* and it has several important functions in the control of respiration. It coordinates the activity of the inspiratory and expiratory muscles, which assures that inspiration and expiration occur in the proper sequence, and makes it impossible for one lung to expire as the other inspires. The respiratory center also controls both the rate and the depth of breathing. The fact that breathing has been observed to be a rhythmical process suggested that the nerve impulses from the respiratory center might be sent rhythmically to the respiratory muscles. It is known, however, that the respiratory center does not discharge its impulses rhythmically, but that in the transmission of its impulses, it, in turn, is influenced by a higher center in the brain and by nerves from the lungs. In addition, the respiratory center is subject to the chemical control exerted by variations in the amount of carbon dioxide in the blood.

External respiration and internal respiration

It is obvious that the ventilation of the lungs is the result of mechanical factors concerned with breathing, but the behavior of gases during external and internal respiration and while being transported in the blood is controlled by chemical and physical factors. These factors in turn are primarily a result of the composition of the air we breathe. Although the term *air* frequently is used as though it were synonymous with oxygen, it should be emphasized that this is a serious error. Air is a mixture of gases of which oxygen is only one, a fact which is brought forcibly to our attention in big cities where the smog leads to respiratory ailments.   In this modern environment, minute particles of solids and greater than average amounts of carbon dioxide greatly alter the composition of the air.   It is not the air for which human beings evolved their respiratory system.   We will, however, consider only air as it should be and will discuss only four of its major components: *nitrogen,*° *oxygen, carbon dioxide,* and *water vapor.*   (Water vapor is listed as one of the gaseous components because it is present in both inspired and expired air and is important in the human respiratory process.)   The *pressure* of the air which surrounds us and the *percentage* of the various gases in the air are the chief elements which control the exchange of gases during respiration.   Each of the gases is said to have a *partial pressure,* which means that the total pressure of the air is equal to the sum of that part of the pressure contributed by oxygen (partial pressure of oxygen), by nitrogen, by carbon dioxide, and by water vapor.   Since the pressure of the air at sea level is equivalent to 760 millimeters of mercury (760 mm. Hg), it is possible to calculate the partial pressure of each of the gases.   Average figures for the percentage of each gas and the partial pressure of each gas in the 350 cubic centimeters of fresh air in the alveoli at inspiration are shown in the table below.

	Alveolar Air at Inspiration	Partial Pressure in mm. Hg
Oxygen	20.80%	158.08
Carbon dioxide	0.04%	0.30
Water vapor	0.66%	5.02
Nitrogen	78.50%	596.60

The partial pressures of oxygen and carbon dioxide can be used to illustrate what occurs in an alveolus which has just received fresh air.   The molecules of oxygen will be exerting a pressure of 158.08 mm. Hg on the walls of the alveolar capillaries, but the molecules of carbon dioxide will be exerting a pressure of only 0.30 mm. Hg on the same capillary walls.   Whether oxygen or carbon dioxide enters or leaves the capillaries will depend on the pressure of these same gases inside the capillary walls in the blood stream.   Hence the movement of these gases will be in accordance with laws of diffusion and osmosis (p. 54).

Therefore, the molecules of the gases will move from greater to lesser concentration through the semipermeable membranes of the alveoli and the alveolar capillaries.   This movement of gases is termed *external respiration,* which we can define more exactly in man as "the exchange of gases between the alveoli of the lungs and the blood stream."   Water vapor and nitrogen will obey the

---

° The rare gases, such as *helium, argon,* and others, constitute less than one per cent of the air.   Because these gases are rare and are physiologically inert, they are included in the nitrogen fraction.

same physical laws which govern oxygen and carbon dioxide.

Having stated the problem of gaseous exchange in the alveoli, let us now examine the actual situation which normally exists. The blood reaching the alveolar capillaries from the body has only 14.0 per cent oxygen, but the carbon dioxide level reached 4.0 per cent and water vapor 6.0 per cent. The carbon-dioxide concentration, therefore, is more than 100 times greater in the alveolar capillaries than it is in the alveoli, and the water-vapor concentration is approximately 10 times greater. Since the percentage of oxygen, and therefore its partial pressure, will be greater in the alveoli than in the blood, a larger number of oxygen molecules will move from the greater concentration in the alveoli to the lesser concentration in the blood than will move in the opposite direction. The oxygen content of the alveoli will be lowered simultaneously with an increase in the oxygen content of the blood. Conversely, there will be a very rapid movement of carbon-dioxide and water-vapor molecules from the capillaries into the alveoli, with the result that the percentages of these gases will be greatly increased in the alveoli while they are being decreased in the blood. Gaseous nitrogen, being physiologically inert, will undergo only comparatively minor changes in concentration. The percentage composition of air in an alveolus immediately before expiration becomes radically different from that immediately after inspiration, as a result of these osmotic changes. Oxygen declines to 14.0 per cent from the original 20.8 per cent; nitrogen drops to about 76.0 per cent from 78.5 per cent; carbon dioxide, however, increases one hundredfold to 4.0 per cent from 0.04 per cent; and water vapor is augmented nearly tenfold to 6.0 per centf rom 0.66 per cent.

External respiration normally occupies only a few seconds of time, and it is not possible for the blood to give up all its carbon dioxide nor for an alveolus to be depleted of its oxygen. The fact that much more gaseous exchange is possible can be demonstrated readily if the breath is held. In this situation, the percentage of carbon dioxide in the alveoli will be significantly decreased, and the percentage of oxygen will decline markedly below that indicated in the foregoing discussion. Thus, although complete exchange of gases does not occur, the rate of respiration and the speed of blood flow are nicely coordinated in a normal, healthy individual to produce a rapid but efficient exchange of gases during external respiration.

External respiration ensures that the blood which leaves the lungs will be high in oxygen and low in carbon dioxide, but when this blood reaches the tissues a situation is encountered which is essentially the reverse of that in the lungs. There is very little free oxygen in the tissues, the percentage seldom reaching as high as 4 per cent. The concentrations of carbon dioxide and water vapor are both in excess of 6 per cent in the tissues, however, since the oxidation of organic materials, with the production of these two gases as waste products, occurs constantly. In compliance with the laws of diffusion and osmosis, molecules of oxygen now will leave the blood stream to enter the tissues, whereas molecules of carbon dioxide and water vapor will leave the tissues to enter the blood stream.   Nitrogen, as in the lungs, is essentially in equilibrium in the blood and tissues, and little change takes place in its percentages.   This exchange of gases through the capillary walls between the blood and the tissues in man is defined as *internal respiration*.   The resultant percentages of gases will be: oxygen, 14 per cent; carbon dioxide, 4 per cent; water vapor, 6 per cent; and nitrogen, 76 per cent.   It will be obvious that these are the same percentages that we gave earlier as characteristic of the blood reaching the alveolar capillaries from the body.

The question may be asked, Why does not all the oxygen leave the blood and enter the tissues, since the tissues have practically no free oxygen?   The answer is a simple one: The blood normally flows too fast through the capillaries to allow time for this complete exchange to occur.   If blood is prevented from leaving a given area, as when a string is tied tightly around a finger, oxygen in the capillaries may be depleted.

Transportation of gases

The final aspect of respiration to be examined is the *transportation of gases* in the blood stream.   The gases are carried either in *solution* in the fluid portion

Figure 19.11.   External and internal respiration.   External respiration (a) involves the exchange of the gases, oxygen and carbon dioxide, between the respiratory organs and the body fluids. Internal respiration (b) involves the exchange of these gases between the body fluids and the cells.

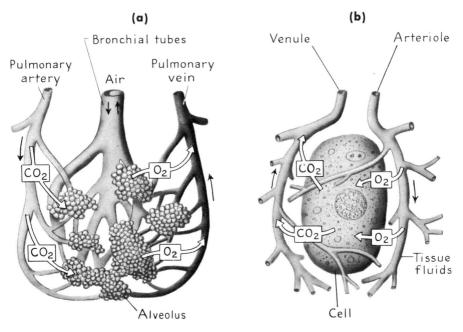

of the blood, the *plasma,* or in *chemical combination.* Two chief variables control the volume of gases which can be transported in solution. These are (1) the partial pressure of each gas, and (2) the solubility of each gas. Only about two per cent of the oxygen can be carried in solution in the plasma, and only about five per cent of the carbon dioxide is carried in solution. It is clear from these figures that another mechanism is necessary for the transportation of these two gases, and it is the chemical combination of oxygen and of carbon dioxide with substances in the blood which accomplishes the purpose. Gaseous nitrogen and water vapor, on the other hand, offer no special problems in transportation under normal conditions. It is only under extreme variations of high pressure (as in deep-sea diving) or in very low pressures (as in high-altitude flying) that nitrogen gas presents any difficulty in respiration. Transportation of water vapor, like nitrogen, can be considered a purely passive phenomenon.

We mentioned earlier (p. 22) that special respiratory pigments exist in many organisms. These substances usually are a copper-protein compound or an iron-protein compound, and they have the ability to carry large amounts of oxygen in loose chemical combination. The respiratory pigment in the earthworm and the clamworm is an iron-protein compound, *hemoglobin,* which is dissolved in the plasma. Man also possesses this same respiratory pigment, but the hemoglobin is present only in red blood cells, the *erythrocytes.*

The chemical nature of the iron-protein complex of hemoglobin is such that it has a remarkable ability to combine with oxygen in an unstable chemical combination which should be spoken of as *oxygenation* rather than oxidation. This combination of oxygen with hemoglobin is reversible and is illustrated in the following equation:

$$Hb + O_2 = HbO_2.$$

Hemoglobin   Oxyhemoglobin

The oxygenated hemoglobin is referred to as *oxyhemoglobin* and has a slightly different color than nonoxygenated hemoglobin. This is responsible for the color difference between arterial and venous blood in the human body. The arterial blood, of course, has a greater amount of oxyhemoglobin and a redder color than does the venous. Approximately 98 per cent of the oxygen in the blood is carried as oxyhemoglobin. When the blood reaches the tissues, oxyhomoglobin dissociates, releasing its oxygen, and the red blood cells then contain the nonoxygenated hemoglobin. The mechanism which causes the release of oxygen from oxyhemoglobin has been studied in great detail and, although a number of factors influence this reaction, one of the most significant is the high concentration of carbon dioxide in the capillaries of the tissues.

Carbon dioxide, when released from the tissues, combines with hydrogen in the water vapor to form *carbonic acid* (H_2CO_3). Carbonic acid increases the acidity of the blood very slightly, but this slight change is sufficient to render oxyhemoglobin completely unstable and to speed the release of its oxygen. Carbon dioxide is carried in chemical combination in the blood as carbonic acid and as various carbonates. Among the carbonates are sodium and potassium compounds such as $NaHCO_3$, $KHCO_3$, and organic carbonates of a class known as *carbamino compounds*. The advantage of transporting carbon dioxide in carbonate form is that the acid-base balance of the blood is not disturbed to any significant degree, even when large amounts of the gas are formed by the tissues. The effectiveness of this form of transportation was questioned by the observation that the sodium and potassium carbonates are relatively stable outside the body and do not give up their carbon dioxide readily. Since carbon dioxide is liberated at almost explosive speed at the lungs, some substance must be present in the blood to facilitate carbon dioxide release from the carbonates. *Carbonic anhydrase*, an enzyme present in the red blood cells, has been shown to be the agent which augments the carbonate dissociation. This enzyme is so powerful that it is effective even when diluted several million times. Its normal action increases the release rate of carbon dioxide more than 1000 times.

Environmental respiratory adjustments

Human curiosity has perpetually led man to attempt to explore and expand his environment. He has plumbed the ocean depths and surveyed the skies with ever increasing intensity. Not content with indirect evidence derived from the use of instruments, men have descended deeper and deeper below the surface of the oceans and ascended higher and higher into the atmosphere above the earth. Suddenly, man has found himself confronted by the physical limitations of his respiratory system. Fortunately, in his endeavors to circumvent these restrictions, man has discovered many of the niceties of the physics and chemistry of his respiratory processes. Certain of these are most interesting and worthy of notice.

A professional diver or a "skin" diver descending below the surface of the water is subjected to an additional pressure of one atmosphere at a depth of about 33 feet. This means that, instead of a pressure of 14.7 pounds per square inch on his body surface as at sea level, at 33 feet a diver experiences a pressure double that at sea level, or 29.4 pounds per square inch. A trained individual in good physical condition can resist this pressure for a brief period without special equipment, but to go farther below the surface requires protection against an ever increasing pressure of the water and demands an adequate air supply for respiration. Within a diving suit a diver is given air under increasing pressure to compensate for the greater external pressure to which he is being subjected. It has been possible in this manner for divers to withstand pressures of more than 147 pounds per square inch, or 10 times that at sea level. Since air is being pumped into a diver at a pressure equal to that of his surroundings, the various gases in the air are also being dissolved in the blood at tremendously high partial pressures.[*]

---

[*] The pressure of air at 147 pounds per square inch would be equal to 7600 mm. Hg. The partial pressure of oxygen, therefore, would be 1580.8 mm. Hg; and that of nitrogen, 5966.0 mm. Hg.

The body can tolerate this unusual situation provided the augmentation of pressure has been gradual. The major difficulty is encountered when the diver ascends and is subjected to decreasing pressure. The various gases are released from solution rapidly, and the excesses of oxygen and carbon dioxide are readily taken care of by the cells and the chemicals in the blood. Nitrogen, however, remains in the capillaries, and if the pressure drop outside the body is too rapid, the diver's blood actually bubbles like a soft drink that fizzes when shaken. The air bubbles block the capillaries, producing a condition called the *bends*, which may be fatal or can cause permanent damage to the brain or heart. This violent release of nitrogen can be avoided by a very slow decrease of pressure that permits the nitrogen to be removed by expiration. The diver who descends 200 feet, for example, may require several hours to return to the surface. A second method of avoiding the bends is to breathe an "artificial air" in which helium has been substituted for nitrogen. The lighter helium gas is rapidly removed from the blood stream and only minutes instead of hours may be required for ascent from a dive.

The situation faced by an aviator who climbs swiftly into the sky is exactly comparable, except for the element of speed, with that which confronts a diver who ascends quickly through the water. Atmospheric pressure, and therefore the partial pressure of each of the gases, declines with increasing altitude. The partial pressure of oxygen at 18,000 feet is only 50 per cent, and at 33,000 feet is only 25 per cent, of that at sea level. Most persons experience difficulty in securing adequate amounts of oxygen when taken quickly to an elevation of 10,000 feet, and above this height oxygen must be administered under pressure. This explains the need for pressurized cabins in modern airplanes, which frequently fly at 20,000 feet or more above sea level. The report of the successful conquest of Mt. Everest illustrates the problem of respiration at high altitudes. During the last 100 feet of climbing, Tenzing and Hillary were each consuming pure oxygen under pressure, at a rate of more than 3000 cubic centimeters per minute.

Persons who live at high altitudes are able to make long-term adjustments to the lower partial pressure of oxygen in their environment. The adaptations are both morphological and physiological. They do not develop quickly but are a result of weeks or even years of adjustment to the high altitudes. The blood volume of Indians living in the high Andes is reported to be 30 per cent greater than of those living at sea level; also, the number of red blood cells per cubic centimeter is approximately 38 per cent greater. Nearly 80 per cent more hemoglobin is present in these Indians, with a correspondingly greater increase in the oxygen-carrying power of the blood. It also has been reported that after long acclimatization to high altitudes many individuals have an increased lung capacity which, therefore, gives them a greater vital capacity.

One of the most interesting side-lights of the studies of high altitudes has been the accumulation of data that emphasize the importance of carbon dioxide in the control of breathing. Although carbon dioxide is a waste product, it provides an essential chemical stimulus to the respiratory center (p. 447). An increase in carbon dioxide of less than one per cent may more than double the amount of air being breathed. A slight decrease in the amount of CO_2 also may produce a temporary cessation of breathing. An increase of carbon dioxide exerts its effect in two ways. The carbonic acid (H_2CO_3) which is produced increases very slightly the acidity of the blood bathing the respiratory center, and this serves as a stimulus to increased ventilation. Likewise, it has been shown experimentally that carbon dioxide acts directly to stimulate the respiratory center independently of any change in blood acidity. The importance of the concentration of carbon dioxide as a chemical stimulus explains why this gas usually is mixed in small amounts with oxygen when it is necessary to administer oxygen to seriously ill persons, and also why carbon dioxide is added to the artificial air which is used by aviators and divers.

It would be logical for oxygen to be the most important gas in the physiological control of the respiratory center. This is not the case and is another example, therefore, of the fact that nature is not always logical. Oxygen does have an important role in the ventilation of the lungs. A decline in oxygen intake is followed by a marked increase in the depth of inspiration and, hence, in better ventilation. A high concentration of oxygen in the alveoli may also be accompanied by a temporary halting of breathing. The stimulating or the inhibiting effects of oxygen, however, are much less marked than are those of carbon dioxide.

A human being who engages in violent exercise or hard work may find that his oxygen consumption is increased by as much as 2000 per cent. The interesting aspect of this increase is that much of the oxygen consumption may not occur simultaneously with the exercise or work but may follow the actual exertion. This means that work can be done in the body during the first few minutes of exertion by nonoxidative release of energy. This, therefore, would be *anoxybiotic respiration*. Such energy releases are not as efficient as those in oxybiotic respiration, in part because lactic acid and other metabolic by-products accumulate which must be oxidized later. In many instances, as in a 100-yard dash, oxidation of the by-products does not take place until after the exercise or exertion has been terminated. When this happens the body is said to have accumulated an *oxygen debt* during the exercise.

It may be stated in summary that the respiratory system of man is remarkably efficient and has a very considerable reserve of vital capacity. Thus, under normal environmental conditions, healthy human beings have the ability to secure oxygen and eliminate carbon dioxide and water vapor at rates in excess of their physiological needs. It is only when man goes exploring into the ocean depths or into the upper atmosphere that he encounters respiratory difficulties and must supplement his natural equipment with artificial aids.

Excretion

The air environment in which man lives and the high metabolic rate of his living processes present problems which complicate human excretion. The major waste materials of the body, for example, must be excreted in solution; but since water conservation is imperative, only limited amounts of fluid can be spared for excretory purposes. Moreover, since large amounts of inorganic salts are ingested, considerable quantities of these must also be excreted if normal osmotic balance within the body is to be maintained. The excretory situation in the human being, therefore, is in marked contrast to that of the frog (p. 371) where an excess of water constantly enters the body through the skin, but, because very little salt is ingested, a dilute urine is consequently excreted. Furthermore, waste materials are formed rapidly in man as a result of his high oxidative rate. Since wastes cannot be stored in a chemically inert form as they are in many invertebrates, they must be eliminated quickly in order to prevent their toxic effects. This may be necessary even at the expense of water loss.

The types of substances which must be excreted by human beings are the same as those eliminated by other organisms (p. 41). These are nitrogenous compounds such as *urea, uric acid,* and *ammonia;* excess *water;* excess *carbon dioxide;* and to a more limited extent, the various inorganic salts of *sodium, potassium, calcium,* and *phosphorus,* as well as considerable quantities of *chloride.*

The excretory system

The structures which are responsible for excretion of these diverse substances are more varied in man than in the other vertebrates. We have already noted the important excretory organs, the *sweat glands* and the *lungs.* The sweat glands eliminate quantities of water and chloride, and the lungs excrete water and carbon dioxide. Excretion is not a major function of the sweat glands or of the lungs, but the body depends on both to supplement the action of the primary excretory organs, the *kidneys.*

The kidneys perform 75 per cent of body excretion, but modern physiologists have stressed that the kidneys are organs primarily responsible for the maintenance of the constancy of the internal environment, a condition technically known as *homeostasis.* An understanding of this concept will explain certain apparent inconsistencies of urine formation which regularly occur. If, for example, large quantities of water are taken into the system, a large quantity of dilute urine will be excreted; conversely, if water intake is decreased, only a small volume of concentrated urine will be eliminated. The kidneys, therefore, have an important role in maintaining the proper *water content* of the body, since they can either eliminate water when it is in excess or conserve it when it is scarce. The kidneys also control the *balance of the salts*—sodium, potassium, phosphorus, and calcium—by removing or conserving them as needed. The *acid-alkaline* balance in the blood can be partially controlled by the ability of the kidney to secrete a more acid or a more alkaline urine as needed to maintain that balance. Even a substance as necessary for life as sugar will be excreted by the kidneys if it reaches abnormally high levels in the blood. In the light of the concept of the constancy of the internal environment, excretion can be thought of as "the elimination of substances which, when present in excess, would alter the internal environment to the harm of the individual."

It might be assumed that an organ capable of such complex physiological actions would have an elaborate structure. The human kidney is somewhat more complex than that of the frog, but a comparison of the functional unit of the human kidney with that of a typical amphibian (p. 369) indicates that the basic organization is essentially the same. The human kidney develops from the posterior part of the *opisthonephros* (p. 368) from the region generally designated as the *metanephric* portion. The kidney duct, the *ureter,* arises during embryonic development as a bud from the posterior part of the *mesonephric duct* and grows into the opisthonephros to establish contact with the kidney.

The adult human kidneys are paired, bean-shaped bodies located to the right and left of the vertebral column in the abdominal cavity. If a kidney is sliced lengthwise, a *glandular region,* composed of a *cortex* and *medulla* and a central *sinus,* is immediately recognizable. The excretory tubules, or *nephrons,* are

Figure 19.12. This drawing of a kidney section with the vessels which provide the circulation of the rich supply of blood shows the structural design of this vital organ of excretion.

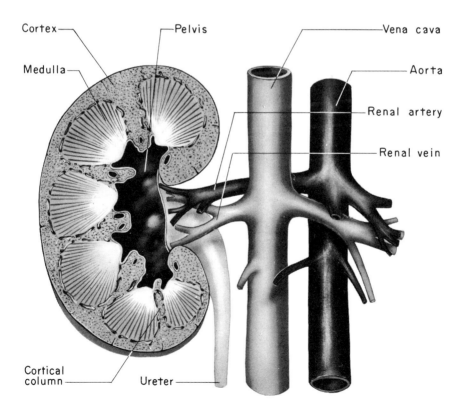

Cortex
Pelvis
Vena cava
Medulla
Aorta
Renal artery
Renal vein
Cortical column
Ureter

located in the cortex, and they drain through *collecting ducts* in the medulla into the cavity of the sinus. This cavity actually is an expanded end of the ureter, which drains the urine from the kidney into the *urinary bladder*. Urine is stored for varying periods of time in the bladder, from which it is discharged from the body through the *urethra*.

Excellent theories of kidney function were developed by Sir William Bowman in 1842 and by Carl Ludwig in 1844, but the modern concept of the manner in which the nephrons excrete might be said to begin with Richards' experiments on the frog kidney in 1922, which were cited earlier (p. 370). The extension of the experimental methods of Richards to the mammals followed very soon, and more elaborate methods of analysis were devised which now make it possible to determine the part played by each portion of the nephron in the excretory process. It has been established that there are three phases of urine formation: (1) the *ultrafiltration* of fluid from the blood into the nephron at the

Figure 19.13. Excretory system. The human kidneys drain by way of the ureters into the bladder, and the latter by way of the urethra to the exterior. In the human being the ureters do not serve as reproductive ducts; in the male, however, the urethra is a urogenital passage (p. 444).

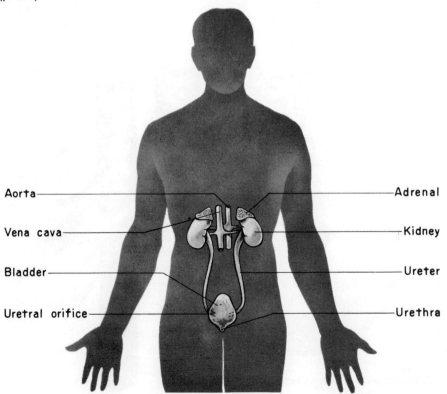

Aorta————————————————————Adrenal

Vena cava————————————————Kidney

Bladder————————————————Ureter

Uretral orifice————————————Urethra

glomerulus; (2) the *selective resorption* of materials from the tubules of the nephron into the blood; and (3) the *secretion of waste materials* into the urine by the tubules of the nephron.   We can gain a better understanding of these processes from a brief description of a nephron of the human kidney.

The *glomerulus* of the nephron is a capillary area between two *arterioles*. These arterioles have well-developed coats of muscle, and the pressure of blood in the glomerulus may be raised or lowered when the pressure of the arterioles is altered by contraction of relaxation of the muscles of their walls.   Blood pressure in a glomerulus may also be altered independently of the contraction of the glomerular arterioles.   Fluid at varied rates from the glomerulus into Bowman's capsule which surrounds it, depending on the pressure of the blood within the glomerulus.   When pressure is high, filtration will be rapid; when pressure is low, the filtration rate will decrease.   The fluid which passes from the glomerulus is an ultrafiltrate containing dissolved substances, chiefly sugar, inorganic salts, urea, and uric acid.   Most proteins, and other molecules larger than 70,000 in molecular weight, normally do not filter through the capillary walls of the glomerulus.

The glomerular region of the nephron is joined to a long tubule which coils on itself and eventually joins a collecting tubule of the medulla.   The tubule of the nephron has several distinct regions and some of the cells are the glandular type, as Bowman first recognized.   We will discuss the function of these tubules in detail later.

	Mg. per 100 cc. of Blood Plasma	Mg. per 100 cc. of Urine	Change in Concentration
Urea	30	2000 to 3000	60 to 100 times
Uric Acid	2	50	25 times
Chloride	370	700	2 times
Sodium	320	350	Same
Glucose	100	None	——

There are 1,000,000 or more glomeruli in each kidney, and recent evidence indicates that in man, in contrast with the frog, all the glomeruli may function at one time.   The amount of fluid filtered per day by these glomeruli varies greatly, depending on the amount of water ingested, activity, age, sex, and many other factors.   It is not unusual, however, for 120 liters of glomerular filtrate to be formed in a 24-hour period.   Usually, only 1.0 or 1.5 liters of urine are excreted daily; therefore, approximately 119 liters of filtrate must be reabsorbed as the fluid passes through the nephrons toward the ureters.   The accompanying table, based on the data reported by Arthur Cushny in 1917, shows the changes in concentration in blood plasma and urine of some of the important materials which pass through the kidneys.   These figures represent averages during normal kidney function, of course, and may be altered considerably under unusual or pathological conditions.

It can be demonstrated that the substances listed in the table are present in the glomerular filtrate at essentially the same concentrations as they exist in the blood. We note, however, that urea may be 100 times more concentrated in the urine and on the other hand, that glucose is not normally present in urine. Substances such as glucose and sodium must, therefore, be completely or almost completely reabsorbed, whereas uric acid and urea are not. The question may be asked whether all the observed amounts of the various substances in the urine can be accounted for solely on the basis of filtration and selective resorption. This point was part of the original debate between Bowman and Ludwig on the mechanism of kidney function, because Bowman believed that actual secretion of waste materials occurred in addition to their filtration, whereas Ludwig believed that only the mechanical factors of filtration and resorption were present. Modern physiologists have gathered impressive evidence to support the idea that the tubular portion of the nephron secretes (excretes) waste material into the urine. Samples of fluid have been drawn by microdissection from various regions of the nephron, and these have been analyzed microchemically. Certain chemicals, such as diodrast, filter very slowly through the glomeruli but are excreted rapidly by the tubules. The injection of such materials has provided a method of measuring the function of the tubules in excretion. Furthermore, the cells of the tubules actually may form (secrete) certain substances such as ammonia or hippuric acid and release them into the urine. The secretion of such nitrogenous compounds is part of the homeostatic mechanism by which the kidney controls the acid-alkaline balance of the blood.

It may be stated in summary that the removal of waste materials from the blood is part of the function of the kidney in maintaining the constancy of the body fluids. The human kidney is aided in the performance of this task by the skin and lungs, and to a limited extent, by the elimination of salts which takes place in the intestine. The functional unit of the kidney, the nephron, accomplishes the work of excretion by:

1. *Ultrafiltration* of fluid containing materials at the same concentration at which they are present in the blood;

2. *Selective resorption* of most of the water and salts and all of the glucose;

3. *Tubular excretion* of certain substances into the urine;

4. *Tubular secretion* of special substances such as ammonia in the urine.

One of the remarkable over-all features of kidney function is the way in which water conservation is practiced. More than 95 per cent of the water filtered through the glomerulus is routinely reabsorbed into the blood stream.

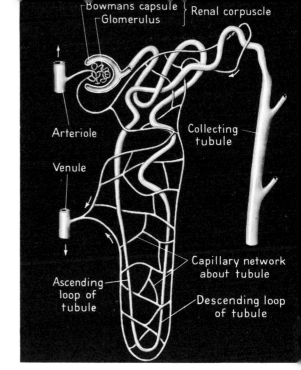

Figure 19.14.   The kidney tubule is a complex filtration-absorption device.

The control of kidney function in the human being is influenced by a number of factors.   We have mentioned previously that blood pressure is an important agent in the rate of filtration.   It also has been demonstrated that various hormones have pronounced effects on the ability of the kidney to excrete some substances or to reabsorb others.   The presence or absence of insulin controls the amount of glucose in the blood and, therefore, has an effect on the rate of glucose excretion; variations in the amount of posterior pituitary hormone alters the ability of the kidney to reabsorb water; and the amount of adrenal cortical hormones influences the excretion of glucose as well as of sodium and potassium.   One of the most striking effects on kidney function is the role of the parathyroid hormone in the excretion of calcium and phosphorus salts.   Its effects are significant because these two substances are vital for normal cellular metabolism, and any marked alteration in the concentration of these salts in the blood can result in death to the individual.   The parathyroid, acting by way of the kidney, therefore exerts a controlling influence on the life of the individual.   We will discuss these hormonal factors in some detail under the section on chemical coordination.

Reproduction

Human beings reproduce sexually.   A moderate number of sex differences, both morphological and physiological, are present. The average human males is larger than the female, and the long bones of the male skeleton are of greater length and of heavier construction than those of the female. Likewise, the shoulders are proportionately broader and the hips narrower in the male than in the female. Men also have a larger larynx, a deeper voice, and coarser facial hair (beard and mustache); but baldness, which is common in older men, is rare in women of any age. There is a greater deposition of subcutaneous fat in the female and the mammary glands are well developed at maturity, whereas in the male they usually are rudimentary. More subtle sex differences also can be observed; for example, the red blood cell count and the basal metabolic rate are higher in men than in women.

The reproductive system

The most significant sex differences, of course, involve the organs of reproduction, their associated glands, and their duct systems. The female reproductive cells, the *ova*, develop in the *ovaries* and pass from the ovaries through *oviducts* (fallopian tubes) to the *uterus*, where the embryo develops. The male reproductive cells, the *sperm* (spermatozoa), develop in the *testes* and exit from the testes through *efferent ducts* into the *epididymis*, and thence to the *ductus deferens* and the penile urethra. Several glands are associated with the male duct system, and their secretions, when added to the *sperm*, constitute the *seminal fluid*. The *seminal vesicles* contribute a thick sticky secretion containing fructose, choline, and globulin; the *prostate gland* releases a thin, watery, alkaline secretion; and *Cowper's glands* secrete a clear fluid. It is not certain how important the secretions of these glands may be in reproduction but the secretions do protect the sperm, provide an alkaline medium to counteract the acidity of the uterus, and supply some nutrient for the sperm. The seminal vesicles or the prostate gland can be removed, however, without affecting copulation (mating). It has been reported, however, that fertility is decreased after such surgery.

The structures concerned with *copulation* differ greatly in the male and female. The uterus is connected to the outside of the body by a muscular tube, the *vagina*, which receives the penis of the male and into which the seminal fluid is deposited. The external genitalia of the female are the *vulva*, composed of folds of skin, the *labia majora* and the *labia minora,* and at the anterior junction of these skin folds an elevation, the *clitoris.* This structure varies considerably in size in different individuals and is homologous with a portion of the penis of the male. The urethra opens separately from the genital tract in the human female. The paired *glands of Bartholin* in the vagina secrete an alkaline fluid which lubricates the vagina and serves also to counteract the acidity of the uterus.

The intromittent organ of the male is the *penis,* through which the urethra also passes to the outside of the body. Since the ductus deferens from the testis joins the urethra near the bladder, the urethra is actually a urogenital duct in the male, in contrast to the existence of separate genital and urinary ducts in the female. Another important difference between the male and female reproductive systems involves the positions of the gonads. The ovaries remain in the abdominal cavity, but the testes migrate through the *inguinal canal* from the body cavity into a pouch of loose skin adjacent to the base of the penis on its ventral side. This pouch is the *scrotum,* and in the human male, as well as in the male of many other mammals, sperm formation does not occur unless the testes are in the scrotum. An individual whose testes have been retained in the body cavity is sterile. The investigations of Carl R. Moore indicate that the temperature in the scrotum is slightly lower than in the body cavity and that this cooler environment is necessary for normal sperm development. Raising the temperature of the scrotum by experimental procedures produces sterility.

The penis has bands of special spongy tissue constituting the *cavernous bodies (corpora cavernosa).* These spongy tissues during sexual excitement fill with blood as a result of the dilation of the arteries leading to the penis. The distention of the cavernous bodies results in the hardening and erection of the penis to enable it to enter the vagina. The contact of the penis with the vagina during copulation stimulates the secretion of seminal fluid by the accessory glands, and at the termination of copulation the forceful contraction

Figure 19.15. Female reproductive system. The structural arrangement of the ovaries, oviducts, uterus, and vagina is illustrated in this sketch. Observe the enlarged openings of the oviducts, which act as funnels to direct the ova into the oviduct. This helps to prevent the occurrence of abdominal pregnancies.

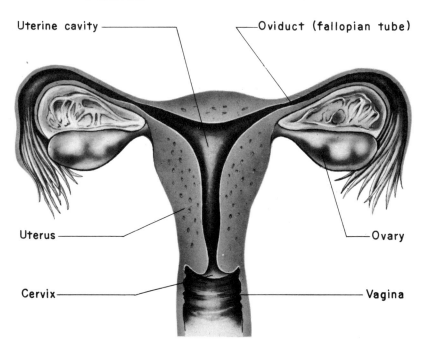

Uterine cavity ————— —Oviduct (fallopian tube)

Uterus —

Ovary

Cervix —

Vagina

of the muscles of the walls of the glands and of the ductus deferens results in the ejaculation of seminal fluid.

The reproductive potential of the human male and female differs considerably. The male reaches sexual maturity during the middle teens, and sperm formation may continue throughout the remainder of his life. Records of men who have begat children in their 60's, 70's, and even 80's are not uncommon. Sexual maturity in the female may begin somewhat earlier than in the male, but the ability to reproduce does not extend throughout life. The span of the reproductive life of women is approximately 30 years. If, for example, sexual maturity is reached at about 15 it may be expected to terminate at about 45 years of age. A wide variation exists, however, in these figures; children have been born to mothers under 10 and to those over 50 years of age.

The number of sperm which can be formed by the male during his lifetime is almost limitless, but the number of egg cells which can reach maturity in the female is restricted. There are several hundred thousand immature ova present in the two ovaries at birth, but this number decreases steadily with age. There

Figure 19.16. Male urogenital system. The relation of the excretory and reproductive systems in the human male is shown by this lateral drawing of the pelvic region. The glands which contribute to the seminal fluid (p. 434) are also diagrammed. The urethra is the only urogenital duct in the urogenital system.

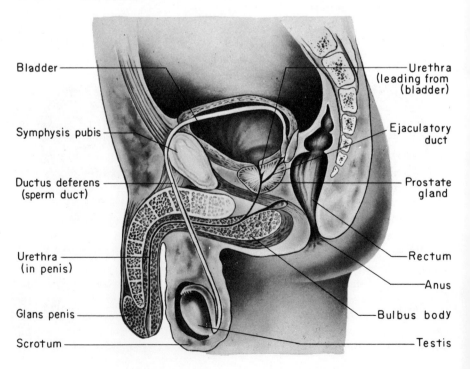

Bladder

Symphysis pubis

Ductus deferens
(sperm duct)

Urethra
(in penis)

Glans penis

Scrotum

Urethra
(leading from
(bladder)

Ejaculatory
duct

Prostate
gland

Rectum

Anus

Bulbus body

Testis

is a tendency for the ovaries to alternate month by month in the release of ova; usually only 12 to 13 ova mature and are released each year.   If a reproductive life of approximately 30 years is assumed, this would mean that a maximum of only 400 to 500 eggs would be ovulted.   Very few ova remain in the ovary when the reproductive life of the female ceases.   The male, in contrast to the female, forms reproductive cells constantly.   The testes are composed of many convoluted tubules, the *seminiferous tubules,* which are cytogenic (cell-form-ing) and produce spermatozoa in great numbers.   The cells of the walls of the tubules reproduce by mitosis and the newly formed reproductive cells undergo a period of *growth* and *maturation* before becoming mature sperm.   It is during maturation that a special type of cell division, *meiosis,* occurs, and we will dis-cuss the significance of this type of division later in conjunction with heredity. Growth and meiosis also occur during the development of an ovum.

The testes and ovaries are endocrine as well as cytogenic glands.   The testes secrete the male hormone, *testosterone,* into the blood stream.   This hormone is responsible for the development and maintenance of most of the male sec-ondary sex characters.   The deeper voice and the accessory glands are influ-enced by this hormone.   Testosterone in the mammal appears to be secreted by special cells, the *interstitial cells,* which lie between the seminiferous tubules.

The ovaries secrete two hormones, *estradiol* and *progesterone.*   These ovarian hormones affect the secondary sex characters and, in addition, are essential for maintaining the proper uterine condition, for the growth and nutrition of the embryo, and for the development of the mammary glands.   We will discuss some details of the effects of the ovarian hormones in the section on chemical coordination.

It is difficult to give precise figures for the times at which various events occur in the female reproductive cycle, because many factors regulate a woman's reproductive physiology.   Nutrition, exercise, psychic disturbances, and social pressures all have profound influence; accordingly, the time intervals which are given in the following account should be considered only as averages subject to wide variation.   The human female at the time of sexual maturity has immature ova in the cortex of the ovary.   These ova are surrounded by a layer of cubical epithelial cells comprising the *follicle cells* of the ova.   An ovum with its surrounding follicle cells is spoken of as an *ovarian,* or *Graafian, follicle.* The follicle cells multiply rapidly at the beginning of a reproductive cycle, so that the ovum is soon surrounded by a many-layered envelope of follicle cells. Once started, this multiplication of follicle cells continues and the ovarian fol-licle becomes larger and larger until it causes an elevation on the surface of the ovary.   The cells on the interior of the follicle are separated by an accumulation of fluid within the follicle, and the ovum finally appears to lie in a fluid-filled blister, the *mature ovarian follicle.*   The size increase of the follicle may easily be more than a hundredfold as a result of the processes of mitosis, growth, and cavity formation which ensue as the follicle matures.   The ovum, however, does not increase appreciably during this period of time and can be observed to rest

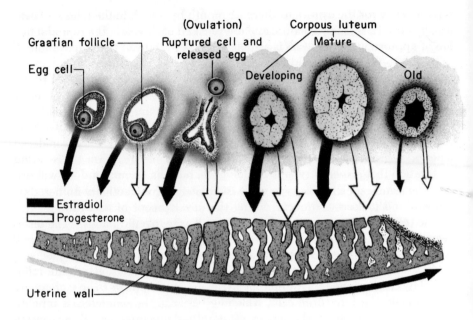

Figure 19.17. Estrus cycle. The relationship between the development of the ovarian follicle and the growth of the uterus is shown in this illustration. It will be noted that all changes are gradual and that the two ovarian hormones, estradiol and progesterone, act cooperatively in producing the uterine conditions which are essential for the implantation of the embryo.

in a small cluster of follicle cells, the *germ hill*, at one side of the follicular cavity.

The mature follicle ruptures, discharging from the ovary not only its fluid contents but also the ovum surrounded by the cluster of cells from the germ hill. This is the process of *ovulation*, and usually in the human female only a single ovum from one ovary is discharged in any one cycle. Another important feature of follicular development is that the developing ovarian follicle is an endocrine gland, estradiol being secreted in ever increasing amounts as the follicle grows. It has been shown that the mature follicle also secretes the second ovarian hormone, progesterone.

The ruptured follicle, after ovulation, undergoes structural reorganization. The follicle cells change in appearance and new cells are added. The cells acquire a characteristic yellow color, and for this reason the mass of cells which develops from the reorganized follicle is called a *corpus luteum*. The corpus luteum, like the ovarian follicle which precedes it, is an endocrine gland and secretes large amounts of progesterone and estradiol. Degeneration of the corpus luteum occurs after a period of time, the time of degeneration depending primarily on whether or not the ovum has been fertilized. A reproductive cycle can be said to close with the degeneration of the corpus luteum, and a cycle which does not include a pregnancy averages a lunar month, 28 days, in duration. There will be, therefore, approximately 13 ovulatory cycles in the course of a calendar year if no pregnancy has occurred.

Several important features of the female reproductive cycle should be emphasized. Ovulation occurs and the ovarian hormones are secreted regardless of whether copulation has taken place. Both estradiol and progesterone exert their effects on the reproductive system, especially on the lining of the uterus, which is prepared for the implantation of the ovum and the work associated with the nourishment of the embryo. Estradiol stimulates the growth of the uterine glands, and mitotic figures are numerous in the uterus. The vascularity of the uterus is greatly increased, and the amount of intracellular fluid is augmented. Cell growth and secretory activity are stimulated in the vagina. The duct system of the mammary glands branches extensively under the influence of estradiol. Progesterone, however, has very little effect in the female unless estradiol is present or has exerted its effects previous to the secretion of progesterone. In a normal cycle, of course, progesterone will be acting on tissues that have been influenced by estradiol. The uterine glands show a marked coiling under the stimulation of progesterone, and their secretory activity is greatly augmented. Likewise, the secretory alveoli of the mammary glands develop in preparation for subsequent milk secretion. The two ovarian hormones also have general metabolic effects which are responsible in part for some of the physiological differences between men and women.

The uterus of the human female is developed to such an extent under the influence of estradiol and progesterone that when the corpus luteum regresses and these hormones are no longer present in adequate amounts, the *endometrium*, or lining, of the uterus degenerates. In the human female, as well as in the females of other primates, uterine degeneration is accompanied by a loss of uterine epithelium and by bleeding from ruptured uterine blood vessels. This is the phenomenon of *menstruation*, which normally continues for three to five days. A new epithelial lining for the uterus is regenerated following menstrual bleeding, and the uterus is prepared for a new cycle.

It should be apparent from the preceding account that menstruation actually marks the termination of one cycle and the beginning of another. Since the duration of menstruation is variable, it has been traditional to consider the first day of the menstrual period as *day one* of a new reproductive cycle, and to date all subsequent events from that time. Average figures for a cycle, therefore, would indicate *days one to four* as menstruation, *days ten to sixteen* as the time during which ovulation may occur, with perhaps the greatest number of ovulations falling on *day fourteen*. The peak of corpus luteum development and function would be reached at about *day twenty-one*, after which regression would begin, leading to the termination of the cycle on *day twenty-eight*. It was pointed out earlier, however, that these averages are subject to considerable individual variation.

Fertilization, embryonic development, and birth

Copulation at the time of ovulation ensures the maximum chance of fertilization because both egg and sperm cells have a limited life span. The ovum is capable of being fertilized and of developing for probably not more than 12 to 20 hours after its release from the ovary. Spermatozoa may remain motile for several days but apparently are capable of fertilizing the ovum only for a period of from 12 to 24 hours. Furthermore, large numbers of spermatozoa, probably well in excess of 40,000,000, must be present to afford a maximum chance of fertilization. It will be remembered also that the egg cell, when ovulated, is surrounded by a "crown," or cluster, of cells from the germ hill. These cells are held together by an adhehive chemical substance, *hyaluronic acid,* which must be dissolved to free the ovum of its cellular coat before sperm can reach the egg and fertilize it. The sperm carry an enzyme, *hyaluronidase,* which accomplishes the dissolution of the hyaluronic acid and enables the sperm to penetrate to the ovum. Since each sperm can carry only a small amount of the enzyme, large numbers of sperm are required in order to accomplish the breakdown of the hyaluronic acid.

The ovum,° when ovulated, is discharged into the abdominal cavity, from which it must migrate into the oviduct. The distance to be traversed is short, and the expanded end of the oviduct, the *ostium,* acts as a funnel to guide the ovum into the oviduct. Since fertilization occurs at the upper end of the oviduct, there are occasional instances in which the ovum is fertilized in the abdominal cavity before reaching the oviduct. The egg actually may begin its development and an abdominal pregnancy may ensue. Such pregnancies must be terminated surgically in order to protect the life of the mother. The ovum, immediately after union with a sperm, forms a fertilization membrane which prevents the entrance of additional sperm, and cleavage begins as the ovum moves down the oviduct. The cilia lining the oviduct facilitate the movement of the embryo to the uterus, and six to eight days are required for the egg to make its journey.

The blastomeres formed during the initial stages of cleavage are essentially equal in size, but the formation of the embryonic layers is somewhat different from that described earlier for a "typical embryo" (p. 112). A hollow ball of cells, the *blastocyst,* is formed during cleavage, and within this ball at one side is a mass of cells, the *inner cell mass.* The outer layer of cells is designated as the *trophoblast,* or nutritive layer, which will provide the connection between the embryo and the uterus and will form the *chorion,* the outer portion of the embryonic membranes. The inner cell mass will give rise to the embryo as well as to a rudimentary *yolk sac* and a vestigial *allantois.* The amniotic cavity does not develop in the human as it does in birds or reptiles but forms in place

---

° In human embryogenesis "ovum" often is used in a very broad sense. Thus, the term *ovum* is used to signify an embryo during its cleavage stages, as well as the unfertilized egg.

by a splitting of the trophoblast and by cavity formation with the inner cell mass. The embryonic layers originate by cell migration and by ingression and not by invagination. The eventual organization of the embryo and its membranes, however, is essentially the same as that of the other vertebrates by the time somite and neural tube formation has been reached. The major exceptions to this generalization are the yolk sac and the allantois, rudimentary structures which are of primary concern only to the student of comparative embryology.

Branching, fingerlike processes, the *villi*, develop on the surface of the chorion (trophoblast). These villi, when they contact the surface of the uterus, have a digestive action which causes the wall of the uterus to be eroded. The embryo slowly sinks into the surface of the uterus, and the villi digest their way through the tissues of the uterus until the blood in many of the smaller uterine vessels is separated from the surface of the villi only by the endothelial lining of the vessel. When the embryonic blood vessels develop they extend into the villi, and thus only the covering of the villi and the endothelium of the maternal blood vessels separate the blood stream of the mother from that of the embryo. The villi eventually break through the maternal blood vessels in their process of excavating space for the embryo to grow, and irregular pools of blood, or *blood sinuses*, are created. These sinuses are supplied with blood by the broken ends of arteries, and blood drains from the sinuses into the broken ends of veins. No mixing of blood takes place, but there is a rapid osmotic exchange of oxygen, carbon dioxide, nutrients, waste materials, and even of hormones, between the mother and the embryo. Most disease-causing organisms, however, cannot pass from mother to embryo.

The devolpment of the chorion of the trophoblast and of the uterus continues throughout pregnancy, leading to a complex interlocking of the chorion with the maternal tissues. This structural and functional connection is the *placenta*, and as a result of this intimate relationship, the placenta becomes entirely responsible for the nutrition, respiration, and excretion of the embryo; and also for the secretion of hormones. The blood vessels of the embryo reach the placenta through the *umbilical cord*, which thus is the embryonic lifeline. An embryo that has successfully established placental connections is spoken of as a *fetus*. Some idea of the extent of the growth of the uterus during pregnancy and under the influence of the hormones of the placenta may be gained from the observation that the cavity of the uterus may increase in volume 100,000 per cent, the weight of the uterus may be augmented by 2000 per cent, and uterine muscle fibers will grow 1000 per cent in length and 500 per cent in diameter.

The placenta also becomes a remarkable endocrine gland. It secretes both estradiol and progesterone, which, of course, are necessary for its own existence. In addition, the placenta secretes an important stimulating hormone, *chorionic gonadotropin*, which prevents the regression of the corpus luteum and augments the production of estradiol and progesterone by that gland. Chorionic gonadotropin probably stimulates the placenta also. The human placenta is so important as an endocrine gland, the removal of the ovaries after one month of pregnancy does not result in damage to the uterus or death to the fetus. The human being is somewhat unique in this respect because only a few other mammals possess such efficient placentae.

The remarkable ability of the placenta and uterus to grow and to maintain the fetus raises the interesting question as to why a pregnancy does not continue indefinitely. This question is more significant since, even when the ovaries are removed, as we mentioned, a pregnancy normally continues to the usual termination time of approximately 10 lunar months, or 280 days. Ovarian changes, such as degeneration of the corpus luteum, therefore, cannot provide the stimuli for birth. The mechanism responsible for the conclusion of pregnancy probably exists within the uterus and placenta. It has been observed that the contractions of the uterine muscles increase in rate and strength as pregnancy progresses. Nervous control of these muscle contractions apparently is not too important, for mothers who are paralyzed in the lower half of the body have uterine muscle contractions and may deliver their babies in essentially a normal manner. The muscle contractions, however, have the effect of clamping off, or occluding, smaller blood vessels in the uterus. Likewise, the pressure exerted on the uterine walls by the rapidly growing fetus during the last two months of pregnancy produces occlusion of other blood vessels. Any portion of the uterus or placenta which is deprived of its blood supply for even a short period of time will begin to degenerate. Perhaps even more important, the degenerating cells and tissues release toxic substances which have adverse effects on the uterus. Once started, therefore, uterine degeneration is speeded, with the result that there is a marked decline in the secretion of the two hormones which are needed for its own survival, and the uterine-placental relationship no longer can be maintained.

There are certain techincal objections to this simplified explanation of the events leading to birth. A very obvious one is the fact that little women may have large babies, and large women little babies. It is probable that the posterior pituitary hormones which stimulate smooth-muscle contractions, together with other factors, are also influential in terminating a pregnancy. We are confronted with a remarkable phenomenon in the birth of a child, but we must admit that at present our explanations for the regularity of this event are inadequate.

We can think of the birth of a baby (labor)* as having three phases: *first,* an enlargement of the opening of the uterus into the vagina; *second,* the forceful muscle contractions of labor and the birth of the baby; and *third,* the expulsion of the placenta (often called the "afterbirth") from the mother's body. The enlargement of the opening into the uterus allows the baby to pass into the vagina (birth canal). Muscle contractions increase in strength and duration as labor advances; likewise, the interval between contractions is decreased. The length of time involved in these muscular contractions preceding birth varies

---

* The technical term for this is *parturition.*

widely. The duration usually is 12 to 24 hours in mothers who are having their first babies, but as a rule, the length of time decreases to 6 to 12 hours in women who are having second, third, or fourth babies. The second phase of birth, the passage of the baby through the birth canal from the body of the mother, is accompanied by additional muscle contractions of the wall of the abdomen. These contractions assist the uterus in the expulsion of the baby. At approximately this time, the amniotic sac ruptures and releases its fluid. This is the phenomenon known as the "rupture of the sac of waters." The umbilical cord which connects the baby to the placenta must be severed and tied at birth. The baby must cease its life as an aquatic organism at this moment, and breathing must begin immediately. The third phase of birth involves the expulsion of the placenta. Forceful muscle contractions in the uterine wall separate the placenta from the uterus. This is then expelled from the body and the birth procedure has been completed.

Multiple births are relatively rare among human beings. Such births are generally spoken of as *twinning* whether they involve two or more than two individuals at one time. Among Americans the rate of twinning is somewhat less than 1 in 100 births. Among the Chinese only about one third as many twins are born as among Americans. There is strong evidence that racial differences are a factor in the number of individuals born at any one pregnancy. A discussion of the types of twins will be considered in the chapter on inheritance.

The development of the urogenital system

The embryonic gonads, both ovaries and testes, develop from the coelomic epithelium adjacent to the mesonephric portion of the kidney (p. 369). The ducts of the mesonephros connect with the tubules of the testes, and the mesonephric duct, therefore, becomes the duct of the testes in the adult. The kidney ducts, however, do not serve as ovarian ducts and separate oviducts for the transport of ova make the appearance. These develop in the male as well as in the female fetus, but the oviducts remain rudimentary in the male whereas they continue to develop in the female. The uterus is formed by a fusion of the lower ends of the oviducts.

The mesonephric and ovarian ducts enter the cloaca and the structural relationship of the cloaca with these ducts in a human fetus of about eight weeks of age is similar to that which we noted in the adult frog (p. 372). The development of the metanephric portion of the kidney, however, alters this condition. The duct of the metanephros, the *ureter*, develops as a bud from the mesonephric duct, and after it has established its connection with the tubular area of the kidney, the function of the metanephric kidney is initiated. The excretory function of the mesonephric portion of the kidney ceases in both the male and female in early fetal life, and the mesonephric area of the kidney then degenerates. The degeneration of the mesonephric portion of the kidney is almost complete in the female, with only a few rudimentary tubules remaining adjacent

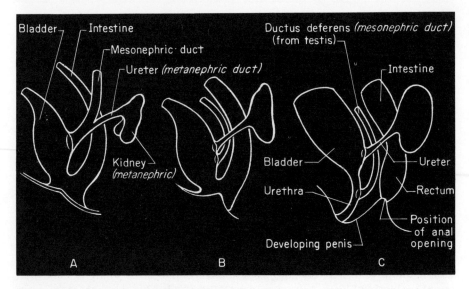

Figure 19.18. Cloacal development. The human embryo possesses a cloaca, but during its development the excretory, digestive, and reproductive systems acquire separate exits from the body. These diagrams illustrate the major changes that occur in the transformation of the cloaca during embryonic development.

to the ovary (p. 440); in the male, however, a considerable portion of the mesonephric region becomes the epididymis, and the mesonephric duct becomes the ductus deferens.

There is a true cloaca present in the fetus at eight weeks of age. The mesonephric duct and the intestine empty into the cloaca, and the developing bladder also is joined to it. A complicated pattern of growth in the cloacal area occurs as development proceeds, and by referring to the accompanying diagram of the cloacal changes in the male it can be seen that the ureter is "split off" from the mesonephric duct and that the cloaca is partitioned into two regions. One region, which becomes the *urethra,* receives the mesonephric duct and the ureter. The bladder likewise empties through this portion. The second region receives only the intestine. This region becomes the *rectum* and has a separate opening to the outside. The situation in the female is somewhat more complicated, since the oviducts, which also open into the cloaca, continue to grow; and when they fuse to form the uterus, they also acquire a separate opening to the exterior through the vagina. The foregoing is only a superficial account of the development of the reproductive system in the human being. It is intended primarily to explain the fate of the cloaca, which is such a prominent anatomical feature of most vertebrates. These brief factual statements perhaps will suffice, and those who are interested in embryogenisis will be able to find detailed accounts of the events of urogenital development in textbooks of embryology.

Nervous coordination

The human nervous system is the most elaborate and the most efficient communication system which has developed in the animal kingdom. The nerve cells number in the billions, perhaps even in the trillions; the speed of transmission of impulses often exceeds 100 yards per second; and an intricate assortment of special receptors is present to inform the body of environmental conditions. The receptors range from simple, tactile sensory structures in the skin to the magnificent image-forming and colorsensitive eyes. The preeminence of the human nervous system as a complex communication system might seem to indicate an unusual structural organization, but the nervous system of man has the same basic structural organization as that of the other vertebrates. The two major divisions—the *central nervous system*, composed of brain and spinal cord, and the *peripheral nervous system*, consisting of cranial and spinal nerves—are comparable to those of the frog (p. 376). Furthermore, the subdivisions of each of these major systems are the same, with only a few minor exceptions.

Central nervous system

The human brain and spinal cord, like those of all the vertebrates, originate from the embryonic neural tube. The tubular nature of the central nervous system is somewhat obscured in the adult, but the *neural canal* can be identified in a section of the spinal cord and can be shown to be continuous with the cavities of the brain—the *brain canals* and the *brain ventricles*. The brain, which is the organ of distinctiion in man, possesses the maximum amount of nervous tissue in the body. The volume of space which it occupies is approximately 1500 cubic centimeters, and the average human brain weighs slightly more than three pounds. This is not the largest brain in the animal kingdom, since the brains of some of the giant mammals exceed it in size. It is in the proportion of the brain to the body size and to the amount of tissue in the spinal cord that the size of the human brain becomes most significant. The brain of man is of a magnitude approximately 50 times that of the spinal cord. This is in sharp contrast to the situation in the frog, in which the brain actually weighs slightly less than the spinal cord (p. 375).

A superficial examination of a human brain might suggest that it is composed almost entirely of *cerebrum* (Figure 18.22). A closer examination, however, will disclose that the cerebrum has grown dorsally and posteriorly to hide almost completely the other parts of the brain. Actually, only the ventral part of the human cerebrum corresponds to the frog cerebrum; but other regions of the two brains—namely, diencephalon, mid-brain, cerebellum, and medulla oblongata—are more nearly alike.

The cerebrum consists of right and left halves, or *hemispheres*, each of which contains a cavity. These cavities are designated as the *first* and *second ventricles* of the brain. The second region of the brain, the *diencephalon*, is represented in man by the *thalamus* and the *hypothalamus*. The dorsally located *pineal gland* and the ventrally situated *pituitary gland* are attached to this region, as in the frog, and serve as excellent landmarks. The *third ventricle* of the brain is in the thalamus.

The *mid-brain*, or optic lobe, is posterior to the thalamus and is characterized by the presence of four rounded structures, the *lateral geniculate bodies*, on its dorsal side. These are the primary visual centers. Only a small *canal* is present in the mid-brain, and this cavity is not considered a ventricle.

The remaining regions of the brain have undergone some important alterations. The *cerebellum*, which in man is second only to the cerebrum in size, is a tripartite body with a central mass in addition to right and left hemispheres. It is actually a portion of what was *embryonic hind-brain* and, therefore, developed from the same embryonic region as the medulla oblongata, which is the most posterior part of the human brain. Directly below the cerebellum is a broad transverse band which carries many nerve fibers from one hemisphere to the other; this region, because it serves to "bridge" these areas of the brain, is called the *pons*. The pons may be considered to be either a separate part of the brain or to be the anterior region of the *medulla oblongata*. The medulla is continuous with the spinal cord and has associated with it two nerves, the *hypoglossal* and the *spinal accessory*, which were not found in the frog. These nerves probably represent an incorporation of the anterior part of the spinal cord with the medulla in man. The *fourth ventricle* of the brain is located in the medulla. This ventricle has a thin but very vascular roof which secretes a considerable portion of the cerebrospinal fluid found in the cavities of the central nervous system. The walls of the other ventricles also secrete some cerebrospinal fluid.

The *spinal cord* is the remaining part of the central nervous system. Associated with the spinal cord are the *dorsal sensory ganglia* and the ganglia of the *autonomic nervous system;* and these, as well as the structure of the cord itself, are strikingly similar to those of other vertebrates. These features will be discussed in connection with the peripheral nervous system.

The brain and spinal cord are sheathed in three layers of connective tissue known as the *meninges*. The outermost of these, the *dura mater,* lines the skull and the vertebral spaces through which the cord runs; the innermost layer, the *pia mater,* is adjacent to the surface of the brain and cord; and the third layer, the *arachnoid,* lies between the other two. Cerebrospinal fluid is secreted into the cavities of the meninges, and the brain and spinal cord thus are provided with a fluid cushion. This is an important protective device against shock and even against the ordinary movements of the body. Incidentally, an infection of any of these layers of connective tissue about the central nervous system may result in the serious disease, *meningitis*.

As we might anticipate, the functions of the several regions of the human brain and of the brains of other mammals have been the subject of intensive investigation. Extensive experimentation has been performed on laboratory mammals, and limited experimentation has been possible even on human beings. It is fortunate, in this connection, that the data from both direct and indirect observations on various mammals and on man correlate so well that we are able to develop a reasonably clear idea of human brain functions.

It is apparent that certain nerve centers, such as the cerebellum, are concerned primarily with the coordination of body activities of a reflex nature. Actions are not initiated in these area but are only regulated, although such regulation may be very complex. The surface, or *cortex*, of the cerebrum, on the other hand, is an association area and can initiate actions. The cerebrum controls *learned behavior;* it is the center of *consciousness,* of *memory,* and of *intelligence.* This is in contrast to the control of reflex actions which is exercised by the other parts of the brain. A very brief account of the functions of the brain regions will serve to illustrate these distinctions. The discussion will begin with that part of the brain most like the spinal cord, the medulla oblongata, and will conclude with the part of the brain least like the cord, the cerebrum.

The medulla is the major pathway from the spinal cord to the brain. The two hemispheres of the cerebrum are connected by nerve fibers in the pons at the anterior end of the medulla. We noted earlier (p. 426) that in the medulla there is a *respiratory center* which influences breathing. Also present are a *cardio-inhibitory center,* a *vomiting center,* a *vasomotor center,* and a center concerned with *visceral reflexes,* such as the emptying of the bladder. The medulla obviously has important regulatory functions, but it does not exert these controls independently of the rest of the nervous system. Its activities, in turn, are regulated by the hypothalamus and even by the cerebral cortex.

The cerebellum can be characterized as that portion of the brain most concerned with *muscle sense* and with muscular coordination. The cerebellum is responsible for the preciseness of muscle contraction and the resultant coordinated movements of parts of the body. Damage to the cerebellum does not prevent muscle contraction or body movements, but the movements of the body become jerky, exaggerated, and inept. Important messages (impulses) reach the cerebellum from the semicircular canals of the ear, and since these canals are the major balancing organs in man, damage to the cerebellum may disturb body equilibrium.

The mid-brain is of relatively little importance in man and is proportionally smaller than in other vertebrates. This region of the brain is of great significance in the lower vertebrates because nerve fibers from the eyes terminate in it and it serves as a visual center. In the human being, however, the thalamus and the cerebrum have assumed much of the function of interpreting visual impulses, and the mid-brain has retained only the function of regulating optic and auditory reflexes. The most prominent structural feature of the mid-brain is the presence of four rounded bodies, the *corpora quadrigemina:* the anterior two are intermediate centers for visual reflexes, and the posterior two participate in auditory reflexes.

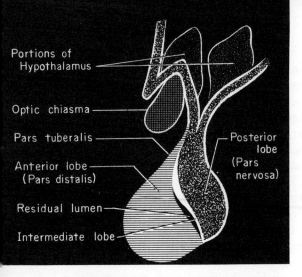

Portions of
Hypothalamus

Optic chiasma

Pars tuberalis

Anterior lobe
(Pars distalis)

Residual lumen

Intermediate lobe

Posterior
lobe
(Pars
nervosa)

Figure 19.19. Hypothalamus and pituitary. The anterior and posterior lobes of the pituitary are complex endocrine glands, but they are partially regulated in their activity by the hypothalamus (p. 446). The intimate structural relationship between the hypothalamus and the pituitary is illustrated in this diagram.

The great importance of the thalamus (diencephelon) as a coordinating center in the brain has become increasingly apparent in recent years. All the major nerve tracts pass through this region of the brain; and in addition, there are special centers which are concerned with some of the most significant physiological activities of the body. The fibers from the retina pass to the thalamus, from where the impulses are directed to the occipital area of the cerebral cortex; likewise, nerve fibers from the ear extend to the thalamus, and auditory impulses are shunted from it to the temporal region of the cerebrum.

The thumb-size lower portion of the thalamus, the hypothalamus, has been shown to be a most important regulatory center. It exerts a very important control over temperature regulation in the body. Various body activities leading to heat production or heat loss are stimulated as a result of changes in the temperature of the blood passing through the hypothalamus. The loss of water or the retention of water in the body is regulated by hypothalamic secretions released in response to variations in the salt or the fluid content of the blood which bathes the cells of the hypothalamus. In some manner not clearly understood at present, the hypothalamus can exert a strong influence on fat and carbohydrate metabolism. Moreover, by a process still undetermined, the emotional state of an individual also is affected by the hypothalamus. It is known that when extensive accidental damage to the cerebral cortex has occurred, slight annoyances which normally would be ignored may produce marked emotional disturbances, even what is called "sham rage." This indicates that the cerebrum normally restrains the hypothalamus. Sleep also may be regulated, in some degree, by the hypothalamus. Finally, the close anatomical association of the hypothalamus with the pituitary gland makes it possible for pituitary activity to be influenced by impulses, and even by chemical substances, from the hypothalamus. This includes the regulation of activity of both the anterior and the posterior lobes of the pituitary.

Several distinctive traits of the cerebrum, such as its large size, its function in memory and intelligence, and its pre-eminence as an association area have

been suggested previously.   We should now stress certain additional characteristics.   The surfaces of the two halves of the human cerebrum, the *cerebral
hemispheres*, are very much folded and furrowed, and this folding considerably
increases the surface area of the cerebrum.   It is significant also that large numbers of nerve cell bodies are present in the surface part of the cerebrum.   These
cells constitute the *cortex*, or *gray matter*, of the brain and are as many as six
cell layers in thickness.   Because the cells simulate a "blanket" for the brain,
this area is referred to as the *pallium;* and since this is a "new" structural feature, it is designated more precisely as the *neopallium*.   The *white matter* of the
cerebrum is internal to the gray matter.   It is composed of an intricate network
of nerve fibers which not only join the two cerebral hemispheres but intercon-
nect all parts of the brain and spinal cord.   The massive fibrous connection
between the two halves of the cerebrum is the *corpus callosum*.

Many attempts have been made to localize functions in restricted areas of
the brain.   The folds of the cerebrum, technically known as *gyri* (singular,
gyrus), provide convenient landmarks for such localization, but with a few important exceptions, the cerebrum appears to act as a unit.   The studies involving
the localization of functions in the cerebrum have been aided by the fact that
there are no pain receptors present in the cerebrum, and direct stimulation of
this brain area, therefore, is not complicated by pain.   Furthermore, studies of
individuals who have suffered brain damage from injury or disease have provided data which can be correlated with the experimental observations made
on normal persons.   A few of the most obvious discoveries are summarized in
the following account.

The *olfactory area* on the anteroventral side of the cerebrum is homologous
with the olfactory lobe of the frog and is associated with the perception of
smell.   This region may be thought of as the most primitive part of the cerebrum.   The back of the brain, the *occipital lobe*, is the *visual center* in man, and
visual impulses are relayed from the mid-brain to this area.   Direct stimulation
of the occipital lobe may cause a sensation of light, as when one "sees stars"
after a blow on the head.   The *temporal lobes* of the brain are the areas concerned with the reception of *sounds*, and they too may be stimulated directly,
as when a person's "ears ring" after he is struck on the side of the head.   It
should be noted that the sensations of sight and sound are perceived in regions
of the neopallium which are either not present or poorly developed in other
vertebrates.

Considerable study has been devoted to the region of the cerebrum which is
marked by a deep furrow, the *fissure of Rolando*.   This furrow starts from the
top of each hemisphere at about the middle and extends laterally.   The fold
(precentral gyrus) immediately in front of the fissure is the *motor area* for the
body, and the fold in back of the fissure (postcentral gyrus) is the *sensory area*
for the body.   An interesting reversal and inversion exists in the folds bordering
the fissure of Rolando.   The right side of the cerebrum is concerned with the
sensory and motor impulses for the left side of the body; and the left side of the

cerebrum with those impulses for the right side of the body.   The areas also are arranged in a linear fashion along the fissure, the points for each motor sub-division being parallel with the corresponding sensory subdivision.   However, the areas are inverted—that is, the motor and sensory divisions for the toes and feet are located at the top of the cerebrum, followed successively by those for the leg, thigh, arm, hand, face, tongue, and jaw as the folds are followed later-ally.   These arrangements are apparent in the accompanying diagram.

It should be evident from the preceding account that there are large areas of the human cerebrum in which specific functions, either motor or sensory, have not been precisely delimited.   These are very extensive in the human being but should not be thought of as blank or nonunctioning regions, because they actually are *association,* or *projection, areas.*   There is little doubt that these as-sociation areas are the domain of *intelligence, reasoning,* and *learning.*   These are the regions which integrate the multitude of impulses that incessantly reach the brain.   Damage to association areas from injury or disease has enabled us to understand some of the functioning of these areas.   Injury to a specific area in the left cerebral hemisphere, for example, may result in the disturbance of speech known as *aphasia,* a disorder in which the individual can recognize words but may not be able to speak them.

The white matter of the brain provides an elaborate series of interconnec-tions with the entire nervous system.   All areas of the right hemisphere of the cerebrum are in constant communication by way of the nerve fibers of the white matter and are also joined with all regions of the left hemisphere, primarily through the corpus callosum.   Motor instructions are sent from the cerebrum to all parts of the brain and spinal cord over special tracts of nerve fibers.   Espe-cially important are those interconnections with the thalamus and the cere-bellum.   Sensory information is also being received constantly by the cerebrum over nerve fiber tracts from all parts of the body.

Many facets of the operation of this fantastically elaborate human central nervous system are as yet poorly understood.   The factors responsible for sleep, for example, are almost unknown.   Modern society has become increasingly aware of the problem of neuroses and psychoses.   When these disorders are a result of brain damage, they may be relatively easy to understand; but when they occur as a by-product of anxiety, fear, inner conflict, or other emotional disturbances, they are much more difficult to analyze and to correct.   The real-ization that physical disorders in remote parts of the body may arise from abnormal mental states has contributed to the growing importance of the field of psychosomatic medicine in dealing with mind-body relationships in modern medical practice.

Peripheral nervous system

The central nervous system is dependent on the bundles of nerve fibers comprising the *cranial* and *spinal nerves* for its connection with the receptors and effectors of the body.   Associated with certain of the cranial nerves and

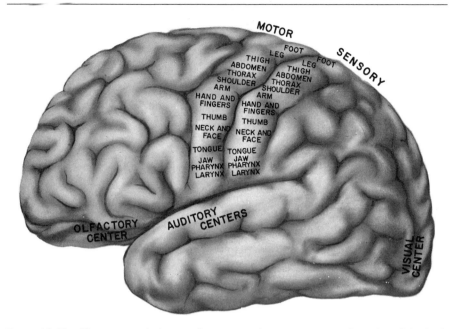

Figure 19.20. The centers which control sensory and motor activities of regions of the body can be mapped on the surface of the cerebrum. This drawing of the left-hand side of the brain shows the relationship of the centers to the fissure of Rolando and other areas of the brain. A knowledge of the function of parts of the brain of other vertebrates, such as the frog, helps us to understand the location of the olfactory, auditory, and visual centers in man.

with all the spinal nerves are aggregations of nerve cell bodies, the *ganglia*. Some of these ganglia are sensory and others are motor in function. The latter are especially important as a part of the autonomic nervous system (p. 378) The cranial and spinal nerves and their associated ganglia constitute the *peripheral nervous system*.

The basic relationships which exist in this portion of the human system are essentially the same as those which we observed in the frog (p. 376). The *spinal reflex*, or *reflex arc*, is the important functional unit in the peripheral nervous system. Again, exactly as in the frog, a stimulus to a receptor will be relayed over a *sensory neuron* through the *dorsal sensory ganglion* to the spinal cord to *synapse* (make connection) with *association neurons* in the gray matter of the cord. These neurons in turn synapse with *motor neurons* in the ventral part of the gray matter of the cord. Impulses are then transmitted over the axons of the motor neuron to the effectors, which respond (see Figure 19.21). In a like manner, the stimulus of a pin prick on the finger will cause muscle contraction which, by pulling the tendons of the finger, will withdraw it from the pin. An action of this kind is a simple reflex and does not require the participation of the brain for successful completion. A message will be delivered to the brain, of course, informing that higher center of the pain and discomfort which has ensued. Additional action could be taken at the command of the cerebrum, with crying, kicking, or other responses being evoked.

Reflexes usually become complicated, involving many regions of the body, and can be modified by participation of the neurons of the cerebrum in the reflex. The famous experiments of the Russian physiologist, Ivan Pavlov, are

HUMAN CRANIAL NERVES		
Nerves	Sensory Function and Origin of Fibers	Motor Function
1—Olfactory*	Smell: epithelium of nose	None
2—Optic†	Sight: retina of eye	None
3—Oculomotor	Muscle sense: muscles of eyeball	Movement of eyeball; constriction of pupil; change of lens shape
4—Trochlear	Muscle sense: muscles of eyeball	Movement of eyeball
5—Trigeminal	Various sense receptors of the skin of face, teeth	Muscles of jaws
6—Abducens	Muscle sense: muscles of eyeball	Movement of eyeball
7—Facial	Taste: taste buds of front of tongue	Facial muscles; salivary glands
8—Acoustic	Hearing, balance: inner ear	None
9—Glossopharyngeal	Taste: taste buds of back of tongue; pharynx	Swallowing muscles; salivary glands (parotid)
10—Vagus	Visceral sensory (lungs, stomach, etc.)	Parasympathetic‡ (heart, stomach, intestine, bladder, etc.)
11—Spinal Accessory	Muscle sense: shoulder muscles	Movement of shoulders
12—Hypoglossal	Muscle sense: muscles of tongue	Movement of tongue

*See page 422.
†See page 422.
‡See autonomic nervous system.

often used to demonstrate a situation of this type. Pavlov was interested in studying what we now call *conditioned reflexes.* This type of reflex can be illustrated by recounting an experiment performed by him.

A bell was rung each time a dog was presented with food, and the rate of the dog's salivary secretion was determined. After a number of trials the bell was rung, but food was not presented. It was discovered that the salivary glands secreted exactly as when food was presented. The dog had become "conditioned" to the ringing of the bell, and the reflex, therefore, proceeded as though the food had been given. Human beings, as a result of learning experiences, have many complicated conditioned reflexes. In fact, it may be stated that most of our reactions are probably in the nature of complex conditioned reflexes rather than of the simple spinal reflex type illustrated by the reaction to pricking the finger.

Autonomic nervous system

An interesting and important subdivision of the peripheral nervous system is the *autonomic nervous system.* Not much is known about the functioning of this part of the nervous system except in mammals, but it is present in other vertebrates (p. 378) and is assumed to perform essentially the same activities as in mammals. The autonomic system of man is somewhat more complex structurally than that of the frog, although the essential features are the same.

The autonomic system consists of nerve fibers which conduct messages to involuntary muscles and to glands in both the superficial and deep areas of the body. The anatomical divisions of the autonomic system are the same as in the frog: the *sympathetic portion,* composed of a complex connected chain of *sympathetic ganglia* on either side of the vertebral column in the thoracic and lumbar regions; and the *parasympathetic portion,* composed of nerve fibers which arise in the cranial and sacral regions of the central nervous system. The most important parasympathetic fibers are to be found in the *vagus nerve.* Nerve fibers from both the sympathetic and parasympathetic divisions extend throughout the body in such a manner as to provide a double innervation to glands and involuntary muscles. More important in a functional sense is the fact that the effects of sympathetic and parasympathetic stimulation are *antagonistic* to each other.

A notable difference exists between the nerve fiber arrangements involved in a simple spinal reflex and those concerned with a reflex in the autonomic system. The motor neuron in a spinal reflex transmits impulses from the cord directly to the structure which is to respond—for example, a voluntary muscle. Impulses traveling over the autonomic system, however, will be carried by two neurons: the axon of the *first neuron,* arising in the spinal cord, will encounter a ganglion somewhere in the autonomic system, where the impulse will be transferred to a *second neuron,* which will convey the message to the involuntary muscle or gland concerned. Since the first neuron transmits the impulse *to* the

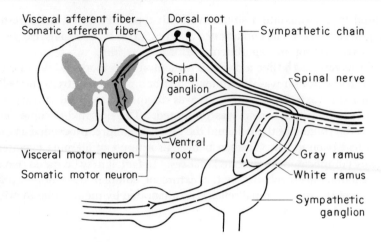

Figure 19.21.   The ganglia and nerve-fiber arrangement in a small section of the autonomic nervous system are shown above.   The relation of the ventral ganglia to the entire system is shown in Figure 19.22.

ganglion, it is designated as the *preganglionic neuron*.   The second, which carries the impulse *from* the ganglion, is called the *postganglionic neuron*.   Generally, the ganglia of the sympathetic system are near the cord, hence the preganglionic neurons are short and the postganglionic neurons are long.   The reverse is true of the parasympathic division in which the ganglia often are on or near the structure to be stimulated; therefore, the preganglionic neurons of the parasympathetic system are long and the postganglionic neurons are short.   An examination of the diagram of the autonomic nervous system (Figure 19.22) will illustrate these differences.

It is important to realize that the autonomic nervous system is not a separate coordinating system but that it operates in cooperation with the central nervous system and the spinal ganglia.   The autonomic system is concerned only with involuntary action—a point which will acquire greater significance when the functions of this division are reviewed.   Stimulation of the *sympathetic* portion of the autonomic system produces an increase in heart rate, blood flow, dilation of the pupil of the eye, elevation of blood sugar level, and an increased blood flow to skeletal muscles and brain.   The blood supply to the digestive system and the contraction of the muscles of the alimentary canal are decreased. Conversely, a stimulation of the *parasympathetic* division produces opposite effects; for example, heart rate decreases and the pupil of the eye contracts. The two divisions, therefore, act antagonistically to each other, as we noted previously.

The importance of the autonomic nervous system appears to be that it facilitates the ability of the organism to make "emergency" responses to a variety of stimuli.   The autonomic nervous system has been removed surgically from several different mammals and all behave essentially in a normal fashion.   They are less efficient, however, in adjusting to adverse situations.   Heart rate, temperature regulation, and blood sugar levels, for instance, do not adjust quickly to the body needs of animals in which the autonomic nervous system has been removed.

It has been especially interesting to discover that the nerve fibers of the autonomic nervous system produce their effects through the release of chemical substances (hormones) at their endings.   The parasympathetic fibers release *acetylcholine*, which was first called *vagus substance* by Otto Loewi, who showed it to be present when the vagus nerve was stimulated.   The sympathetic fibers secrete *epinephrine* (adrenalin) and *norepinephrine*.   These are also secreted by the medulla of the adrenal gland.   The secretions of the sympathetic fibers originally were called *sympathin* by Cannon, who first demonstrated their presence.

Figure 19.22.   The autonomic nervous system.   The sympathetic nerves are shown as solid lines; the parasympathetic nerves, as dotted lines.   Sympathetic ganglia are shown as the circles just to the right of the spinal cord; parasympathetic ganglia are located on the organs they innervate.

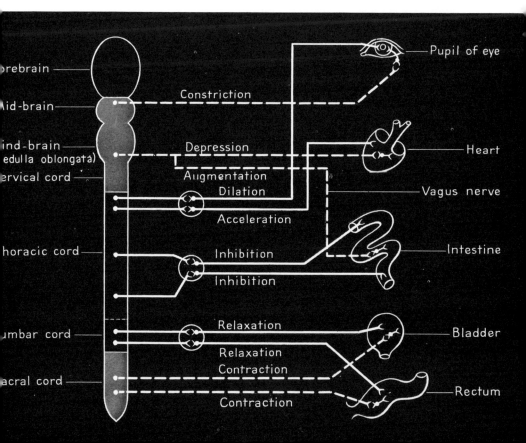

Sense perception

The customary designation of the "five senses" is not adequate to describe sense perception, or the ability of man to interpret the stimuli which affect him. The basic five senses—*touch, taste, smell, sight,* and *hearing*—are supplemented in man by the capacity for recognizing *pressure, temperature, pain, hunger, thirst,* and *muscle sense,* or *tension.* Even sight is facilitated, since human beings are capable of recognizing a wide range of colors as well as objects. It is necessary, because of these sensory complexities, to classify in some manner the receptors which interpret the stimuli.

Sense receptors and special-sense organs

It is a comon procedure to designate the receptors which provide an awareness of the immediate external environment as the *surface receptors,* or *exteroceptors,* and the receptors which supply information from the deep tissues of the body as the *proprioceptors.* There are obvious difficulties with this simplified classification since, for example, the receptors in the lining of the digestive tract are *surface receptors,* but they provide information about internal conditions. These, therefore, usually are referred to as *interoceptors.*

Exteroceptors provide the body with sensations relative to *contact* and *distance,* and their information is localized, distinct and, typically, is of a conscious nature. The contact receptors are those for pain, touch, and temperature; whereas the distance receptors, which have their sensations "projected" outside the body, are those of sight, hearing, and smell. Although structurally taste must be considered as interoceptive with contact receptors, it is difficult to classify functionally since taste sensations are also projected. Taste can be considered, therefore, as a distance receptor.

The proprioceptors, in contrast to the exteroceptors, provide the body with less distinct sensations, generally of an unconscious nature. These are important receptors, however, because the reactions evoked as a result of their stimulation involve large numbers of muscles and important internal changes.

SIMPLE RECEPTORS • The majority of sensations received in the skin and deep tissues of the body are interpreted by minute receptors composed of small clumps of specialized cells associated with nerve fibrils. It appears, however, that *pain* is not associated with any specific type of receptor but can be produced by a variety of stimuli which stimulate directly the free endings of sensory nerves and the exteroceptors in general. It also is difficult to assign definite functions to most of the histological structures which have been suggested as being specialized receptors. *Neuromuscular spindles* are present in skeletal muscle, especially at the junction of tendons with muscles. These contain both nerve and muscle fibers enclosed in a connective tissue sheath. The function of the neuromuscular spindles definitely is associated with the sensations generally referred to as *muscle sense,* which inform the body concerning the variation in tension of muscles or tendons. Normal muscle coordination and balance depend on these receptors. *Nerve baskets* composed of coils of nerve fibers around the bases, or follicles, of hairs provide an excellent means of interpreting touch.   It is presumed that special bodies known as *Meissner's corpuscles* and *Merkel's discs* also are touch receptors, but the evidence is not conclusive.   Scattered through the loose connective tissue of the body and especially in the deeper layers of the skin are the relatively large *Pacinian corpuscles*, which appear to be pressure receptors.   Finally, certain bodies in the skin, known as *Krause's end-bulbs*, are reported to be cold receptors; and others, *Ruffini's endings*, are described as warm receptors.   These, however, are not positively known to be associated with temperature reception.

Taste receptors

The receptors for the chemical sensations of taste and smell are better known and understood than are those for the sensations just described.   Taste buds

Figure 19.23.   Receptors in skin.   The skin possesses remarkably diverse receptors, which make it an excellent sense organ.   The more important skin receptors are shown below.   Although they are sketched diagrammatically, they illustrate the range of variation that exists.

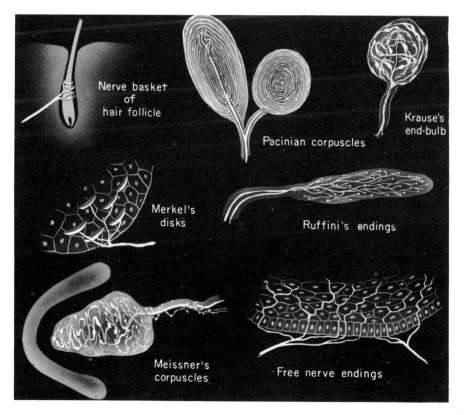

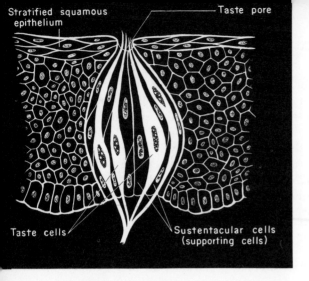

Stratified squamous epithelium

Taste pore

Taste cells

Sustentacular cells (supporting cells)

Figure 19.24. The taste buds, in common with the olfactory epithelium, are relatively simple, being composed of sensory, or taste, cells and sustentacular, or supporting, cells. Structurally, we have no clue as yet concerning the manner by which the sensory cells detect the difference in taste of various substances.

are located chiefly on the *papillae*, small elevations on the upper surface of the tongue; but these are also present in small numbers on the soft palate, cheeks, and pharynx. The taste buds are flask-shaped and are composed of two cell types: the *supporting cells*, and the *taste cells*. The latter are elongated, with sensory hairlike processes directed toward the surface of the papilla, and are joined at their base to the sensory neurons. The "neck" of the flask-shaped taste bud has a small pore which opens onto the surface of the papilla and is connected internally with a small cavity. Taste buds are specific in their sensitivity to stimuli, but a papilla may contain more than one type of taste bud. The distribution of the buds in the tongue follows a regular pattern: the buds which are receptors for *salty* are located at the tip and anterolateral margins; the receptors for *sour* (or acid) are on the lateral edges; the receptors for *sweet* overlap with those for salty on the tip of the tongue; and finally, the receptors for *bitter* are at the base of the tongue. In spite of the differences in the taste buds with respect to their ability to distinguish between salty, sweet, sour, and bitter, it has not been possible to distinguish structural differences in the taste buds.

Considerable individual variation exists in the ability to taste. A few individuals are actually "taste-blind," others are unable to taste certain substances, and still other persons can taste a material only when it is in a relatively high concentration. The ability to taste the chemical PTC (phenylthiocarbamide) provides an interesting illustration of some of the variations which we can observe. Some people can detect PTC when it is present in amounts as low as 0.000005 per cent, whereas many other persons require PTC at a concentration of 0.1 per cent before it can be tasted. A few people actually are nontasters. It has been demonstrated that this ability to taste PTC is a trait which is inherited in a Mendelian fashion (Chapter 20).

The taste buds cease to respond to a given substance after prolonged stimulation. The ability to taste other materials, however, may be augmented simultaneously. In addition, certain substances may mask the taste of others. The complexity of the possible taste combinations in conjunction with individual taste variations accounts for the fact that a food which may be a gustatory delight to one person may be insipid or even distasteful to another. The most important single factor which modifies taste responses is the fact that much of what we commonly consider to be taste actually is smell. Everyone probably has observed that while suffering from a head cold, food tastes "flat," or insipid. A classic experiment frequently used in beginning biology classes illustrates this situation very well. A blindfolded subject who has his nostrils blocked with cotton, or by a clamp, is given a bite of apple and a bite of onion, and is unable to taste a difference between the two foods under these conditions.

Smell, or olfactory, receptors

We are accustomed to think of man's olfactory sense as being poorly developed. This actually is not the case, since human beings are able to detect a wide variety of odors in dilute concentration. Some mammals do exceed man in their ability to smell, but, as we noted previously, man is exceeded by other animals in many of his attributes. The human olfactory receptors are located in the nasal epithelium on the roof of the nasal cavity and on each side of the nasal septum. The total area of these receptors is not large, averaging about 500 square millimeters, or less than one square inch, of surface. The olfactory epithelium contains three types of cells: the long, slender *supporting cells;* the small, rounded *basal cells;* and the bipolar *olfactory cells.* The olfactory cells are broad on the surface, and have six or eight short cilia which project into the nasal cavity. At their base the cells are drawn out to a slender axon which makes synaptic connection with the nerve cells of the olfactory bulb. The olfactory cells, therefore, are modified nerve cells which both receive the olfactory stimuli and relay impulses to the olfactory bulb.

Numerous attempts have been made to classify odors into types, but these

Figure 19.25. The olfactory epithelium is a relatively simple sensory device insofar as structure is concerned. The complex functioning of the olfactory cells in the interpretation of odors, however, is very poorly understood.

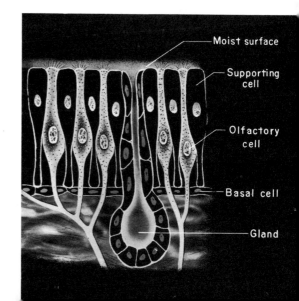

Moist surface

Supporting cell

Olfactory cell

Basal cell

Gland

classifications have not withstood experimental analysis. The ability of the olfactory cells to detect minute quantities of material, however, is remarkable. Many substances can be detected when present in amounts as low as one part in several billion. Certain chemicals (such as musk, common in perfume) are noteworthy in this regard. Although it is not clear how the olfactory receptors distinguish between various odors, it is known that substances must be in solution on the surface of the olfactory cells in order to be smelled. The more volatile the substance, the easier it is to smell it. The olfactory epithelium, like the taste buds, may lose the ability to respond to stimulating substances after prolonged contact. This explains why a strong or pungent odor which at first is most unpleasant will seem to fade and will be unnoticed after a short period of exposure to it.

Visual receptors

Human eyes embody in their structure and function all the main advancements which are present in the eyes of other vertebrates. They are, of course, *light-sensitive* and *image-forming;* and, even more impressive, they are able to *perceive color* over a wide range from red to violet in the spectrum. An additional faculty possessed by human eyes is rare among vertebrates: namely, the two eyes cooperate to provide *three-dimensional,* or *stereoscopic, vision.* It is frequently stated that many of the features of the human eye are comparable to those of a camera. There is, for example, a *lens system,* the cornea and the crystalline lens, which focuses the light rays on a *photorecptive area,* the retina; and an adjustable *diaphragem,* the iris, which regulates the amount of light that can enter the eye and fall upon the retina. The eye in its function, however, is superior to any camera, especially in its sharpness of focus and its color reception. The human eye is undoubtedly the most magnificent sensory structure in the animal kingdom, and only the human ear approaches its excellence as a sense organ.

Eye structure and function

The eye is almost spherical in shape and in an adult averages approximately one inch in diameter. The wall of the eye is composed of three layers which are different in structure and in function. The outermost layer is a tough, fibrous tunic called the *sclera,* which is opaque except over the front of the eye, where it is transparent; and in this region it constitutes the *cornea.* The sclera is chiefly responsible for the maintenance of the shape of the eyeball. The second layer of the eye is the *choroid coat.* This is a vascular membrane over most of its extent, and anteriorly it forms the *ciliary body* and the curtainlike *iris.* The innermost of the three tunics of the eye is the photosensitive *retina.* This layer adheres to the choroid coat and is pigmented on its outer surface. Portions of the retina extend over the inner surface of the ciliary body and the iris, but these areas are not photosensitive.

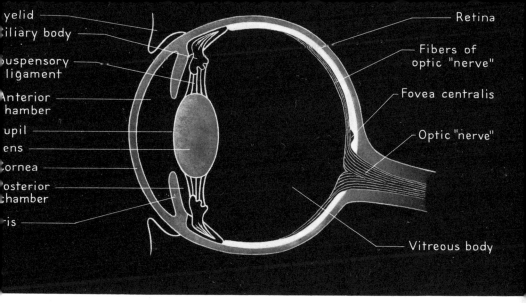

Eyelid
Ciliary body
Suspensory ligament
Anterior chamber
Pupil
Lens
Cornea
Posterior chamber
Iris

Retina
Fibers of optic "nerve"
Fovea centralis
Optic "nerve"
Vitreous body

Figure 19.26. This section drawing shows the structures of the human eye and indicates their relationships. Compare this drawing with that of the complex eye of the squid (Figure 14.13) and the eye of the frog (Figure 18.11).

A prominent feature within the eyeball is the *crystalline lens,* which is a transparent sphere suspended in a circular *ciliary ligament* extending from the ciliary body. The lens is placed directly posterior to the opening in the iris, the *pupil.* The positioning of the iris, lens, and ciliary body creates three distinct chambers within the eye. The cavity between the cornea and the iris is the *anterior chamber;* the small space bordered by the iris, the ciliary ligament, and the lens is the *posterior chamber;* and the largest eye cavity, which is between the lens and the ciliary ligament posterior to the wall of the eye, is the *vitreal chamber.* The anterior and posterior chambers are filled with *aqueous humor,* a watery substance similar chemically to cerebrospinal fluid. The vitreal chamber, however, is filled with *vitreous humor,* a thick semifluid substance sometimes called the *vitreous body.* The pressure of the aqueous and vitreous humors within the eye aids the sclera in maintaining the shape of the eyeball. The relationships between the cornea, lens, aqueous humor, and vitreous humor are the determining factors in the focusing of the light rays on the retina, and therefore, of the individual's ability to see objects clearly. The significance of these relationships can be illustrated by describing the path followed by a light ray from the outside through the eye to the retina.

A ray of light entering the eye obliquely from an external object passes through the transparent cornea and is influenced in its direction by two factors: the convex curvature of the cornea and the density of the cornea. An oblique ray of light is deflected toward the perpendicular by the curvature of the cornea (that is, it is bent toward the center of the eye). The bending produced by the convex surface of the cornea is supplemented by the effect of the density of the cornea, because oblique rays of light passing from a medium of lesser density (air) to one of greater density (cornea) are deflected toward the perpendicular. The aqueous humor has the same bending effect as the cornea; and the two, therefore, can be considered as a single lens system producing the initial focusing of the light rays that enter the eye. This system accounts for two thirds of the deflection of light rays which occurs. The crystalline lens is the third element in deflection of light, the effect of the vitreous humor being negligible in focusing. The cornea and the aqueous humor function as a fixed-focus lens; but since the curvature of the crystalline lens can be changed, its focusing power can be altered. This point will be discussed in greater detail when certain abnormalities of vision are considered.

Two properties of the stimuli reaching the retina should be mentioned before proceeding with the discussion of retinal function: (1) the image produced on the retina is *smaller than the object being viewed;* and (2) *the retinal image is an inverted one.* Obviously, we do not "see" either miniature or inverted objects, and the reason that we do not is because of two phenomena: *righting* and *projecting.* The "righting" of the objects is accomplished through psychological adjustment during infancy and childhood. Likewise, we learn to "project" the image of the object—that is, to locate the object external to the body and at a distance from the eye. Projecting occurs through our past association of the relative positions of various objects, and by the use of other receptors such as touch for establishing their exact locations.

The two phenomena of righting and projecting can be illustrated rather simply. If a person with normal vision is fitted with a pair of special lenses that will reverse the rays of light entering the eye, any object viewed through these lenses will appear at first to be reversed. If the person continues to wear such lenses, however, a psychological adjustment will be made, and the objects will once more be seen in their "normal" positions. If the lenses are removed following this new adjustment, the eyes once more present a "topsy-turvy" world to the person. This condition persists until a new psychological readjustment has been made.

Projection can be demonstrated even more simply. If one presses the index finger lightly against the left eyeball at the lower left corner of the closed eye, a dark spot surrounded by a bright ring will be observed at the nasal side of the eye. When the eye is opened slowly, the ring-spot will appear to float in

Figure 19.27. Blind-spot demonstration. Close your left eye and hold this book so that the illustration is about six inches in front of your right eye; then look steadily at the cross. Move the book slowly toward your eye until the circle disappears. When this happens, the image of the circle has fallen on the entrance of the optic nerve, in which rods and cones are absent and which is therefore insensitive to light.

space over the bridge of the nose. This occurs because we have learned to associate stimulation of the retina at the lower left corner with the presence of objects in the region of the bridge of the nose; accordingly, we "project" an image to that position when we merely stimulate the retina by finger pressure.

It should be apparent from this brief account, and by reference to the illustration of the human eye (Figure 18.11), that the cornea and lens focus the light rays on the retina. It is the function of the retina, therefore, to interpret the stimuli provided by these light rays and transform the messages into a visual image. This interpretation is accomplished by special receptor cells, the *rods* and the *cones*, which are found only in the retina. There are approximately 13,000,000 rods and 7,000,000 cones in a normal retina. A quirk of embryonic development has placed these receptors at the back of the retina, adjacent to the pigment layer. The association neurons and the nerve fibrils, therefore, lie between the rods and cones and the lens. Light rays must pass through several layers of nerve cells and nerve fibrils before reaching the receptor cells. This is merely one more example showing that nature does not always build in the most efficient or logical manner. The nerve fibrils of the retina converge at the back of the eye to form the optic nerve and pass from the eye at that point. This area has no rods and cones, which results in a *blind spot* on the retina. Again by psychological adjustment we "fill in" this area when we project, and hence we observe no blank area before our eyes. The presence of the blind spot, however, can be demonstrated easily with the illustration below.

The rods and cones are not uniformly distributed over the retina. The cones are relatively most numerous in the exact center of the retina in a small depressed region, the *fovea;* whereas the rods are more abundant in the remainder of the retina. The cones are sensitive to bright light and to color. The rods, on the other hand, are color-blind, but they are very sensitive to small amounts of light. The fact that rods are much more receptive to dim light than are the cones explains an interesting phenomenon in night vision. An object, for example, can be seen more clearly at night if one looks slightly to one side rather than directly at it. The concentration of the cones in the fovea provides the sharpest vision in daylight or under bright lighting conditions and is the point of maximum reception on the retina.

The similarity of the photosensitive retina to a light-sensitive photographic film suggests that chemical reactions initiated by light falling on the retina (photochemical reactions) might provide the stimuli for the visual impulses. Investigations of retinal function, therefore, have been concerned not only with the physical connections between the receptor cells and the brain, but also with the chemical changes which can be correlated with vision.

The structural relationship of the retinal cells is complex, but in its simplest form this consists of the transmission of impulses from the deep-lying *rods and cones* to the *bipolar association cells,* and from these to the *ganglion cells* in the retina adjacent to the vitreal cavity. Both the bipolar and the ganglion cells, however, may be interconnected to a large number of other cells, with the

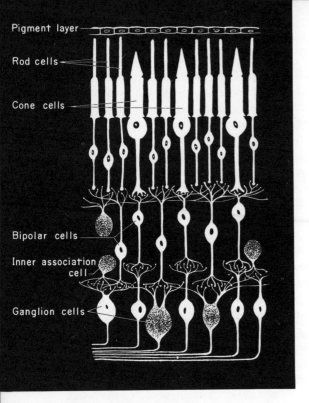

Pigment layer

Rod cells

Cone cells

Bipolar cells

Inner association cell

Ganglion cells

Figure 19.28. This diagrammatic drawing shows the retinal cells and indicates their structural design and relationships.

result that they can relay impulses from many photoreceptors. The fibrils from the ganglion cells leave the retina and join to become the optic "nerve."

The studies of G. N. Wald on the photochemical reactions in the retina have been especially valuable for understanding the generating of visual impulses. Wald and many others have demonstrated that several *visual pigments* closely related chemically to vitamin A_1 are present in the retina of the higher vertebrates. Notable among these pigments is *visual purple*, or *rhodopsin*, which is responsible for vision in reduced light in human beings. The exposure of visual purple to light (either in the eye or in solution) bleaches the pigment, and the chemical changes which occur during this bleaching process have been studied in detail. The intermediate chemical substances have been identified, and it has been demonstrated that vitamin A_1 is one of the by-products. Visual purple will be resynthesized when the retina is subjected to darkness, and vitamin A_1 is essential for this resynthesis. Any person who lacks adequate amounts of vitamin A_1 in the diet, therefore, will not be able to produce normal quantities of visual purple and will suffer from night blindness. Only a minute amount of light is needed to disintegrate visual purple, and less than a dozen rods need to be stimulated to elicit a visual response. The amount of light which can be detected by an eye which has been dark-adapted for at least 30 minutes is approximately 0.00000001 per cent of the maximum amount of light which can be observed in a light-adapted eye.

Color perception

The ability of the retina to "see" color is another interesting aspect of human vision. Color can be perceived only in the light-adapted eye, and color detection definitely is a function of the cones, since the rods are color blind. It is possible to map the retina with respect to its ability to detect color in its various regions, and such studies have demonstrated that there are four restricted areas of the retina in which the primary colors are perceived. These areas are in a concentric arrangement about the fovea. The innermost, the *green area*, perceives the colors red, green, and blue; next to it is the *red area*, which perceives red and blue; then a third, the *blue area*, which perceives blue and, to a limited extent, yellow; and finally, the outermost region, the *white area*, which encompasses the remainder of the retina and is sensitive only to white light. The cones in the various regions of the retina thus vary in their ability to detect color, and several theories have ben advanced in an attempt to explain this color reception.

The Young-Helmholtz theory assumes the presence of three chemical substances in the cones: one sensitive to red; a second sensitive to green; and a third sensitive to violet. If, for example, red light falls on the cones, the red substance is broken down and a photochemical reaction follows which provides the necessary stimulus for the impulses which will be sent to the brain. According to this theory, black is due to an absence of stimulation, white to the presence of all the colors, and the color variations are a result of the breakdown of different color substances. It is difficult, however, in the Young-Helmholtz theory to account for the fact that the eye can see gray and white in areas of the retina where colors are not seen. Similarly, no adequate explanation is offered for the ability of the eye to see yellow in the blue area of the retina. The several other theories of color vision also are subject to criticism. The fact remains that the normal human eye can see color, but the mind has not as yet devised an adequate explanation for this remarkable phenomenon of vision. It is likely, however, that investigation will produce a satisfactory explanation for it.

Accommodation

It was stated earlier that about one third of the bending, or deflection, of the light rays in the eye is accomplished by the crystalline lens. More important than the amount of bending produced is the ability of the lens to change its shape and, therefore, to vary the degree of deflection of the light rays. As we indicated, the cornea may be considered as a *fixed-focus* lens; the crystalline lens is a *variable-focus* lens. This ability of the lens to change its shape makes it possible for the human eye to see objects clearly as much as 20 miles distant or only 20 centimeters away. The technical designation of this focusing process is *accommodation*.

The mechanical processes in the human eye differ somewhat from those of the frog (p. 357) and of certain other vertebrates. We should recall that the human lens is a transparent, elastic, biconvex sphere which is slightly more curved on its posterior side than on its anterior, and that it is located directly behind the pupil, suspended from the ciliary body by the ciliary ligament. Tension is exerted on the ligament and the lens is slightly flattened when one is looking at distant objects (that is, objects more than 20 feet away). The minimum degree of bending of the light rays occurs at this time. Light rays from objects nearer than 20 feet enter the eye from more oblique angles, and in order to focus such light rays on the retina, they must be deflected, or bent, considerably. The lens, therefore, must have greater curvature. Direct observation and experimentation demonstrates that the following sequence of events occurs during accommodation for near objects: *first,* the ciliary muscle contracts and actually pulls the choroid coat slightly forward; *second,* this decreases the tension on the ciliary ligament; and *third,* the lens released from the pull of the ligament becomes spherical by its own elasticity. The ciliary muscle thus is at rest when the eye is viewing distant objects but is contracting when near objects are being observed.

A second important factor for good vision is the change in position of the two eyes during accommodation. As an object is brought nearer the eyes they *converge;* thus when an object is very near the face, one appears to be looking "down the nose," or "cross-eyed." Conversely, when the eyes are focusing on distant objects the two eyes look straight ahead or even *diverge* slightly. This change in the position of the eyes adds the advantages of stereoscopic vision to those of sharpness of focus through accommodation.

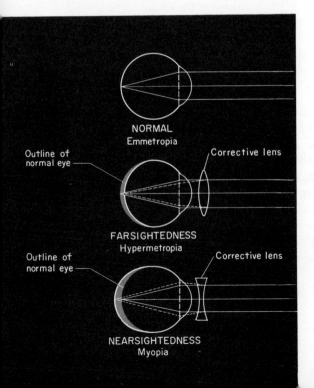

NORMAL
Emmetropia

Outline of
normal eye

Corrective lens

FARSIGHTEDNESS
Hypermetropia

Outline of
normal eye

Corrective lens

NEARSIGHTEDNESS
Myopia

Figure 19.29. Normal, farsighted, and nearsighted eyes. The length of the eyeball may vary in individuals. When the eyeball is longer than normal, light rays will focus in front of the retina, causing nearsightedness (myopia); with shorter than normal, the rays will focus behind the retina and the individual will have farsighted vision (hypermetropia). Light rays can be brought to focus on the retina by means of corrective lenses which cause the rays to diverge or converge before striking the cornea.

Abnormal vision

Three common eye defects—*nearsightedness,* or myopia; *farsightedness,* or hypermetropia; and *unequal focusing of light rays,* or astigmatism—may be analyzed rather simply in terms of the accommodation process. The eyeball of a nearsighted person is elongated in the anterior-posterior axis, and the light rays are brought to focus in front of the retina. Conversely, the eyeball of a farsighted person is too short, and the light rays are not focused on the retina. The theoretical focus of such rays is in back of the retina. The cornea in the astigmatic eye is not curved to the same degree in all planes, with the result that light rays which fall on the irregularly curved portion are not brought into focus on the retina. All three of these conditions result in blurred vision, but each can be corrected by the use of the proper type of lens in front of the eye. Concave lenses, which cause a greater divergence of the light rays before they enter the eye, will correct for myopia; and convex lenses, which cause greater convergence of the light rays, will correct for hypermetropia. Special lenses which will alter the focus for the unequal curvature of the cornea will adjust the eye for astigmatism.

Pathway of visual fibrils

The nerve fibers extend from the retina to the geniculate bodies of the mid-brain (p. 446) and thence to the area striata of the occipital cortex of the cerebrum. The optic "nerve" is composed of nerve fibrils from the ganglion cells of the retina, and since the retina originated from the fore-brain of the embryo, the optic nerve technically is a *brain tract.* The optic tracts cross before reaching the geniculate bodies, creating what is known as the *optic chiasma;* and the distribution of the nerve fibrils in this region is especially important. The fibrils from the temporal half of each retina pass through the chiasma on the same side as their origin and extend to the geniculate bodies on the same side. The fibrils from the nasal half of each retina cross over the chiasma and extend to the geniculate body on the opposite side. The importance of this distribution will be apparent by reference to the accompanying diagram. Light rays from an object at the *left* of the face will fall on the *nasal side* of the retina of the *left eye,* but on the *temporal side* of the retina of the *right eye.* The fibrils from these areas will be seen to terminate in the same region of the brain because of the crossing-over at the chiasma. This assures that although light rays from a single object may fall on different areas of the two retinas, the messages from these areas will terminate in and be interpreted by the same region of the cerebral cortex.

Receptors for audition and equilibrium

There is considerable variation in the ability to "hear," and certain vertebrates exceed man in the reception of high-frequency sounds, as well as in the detection of faint sounds.   The unique ability of human beings to communicate by means of vocal sounds, and the fact that the human voice has a wide range both in tone and volume, demonstrates that although not pre-eminent, the ear of man is an excellent sense organ.   The human ear has also retained its primitive function as a balancing organ and hence is a dual sense organ.   The two functions of audition and equilibrium are so diverse, however, that it is necessary to consider them separately.

Sound: frequency and intensity

Some acquaintance with two characteristics of sound is necessary for our understanding of hearing.   These characteristics are: the *frequency*, or the number of vibrations (cycles) per second; and the *intensity*, or loudness, of the sound waves.   The normal human ear is able to detect sounds in a wide range of vibrations per second (from 20 to 20,000), but the maximum sensitivity is to tones of from 2000 to 5000 vibrations per second.   It is significant that most speech sounds fall in the latter range.   The ability of the ear to distinguish intensity of sound is fantastic.   The range of sensitivity is from a faint whisper to the sound of thunder, or in terms of the comparative measurement used, from one decibel to one trillion decibels.   It has been pointed out by physiologists that the human ear has nearly reached a practical limit of efficiency in sound-

Figure 19.30. Visual pathways. This drawing illustrates the arrangement of the fibers of the optic tracts which make possible the binocular vision of vertebrates. The fibers cross at the optic chiasma, and visual stimuli which fall on different areas of the two eyes may be interpreted by one area of the brain. In this drawing the dark lines illustrate the pathways of stimuli from the retinas to the brain.

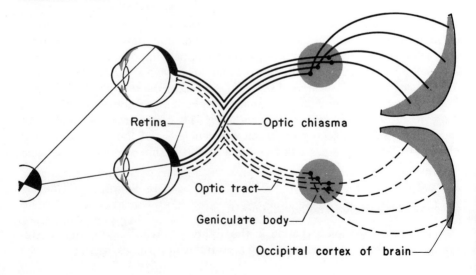

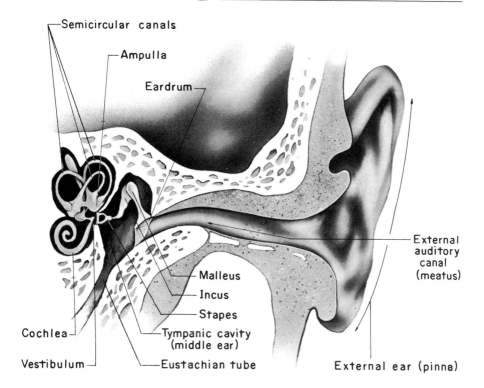

Semicircular canals

Ampulla

Eardrum

External auditory canal (meatus)

Malleus

Incus

Stapes

Cochlea

Tympanic cavity (middle ear)

Vestibulum

Eustachian tube

External ear (pinna)

Figure 19.31.   The human ear is second only to the eye as an elaborate sense organ.   This diagrammatic section shows how the external ear serves as a funnel to "collect" sound waves and channel them into the middle ear.   The connection of the middle ear with the inner ear via the ear bones is shown clearly.   The dual function of the ear as a hearing organ and as a balancing organ is shown by the cochlea and by the semicircular canals, respectively.

intensity detection.   If the ear were much more efficient, we might be driven to distraction by the sound of our own heartbeats or by flies walking on the ceiling —sounds which now are near our limit of hearing ability.

Ear structures

Three distinct structural units comprise the auditory apparatus: the *external ear,* the *middle ear,* and the *inner ear.*   These vary in complexity, with the inner ear being the most elaborately constructed and the most diversified in its function.   The external ear consists of two parts: the *pinna,* a projecting wing of cartilage covered with skin; and a tubular *auditory canal* leading to the middle ear.   The auditory canal is separated from the middle ear by the

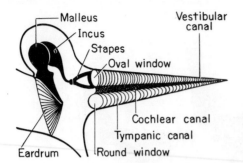

Malleus

Incus

Stapes

Oval window

Vestibular
canal

Cochlear canal

Tympanic canal

Eardrum

Round window

Figure 19.32. This is a schematic drawing of the arrangement of the canals of the inner ear. Pressure changes are produced by the movement of the stapes against the membrane of the oval window. Since the vestibular canal and the tympanic canal are continuous, there are compensating movements of the membrane of the round window.

membranous *ear drum*. The pinna serves to funnel sound waves into the auditory canal.

The *middle ear* is much smaller than the auditory canal and contains a flexible chain of small bones: the *malleus,* or hammer; the *incus,* or anvil; and the *stapes,* or stirrup. The hammer touches lightly on the inner surface of the ear drum, and as the ear drum moves in response to sound waves entering through the auditory canal, the vibrations produced are transmitted across the middle ear by the movements of the ear bones. Since the stirrup beats against a membrane covering the *oval window* of the inner ear, the movements of the stirrup are translated into vibrations of this membrane and are thus transmitted to the inner ear. Another important feature of the middle ear is the *Eustachian tube,* a canal which extends ventrally from the middle-ear chamber to the pharynx and makes possible the equalization of air pressure on the two sides of the ear drum. The experience of ascending or descending rapidly in an elevator or in an airplane can be used to illustrate the effectiveness of this system. If a person swallows at such times, pressure on the two sides of the ear drum is equalized, and the discomfort of having the ears "pop" is reduced.

It is obvious that the external and middle ears serve to transmit sound waves to the inner ear. It is in the inner ear that the transformation of the vibrations into nerve impulses for relay to the cerebral cortex occurs. That portion of the inner ear which functions in audition is the *cochlea*, a spirally coiled structure which superficially resembles a snail shell of two and a half turns. Close examination of the cochlea discloses that it tapers from a broad base to an almost pointed apex and that internally it is composed of three fluid-filled chambers, or canals. One of these, the large *vestibular canal,* is closed at one end by the membrane of the oval window previously mentioned. A second, the large *tympanic canal,* is continuous at the apex of the cochlea with the vestibular canal and is closed by a membrane at the *round window,* adjacent to the middle ear. A triangular, smaller chamber, the *cochlear canal,* is wedged between the vestibular and tympanic canals. The three chambers are separated from each other by thin membranes (expect at the apex where there is a junction of the vestibular and the tympanic canals). The fluid within the cochlear canal is called the *endolymph,* whereas the fluid in the other two canals is designated as

the *perilymph*.   The arrangement of the canals is such that the vibration of the
membrane of the oval window produces pressure waves in the fluids of the
canals.   Since the fluid cannot be compressed, the pressure waves pass through
the vestibular canal to the tympanic canal, where the movement of the membrane of the round window compensates for the pressure changes.   The canals,
like the ear drum and the ear bones, are concerned with the transmission of vibrations from the exterior of the body to the primary sound receptors.   These
receptors are in the *basilar membrane* and in the associated *organ of Corti* of
the cochlear canal.

The organ of Corti is an extremely complicated structure, the minute details
of which are beyond the scope of this account.   Reference to Figure 19.33,
however, will assist us in comprehending at least its major features, and in
understanding a simplified explanation of its action.   The organ of Corti rests
on the basilar membrane which separates the cochlear and tympanic canals.
This membrane is abundantly supplied by fibers from the auditory nerve and
has two other significant structural features: *first*, the basilar membrane gradually increases in width as it spirals through the cochlea, ranging from 80 microns

Figure 19.33.   Organ of Corti and cochlear canals.   The organ of Corti, which is shown here
with its relationship to the cochlear canals, is the structure responsible for the transformation of
sound waves into nerve impulses.   As is indicated in the text, the exact functioning of the organ
of Corti is not clearly understood.

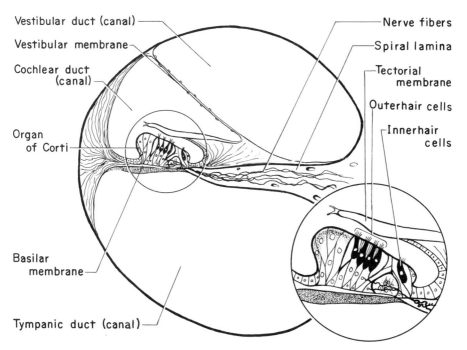

Vestibular duct (canal)

Vestibular membrane

Cochlear duct
   (canal)

Organ
   of Corti

Basilar
   membrane

Tympanic duct (canal)

Nerve fibers

Spiral lamina

Tectorial
   membrane

Outerhair cells

Innerhair
   cells

at its narrowest to 500 microns at its widest point; *second,* numerous fibrils of varying lengths are also present in the membrane. These differences in membrane width and fibril length cause the basilar membrane to vibrate at definite points in response to sounds of different pitch just as piano strings of varying lengths vibrate differently. Pressure waves in the perilymph are produced by the action of the stapes on the membrane of the oval window and are responsible for the vibrations in the basilar membrane. In addition to these actions, movements of the basilar membrane influence the cells of the organ of Corti above it. Special *hair cells,* with as many as 100 fine processes, or "hairs," on the surface of each cell, are located immediately above the membrane. Some 3000 of these hair cells are arranged in a single row; and approximately 20,000 more are arranged in three rows. The "up and down" movements of the basilar membrane produce varying degrees of bending in the hair cells by pressing them against the overlying *tectorial membrane.* The variable stimuli produced in this manner are translated into impulses in the auditory nerve.

We may state in summary that the transmission of sound waves from the environment to the place of their interpretation in the temporal lobes of the cerebrum is a result of the transformation of the vibrations in the air to waves of pressure changes in the perilymph and endolymph. The waves produce minute vibrations as well as gross movements of the basilar membrane. These vibrations interpret pitch, and the intensity of sound is interpreted by the major position changes of the basilar membrane which press the hair cells of the organ of Corti against the tectorial membrane.

The activity of the inner ear as an organ of equilibrium is remarkably similar among all the vertebrates. This function is independent of the cochlea and is associated structurally with two sacs, the *utriculus* and *sacculus,* and a labyrinth composed of three *semicircular canals.* The labyrinth and the sacs also are filled with endolymph. A special sensory receptor, the *macula,* is located in each of the sacs. The macula of the utriculus is horizontally positioned on the floor of the sac, whereas that of the sacculus is on the inner wall and is vertical in its

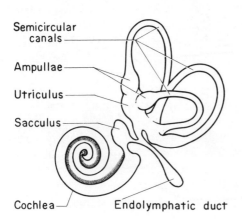

Semicircular canals

Ampullae

Utriculus

Sacculus

Cochlea

Endolymphatic duct

Figure 19.34. Canals of ear. The functioning of the ear as a balancing organ is possible because of the structure and relationship of the semicircular canals, which lie in different planes, and the utriculus and sacculus. A description of the operation of the system is given in the text.

position. Each of the semicircular canals is enlarged at one end to form a bulb, or *ampulla,* and within each bulb is another special receptor, the *crista.*

Special hair cells are present in the macula and the crista, and a gelatinous material containing small particles of calcium carbonate, the *otoliths,* covers the surface of the hair cells. When the head is moved up or down or is rotated, the position of the otoliths is changed and, in turn, the pressure they exert on the hair cells is changed, thus producing stimuli. The utriculus and sacculus appear to be concerned with those stimuli which inform concerning the *position* of the head, whereas the semicircular canals inform concerning the *movements* of the head. The canals are especially effective in this respect because of their arrangement at right angles to each other. Furthermore, one of the canals is positioned horizontally, and the other two, the anterior and posterior canals, are positioned vertically. The actual role of the endolymph in the functioning of the labyrinth is not clear. Since the canals are a closed system surrounded by bone, movements and pressure changes in the endolymph certainly are not so extensive as those which occur in the cochlea.

Disturbances of the inner ear are accompanied by difficulties in balancing; similarly, variable "up and down" disturbances produce nausea, as is illustrated by seasickness and car sickness. The inner ear, however, is not the sole determinant of equilibrium. The proprioceptors, especially those concerned with stimuli from the feet and legs, are important for balance. Even when there has been extensive damage to the inner ear, a person can maintain balance by means of the proprioceptors and by sight. Such an individual obviously has great difficulty walking or remaining erect when in the dark.

Chemical coordination

The impressive features of the nervous system in man are paralleled by an equally remarkable development of chemical coordination, especially through the *endocrine system* (p. 378). We should recall, in this connection, that each cell of the body, as a result of its metabolic activities, produces chemical substances that may influence other cells, and that the body may be dependent on certain of these substances. Carbon dioxide, lactic acid, and urea are examples of chemicals which diffuse or circulate variable distances through the body and affect different cells. The action of carbon dioxide on the respiratory center (p. 379) is an excellent illustration of a metabolic by-product with significant physiological effects. Such chemicals are called *parahormones,* and in contrast to them are the *hormones* which also diffuse or circulate but which are special secretions of glands, tissues, or cells. Some examples of hormones, already mentioned in our discussion of human physiology, are: acetylcholine, secreted at the nerve endings of the parasympathetic system; cholecystokinin, formed by the lining of the duodenum; and insulin, released by the pancreas. Finally, it has been demonstrated that the hypothalamic region of the brain secretes hormonal substances which profoundly affect the anterior and the

Hormones in Man

Gland, tissue, or cell	Action on	Hormones
Pituitary		
Anterior lobe	Reproductive system	Gonadotropins
	Mammary glands and behavior	Luteotropin
	Adrenal cortex	Adrenocorticotropin
	Thyroid	Thyrotropin
	Growth	Somatotropin
Intermediate	Pigmentation	Intermedin
Posterior lobe	Uterine contraction	Oxytocin
	Smooth-muscle contraction	Vasopressin
	Water balance	
	Antidiuretic	
Thyroid	Metabolic rate of cells	Thyroxine*
Parathyroid	Calcium and phosphorus balance	Parathormone
Pancreas		Insulin
(islets of Langerhans)	Carbohydrate metabolism	Glucagon
Adrenal		
Cortex	Carbohydrate metabolism	Hydrocortisone
	Sodium and potassium balance	Aldosterone
Medulla	"Emergency" reactions	Epinephrine (adrenalin)
		Norepinephrine
Gonads		
Ovary	Secondary sex characters	Estradiol
	Maintenance of pregnancy	Progesterone
		Relaxin
Testes	Secondary sex characters	Testosterone
Placenta	Maintenance of pregnancy	Chorionic gonadotropin
		Estradiol
		Progesterone
Lining of duodenum	Flow of pancreatic juice	Secretin
	Gall bladder contraction	Cholecystokinin
	Stomach contraction and secretion	Gastrin
Sympathetic nerve cells	"Autonomic" reactions	Epinephrine
		Norepinephrine
Parasympathetic nerve cells		Acetylcholine

*Or triiodothyronine; both associated with a protein.

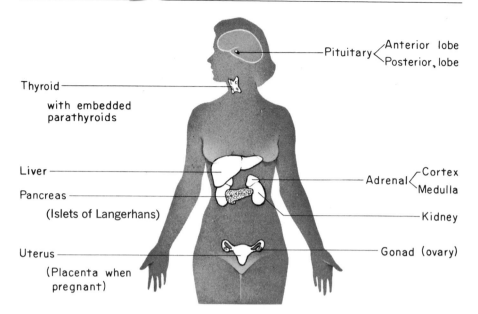

Pituitary — Anterior lobe / Posterior, lobe

Thyroid

with embedded
parathyroids

Liver

Pancreas

(Islets of Langerhans)

Uterus

(Placenta when
pregnant)

Adrenal — Cortex / Medulla

Kidney

Gonad (ovary)

Figure 19.35. Endocrine glands of the female. The endocrine glands of the female and male
are alike. The gonads differ in their cytogenic function (p. 384) and in the type of sex hormones
they secrete; otherwise, the endocrine secretions are comparable.

posterior lobes of the pituitary. This brain region, as well as the lining of the
intestine and the endings of the autonomic nerves, should therefore be considered as endocrine in function even though this may not be their major
activity. It is evident that chemical coordinators in man are diverse, both in
origin and nature.

Our present knowledge of the hormones and their activities is incomplete.
A listing of the major hormones in man and the glands with which they are
associated is presented in the accompanying table. This brief tabulation, however, does not give a complete résumé of the subject. *Glucagon* and *aldosder-
one,* for example, are recent additions to the list of hormones and much remains
to be discovered concerning their action. We are uncertain about the chemical
nature of the thyroid hormone and whether *thyroxine* or *triiodothyronine* is the
active principle. It also remains to be established whether the effect of anterior
pituitary extracts in diabetes is merely one of the physiological effects of the
growth hormone or is due to a separate chemical substance.

The anterior lobe of the pituitary, as we mentioned elsewhere, frequently has
been called the "master gland" of the endocrine system. Although it is the most
versatile and does exert an influence over most of the other endocrine glands,
the anterior pituitary itself is affected by variations in the activity of the endocrine system. Thus, if the thyroid gland secretes its hormone at a subnormal

rate, the rate of secretion of the anterior lobe will be depressed. Changes in the level of the circulation of gonadal hormones and of adrenal cortical hormone also will produce alterations in anterior pituitary function. These *reciprocal interactions* among the endocrine glands are characteristic of the complexity of hormonal interrelationships.

The anterior pituitary lobe

It has been established that six chemically distinct hormones are secreted by the anterior lobe of the pituitary. Two of these are the gonadotropins: the *follicle stimulating hormone* (FSH), and the *interstitial cell stimulating hormone* (ICSH). These regulate the growth and maturation of the ovary and the testis. A third hormone, *luteotropin* (LTH), or *prolactin*, is necessary for the continued secretion of hormones by the corpus luteum of the ovary and is needed also to provide a stimulus for the secretion of milk by the mammary glands. *Thyrotropin*, the *thyroid stimulating hormone* (TSH), and *adrenocorticotropin*, the *adrenal cortex stimulating hormone* (ACTH) are important in stimulating the activities of the thyroid and adrenal cortex respectively. Finally, *somatotropin* (STH), the *growth and diabetogenic hormone*, is necessary for normal bone development, protein anabolism, and general tissue growth of the body.

Figure 19.36. For those proverbial sideshow wonders, the giant and the dwarf, the circus is indebted to the pituitary gland. In the case of the giant, this gland has secreted too much of the growth hormone; in the case of the dwarf, too little. (Courtesy H. A. Stillwell Studio.)

Any one, or all, of the anterior pituitary hormones may be secreted in an overabundance or in subnormal quantities. If, for example, an excess of somatotropin is present in a child, gigantism may be produced; whereas a child with a deficiency of STH may become a dwarfed individual. The thyroid gland, likewise, may be overstimulated by TSH, or an inadequate quantity of TSH will result in subnormal thyroid function.

The intermediate lobe of the anterior pituitary secretes a hormone which stimulates skin pigmentation. This hormone usually is referred to as *intermedin,* or the melanophore stimulating hormone (MSH). This hormone also is found in the vertebrates which do not possess a separate intermediate lobe and could be considered, therefore, as a seventh anterior lobe hormone.

The posterior pituitary lobe

This gland, also called the *pars nervosa,* releases hormones which affect smooth-muscle contraction and water balance. The investigations of Vincent duVigneaud and his associates have demonstrated that it is possible to isolate two hormones from the gland, and the exact molecular weights and amino acid compositions of these hormones have been determined. They are polypeptide hormones: one, *oxytocin,* causes a marked contraction of uterine muscles; whereas the second, *vasopressin,* produces an elevation in blood pressure and decreases urine secretion. The latter hormone, therefore, is often called the antidiuretic hormone (ADH). A lack of vasopressin in man is accompanied by an excessive excretion of urine, a disorder known as diabetes insipidus. During the course of this disease, several gallons of urine may be excreted daily. The antidiuretic hormone also regulates the passage of water through the skin of amphibians. There exists an interesting and intimate relationship between the brain and the posterior pituitary. Nerve fibers from the brain (hypothalamus) terminate in the pars nervosa and secretory substances migrate to the posterior pituitary along these nerve fibers. The "posterior pituitary hormones" actually are secreted by the brain and are merely "stored" in the gland. We will comment on the full significance of these observations when we discuss the regulation of anterior pituitary-gland function.

The thyroid gland

The thyroid gland of man has a function comparable with that of the frog thyroid. Normal growth and maturation are possible only when the thyroid gland secretes adequate quantities of thyroid hormone. If the secretion of the gland is insufficient before birth, normal body development may be impossible and permanent damage to the brain may result. The most extreme condition of this type is known as *cretinism.* Failure of the gland to secrete normal quantities of hormone during early childhood may produce *childhood myxedema,* which resembles cretinism but can be corrected if it is recognized and is treated early. Muscular weakness and mental sluggishness accompany

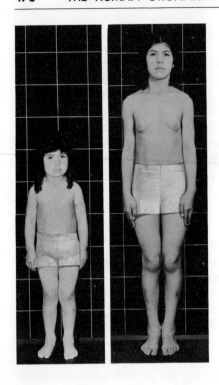

Figure 19.37. (a) Girl, age 10, with childhood myxedema, a condition caused by malfunction of the thyroid gland. In (b) the same girl after five years of a treatment for the disorder. (Courtesy E. Kost Shelton and *Endocrinology*.)

insufficient thyroid hormone secretion at any age and are characteristic of *adult myxedema*.

The thyroid hormone in man has a pronounced effect on cellular metabolism. An excess of the hormone produces a great increase in oxidative rate and body temperature; blood pressure and heart rate will be elevated; and tremors, nervousness, and irritability may be present. One of the notable malfunctions of this type is *Graves' disease*. The marked effect of the thyroid hormone on oxidation which is demonstrated in man appears to be lacking in cold-blooded vertebrates.

The parathyroid glands

These vital glands secrete *parathormone*, which is necessary for the maintenance of the proper balance of calcium and phosphorus in the body (p. 7, 58). Although these two chemicals constitute only a small percentage of the total body substance, they are necessary for bone growth and for the proper physical-chemical balance in osmosis and are essential for normal muscle contraction. The parathyroid hormone exerts its influence by regulating the amounts of calcium and phosphorus deposited in the bones and the rate of excretion of these salts by the kidneys. Extensive damage to the parathyroids, or their surgical removal, will cause the level of calcium in the blood to drop rapidly, with the result that *muscular tetany* is produced.   In this condition there is a great increase in neuromuscular irritability and a forceful contraction of the muscles follows.   Death occurs quickly unless the blood calcium is restored to and maintained at a normal level.   Parathyroid disorders, therefore, are extremely serious.

An overabundance of parathyroid hormone produces a decalcification of the bones, which are reduced to ropelike structures.   Simultaneously, the rate of phosphorus excretion, but not that of calcium, is increased.   The result is a marked increase in blood calcium and localized areas of calcification in the body.   Cataracts of the eye, for example, are common in this disease.

The pancreas gland

The discovery of the endocrine function of the pancreas was made in the 1890's, but the isolation and purification of its hormone, *insulin,* was not achieved until 1922.   The investigations of Banting and his associates at that time established that insulin is a protein hormone produced by the beta cells of the *Islets of Langerhans* of the pancreas.   We know more now about the chemistry of insulin as a protein than we know about any other protein, either hormone or nonhormone.   Its physiological function in the body has been investigated more thoroughly than that of any other hormone.   Although we are uncertain exactly how its effects are produced, the action of insulin is now being investigated at the level of intracellular chemical reactions.

Lack of sufficient amounts of insulin in the body is associated with disturbed carbohydrate and fat metabolism.   The disease produced is *diabetes mellitus,* or sugar diabetes, once called "the scourge of mankind."   Before insulin became available the average life of a diabetic person was about four years, but now that this disorder can be controlled by diet and insulin treatment, diabetics can lead normal lives if they adhere to the prescribed treatment.   It has become increasingly apparent that insulin does not act alone on carbohydrate metabolism.   The anterior pituitary secretes a diabetogenic (diabetes-causing) factor.   This factor, usually identified simply as DBG, is antagonistic to insulin.   Thus, if there is an excess of DBG in the body, a person may have diabetes mellitus even though insulin is present.   This condition of excess pituitary DBG frequently occurs in gigantism and is one of the lines of evidence which suggest that somatotropin and DBG may be the same substance.   Thyroid hormone and adrenal cortical hormone also increase the blood sugar level and thus have actions which are essentially contrary to the effect produced by insulin.

It was noticed for many years that a temporary increase in blood sugar often occurred when insulin was injected.   Since the primary effect of insulin is to decrease the blood sugar level, this observation suggested that insulin preparations might be contaminated with another hormone.   This proved to be true, and since 1950 there has been great interest in a second pancreatic hormone, *glucagon,* or the hyperglycemic factor.   This hormone also is secreted by the

Islets of Langerhans, but by the alpha cells, a different cell type than those which secrete insulin. The chemical nature of the glucagon molecule recently has been determined, and as in the case of insulin, its amino acid composition has been established.

It is evident from this brief account that carbohydrate metabolism in the human body is under polyglandular control. Hormones from the anterior pituitary, thyroid, adrenal cortex, and pancreas all have major roles to play in sugar utilization. It will be noted later that the adrenal medulla likewise has some effect on the blood sugar level. It is not surprising, therefore, that diabetes mellitus is a difficult disease to combat in human beings.

The adrenal gland

This also is a dual gland (p. 383), the two parts being different in embryonic origin and radically dissimilar in function. The portion of the human adrenal gland derived from the coelomic epithelium surrounds that part which is of nervous origin, and this superficial region of the gland is accordingly called the *cortex*, whereas the inner region is designated as the *medulla*. The function of the medulla is much less complex than that of the cortex and will be considered first.

The *adrenal medulla* secretes *epinephrine* (often called adrenalin) and *norepinephrine* into the blood stream (p. 379). These hormones mimic the effect of the stimulation of the sympathetic nervous system and can be thought of as actually supplementing its action, since their effects will be of longer duration. The hormones of the adrenal medulla produce an increase in heart rate and blood pressure, an elevation in blood sugar, a more rapid clotting of the blood, an enlargement of the air passages to the lungs, a dilation of the pupils of the eyes, and a shift of blood from the viscera to the brain and skeletal muscles. This interesting set of responses suggested to Cannon that the primary function of the adrenal medulla is to adapt an organism to meet emergencies! Whether this *emergency theory* is correct remains to be proved by additional work, but there is ample *evidence* that man is better able to adjust to unusual conditions for short periods of time as a result of the secretion of medullary hormones.

The *adrenal cortex* is second in importance only to the anterior lobe of the pituitary in the endocrine system. This gland plays an important role in sodium and potassium balance in the body (p. 55) and has a significant function in carbohydrate metabolism. During the 1930's, when the first extracts of the adrenal cortex became available, it was thought that there were two separate hormones, and these were usually referred to as the *salt principle* and the *sugar principle*. The painstaking chemical work of E. C. Kendall and others has shown that a series of steroid substances closely related to cholesterol can be extracted from the adrenal cortex. Subsequent synthesis of these and related chemicals has demonstrated that both the sugar and salt effects can be produced by one substance—for example, by *hydrocortisone*. A second chemical designated as *aldosterone,* however, has an effect on sodium and potassium balance a thousand times greater than that of hydrocortisone. The exact nature of the hormone or hormones secreted by the adrenal cortex is a subject which requires further investigation.

One of the first of the hormonal disorders to be described accurately and to be related to an endocrine gland is *Addison's disease,* which was characterized by the English physician, Thomas Addison, in 1855. It involves a disorder which is produced when the adrenal cortex degenerates or is destroyed by disease. The resulting lack of adrenal cortical hormone is accompanied by an excessive excretion of sodium and, coincidentally, of chloride by the kidneys. Conversely, potassium is reabsorbed by the kidney at a rate greater than normal, with the end result that the vital sodium-potassium balance of the fluids and tissues is altered. There is a marked dehydration of the body as a consequence: the blood thickens; and the osmotic relationship between the cells and the body fluids becomes abnormal. Carbohydrate metabolism also is considerably disturbed: blood sugar level declines, and cells, therefore, suffer from an inadequate supply of energy. The abnormal osmotic conditions coupled with the decrease in energy lead to progressive cellular deterioration, resulting in body weakness and eventual death. An interesting secondary effect, a marked bronze pigmentation of the skin, can be observed in many human beings suffering from Addison's disease. The lack of adrenal cortical hormone results in a greater stimulation of pigment production by intermedin, since the cortical hormone partially counteracts the action of intermedin.

A reasonably accurate picture of what happens when too much adrenal hormone is present can be gained by reversing the basic conditions of Addison's disease. An excess of cortical hormone causes the kidneys to excrete larger than normal amounts of potassium and to reabsorb more sodium and chloride than usual. A marked hydration of the body may follow. Likewise, the level of blood sugar rises very considerably when there are extra quantities of cortical

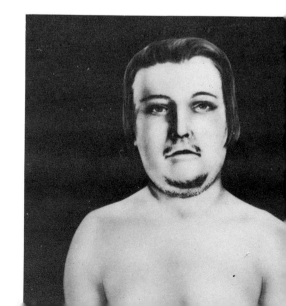

Figure 19.38. This woman is afflicted with adrenal virilism, a condition which results from an imbalance of adrenal hormones. The excess of the cortical hormone has produced the side effect of masculinization, discussed in the text above. (Photograph by Schick Publishing Company, Arlington, Mass.)

hormones present. Hydration, of course, will be associated with altered osmotic conditions, and the elevation of blood sugar is also harmful because the extra sugar in the blood is derived primarily from a breakdown of body proteins. Among the many other side effects of the excess of cortical hormone which may occur, one of the most startling is *masculinization*. Some of the excess cortical secretions have actions comparable to those of the testicular hormone. A woman with an excess of cortical hormone may develop a heavy beard, a deep voice, and even undergo slight skeletal and muscular changes in the direction of maleness. The "bearded lady" of the circus often is a person afflicted with an overactive adrenal cortex. If the amounts of cortical hormones are excessive during early childhood, a condition of *pseudohermaphroditism* (false hermaphroditism) may occur, in which even the female reproductive organs are modified and simulate those of the male.

The gonads

The remaining endocrine glands in man are those associated with the reproductive system, and we have already briefly discussed their actions (p. 437). The male sex hormone, *testosterone*, secreted by the testis, is primarily concerned with the secondary sex characters of the male, such as the beard, voice, and skeletal configuration. One female sex hormone, *estradiol*, from the ovarian follicle, has an effect on the secondary characters of the female. Estradiol, in cooperation with a second hormone, *progesterone*, from the corpus luteum of the ovary, prepares the reproductive organs for pregnancy and helps maintain the uterus during the period of fetal development (p. 439). The most remarkable of the endocrine organs associated with the reproductive system is the placenta, for it produces hormones which are comparable to the gonadotropins of the anterior pituitary and to the two ovarian hormones. Recently, interest has been revived in another female sex hormone, *relaxin*, which was first reported many years ago by F. L. Hisaw. This hormone causes a "relaxing" of pelvic ligaments and thus facilitates the enlargement of the birth canal, which is necessary for normal parturition.

The regulation of anterior pituitary secretions

Since the anterior pituitary gland appeared superficially to be omnipotent in its control of endocrine functions, it was important to determine what factor or factors might in turn regulate its activity. One of the first suggestions was that there exists a *feedback* mechanism between the anterior pituitary gland and each of its target organs. It was visualized that this feedback could alternately inhibit or release from inhibition the pituitary gland. The relationship between the thyroid gland as a target-organ for thyrotropin (TSH) from the anterior pituitary can serve as an illustration of the mechanism. The idea was that thyrotropin stimulates the thyroid to produce more thyroxin but, when this hormone reaches a certain high level in the blood, it will inhibit either

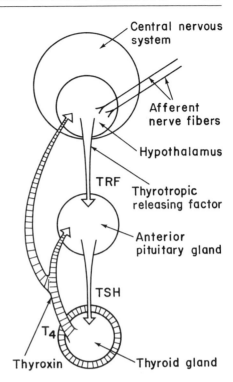

Figure 19.39. The complex interrelationships between the hypothalamus, anterior pituitary, and thyroid are shown in this diagram. Similar relationships exist among most other endocrine glands.

THYROID FEEDBACK

the production or release of thyrotropin by the pituitary. Subsequently, the decrease in the amount of TSH reaching the thyroid will be accompanied by a decreased output of thyroxin. The lower level of thyroxin in the blood now would not be sufficient to inhibit the pituitary production or release of TSH. This hormone will again increase in quantity and the cycle will begin again. For obvious reasons, this has often been called "teeter-totter" theory of anterior pituitary regulation. The cycle is shown in Figure 19.39.

The feedback hypothesis has been studied experimentally by a multitude of investigators who have analyzed such relationships as those between the gonad stimulating hormones of the anterior pituitary and the ovarian and testicular secretions. The relationship of the adrenal cortex stimulating hormone (ACTH) and the adrenal cortical secretions has also been investigated. All the experiments have supported the concept that high levels of target-organ hormones will inhibit the secretion or release of their respective stimulating (tropic) hormones from the anterior pituitary. Thus, estradiol will inhibit the secretion of the follicle stimulating hormone (FSH) and cortisol will inhibit ACTH secretion.

There are, however, objections to the feedback mechanism as the sole regulator of anterior pituitary function. For example, the levels of target-organ hormones which are employed experimentally to inhibit usually are much higher than the amounts which are normally present in the blood. Even more significant are the repeated observations that the pituitary can secrete extra tropic hormones even though there may be high levels of target-organ hormones present. The release of extra TSH occurs when an animal is subjected to cold and the level of thyroxin will be elevated above normal. In a very spectacular fashion, it can be demonstrated that a man subjected to stress will secrete large quantities of ACTH and greatly increase the quantity of cortisol in his blood. Obviously, there must be other significant mechanisms involved in the regulation of anterior pituitary function.

The preceding experiments, and countless others, suggest that the nervous system must play an important role in regulation. There is, however, no major nerve supply to the anterior pituitary which would seem to be adequate to provide reflex pathways for nervous control. How is it possible, therefore, that external stimuli as temperature changes or stress conditions which must act by nervous pathways can alter anterior pituitary function? We mentioned previously that frequently in biological research seemingly unrelated or distantly related observations dovetail like pieces in a jig-saw puzzle to provide a complete picture. This is the case for the present problem.

Pituitary portal system

In the late 1920's the existence of an unusual circulatory relationship between the floor of the brain and the anterior pituitary was discovered. Primarily due to the initial leadership of G. B. Wislocki, the anterior pituitary was found to be supplied by blood vessels that begin in a capillary-network on the floor of the brain and end in sinuses within the gland itself. This system has been designated as the *pituitary portal system*. G. W. Harris and other investigators were intrigued by this vascular connection between the brain and the anterior pituitary, especially when it was realized that the hypothalamic region of the brain was involved. This brain area is immediately above the pituitary stalk and is essentially a complex switchboard which shunts messages from the body to the higher brain centers and also relays messages in the opposite direction. Within the hypothalamus there exist concentrations of nerve cells called nuclei (not to be confused with the nuclei in the cells). Some of these concentrations of nerve cells are rather well delimited from surrounding tissues, and electrodes can be placed in them by special surgical procedures. It is possible to subject a hypothalamic nucleus to an electric current of sufficient intensity to cauterize it and thus destroy its function and also possible to stimulate a nucleus by means of a mild electric current.

Experiments have shown that when one of the nuclei in the region of the optic chiasm is destroyed, there is a cessation of the release of TSH by the pituitary. Conversely, stimulation of this area is followed by an increase in TSH release. In a similar fashion, other nuclei have been found to be associated with the regulation of ACTH or of LH and FSH production by the pituitary.   Mating behavior can also be inhibited or stimulated in animals by destroying or stimulating other nuclei.   One major question has been answered by these investigations: namely, that the nervous system does exert an influence on anterior pituitary function and that it does so through hypothalamic nuclei. It remained to be determined, however, how the nuclei could produce this regulation, and once again other pieces of information were available to fit into the jig-saw puzzle.

W. B. Cannon and O. Loewi had demonstrated that nerve cells of the autonomic nervous system secrete *neurohumoral* substances at their endings.   It occurred to endocrinologists that the various hypothalamic nuclei also might secrete neurohumoral substances which could be carried by the pituitary portal system to the anterior pituitary where they would then influence the release of specific tropic hormones.   This idea had strong support from other observations related to the posterior pituitary, and it is profitable to digress for a moment and discuss these data before completing the account of anterior pituitary control.

Origin of posterior pituitary hormones

The posterior pituitary (*pars nervosa*) originates during embryonic development as an outgrowth of the floor of the brain.   It is not surprising, therefore, to observe that bundles of nerve fibers from two of the major hypothalamic nuclei extend into the posterior pituitary.   Observations of living animals and electron-microscope observations show clearly that granules move along the nerve fibers from the nuclei to the posterior pituitary where they are stored. Furthermore, when radioactive sulfur (S^{35}) is administered, it is incorporated into protein in the nuclei and the radioactive protein is then transferred to the posterior pituitary.   Finally, when the nerve fiber bundles are cut there is an absence of antidiuretic hormone (ADH) and *diabetes insipidus* is produced. There is clear evidence, therefore, that what we have designated as "posterior pituitary hormones" are actually produced in the hypothalamus, associated with a protein, transferred along the nerve fibers to the posterior pituitary for storage, and are split from the protein to be released as the active peptide hormones oxytocin or vasopressin (ADH) when they are needed.

Hypothalamic releasing factors

The relationship between the hypothalamus and the posterior pituitary strongly suggests that there also might be neurohumors from the hypothalamic nuclei which could influence anterior pituitary function.   The adverse effects on anterior pituitary function which followed the destruction of certain hypothalamic nuclei by electrocautery, therefore, could be interpreted as removing the source of the neurohumors.   Similarly, the augmented secretions after mild electrical stimulation could be a result of an increase in the release of neurohumors from the hypothalamic nuclei.   Since there are no major nerve trunks leading from the hypothalamus to the anterior pituitary, it was assumed that the neurohumors would be carried by the *pituitary portal system*. Several investigators using several different experimental animals interrupted the flow of blood in the pituitary portal system by surgical means and observed that the release of most of the tropic hormones was prevented. These experiments, however, could be criticized on the grounds that the anterior pituitary was made anemic by the surgery and hence could not be expected to function normally. Additional supportive evidence, therefore, was needed and it was immediately forthcoming.

Extracts were made of various regions of the hypothalamus, and modern chemical procedures were utilized for the purification of these extracts. It was discovered that it was possible to isolate substances which were very specific in their actions on the anterior pituitary. A *corticotropic releasing factor* (CRF) was prepared which increased the pituitary output of ACTH. A second factor, the *thyrotropic releasing factor* (TRF) differed from CRF and was able to augment the release of thyrotropin. A third substance, the *luteinizing hormone releasing factor* (LRF) increased the output of luteinizing hormone. Since LH is the hormone which "triggers" ovulation, an excellent end point for determining its presence was available. The release of the follicle stimulating hormone (FSH) also appears to be under the control of a releasing factor from the hypothalamus.

The next obvious question is: what is the chemical nature of the releasing factors? It would be significant if either oxytocin and/or vasopressin should prove to be the "releasing factors." Vasopressin does have some effect on the ACTH release but is much less potent than CRF. Certainly, the releasing factors appear to be polypeptides closely related chemically to vasopressin, and exciting biochemical studies currently are being directed toward a determination of the nature of the releasing factors.

Relationship of nervous and chemical coordination

The two coordinating mechanisms in the vertebrates of nervous and chemical coordination have been brought together into a single integrating system by the striking studies of the relationship of the hypothalamus to the anterior pituitary. There is little doubt that this is a fundamental relationship of great biological significance in the animal kingdom because we recall that some of the hormones of the insects originated in nervous tissue. The "brain hormone" of the moth, for example, stimulated the production of the prothoracic gland hormone, ecdysone, and the corpus cardiacum "stored" the brain hormone. The analogy between this case and the posterior pituitary storage of oxytocin and vasopressin is striking.

Circulation

The circulatory system of man, like that of other mammals and the birds, is a complete *double circulation*. There is no mixing in the heart of the oxygen-

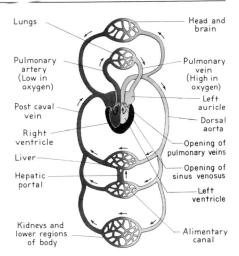

Lungs

Pulmonary artery (Low in oxygen)

Post caval vein

Right ventricle

Liver

Hepatic portal

Kidneys and lower regions of body

Head and brain

Pulmonary vein (High in oxygen)

Left auricle

Dorsal aorta

Opening of pulmonary veins

Opening of sinus venosus

Left ventricle

Alimentary canal

Figure 19.40. Diagram of double circulation, indicating the flow and distribution of blood in the human system. The relationship of the capillaries to the arteries and veins cannot be shown in this diagram but is implied.

rich blood from the lungs with the oxygen-poor blood from the body. This separation is possible because the human being has a four-chambered heart consisting of two auricles and two ventricles, in contrast to the three chambers of the frog heart (Figure 18.16). Blood returning to the heart from the body enters the *right auricle* and passes to the *right ventricle,* from which it is pumped through the *pulmonary arteries* to the lungs. Blood from the lungs returns to the *left auricle* of the heart through the *pulmonary veins* and passes from the *left auricle* to the *left ventricle,* from which it is pumped into the *aorta* and thence throughout the body. The route followed by the blood from the heart to the lungs and return is called the *pulmonary circulation;* the route of the blood through the body is the *systemic circulation.* It is obvious that this double circulation is much more efficient with respect to the respiratory function of the blood than is the incomplete separation of the systematic and pulmonary circulations observed in the frog.

The human heart is a remarkable pumping device and the amount of work performed by this organ during an average lifetime is fantastic. The first glimmering of how remarkable its performance really is was gained by the pioneering researches of Sir William Harvey in the seventeenth century. Harvey's observations and experiments were so important that a short description of his studies should be included here. Furthermore, it has often been stated that this work marked the introduction of the experimental method into biological science.

Harvey's determination of the rate of blood flow proved to be the key which unlocked the puzzle of the mechanism of blood circulation. Although he made several errors in his calculations, the general conclusions which he reached were irrefutable. Harvey measured the volume of the left ventricle of the heart of a cadaver and estimated that it would hold approximately two ounces of blood. He believed, however, that only a fraction of this amount of blood was pumped at one time. He calculated, in a very conservative fashion, that the heart output was approximately ⅙ ounce per beat; but we know now that the heart empties completely, and that nearly four ounces of blood, or more than twenty times as much as Harvey suspected, is pumped each time the ventricles contract. Harvey then calculated that the rate of beat averaged 33 per minute—again an error, because the average rate usually is twice as great. Using these ultraconservative calculations, Harvey estimated that in 30 minutes over 17 pounds of blood would be pumped by the heart into the arteries. Since a person weighing 150 pounds was known to have about 15 pounds of blood, the equivalent of all the blood in the body would be circulated in 30 minutes, and it was inconceivable to Harvey that this quantity of blood could be formed constantly in the liver, as Galen and many of the earlier anatomists had thought. Corrections in Harvey's calculations which take into account greater heart output and more rapid heart beat proved, of course, that the equivalent of all the

Figure 19.41.   Chemical and nervous coordination.   The nervous system sends and receives messages rapidly.   The blood and body fluids also carry chemical messages to and from all parts of the body, but such chemical response is much slower than nervous stimulation.

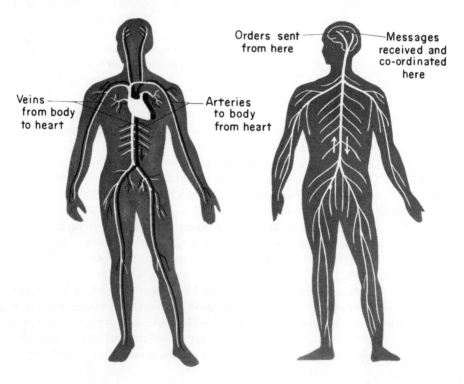

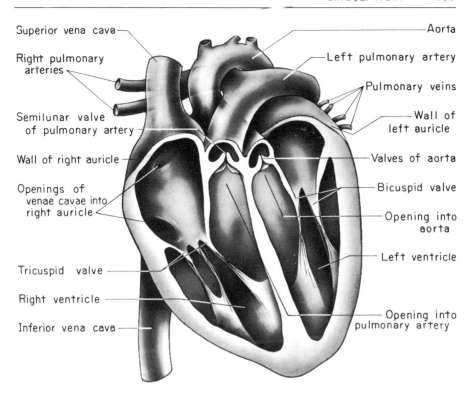

Superior vena cava

Right pulmonary arteries

Semilunar valve of pulmonary artery

Wall of right auricle

Openings of venae cavae into right auricle

Tricuspid valve

Right ventricle

Inferior vena cava

Aorta

Left pulmonary artery

Pulmonary veins

Wall of left auricle

Valves of aorta

Bicuspid valve

Opening into aorta

Left ventricle

Opening into pulmonary artery

Figure 19.42.   The four-chambered heart of man is a remarkable pumping mechanism.   The arrangement of the valves within the major vessels of the heart also regulates in a very exact fashion the direction of blood flow.   The complete double circulation of blood, systemic and pulmonary, is possible because of the complete separation of the right and left sides of the heart.

blood in the body must pass through the arterial circulation in *less than one minute*, rather than the conservative 30 minutes determined by Harvey.   The importance of Harvey's observations and conclusions is great, however, and overshadows the errors in his calculations.   Furthermore, his work provided the impetus for the extension of the experimental method to other biological problems and aroused an interest in the study of living rather than preserved organisms.   The simplicity of his experiments and the logic of his deductions established a pattern for investigators which was most influential.

Harvey's observations emphasized that the heart does a tremendous amount of work; and we know now that the various factors which are involved in the control of the heart beat are quite as remarkable as the amount of work which is done by that organ.   The cardiac muscle possesses the ability to contract rhythmically and independently of outside stimuli;   a condition known as the *automaticity* of the heart.   Bits of mammalian heart tissue, for example, will continue to contract for long periods of time outside the body.

Furthermore, the contraction of normal heart muscle follows a definite sequence.   A contraction wave originates at the right auricle and progresses over the heart in such a fashion that the blood is transferred from the auricles to the ventricles and from the ventricles to the great arteries leading to the body and lungs.   Careful observation and experimentation have demonstrated that the *beat* originates in a small nodule of tissue known as the *sinuauricular node* (SA node).   This is located on the wall of the right auricle at the base of the vena cava.   The sinuauricular node is composed of specialized muscle tissue which is able to conduct messages but which has lost the ability to contract.   It is the remnant of the sinus venosus which was seen in the frog (Figure 18.8).   Special conduction pathways of modified muscle, the *neuromuscular bundles,* relay impulses from the SA node to the other regions of the heart, thus controlling the contraction of the heart.   Since the sinuauricular node initiates the beat, it is often designated as the "pacemaker" of the heart.

A second concentration of neuromuscular tissue, the *auriculoventricular node* (AV node), is present at the base of the septum which divides the two auricles. Two bundles of tissue extend from the AV node into each ventricle, where the bundles repeatedly subdivide to form a network in the walls of the ventricles. Damage to the AV node or to one of the AV bundles results in a nonsynchronized beat of the ventricles, and this may lead to circulatory failure and death.

It is clear that although the origin and rhythmic nature of the heart beat is a function of the SA and the AV nodes and of the neuromuscular bundles of the heart, the rate of heart beat is largely influenced by nervous control exerted through the autonomic nervous system.   Nerve fibers of the sympathetic nerves and from the vagus nerve of the parasympathetic system terminate in the two nodes; and, in addition, the sympathetic nerves send numerous branches to the heart muscle itself.   Stimulation of the vagus nerve slows or even stops the heart beat, but stimulation of the sympathetic system by way of the *stellate ganglion* accelerates the rate of heart contraction.   That each of these portions of the autonomic system exerts a slight but continuous effect on heart action can be demonstrated by blocking the effect of one or the other by drug action or by cutting the nerves.   If, for example, the effect of the vagus is blocked, heart rate will increase because of the lack of inhibitory action.   Conversely, a blocking of the sympathetic innervation of the heart results in a slowing of the heart rate because of the removal of the accelerating stimulus of the sympathetic nerves.   It might be stated by way of analogy that the normal action of the heart is much like that of an automobile moving along slowly with both brake pedal and accelerator slightly depressed.

The vascular system

The major arteries and veins in man are comparable to those which were noted previously in the frog (Figures 18.17, 18.18).   Figure 19.42 illustrates this

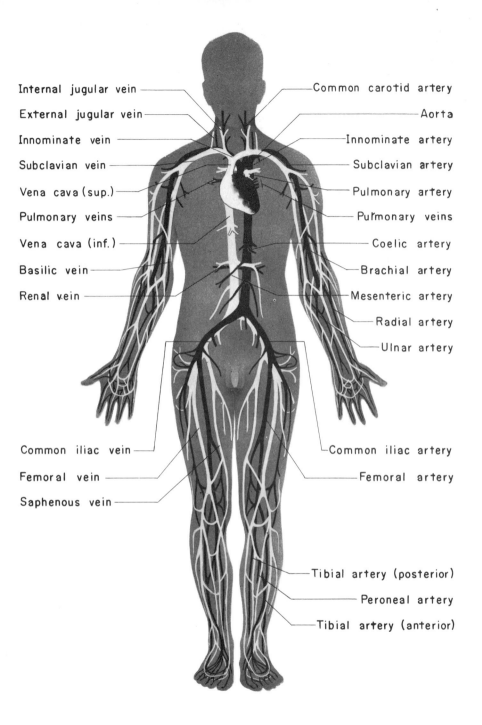

Internal jugular vein

External jugular vein

Innominate vein

Subclavian vein

Vena cava (sup.)

Pulmonary veins

Vena cava (inf.)

Basilic vein

Renal vein

Common carotid artery

Aorta

Innominate artery

Subclavian artery

Pulmonary artery

Pulmonary veins

Coelic artery

Brachial artery

Mesenteric artery

Radial artery

Ulnar artery

Common iliac vein

Femoral vein

Saphenous vein

Common iliac artery

Femoral artery

Tibial artery (posterior)

Peroneal artery

Tibial artery (anterior)

Figure 19.43. Circulatory system. The major arteries and veins in man are shown in this diagram. Here, as with the skeletal and muscular systems, it is easy to recognize the vertebrate similarity: many of the arteries and veins are the same as those identified in the frog.

similarity. Note that the carotid, subclavian, pulmonary, renal, and femoral arteries, as well as the jugular, brachial, vena cava, hepatic, and femoral veins, are similar to those of the frog, not only in name but also in location.

Lymph vessels also were observed in the frog, and these drainage channels are even more important in man. The higher blood pressure in human beings makes it possible for more fluid to filter from the capillaries into the tissue spaces, but this pressure also renders it difficult for the fluid to return to the blood stream. The lymph vessels open into the tissue spaces at one end and convey the tissue fluids back into the blood stream at their other end. The most prominent lymph vessel providing this drainage is the *thoracic duct,* which joins the vena cava as the latter empties into the right auricle of the heart. Especially important among the lymph vessels are the *lacteals,* which drain the small intestine. These become quite "milky" after a high fat-content meal, because the digested fats are picked up by the lacteal branches in the villi of the intestine and emptied into the thoracic duct.

The blood as a defense mechanism

The role of the blood in body defense is significant in man, and there are two important phases to this function: the prevention of blood loss when blood vessels are severed; and the occurrence of phagocytic and chemical reactions against bacteria and other foreign materials. The effects of these defensive mechanisms are apparent, but much remains to be learned concerning how the processes occur. The deceptively simple formation of a blood clot will serve to illustrate some of the complexities.

Figure 19.44.   The fine branches of the capillary bed, shown in this high-power photomicrograph (a), are so tiny that to get through them the red blood cells must go in single file.   (b) The flaplike valve, the lymph heart in the lymph vessel (p. 367) which allows the lymph to flow in only one direction, toward the heart.   (a) Courtesy Dr. W. B. Zweifach, New York University.

(a)   **(b)**

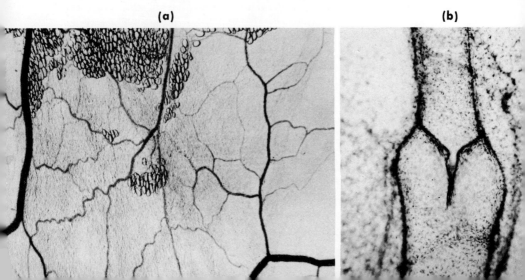

When a blood vessel is severed, blood can be observed to flow freely for a short period of time. Soon, however, the blood becomes more viscous and gradually solidifies to form a clot, or *thrombus*. Microscopic examination of a clot discloses that it is composed of a network of filaments, with fluid and blood cells trapped within the spaces between the filaments. The clot slowly contracts, squeezing out a straw-colored fluid, the *serum*, and eventually this clot becomes a compact plug sealing the incision and preventing hemorrhage. Clots are slowly absorbed by the system, disappearing completely as a wound heals. Occasionally, however, a clot will break free of its point of origin and enter the blood stream. Such a migrating clot, or *embolus*, is dangerous because it may lodge in a small blood vessel of the brain or heart as an *embolism* and shut off the blood supply to the area. An embolus, therefore, may produce paralysis, serious heart damage, or death. The use of anticoagulating drugs in cases where an embolism is threatened has become a valuable medical and surgical procedure in recent years.

Physiologists are not in complete agreement concerning the chemical changes which occur in the blood preceding the formation of a clot. The nature of the events, however, appears to be established.   The clot is formed of *fibrin*, which does not exist in the circulating blood but is produced only by transformation of a precursor, *fibrinogen*, which is present in the blood. The stimulus for the production of fibrin from fibrinogen is provided by another substance, *thrombin*, which also is not normally present in the blood but is a product of *prothrombin*. It has been established that these substances are protein in nature and are formed by the liver, but the exact chemical nature of the stimulus which initiates the chain reaction leading to fibrin formation remains uncertain. The most acceptable explanation of the mechanism involved probably is that given in the following paragraph.

Each cubic millimeter of blood contains 300,000 or more small, nonnucleated particles of protoplasm, the *platelets*, or *thrombocytes*. These bodies are fragile and very sticky.   They adhere readily to any foreign matter in the blood stream and aggregate on any injured surface, where they rapidly disintegrate.   The breakdown of the platelets is accompanied by the release of *thromboplastin* which, in the presence of adequate amounts of calcium and a cofactor, converts prothrombin to thrombin and thus starts the clotting reaction.   The events leading to the production of a fibrin clot can be summarized as follows:

Wound with aggregated platelets

↓

Release of thromboplastin from platelets
   (with adequate amounts of calcium and co-factor)

↓

Conversion of prothrombin to thrombin

↓

Conversion of fibrinogen to fibrin

The serious human disease, hemophilia (p. 516), is characterized by the failure of the blood to clot properly. The cause appears to be the inability of the body to produce sufficient thrombin as a result of inadequate thromboplastin activity. If untreated, the hemophiliac may bleed to death from a very slight cut or scratch, or from a minor internal injury which would be of little consequence to a normal individual. Vitamin K is necessary for the production of prothrombin in man, and the blood will fail to clot properly without adequate amounts of this vitamin; spontaneous hemorrhages may even occur. Since new-born infants have a very low concentration of prothrombin in the blood, vitamin K is often administered to mothers before childbirth to prevent infant hemorrhaging. Chronic alcoholics frequently suffer from vitamin K deficiency because they substitute alcohol for essential foods in their diet.

Another important defensive mechanism in the blood is that associated with the activities of the white blood cells, the *leukocytes*. The number of white blood cells in man is much lower than that of the red blood cells. The average number of leukocytes is approximately 7000 per cubic millimeter of blood, with a normal range of from 5000 to 10,000 per cubic millimeter. There are three major types of white blood cells: the *granulocytes*, which constitute about 67 per cent of the total; the *lymphocytes*, approximately 27 per cent of the total; and the *monocytes*, the remaining 5 or 6 per cent. White blood cells may increase rapidly in numbers during infection or during certain abnormal physiological states, sometimes reaching a concentration of 50,000 or more per cubic millimeter. These cells can leave the blood stream through the capillary walls and may aggregate about foreign matter. The granulocytes in particular are able to ingest foreign bodies such as bacteria, and this *phagocytic* action is comparable to the amoebocyte action observed elsewhere in the animal kingdom. The leukocytes contain several different enzymes, and when these cells disintegrate at the site of an infection, the enzymes are released to aid in the digestion of necrotic tissues.

The blood also performs a major function in counteracting bacterial action by chemical means, in producing protective chemicals, the *antitoxins* and the *antibodies*. Many bacteria release poisons, or *toxins*, and the body is stimulated to produce *antitoxins* which are able to prevent or to alleviate the effects of the toxins. Bacteria and foreign proteins also behave as *antigens*—that is, they augment the production of *antibodies* and the release of these into the blood stream. The antibodies that are produced usually are specific in their action and will react only with the particular protein (antigen) which has stimulated their production. There is considerable variation in action, however, among antibodies. Some antibodies, the *agglutinins*, cause bacteria or other foreign cells to stick together, or agglutinate; others, the *precipitins*, precipitate foreign bodies; and still others, the *cytolysins*, are capable of dissolving, or lysing, foreign cells which have been introduced into the body.

One fact of particular significance is that human beings and many other vertebrates produce antibodies against their own red blood cells. This was established first about 1900 by Karl Landsteiner, but the observation that blood transfusions in man can be fatal as well as beneficial was known for many decades previous to that time. The classification of blood types with respect to the major antigen-antibody reactions is essentially that which was first suggested by Landsteiner. The red blood cells contain two types of substances designated as A and B, and four types of cells can be recognized, depending on the presence or absence of these substances: (1) type A contains A substance; (2) type B possesses B substance; (3) type AB has both A and B substances; and (4) type O contains neither A nor B substance. It is obvious that the plasma of an individual with type A cells could not contain appreciable amounts of antibodies for A (anti-A antibodies) or the cells would be agglutinated. Likewise, anti-B antibodies must be absent or negligible in type-B individuals. Both anti-A and anti-B antibodies must be absent or negligible in type-AB persons; but both anti-A and anti-B antibodies can be, and are, present in type-O individuals. This relationship is indicated in the following table.

Type	Red Blood Cell	Plasma of Blood
A	Contains A substance	Contains anti-B antibody
B	Contains B substance	Contains anti-A antibody
AB	Contains A and B substances	Contains neither anti-A nor anti-B antibodies
O	Contains neither A nor B substance	Contains both anti-A and anti-B antibodies

It is apparent that if a blood transfusion is needed, the most advantageous situation would be to have both the donor and recipient of the same blood type. This is not absolutely necessary, however, as limited mixing of blood types is possible. The cells of a type-O individual, for example, have neither A nor B substance; therefore, blood from a type-O individual in some instances may be given to any of the other types, because the cells will not agglutinate. A type-O individual is sometimes designated as a *universal donor*. Conversely, since type AB does not contain antibodies for either A or B, an AB individual can receive blood from any other type and hence often is called a *universal recipient*.

The terms *universal donor* and *universal recipient* have fallen into disuse in recent years because of the discovery of other important blood factors, one of the most important being the Rh group. It is now known that there are several subgroups of A, and that there are M, N, P, and S blood types, as well as the Rh-positive and Rh-negative blood types. It is important, therefore, that the blood of both donor and recipient be matched with respect to these group differences, in order to avoid complications during transfusions.

The inheritance of blood types in man has been studied in considerable detail and will be discussed in Chapter 23. We may remark at this time that the pattern of inheritance follows well-established laws of heredity; and that a comparison of blood types can be used to determine relationship or non-relationship between individuals.

The pineal and thymus glands

Two organs have been omitted from our discussion, the *pineal* and the *thymus*. The former, which is located on the dorsal surface of the brain, is still an unknown entity with respect to its activity. On the other hand, exciting discoveries have been made about the thymus function since 1960. This gland usually is located under the breastbone and in front of the aorta. It is large at birth and normally atrophies after puberty and once was thought to be associated with sexual development because of this relationship to puberty. Studies over the years involving removal of the thymus, implantation of extra thymus glands, and the preparation and injection of extracts all gave conflicting results. Jacques F. P. Miller, however, discovered the critical factor relative to the thymus function. He removed the gland *during the first day after birth* in mice and found that very significant effects were produced. The animals operated upon were unable to form antibodies and would not reject skin grafts from other animals. These results have been widely confirmed, and it is now apparent that the thymus either provides lymphocytes (the source of antibodies) to the lymph nodes and spleen or releases a chemical substance that determines the type of lymphocytes which will be formed. The thymus does this immediately after birth and may even begin the process shortly before birth.

It is interesting to note that in the chicken the bursa of Fabricius located dorsal to the cloaca also functions in the determination of antibodies. When the bursa is removed or is prevented from developing by injecting chick embryos with male hormone, antibodies will not be formed. Skin grafts, however, will not "take." When both the thymus and bursa are removed, the skin grafts will take and antibodies will not be formed. These two glands in chickens, therefore, appear to have a division of labor with the thymus regulating tissue reaction (for example, skin grafts) and the bursa of Fabricius determining the antibody formation.

A résumé of the features of the human organism illustrates that man is a typical vertebrate, generalized in most structures and functions, and specialized primarily in the remarkable development of his brain. Man has been able to manufacture tools, to build locomotive devices, and to construct shelters which protect him from adverse environmental conditions. These developments and the countless others which are products of man's ingenuity give human beings greater independence than is possessed by any other organism, or than was possessed by any living thing of ages past. In a philosophical vein, the future of *Homo sapiens* appears to be unlimited provided that human beings do not destroy themselves in intraspecific warfare.

REFERENCES

AREY, LESLIE B., *Developmental Anatomy*, 6th ed.   W. B. Saunders Company, Philadelphia, 1954.

CANNON, WALTER B., and A. WASHBURN, *American Journal of Physiology, 29*, 1912, p. 441.

CARLSON, A. J., and VICTOR JOHNSON, *The Machinery of the Body*, 4th ed.   University of Chicago Press, 1953.

CORNER, GEORGE W., *Ourselves Unborn*.   Yale University Press, New Haven, Conn., 1945.

HAYMAN, J. M., *American Journal of Physiology, 79*, 1927, p. 389.

HUNT, J., *The Ascent of Everest*.   Hodder and Stoughton, London, 1953.

HOUSSAY, BERNARDO A., *Human Physiology*.   2nd ed.   McGraw-Hill Book Company, New York, 1955.

LEVEL, RAPHAEL H., "The Thymus Hormone." *Scientific American, 211*, July 1964, pp. 66–77.

MAXIMOW, A. A., and WILLIAM BLOOM, *A Textbook of Histology*, 6th ed.   W. B. Saunders Company, Philadelphia, 1953.

MOORE, CARL R., *Biology of the Testes*.   Williams and Wilkins Company, Baltimore, 1939.

ROMER, ALFRED S., *The Vertebrate Body*.   University of Chicago Press, 1950.

ROMER, ALFRED S., *Man and the Vertebrates*.   Penguin Books, Harmondsworth, Middlesex, 1954.

STAUB, A., L. SINN, and OTTO BEHRENS, "Purification and Crystallization of Glucagon." *Journal of Biological Chemistry, 214*, 1955, pp. 619–632.

TEPPERMAN, J., *Metabolic and Endocrine Physiology*.   Yearbook Medical Publishers, Chicago, Illinois, 1962.

TURNER, C. DONNELL, *General Endocrinology*, 3rd ed., pp. 463–481.   W. B. Saunders, Philadelphia, 1960.

WEICHERT, CHARLES KIPP, *Anatomy of the Chordates*.   McGraw-Hill Book Company, New York, 1951.

WINCHESTER, A. M., *Genetics*.   Houghton Mifflin Company, Boston, Mass., 1951.

WILLIAMS, Robert H., *Clinical Endocrinology*, 2nd ed.   W. B. Saunders Company, Philadelphia, 1955.

Like Father,	**20**
Like Son;	
Yet Different:	**Genetics**

●

The value and utility of any experiment are determined by the fitness of the material to the purpose for which it is used, and thus in the case before us it cannot be immaterial what plants are subjected to experiment and in what manner such experiments are conducted.—Gregor Mendel, 1865

The search for an integrating principle which would have universal application in biology has been a long and difficult one.   Living things display amazing individuality, whether one considers them individually as organisms, or collectively as species or phyla.   We have had the opportunity to survey and discuss only a few of the multitude of variations which are expressed by animals, and our observations have tended to emphasize the differences.   Undoubtedly, this approach has suggested that each species behaves as a "law unto itself."

Figure 20.1.   Gregor Mendel.
(Courtesy Historical Pictures Service.)

This, however, is not a true evaluation of biological systems because in reality the opposite is true. Reflection will indicate that in spite of differences which exist, most of the major characteristics of living systems are common to all plants and animals whether their body forms are simple or complex. Let us briefly restate some of the basic concepts which apply universally in biology.

Protoplasm

Its chemical composition is variable but it is a colloid, it has monomers and polymers of carbohydrates, fats, and proteins, and it grows, reproduces, moves, and responds. Protoplasm is synonymous with life.

Organization

The cell is the structural unit of life, and associated with all cells we observe nuclei, mitochondria, endoplasmic reticulum, ribosomes, ground substance, and a regulatory plasma membrane.

Functions

All organisms practice nutrition, respire, excrete, reproduce, and coordinate their activities. These functions are as complex in the one-celled organisms as they are in the multicelled organisms. Enzymes are the ubiquitous agents in all functions.

Metabolic processes

The energy relationships of the Krebs cycle, of high-energy phosphate, of enzyme activities in synthesis or hydrolysis, and the balance between anabolism and catabolism are as common to yeast cells as to the brain cells of man.

Biologists have realized that similarities exceed differences among organisms. The idea gradually emerged that *determiners* must exist which are responsible for the maintenance of a high degree of uniformity among the members of each species and which regulate protoplasmic activities. The transmission of characteristics from parent to offspring is never a haphazard process. Human beings, for example, reproduce only human beings with human enzyme systems, human proteins, and human behavior. On the other hand, mice beget only mice and paramecia beget only paramecia. This is the essence of the problem of inheritance.

Scientists, in their endeavors to find universal determiners for the multiplicity of integrations which must be explained, have sought the answer by attempting to resolve three important questions: (1) What is the location of the determiner or determiners? (2) How are the determiners transmitted? and (3) What is the nature of the determiners and how do they regulate protoplasmic activities? Obviously, if the third question can be answered we will have the unifying principle we have been seeking in biology.

The observations which have led us step by step to the discovery of the location of the determiners and how they are transmitted provide us with a spectacular example of scientific achievement. This is especially impressive when we realize that all the major discoveries have been made in only slightly more than 100 years. These observations and discoveries are the basis for the science of genetics.

Modern genetics was begun by Mendel with a study of the inheritance of characters in garden peas. His experiments were brilliantly conceived, and the results were published in 1866 in the proceedings of the scientific society at Brünn. The paper was distributed thoughout Europe through an excellent system of exchange maintained between the society and the libraries on the Continent. His conclusions, by a strange series of circumstances, were not received with any enthusiasm, and Mendel himself was bitterly disappointed that recognition was not given to his endeavors. Many of the biologists who should have been interested in Mendel's work were occupied at the time in attempting either to confirm or discredit the theory of the origin of species advanced by Darwin in 1859. Mendel himself contributed to the lack of acceptance of his work, because after the experiments with garden peas he transferred his attention to the study of inheritance in hawkweeds. Unfortunately, the hawkweeds had an unusual and complicated type of inheritance, and he was unable to duplicate his observations on peas. A controversy between church and state, furthermore, diverted Mendel's attention from his research: the government at that time levied a tax on religious institutions; this infuriated Mendel and, as a church official, he refused to pay the tax which was levied on his church. He expended his energies during the remaining years of his life attempting to have the tax law repealed. Mendel, therefore, published no further substantiating evidence for his theory of inheritance; and it remained for three papers, published independently by Hugo de Vries, Karl Correns, and Erik Tschermak in the year 1900, to confirm Mendel's observations. His paper was discovered at this time, and its significance was appreciated for the first time. The three workers acknowledged his prior discovery of the laws. In 1951, Tschermak, the only living member of the trio, wrote an interesting résumé of the rediscovery of the Mendelian laws.

Few scientific concepts appear suddenly as a product of one man's discoveries. Many investigators before Mendel's time had been interested in the transmission of characteristics from parent to offspring in both plants and animals. Josef Koelreuter in the eighteenth century learned the details of plant fertilization and studied cross-bred plants. Although he did not advance a satisfactory explanation for the variations which occurred in his experiments, he realized that characteristics often disappeared and would reappear in later generations. Practical genetic experiments were made with domestic animals by Robert Bakewell in England in the late 1700's. He inbred cattle and sheep, and in spite of the fact that his experiments were considered to be immoral because of this inbreeding, he was able to increase the weight of both the cattle

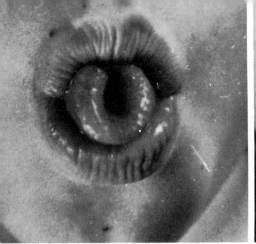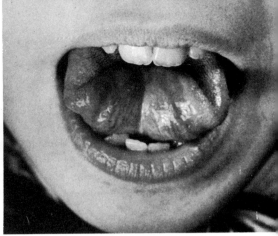

Figure 20.2. These unusual gymnastics are inherited abilities in man. Many people have inherited the ability to roll the tongue as in (a), but only one in a thousand can fold it (b). (Courtesy Dr. A. M. Winchester, Stetson University.)

and the sheep. Louis L. deVilmorin performed "selection" experiments in the mid-nineteenth century in an attempt to improve the quality of sugar beets and made the important observation that individuals that looked alike could be hereditarily different. A statistical method of genetic analysis was used extensively by Sir Francis Galton in the nineteenth century, at a time when Mendel's studies were yet undiscovered. Mendel was familiar with the work of his predecessors, and in his paper he discussed the significance of some of these results.

The Basic Laws of Inheritance

It may seem unorthodox to initiate the study of inheritance in animals by describing Mendel's experiments with plants, but it is essential to remember that *the hereditary mechanisms are alike in all organisms.* Mendel's innovations were so important that they determined the pattern of modern genetic study, and his experiments were planned with a precision which had been lacking in previous investigations. Furthermore, he was greatly influenced by the training he had received as a mathematician and designed his experiments so that the results could be tabulated and analyzed with exactness. The novelty of his methods is best indicated in his own words describing the inadequacies of previous investigations: "Among all the numerous experiments made, not one has been carried out to such an extent and in such a way as to make it possible to determine the number of *different forms* under which the offspring of hybrids appear, or to arrange these forms with certainty *according to their* separate generations, or to ascertain their *statistical* relations." (The italics are ours.) It has been stated frequently that Mendel was fortunate in his selection of the garden pea as an experimental form. This statement is misleading. The pea plant was chosen only after he had made preliminary studies of beans, snap-dragons, pumpkins, four-o'clocks, and other plants. He also carried on experiments for many years with bees. Mendel observed that the characters in the peas were constant, that the plants could be protected from uncontrolled fertilization, and that the cross-bred peas (hybrids) would themselves reproduce. It is also significant that since the pea plants are hermaphroditic, they could be self-fertilized. The only accidental element of good fortune in his selection was that the plants had an uncomplicated type of inheritance. The important features of Mendel's contributions to the *method* of the study of inheritance are fourfold. *First,* he studied each hereditary character separately. *Second,* he made certain that each character was selected from a pure breeding line. *Third,* he kept an accurate record of each generation. *Fourth,* he crossed large numbers of plants and enumerated the different types of offspring. The effectiveness of these criteria in a genetic study can be illustrated best by giving the details of a specific experiment made by Mendel. This and similar experiments led to the establishment of Mendel's first law, the *law of segregation.*

Determining the law of segregation

Mendel selected seven sets of characters for study, one of them being the variation in height of plants. *Tall* pea plants reach a height of six or seven feet, but *dwarf* pea plants grow only ¾ to 1½ feet high. The plants used as parents in the experiment were selected from lines which were *pure* for the character. Thus, for several generations, the tall plants had only tall ancestors, and the dwarf plants only dwarf ancestors. The first generation of plants from the cross of tall × dwarf was designated as the *first filial generation,* F_1 in genetic short-hand; and those plants which resulted from the crossing of the F_1 were called the *second filial,* or F_2, generation. The F_2 generation in this experiment had a

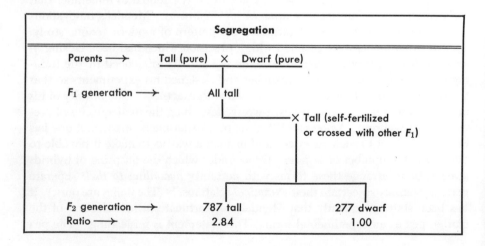

Segregation

Parents ⟶ Tall (pure) × Dwarf (pure)

F_1 generation ⟶ All tall

⟶ × Tall (self-fertilized or crossed with other F_1)

F_2 generation ⟶ 787 tall   277 dwarf
Ratio ⟶ 2.84   1.00

total of 1064 plants. It is obvious that the four features of his experimental plan were applied exactly in this study.

Dominant and recessive characters

The simplicity of Mendel's experiment and the organized way in which the data are presented bring to attention several salient facts in heredity. Mendel noted that in the F_1 generation all the plants were tall, and that the dwarf parents seemingly had no influence on the offspring. For this reason, Mendel spoke of the character tall as *dominant* over the character dwarf, which he referred to as *recessive*. Dominant and recessive characters are relatively common in plants and animals, but dominance or recessiveness is of no special significance in the hereditary mechanism. Mendel recognized this, but his successors were sometimes confused concerning the importance of dominance. The second fact which impressed Mendel was that the dwarf plants reappeared in a definite ratio in the F_2 generation. The total number of plants in this experiment could be subdivided, therefore, into two groups in the F_2, with an approximate ratio of 3 tall to 1 dwarf. Mendel realized that although the F_1 plants were as tall as the tall parent type, nevertheless, they must have contained hidden potentialities for the dwarf condition because the undersize plants reappeared in the F_2 generation. Mendel, therefore, set about to devise a theory which could explain the reappearance of dwarfs and the ratio which was observed. He assumed that a "factor" for tall and another "factor" for dwarf were present in the plants. The nature of this "factor" was unknown to him.

The genes and their symbols

The rediscovery of Mendel's laws was accompanied by the adoption of the name *gene* for the unit of inheritance instead of Mendel's term "factor." It also was more convenient to use symbols to represent genes instead of employing descriptive words for each gene. We will observe soon that there can be

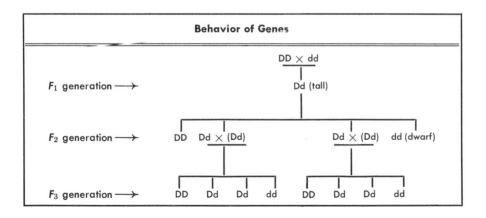

several recessive variations of a normal (dominant) character. The symbols which are given to the genes are designed, therefore, to express the recessive character rather than the normal trait and the symbols are written in algebraic form. A small letter is used to indicate a recessive gene and a large letter to represent the dominant gene. Thus, the experiment we have just described involving tall and dwarf plants can be rewritten in genetic "algebra." We write d *for a dwarf gene* and D *for a tall gene.* Mendel assumed that in the tall F_1 plant a gene for dwarf must be present and that the F_1 individual would contain, therefore, both tall and dwarf genes. Accordingly we will indicate the genetic makeup of the F_1 plant as Dd. Each of the two parent types, on the other hand, had been selected from a pure breeding line, and thus the tall parent should be written as DD and the dwarf parent as dd.

Mendel was forced to assume that a single gene (D) produces an effect on height which is equal to that of two tall genes (DD), and that the dwarf plants could appear only if the two dwarf genes (dd) are present. It was especially important for him to analyze more carefully the kinds of genes (factors) that were present in the tall plants in the F_2 generation. Mendel self-fertilized these plants and discovered that the tall plants were not alike but differed in the kinds of genes they possessed. One third of the tall plants bred "true," having only the genes for tall (DD). Two thirds of the tall plants, however, gave rise to both tall and dwarf plants and in the ratio of three tall to one dwarf. These plants, therefore, must have possessed both kinds of genes (Dd). The cross which illustrates these data is shown as the third filial, F_3, generation in the accompanying chart.

The separation and recombination of genes

Mendel was now forced to make additional assumptions in order to explain these results. First of all, only two genes were assumed to be present in each generation. The question immediately raised was: Why should there not be four genes in the next generation when a tall plant is crossed with a dwarf plant? The theory advanced to explain the behavior of the genes was Mendel's most brilliant contribution. Mendel postulated that the only possible hereditary bridge between two generations was by way of the reproductive cells: namely, the egg cells and the pollen, or male, sex cells. Mendel suggested that if genes *separated* during the development of the reproductive cells in such a manner that the mature egg or the pollen cell received only one half the genes, the results would be explained. The reproductive cells formed by DD plants, therefore, would each receive only one D, and the reproductive cells formed by the dwarf plants would each receive only one d. The combination of a pollen cell containing d with an egg cell containing D would produce an individual in the F_1 generation which would be Dd. This is an agreement with the original suggestion that a dwarf gene must have been present in the F_1, even though its effect was not visible. We realize now that this result is quite

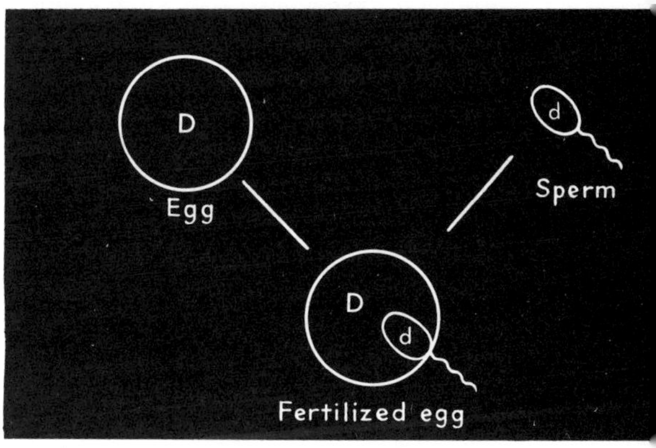

Figure 20.3. Fertilization and gene behavior. In this example, the egg contributes the D gene; the sperm, the d gene. The new individual, therefore, has a Dd gene combination.

characteristic of most recessive genes.   The critical test for Mendel's theory that the genes separated in the formation of the reproductive cells, however, is the analysis of the F_2 generation.   Theoretically, both male and female reproductive cells of the F_1 plants would be of *two types*.   One reproductive cell type would contain the D gene, and the other would contain the d gene. Mendel then made one final assumption: namely, that large numbers of both types of reproductive cells were produced, and any cell of one type had an equal opportunity to combine with any cell of another type.   The theoretical possibilities of such combinations are usually presented in what is referred to as a "checkerboard," in which the reproductive cells of the female (♀) are written, say, at the top of the checkerboard and the reproductive cells of the male (♂) at one side.   Frequently, instead of using the symbols in such diagrams, the male reproductive cells of plants or animals are shown as a circle with a tail, to differentiate them from egg cells.

If such a box is made, with egg cells of the Dd plant heading the two vertical columns and pollen cells of the Dd plant facing the two horizontal columns, then the combination of D pollen cells with the egg cells will produce DD and Dd individuals.   The combination of d pollen cells with the egg cells would produce Dd and dd individuals.   It should be observed that the squares in the checkerboard represent the individuals of the next generation.   If we now examine the squares, it will be noted that at least one D appears in three of them; in one case DD, and in two cases Dd.   The fourth square contains the dd and would represent a dwarf plant.   The ratio, therefore, is 1 DD : 2 Dd : 1 dd.   The actual cross performed by Mendel

Checkerboard Showing Theoretical Possibilities in F_2

		Eggs (♀)	
		D	d
Pollen, or male cells (♂)	D	DD	Dd
	d	Dd	dd

which produced the F_3 generation proved that the 3 to 1 ratio in the F_2 could have been written as a 1:2:1 ratio. The *theoretical crosses* in the checkerboard gave exactly the same results which had been observed for the *actual crosses,* and the assumptions which were made by Mendel were verified.

Law of segregation

The statement of the *law of segregation* is relatively simple in the light of Mendel's experiment and his assumptions. It can be summarized briefly as follows:

1. There are two genes for an inherited characteristic.

2. The genes *segregate* (separate), and each reproductive cell receives only one half the genes (one of the two for each inherited character).

3. Any reproductive cell of one type has an equal opportunity to combine with any reproductive cell of another type.

Each of the seven characters studied by Mendel followed the pattern of inheritance described for height, and his most extensive experiment involved the inheritance of seed color, which is either yellow or green. Yellow is dominant; green is recessive. A cross of F_1 hybrids gave a count of 8023 seeds; of these 6022, or 75.05 percent, were yellow, and 2001, or 24.95 percent, were green. This gives a ratio of 3.01 to 1.00 and is extraordinarily precise. Arthur D. Darbishire in 1909 repeated the cross; and in a total of 145,246 seeds, noted that 109,060 (75.09 percent) were yellow and 36,186 (24.91 percent) were green.

It is necessary to introduce here certain terms which are used in describing genetic experiments. A fertilized egg is spoken of as a *zygote* and if, in such a fertilized egg, the two genes which control a given character are alike, it is said that the egg (and the individual which develops from it) is *homozygous* for the character. When, for example, a pollen cell containing D fertilizes a D egg cell, the resultant zygote is homozygous for tall (DD). A dwarf plant (dd) likewise is homozygous for dwarf. When the genes in the zygote are unlike, however, as in the case of the union of a D pollen cell with a d egg cell to produce a Dd fertilized egg, it is designated as *heterozygous* for the character. A group of zygotes (and the individuals which develop from the zygotes), classified according to the *kind of genes* which are present, is called a *genotype.* It will be remembered, however, that the DD plants and the Dd plants were identical in their appearance, and these or other organisms which *appear* alike to our senses (not only sight but sometimes taste, touch, or smell) are classified as similar *phenotypes.* The phenotypes are the "look alikes," and may or may not have the same kind of genes. The Dd and the DD plants, for example, are the same phenotype but are different genotypes.

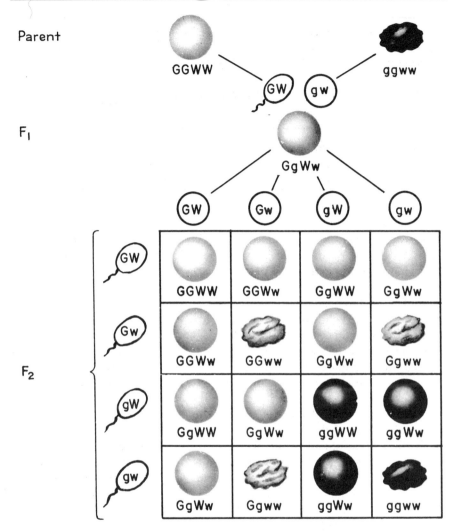

Figure 20.4. The results of the cross for seed color and form in peas are shown above (also see chart page 509).

Determining the law of independent assortment

Gregor Mendel, after he had determined the distribution of the genes that controlled the inheritance of a single character, turned his attention to crosses in which *two characters* were observed simultaneously. We may again take one of his own experiments to illustrate the results of such an investigation. Pure-breeding plants with *round yellow* seeds were crossed with other pure-

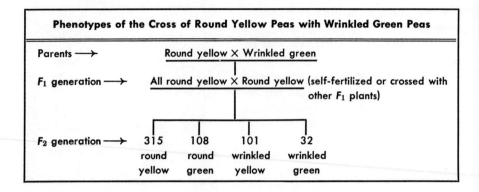

Phenotypes of the Cross of Round Yellow Peas with Wrinkled Green Peas

Parents ———→   Round yellow × Wrinkled green

F_1 generation ———→   All round yellow × Round yellow (self-fertilized or crossed with other F_1 plants)

F_2 generation ———→   315   108   101   32
                        round   round   wrinkled   wrinkled
                        yellow   green   yellow   green

breeding plants with *wrinkled green* seeds. *Round* is dominant; *wrinkled* is recessive. Plants from the F_1 generation, when crossed with others like themselves or self-fertilized, produced a total of 556 seeds in the F_2 generation. Mendel made an accurate count of these seeds and found that they fell into four phenotypes, as shown in the following chart. The numbers of the different kinds of seeds also occurred in a ratio of approximately 9:3:3:1.

Since round is dominant over wrinkled, and yellow is dominant over green, the fact that the phenotypes of the F_1 seeds were all round yellow was exactly as expected. Furthermore, if the number of round seeds in the F_2 are added together and compared with the number of wrinkled seeds, we observe that there are 423 round and 133 wrinkled. Similarly, the totals for yellow and green seeds are 416 yellow and 140 green. Both ratios are approximately 3 to 1. It was obvious to Mendel, therefore, that the genes for one character did not change the effect of the genes for the second character in either the F_1 or F_2 generations. The significant problem, however, was to find an adequate explanation for the four different phenotypes in the F_2 generation and the definite ratio in which they appeared. We can again write the cross in genetic shorthand. The dominant genes for round and yellow can be designated by W and G, respectively, and the recessive genes by w and g. It is a regular practice in genetics to write a dash (—) when the complete genotype is unknown, or when the organism might be either homozygous or heterozygous. Round seeds, for

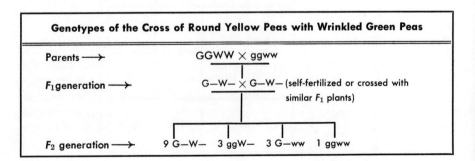

Genotypes of the Cross of Round Yellow Peas with Wrinkled Green Peas

Parents ———→   GGWW × ggww

F_1 generation ———→   G—W— × G—W— (self-fertilized or crossed with similar F_1 plants)

F_2 generation ———→   9 G—W—   3 ggW—   3 G—ww   1 ggww example, could be written as W—, because the genotype might be either WW or Ww. The cross, therefore, can be written as shown.

Mendel assumed that segregation of the genes occurred in the usual fashion and that each reproductive cell received *one and only one of each pair of genes.* The WWGG parent, therefore, would form WG reproductive cells, and the wwgg parent would form wg reproductive cells. The union of these cells would produce a heterozygote with a WwGg combination of genes. We can, if this assumption is correct, replace the dashes in the F_1 plants and write them WwGg. The formation of the reproductive cells by such plants could result in WG and wg cells, but if this possibility is tested a difficulty is encountered. It is obvious that only four types of plants would appear, in a ratio of 3 round yellow to 1 wrinkled green. There would have to be additional types of reproductive cells if a 9:3:3:1 ratio were to be produced. Mendel theorized that there must be a random distribution of genes in such a fashion that either one of the two genes for seed form might be associated with either one of the two genes for seed color. He concluded that *four types* of reproductive cells must be formed: WG, Wg, wG, and wg. Finally, if all the combinations of these reproductive cells were possible and were tested, the following would result.

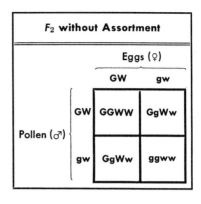

F_2 without Assortment

	Eggs (♀)	
	GW	gw
Pollen (♂) GW	GGWW	GgWw
gw	GgWw	ggww

Checkerboard for the Cross of Heterozygous Round Yellow Peas

	Eggs (♀)			
	GW	Gw	gW	gw
Pollen (♂) GW	GGWW	GGWw	GgWW	GgWw
Gw	GGWw	GGww	GgWw	Ggww
gW	GgWW	GgWw	ggWW	ggWw
gw	GgWw	Ggww	ggWw	ggww

The law of independent assortment

It is possible to summarize briefly the *law of independent assortment* as follows:

1. The genes which are associated with two or more characters segregate independently of each other.
2. The genes for a character will assort independently, and may be associated with either of the genes for a second (or third, etc.) character.
3. All combinations of reproductive cells are possible.

Inheritance in *Drosophila melanogaster*

The rediscovery of Mendel's work in 1900 focused attention on the problem of hereditary mechanisms in animals as well as in plants. In the next decade a brilliant group of investigators under the leadership of T. H. Morgan at Columbia University began the study of the inheritance of characters in the fruit fly, *Drosophila melanogaster*. These animals have been extremely valuable for genetic research because they reproduce rapidly and can be cultured easily in the laboratory. A generation from egg to egg requires only about 10 days. It was apparent immediately that the laws of segregation and independent assortment are applicable to these animals as well as to the plants with which Mendel worked. The inheritance of hundreds of characters has now been studied and catalogued in *Drosophila*. One of the experiments which will depict the behavior of the genes in *Drosophila* is shown by a cross involving body color and wing length. The body color of the wild-type fly is *grey*, and one of the inherited color variations is a dark color called *ebony*. The wings of the wild-

Figure 20.5. Independent assortment in the fruit fly.

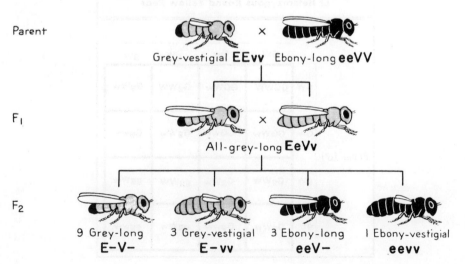

Parent

Grey-vestigial **EEvv**   Ebony-long **eeVV**

F₁

All-grey-long **EeVv**

F₂

9 Grey-long **E–V–**   3 Grey-vestigial **E–vv**   3 Ebony-long **eeV–**   1 Ebony-vestigial **eevv**

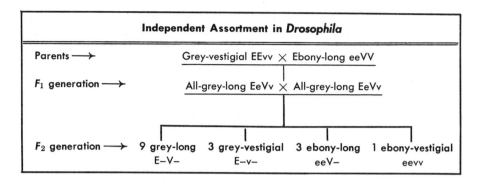

type animals are *long*, but there are several variations in wing length, one of which is designated as *vestigial* wing.   Grey color is dominant over ebony, and long wing is dominant over vestigial.   When an ebony-long-winged fly is crossed with a grey-vestigial-winged fly, both segregation and independent assortment can be demonstrated.   Thousands of crosses involving other characters in *Drosophila* have given the same pattern of results.

It will be noted that these results are exactly like those in the cross of round yellow peas with wrinkled green peas, and that the genes for body color and wing length must have segregated and assorted independently.

Function of the genes and chromosomes in inheritance

Mendel had theorized that the egg and sperm cells (usually simply referred to as the *germ cells*) provide the only connecting link or bridge between generations, and that the genes must be transmitted by these cells.   Of even more significance was Mendel's belief that segregation (separation) of the genes occurs during the formation of the reproductive cells.   Neither Mendel nor others at that time knew of any mechanism which could explain the regularity with which the genes were shuffled within the germ cells.   During the period when Mendel's discoveries lay unnoticed, many careful studies were being made of the development and division of cells.   The details of mitotic cell division were clarified, and it was discovered that chromosome number was remarkably constant in all cells.   Several investigators, however, noted that the chromosome number is reduced during the later stages of the development of germ cells, with the result that the mature egg and the mature sperm cell possess only half as many chromosomes as the other cells of the body.   This observation stimulated an intensive investigation into the manner of chromosome distribution in the reproductive cells to ascertain, if possible, whether the chromosomes could be serving as vehicles for the transportation of the genes. A brief exploration, therefore, into the development of the germ cells is necessary at this time in order to describe the details of the process which results in the halving of the chromosome number in the mature reproductive cells.

In 1902 W. S. Sutton suggested that the *genes are located on the chromosomes,* because he observed that there is a striking similarity in the behavior of the chromosomes during mitosis and meiosis and of the genes during inheritance. *First,* the life of a new individual begins when a sperm combines with an egg. The male parent contributes one set of chromosomes encased in the sperm and these, together with the chromosomes contributed by the female parent in the egg, are the chromosomes of the new individual. When an individual reaches sexual maturity and the pairing of the chromosomes occurs in meiosis, it can be demonstrated that one member of each pair of chromosomes was contributed by the male parent and the other member of the chromosome pair by the female parent. Genetic experiments have established

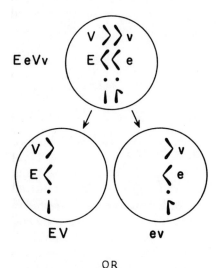

Figure 20.6. Different types of germ cells are necessary for independent assortment. The formation of these cells can be explained by assuming (1) the location of the genes on the chromosomes; and (2) the separation of paired chromosomes with their random distribution to the germ cells.

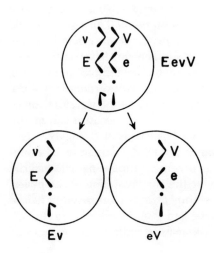

that the genes also are paired, and that one member of each gene pair is contributed by the male parent, the other by the female parent. *Second,* the fact that mature reproductive cells have only half of the chromosomes and that this half number results from the separation of the paired maternal and paternal chromosomes is particularly significant. This observation parallels the law of segregation: namely, that only half the genes are present in mature germ cells, and that these genes represent one member from each pair of genes. *Third,* although members of a pair of chromosomes separate during meiosis, any member of one pair may be accompanied by either chromosome of a second, or third, or fourth pair, etc. This fact can be validated by direct observation of meiotic division, and this behavior is also comparable to that of the genes in the law of independent assortment.

In the light of the foregoing facts and on the basis of additional evidence not discussed here, it is not surprising that Sutton's original suggestion of the location of the genes on the chromosomes gained wide acceptance. This concept has been tested repeatedly in plants and animals, and the evidence more than adequately supports this gene-chromosome relationship. A single example of this relationship in *Drosophila* will serve to illustrate how the distribution of the chromosomes can account for the mechanics of both segregation and independent assortment.

The four pairs of chromosomes in *Drosophila melanogaster* differ in both size and shape. We find a pair of small dotlike chromosomes, also a larger elongated pair, known as the XX pair in the female and the XY pair in the male, and finally two similar pairs of chromosomes even larger than the elongated ones. If we now turn our attention to the known behavior of the genes in *Drosophila,* we can again use the example of the inheritance of body color and wing length (Figure 20.5). The genes for these characters are associated with the dominant *grey* body color, and the recessive *ebony* body color, the genes for dominant *long* wing, and for the recessive *vestigial* wing. Let us choose a fruit fly which is heterozygous for both body color and wing length. The phenotype of this fly would be grey in body color and would have long wings, because grey and long are dominant. The genotype, however, would be EeVv (E = grey, e = ebony, V = long wing, v = vestigial wing). If we now make two assumptions—that the two genes for body color are located on one pair of chromosomes (one on each chromosome), and that the two genes for wing length are located on a second pair of chromosomes (also one on each chromosome)—it is possible on the basis of chromosome behavior to analyze the possible types of reproductive cells that can be formed.

Since we have assumed that the grey gene (E) and the ebony gene (e) would be located on chromosomes that pair, the separation of these paired chromosomes during meiosis would automatically segregate these genes. Likewise, the separation of the two members of the second pair of chromosomes would segregate the long gene (V) from the vestigial gene (v). Reference to the top part of the diagram (p. 512) will show that two genetically different types of reproductive cells could be formed: one would contain the genes EV and the other ev.

It is known, however, from direct observation of meiotic divisions that the chromosome pairs will arrange themselves in the equatorial plate in a random fashion. It should be expected, therefore, that in 50 per cent of the cases the chromosomes would be arranged as they are shown in the lower division in the diagram, and that the distribution of the genes would be altered. The separation of the chromosomes during meiosis would then produce two other genetically different types of germ cells. One of these could contain the genes Ev and the other eV. We would expect in a gene-chromosome situation of this kind to find four genetically different types of germ cells, and that the four different kinds would appear in equal numbers. These results agree exactly with the independent assortment of the same genes in an actual cross (p. 511). It is evident, therefore, that the distribution of the genes can be explained by the assumption that the genes for one character are located on one pair of chromosomes, whereas the genes for the other character are located on a second pair of chromosomes. Subsequent experiments which were designed to study in more exacting detail the transmission of the genes for grey-ebony body color and long-vestigial wings have made it possible to identify the actual chromosomes on which these genes are located. It is easier to illustrate the location of specific genes on specific chromosomes in a more striking fashion by analyzing the transmission of certain characters which are linked with the sex of an individual.

Chromosomes and sex determination

A study of the germ cells of the fruit fly revealed that one of the chromosome pairs in the male, the XY pair (below), was different from the corresponding chromosome pair in the female, the XX pair. Similar differences in the chromosome pairs of males and females of other animals had been observed previous to this discovery in the fruit fly, and such chromosomes had been designated as X chromosomes because their function was unknown. Since these chromosomes differed in the sexes, it was suggested that the XX or XY pairs might be concerned in some way with sex determination. The task of analyzing this possibility was made somewhat easier by the discovery that the Y chromosome of *Drosophila* is hook-shaped and can therefore be followed

6 + X X = Female   6 + X Y = Male

Figure 20.7. Chromosomes and sex determination.

easily through the stages of mitosis and meiosis. The behavior of the XX and XY chromosomes in the maturation of the egg and sperm is given in the following paragraphs; for convenience the chromosomes of the female will be shown here as X ♀ X ♀ and those of the male as X ♂ Y ♂ .

Since the X ♀ X ♀ and the X ♂ Y ♂ chromosomes are paired and will separate during the formation of the egg cells, each egg cell will receive only one X ♀ chromosome, and as far as the X ♀ chromosomes are concerned, the eggs are identical. The maturation of the sperm, however, results in sperm cells which always differ in their chromosome composition. One type of sperm will receive the X ♂ chromosome and the other type must contain the Y ♂ chromosome.

If an X ♂ sperm fertilizes an egg cell, the new individual will be female, with X ♂ X ♀ chromosomes. On the other hand, a union of Y ♂ sperm with the egg produces a male with X ♀ Y ♂ chromosomes. Three facts of considerable genetic importance may be gained from these observations: *first*, the Y chromosome is found only in the male; *second*, the X chromosome of the male always will be transmitted to the daughters (X ♂ X ♀); and *third*, the X chromosome in the male must come from the mother (X ♀ Y ♂). This remarkable interrelationship of the chromosomes to sex justifies the modern designation of the X and Y chromosomes as *sex chromosomes*. The manner in which these operate to determine sex is a very complicated problem, however, and is beyond the scope of our discussion.

Sex linkage

In 1910 Morgan observed a peculiar fruit fly in one of the laboratory cultures. This fly possessed white eyes instead of the normal red eyes of the wild-type

Figure 20.8. Sex differences in male and female fruit flies are usually obvious, like, for example, the larger size of the female and the dark tip of the male's abdomen. The difference in eye color shown in this photo is a matter of genes and not a characteristic sex difference. (Courtesy Clarence Flaten.)

animal.   It has been found that when a white-eyed male is crossed with a red-eyed female, only red-eyed flies are present in the F_1 generation.   Furthermore, when the brother and sister flies of the F_1 generation are mated, both red-eyed and white-eyed flies appear in the F_2 generation and in a ratio of 3 red-eyed to 1 white-eyed.   The white-eye character clearly is a recessive character controlled by a recessive gene, and the cross seems comparable to that observed when tall and dwarf peas were crossed.   Two important differences, however, were noted by Morgan and his co-workers: *first,* the F_2 white-eyed flies in the above cross were always males; and *second,* only the daughters of the white-eyed male parent could transmit the gene for white eyes to the F_2 generation.   (This was shown by crossing the F_1 males to normal red-eyed flies, in which case only red-eyed flies appeared.)   It became apparent that the gene for white eye was not passed from father to son but was always transmitted to the daughters.   This fact recalled the similar behavior of the X ♂ chromosome, because it will be remembered that this chromosome is never transmitted from father to son but always must be transmitted from father to daughter.   The parallel behavior of the gene for white eye and the X ♂ chromosome was interpreted by Morgan to mean that this gene is located on the X chromosome.   Here, then, was an opportunity to locate a specific gene on a specific chromosome.   Figure 20.9 illustrates the inheritance of white eye color in fruit flies and demonstrates the validity of the conclusion that the gene for white eye color is located on the X chromosome.   Such an association of genes with the sex chromosomes is spoken of as *sex linkage.*

An additional interesting fact was also discovered about the inheritance of sex-linked genes.   White-eyed female fruit flies are much rarer than white-eyed males; and this observation, coupled with the peculiar transmission of the gene for white eye through the F_1 generation, suggested the possibility that the *Y chromosome carries no gene for eye color.*   If this is true, a recessive character would appear in the male when a single recessive gene for the character is located on the X ♂ chromosome, because there would be no dominant gene on the Y chromosome to counteract its effect.   Also, in the female both X ♀ X ♀ chromosomes would be required to carry the recessive white eye genes in order for the recessive character to appear; therefore, it would show up less frequently in the female than in the male.   Repeated experimentation has verified the conclusion that the Y chromosome does not carry a gene for eye color, and it has been shown further that there are only a very few genes present on this chromosome.

It has been possible to demonstrate that there are many genes located on the X chromosomes.   Yellow body, white eye, miniature wings, and forked bristles are some of the known characters controlled by additional genes located on the X chromosomes of *Drosophila*.   The presence of genes on the X chromosomes of man also is known, and the transmission of these genes from generation to generation is exactly like that which occurs in the fruit fly.   Red-green color blindness and hemophilia (failure of the blood to clot properly) are well-known

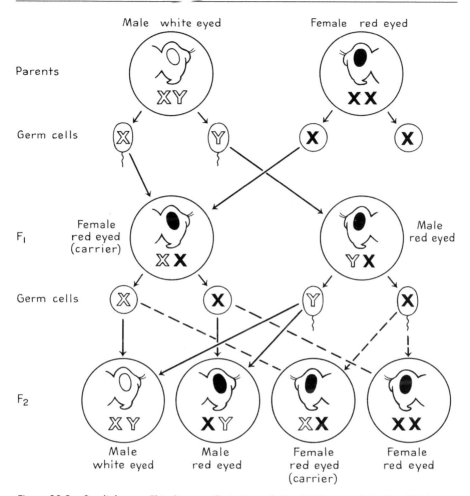

Figure 20.9. Sex linkage. This diagram illustrates only the distribution of the X and Y chromosomes. Chromosomes which carry the recessive gene for white eye or have no gene (Y) are shown in white; chromosomes with the gene for red eye are shown in black.

examples of sex-linked characters. Hemophilia, fortunately, is a rare disease, and it is likely that few females are ever born who possess the two recessive genes for this blood disorder. A cross involving a woman with one recessive gene for hemophilia and a man who has hemophilia is illustrated in the diagram above.

An interesting side light on the transmission of hemophilia is the high incidence of this abnormality in certain of the royal houses of Europe. Cousin marriages were politically expedient among some members of the royalty, and the mating of these individuals concentrated the number of the abnormal genes

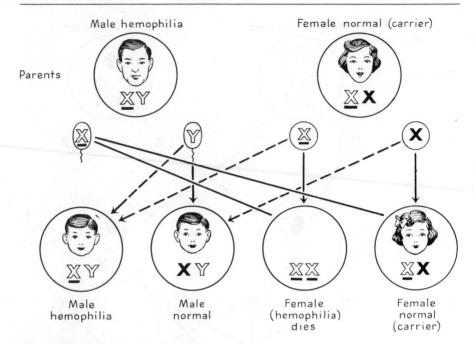

Figure 20.10. Sex-linked inheritance in man follows exactly the same pattern as that in fruit flies. The inheritance of hemophilia is a case in point. This diagram shows the genetic results when a man with the disease marries a woman who is a carrier.

in their descendants, with the result that many cases of hemophilia appeared. This is shown graphically in the diagram of the progeny of a woman carrying the gene married to a man who has hemophilia. Only two of the four possible types of children could be normal, and even one of these two would carry a gene for hemophilia. The Russian and Spanish royal houses especially were cursed by this hereditary ailment, and the results emphasize the danger of inbreeding (the mating of closely related individuals).

Linkage on other chromosomes

With the discovery of sex linkage, it was only natural that the geneticists would look for similar groups of genes on other chromosomes (those not associated with sex are called *autosomes*). Many genes have been located on each of the autosomes in man, and this has been true in every organism which has been studied. It has been established, for example, that there are approximately 30,000 genes in man, but there are only 46 chromosomes present. When several genes are located on the *same pair* of chromosomes, they cannot assort independently because they are linked together. This situation, which has been designated as *linkage*, therefore is an exception to independent assort-

ment.   An illustration of linked genes in human beings is provided by hemophilia and red-green color blindness.   A man who has these characters
possesses a recessive gene for each located on his X chromosome; hence, these
two genes would be "linked" and transmitted as a unit to his offspring.   No
independent assortment could take place between these genes.   In a similar
way, in *Drosophila melanogaster* the characters of white eye color, yellow body
color, miniature wings, and forked bristles which we previously mentioned are
linked because they are controlled by genes located on the X chromosome.

Linkage groups

A study of linkage in different organisms has shown that the number of groups
of linked genes is always equal to the number of pairs of chromosomes.   In
Drosophila melanogaster, where there are four pairs of chromosomes, we would

Figure 20.11.   The chromosome basis of linkage.   This diagram gives a further example of the
linkage of genes on chromosomes and shows the behavior in germ-cell formation of the genes
for black body color and vestigial wings.   The figures at the top refer to the relative distances,
in cross-over units, between the genes on the chromosomes (see page 522).   It should be noted
that B denotes grey and b signifies black.

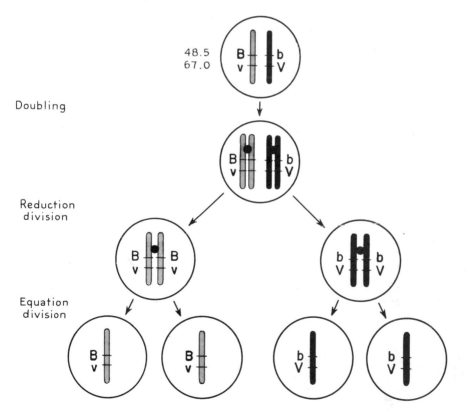

expect each pair to have its own group of genes, and there should be four linkage groups. There are four! *Drosophila willistoni*, on the other hand, has only three pairs of chromosomes and only three linkage groups. It is amazing that Mendel did not report linkage. Modern investigations show that the pea plants with which he worked have seven pairs of chromosomes and seven linkage groups. Mendel either did not observe linkage—which seems improbable—or he was so engrossed with independent assortment that he ignored linkage.

Crossing over

Early in the study of linkage it was discovered that there are instances in which linked genes do not remain together. This break in linkage is infrequent, but the percentage of breaks is very consistent for any given pair of genes. It soon became possible to predict the occurrence of these exceptions to linkage, and it became evident that this was a regular phenomenon. Any break in linkage must involve a *separation of genes* which are located on the same chromosome; so once again attention was directed to the behavior of the chromosomes in the reproductive cells. Meiotic divisions, therefore, were examined with great care in the search for clues that could explain linkage breaks.

We mentioned casually during the discussion of the prophase of meiosis that the chromosomes first appear as long coiled threads which lie side by side and are entwined. A closer examination discloses that by the middle of prophase the two homologous chromosomes are completely paired and are tightly coiled about each other. The two paired chromosomes are called *bivalents* and have four chromatids. In next to the last stage of prophase, the coiled bivalents partially uncoil and the four chromatids are apparent. The uncoiling is not carried to completion, however, and the chromatids continue to be in contact at various points along their lengths. The number of points of contact will vary for different bivalents. Longer bivalent chromosomes usually have a greater number of contacts than do shorter bivalents. It can be demonstrated conclusively that

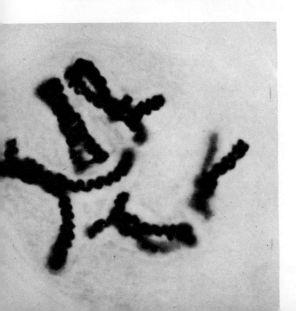

Figure 20.12. As this photograph beautifully illustrates, the coiling of chromosomes is a real phenomenon and not merely a theoretical possibility.

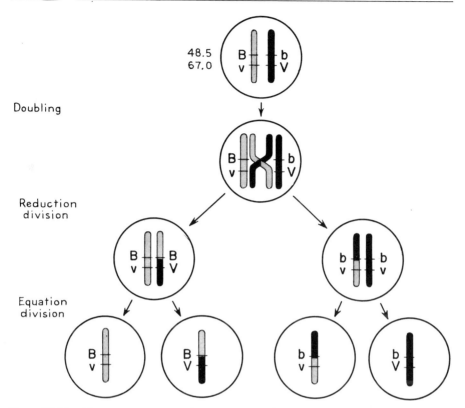

Figure 20.13. Chromosomes may exchange pieces as this diagram of crossing over indicates. This exchange results in "new" chromosomes with "new" gene combinations.

regions of nonsister chromatids are exchanged at the point of contact, that is, sections of chromatid strands which comprise the bivalent chromosomes are transposed. These points of contact and exchange are called *chiasmata*, and Figure 20.13 illustrates what can happen when transposition occurs between the genes for ebony body color and vestigial wings which are located on bivalent chromosomes.

A. H. Sturtevant, working in Morgan's laboratory, was the first to suggest that the linked genes are arranged in a line along the chromosomes, and that when pieces of chromosomes are exchanged, the groups of genes which are located on those sections of chromosome also will be exchanged or "crossed over" from one chromosome to another. It is interesting that Sturtevant made this suggestion before our detailed knowledge of the behavior of the chromosomes in meiosis was known. The term *crossing over* was used by Sturtevant to designate this breakage of linkage groups which is a product of chiasmata formation. Crossing over has been amply verified as providing *the mechanism*

Parent

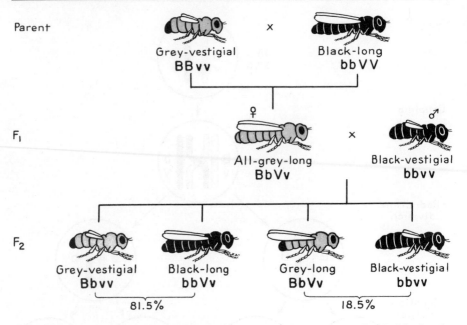

Figure 20.14. This diagram shows the results of a cross involving the genes for black body color and vestigial wings and indicates the degree of crossing over. Note the percentage indicated for the types of F₂ individuals.

for the breaking of linkage, but an additional question remains to be answered. Why is there a *predictable regularity* in the crossing over for specific genes, or, conversely, why does the percentage differ for various pairs of linked genes?

The problem of the predictable regularity with which crossing over takes place is subject to a simple explanation. The greater the distance between genes, the more likely it is that chiasmata will occur between them and that exchanges will result. The closer together the genes are, the less likely it will be that chiasmata are interposed.

Chromosome mapping

Utilizing the information derived from crossing-over percentages, it is possible to plot the *relative positions* of the genes on the chromosomes. This has been done for a number of organisms, and in the greatest detail for *Drosophila melanogaster*. The position of the genes remained on this relative basis for a number of years until new information made a more exact location possible.

There exist in the salivary glands of fruit flies giant chromosomes which have a very characteristic banding. This banding is different on each chromosome, and it is possible to locate the genes relative to these bands. The electron microscope has demonstrated the presence within these bands of bodies about the

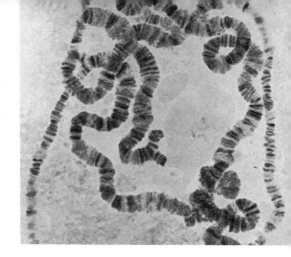

Figure 20.15. The giant salivary chromosomes show a characteristic banding. It has been possible to locate the positions of the genes relative to these bonds. (Courtesy Clarence Flaten.)

size that the genes are calculated to be.

It is known now that these bodies are *not* the genes. However, the bands do provide visible locations for the genetic units as we know them to be (p. 544) Therefore, by observing changes in the bands, it is possible to observe when genetic material has crossed over or even when genes have been lost ("deleted").

Multiple-gene inheritance

The Mendelian theory of heredity originally was based on the concept that *two genes* control a given character. It is now well known that characters in organisms often are influenced or controlled by more than two (a single pair) of genes. It should be emphasized, however, that the behavior of the several genes which are involved in such *multiple-gene* (often called *multiple-factor*) inheritance is in accord with the basic laws of segregation and independent

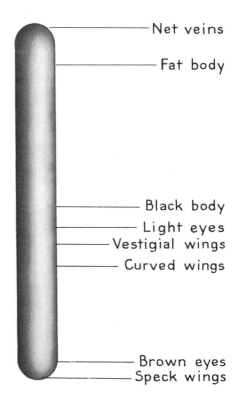

Net veins

Fat body

Black body

Light eyes

Vestigial wings

Curved wings

Brown eyes

Speck wings

Figure 20.16. Chromosome map. This diagram shows the relative positions of some of the genes which have been located on one of the chromosomes of the fruit fly. Included among them are the genes for black body and vestigial wings discussed in text.

Figure 20.17.   Human skin pigmentation.

assortment.   Exception to Mendel's ideas lies solely in the fact that more than two genes are involved in the determination of the particular character.   The inheritance of human skin pigmentation, for example, involves *at least* two pairs of genes.   These pairs of genes are located on different pairs of chromosomes, and both segregation and independent assortment of the individual genes occur. These genes do not show the type of dominance and recessiveness which we discussed earlier.   This is illustrated by a cross between Negro and white in which the children, *mulattoes,* are lighter than the Negro parent but are darker than the white parent.   Such an effect may be called *incomplete dominance* or *blending inheritance.*   When mulattoes marry, their children will show varying degrees of pigmentation, and a range from white to Negro is possible.

Inheritance of Human Skin Pigmentation					
Parents	Repro- ductive cells	F_1 gener- ation	Repro- ductive cells		F_2 generation
Negro (BBB′B′) × White (bbb′b′)	BB′ bb′	Mulatto BbB′b′ × BbB′b′	BB′ Bb′ bB′ bb′ BB′ Bb′ bB′ bb′	BBB′B′	$\frac{1}{16}$ Negro; 4 genes for black
				BBB′b′ BBb′B′ BBb′B′ bBB′B′	$\frac{4}{16}$ chocolate; 3 genes for black
				BbB′b′ bBb′B′ bbB′B′ bBB′B′ BBb′b′ Bbb′B′	$\frac{6}{16}$ mulatto; 2 genes for black
				Bbb′b′ bbb′B′ bbb′B′ bBb′b′	$\frac{4}{16}$ brunette (skin); 1 gene for black
				bbb′b′	$\frac{1}{16}$ white; 0 genes for black

We have already touched upon evidence which demonstrates that multiple-gene inheritance is present in fruit flies. We directed our attention to the fact that the gene for *black body color* is different from the gene for *ebony body color* and that these genes are located on different chromosomes (p. 519). Still another gene, that for yellow body color (p. 516), is on the X chromosome. The wild-type body color, *grey,* is due to a series of gene pairs, and at least *one dominant* (grey) gene must be present in *each pair* in order to produce the grey body color. It has been demonstrated also that there are at least eight different gene pairs concerned with eye pigmentation in fruit flies. Each of the eight pairs must also contain at least one dominant (red) gene if red eye color is to develop. Conversely, if any one of the eight pairs is made up of two recessive genes, the eye color will not be red. It has become increasingly evident that most characters are controlled by more than a single pair of genes, and that multiple-gene inheritance is the rule rather than the exception.

Mutation

The wild-type fruit flies have a grey body color which we have just noted to be a result of the presence of a series of dominant grey genes. Fruit flies with grey body color can be bred in the laboratory for many generations, and all the offspring will have the grey color. Sooner or later, however, there will appear one or more flies with a different body color. Yellow body is one such example of a color variation which may appear suddenly in a population of grey flies, and this new color variation will be inherited. Any such hereditary deviation of a character from the normal is spoken of as a *mutation;* both the reason for its sudden appearance and the method of its inheritance are of great significance to the geneticist. Let us, therefore, analyze the occurrence of the yellow body color in *Drosophila melanogaster.*

It is a simple matter to cross yellow-bodied and grey-bodied flies and to observe that yellow is recessive. Furthermore, because of the regularity of the results, the cross indicates that the yellow color is gene-controlled.

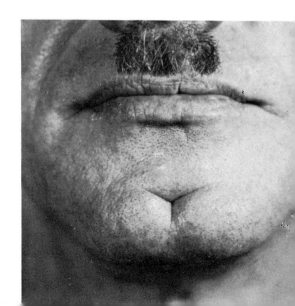

Figure 20.18. This cleft chin is due to a dominant gene. (Courtesy Clyde E. Keeler.)

Figure 20.19. Mutations, occurring in all organisms, can be good or bad. The famous mutation that produced short-legged sheep was obviously good, at least from man's point of view: the sheep are easier to herd and can be kept in by very low fences. (Courtesy Christian Wreidt.)

A more careful analysis shows that half the males in the F_2 have yellow bodies, and this is comparable to the inheritance of white eye color noted on page 517. We are reasonably certain, therefore, that the gene for yellow is on the X chromosome. It is possible, of course, to make a cross of red-eyed, grey-bodied flies with white-eyed, yellow-bodied flies, and to determine if the genes for yellow body and white eye are linked. This has been done and shown to be true! It is possible in this latter cross not only to determine that the genes are linked, but also to determine the percentage of crossing over and the relative position of the genes for grey and yellow. Such crossing-over data prove that the grey and yellow genes are located at the same point on the X chromosomes, and that the two genes never can be found simultaneously on one X chromosome. The conclusion is that a dominant grey gene has undergone a change to become a recessive yellow gene. This hereditary change, therefore, is usually spoken of as a *gene mutation,* or a *point mutation.*

Gene mutations, however, are not the only mutations that can occur in the genetic composition of plants and animals. Chromosomes may fragment during mitosis, and *pieces of chromosomes* may be distributed atypically to the daughter cells. One new cell formed as a result of such an abnormal cell division may receive an *extra portion* of one chromosome, and conversely, another cell may have a corresponding *partial* chromosome. Groups of genes, because of their location on these pieces, will either be added to or subtracted from the resulting new cells. *Entire chromosomes* may sometimes be distributed in an unusual manner, and at division one cell may gain an entire *extra chromosome* at the expense of another cell, which will lose an entire chromosome. A more striking phenomenon is the duplication of an *entire set of chromosomes.* Thus, a *Drosophila* egg cell, as a result of the failure of the chromosomes to undergo meiotic division, might receive 8 chromosomes and the new individual formed at fertilization might have 12 chromosomes—8 from the egg and 4 from the sperm. Instead of having two genes per character, such an animal would have three. Cells with four full sets of chromosomes, and consequently four sets of genes, have also been observed. It is possible to modify cell divisions experimentally in plants by treating them with the chemical substance, *colchicine.* These colchicine-treated plant cells undergo chromosome duplication without undergoing cell division, with the result that the chromosome number in the reproductive cell is doubled. Such cells, when combined with similar reproductive cells of the opposite sex also having a double number of chromosomes, produce an individual with four full sets of chromosomes. Plants containing an extra set or two extra sets of chromosomes may differ radically from parent-type plants. Such plants frequently are larger than the parent and may be so strikingly different in appearance that they might easily be mistaken for new species. Plants which have four full sets of chromosomes may reproduce in a normal manner, forming reproductive cells, each of which contains two full sets of chromosomes. The next generation, therefore, will contain the four complete sets.

The extremely slow rate at which mutations occur led the geneticists many years ago to seek a means of increasing the mutation rate. One of the first successful experiments was reported by Muller, who had treated *Drosophila* with X-radiation. It was found that the mutation rate was increased approximately 100 times by such radiation. It was further noted that the rate of mutation was directly proportional to the dosage of X-rays used. Subsequent to the work of Dr. Muller, for which he received the Nobel prize, other investigators have discovered that ultraviolet light, temperature, mustard gas, and the radiation from atomic energy sources are also effective in producing mutations. These cause not only gene mutation but also chromosome fragmentation; alteration of the number of sets of chromosomes may also result. This experimental

Figure 20.20. The apple on the left is a normal apple; the one on the right has a double set of chromosomes, resulting in the obvious increase in size. (United States Department of Agriculture; courtesy Haig Derman.)

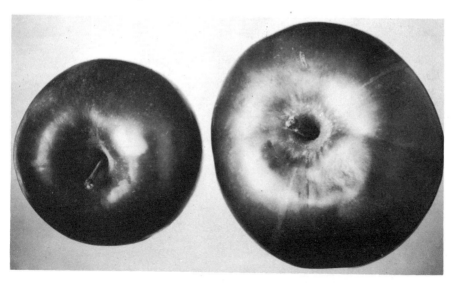

production of mutations has greatly facilitated the work in genetics. The basic advantage of using *Drosophila*, which accrued from the fact that a single generation could occur in the short period of 10 days, has now been supplemented by mutations produced almost at will. These studies have expanded our understanding of genetic mechanisms and of the creation of new characters in organisms.

It has now been shown that most mutations are recessive. These mutations produce alterations in the enzyme systems of the organisms, which for the most part are slight; but when several successive mutations are present in a given organism, the accumulative effects may be considerable. It has been amply demonstrated that accumulated recessive mutations may greatly reduce the viability of the organism; and mutations, when present in the homozygous condition, frequently are lethal to the organism.

Our knowledge of mutations has been used to economic advantage. The use of crosses of distantly related plants and animals to introduce new dominant genes into a stock to replace recessive genes is an application of this knowledge.

Figure 20.21. This bizarre collection of abnormal fish is the result of exposure to radiation. (Courtesy University of Washington, Applied Fisheries Laboratory.)

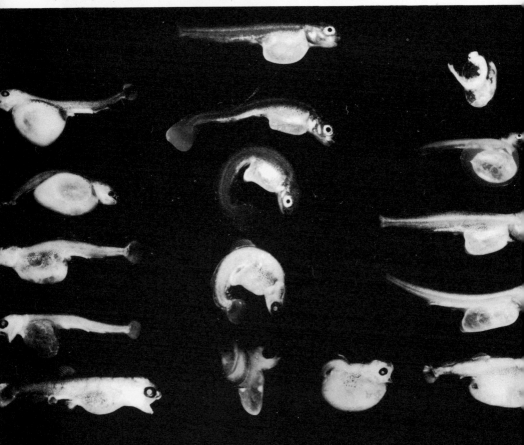

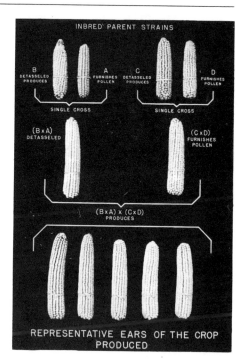

Figure 20.22. Hybrid corn. (Courtesy United States Department of Agriculture, Bureau of Plant Industry.)

When two distantly related organisms are crossed, the dominant genes frequently produce a condition which is known as *hybrid vigor*. Hybrid plants and hybrid animals frequently are superior to either of the parent stocks. The example which has attracted the greatest attention in recent years has been the development of hybrid corn. Stocks selected for the presence of certain favorable characteristics are used for controlled breeding. These characteristics may involve the size of the ear, the thickness of the stalk, the uprightness of the stalk, or the starch content of the grains. These features are combined in the offspring by bringing together parent plants which contain the necessary genes for each of the desired characters.

The results of corn hybridization are so well known that they probably require little comment, but we might point out that during the period of World War II the hybrid corn produced in the United States was 300,000,000 bushels greater than before the introduction of hybridization; and 23,000,000 fewer acres of land were needed to produce this increased amount of corn. The value of the extra corn produced during the World War II period was valued at more than enough to pay for the total cost of the Manhattan project for atomic research.

The use of hybridization to improve domestic animals is not new. Startling progress has been made, however, in recent years in the improvement of cattle and poultry by hybridization. It is possible to hybridize fowls, either to increase their size for the meat production, or to increase egg production. It is often advantageous also to *inbreed* animals or plants.   It will probably be obvious, however, that inbreeding, while it may be helpful, also increases the probability that recessive genes may be accumulated in greater numbers as a result of the inbreeding.   Brothers and sisters are more likely to have the same recessive genes than are distantly related organisms.   The cross of brother to sister, which is often done in animal inbreeding, will increase the possibility of characters being homozygous for recessive genes.   The breeder who is making such crosses should eliminate from each generation any animal which shows harmful recessive characteristics but retain those organisms in which the dominant genes are accumulated.   The dominant genes in the homozygous condition will, of course, accent the desired character.

It is obvious why inbreeding is sometimes a problem in human populations, and why there are social taboos and even laws against cousin marriages.   The difficulties which arise from human inbreeding are as much sociological as they are biological.   Humane considerations deter us from callously eliminating unfortunate individuals who receive an overabundance of harmful genes as a result of inbreeding.   As a matter of fact, subnormal persons usually receive institutional care and welfare help at considerable expense to their more fortunate kinsmen.   The example cited previously of the occurrence of hemophilia in certain royal families is an excellent illustration of the harm of inbreeding.

REFERENCES

ALTENBERG, E., *Genetics*. Henry Holt and Company, New York, 1945.

BARRY, J. M., *Molecular Biology. Genes and the Chemical Control of Living Cells*. Prentice Hall, Englewood Cliffs, New Jersey, 1964.

BONNER, DAVID M., *Heredity*. Prentice Hall, Englewood Cliffs, New Jersey, 1964.

DOBZHANSKY, T., *Genetics and the Origin of Species*. Columbia University Press, 1951.

GARDNER, ELDON U., *Principles of Genetics*. John Wiley and Sons, New York, 1964.

LEVINE, R. P., *Genetics*. Holt, Rinehart, and Winston, New York, 1962.

McELROY, WM. D., and BENTLEY GLASS, *The Clinical Basis of Heredity*. The Johns Hopkins Press, Baltimore, Maryland, 1957.

MENDEL, GREGOR, *Experiments in Plant Hybridisation* (Translation). Harvard University Press, 1938.

MORGAN, T. H., *The Theory of the Gene*. Yale University Press, 1928.

MULLER, H. J., "The Gene." Pilgrim Trust Lecture for 1945. Proceedings of the Royal Society, Series B, *134*, 1947.

MULLER, H. J., C. C. LITTLE, and L. H. SNYDER, *Genetics, Medicine, and Man*. Cornell University Press, 1947.

SCHEINFELD, A., *You and Heredity*. J. B. Lippincott Company, Philadelphia, 1951.

SNYDER, L. H., *Medical Genetics*. Duke University Press, 1941.

STERN, C., *Principles of Human Genetics*. W. H. Freeman and Company, San Francisco, 1949.

WILSON, E. B., *The Cell in Development and Heredity*. The Macmillan Company, New York, 1928.

WINCHESTER, A. M., *Genetics*. Houghton Mifflin Company, Boston, 1951.

21

The Genetic

Determiners

•

"I have said before, that a Man did excell all other Animals in this faculty, that when he conceived any thing whatsoever, he was apt to enquire the conse-quences of it, and what effects he could do with it. And now I adde this other degree of the same excellence, that he can by words reduce the consequences he findes to general Rules . . ." Thomas Hobbes, *Leviathan*, 1651

The nature of the determiners

Three questions were asked at the beginning of Chapter 20. The first was: What is the location of the determiners which regulate living processes? The second was: How are the determiners transmitted? Modern Mendelian ge-netics has given us the term genes to designate the determiners, has confirmed their location on the chromosomes and the manner of their transmission. The third question, however, remains to be analyzed. It is a two part query: What is the nature of these determiners, and how do the determiners regulate cell activities? Fortunately, biochemical research during the last two decades has provided us with the clues necessary to decipher the puzzles of the nature of the gene and its regulatory action. We outlined much of the basic information in our earlier discussion of the polymers of the cell. It is important now to expand that discussion to embrace an account of the dynamic relationship among the macromolecules of living systems.

We recounted earlier that Meischer had discovered nucleic acids and pro-teins in the nucleus. Other investigators subsequently established the fact that one of the nucleic acids, *DNA*, was found only in chromatin material. When it was determined that the genes are located on the chromosomes, it seemed logical to assume that the genes might be proteins. The studies of H. J. Muller, who produced mutations in fruit flies by X-ray treatments, suggested that ap-parently gene size was compatible with the size of protein molecules. Proteins also are complex molecules composed of combinations of many amino acids, and this almost infinite variety in the chemical composition of proteins could provide a theoretical basis for the impressive diversity of genes.   There are serious objections, on the other hand, to the hypothesis that genes are proteins. We know that genes are arranged in a linear fashion on the chromosomes and that they duplicate themselves exactly when a cell divides.   It is difficult to imagine how a complex protein molecule could do this.   If the molecule were to split lengthwise, one would expect each new half to be the mirror image of the original rather than to be the exact duplicate.   It is possible to assume that a template could be formed by a "protein-gene" and that a "new gene" could be formed by the template.   Proteins, however, are three-dimensional molecules and so it is difficult to visualize how a template might organize a complex three-dimensional "protein-gene."   Fortunately, biophysicists and biochemists were directing their attention to the nucleic acids as well as to the proteins of the chromosomes.   The direction taken by these studies provided the "yeast" that has created a "ferment" in all of biology today.

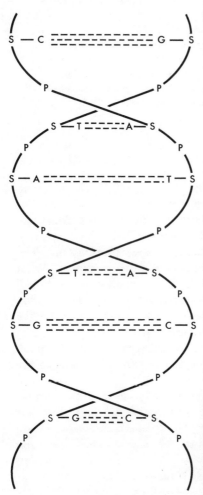

DNA as the gentic material

In the 1950's it became possible to analyze the nucleic acids—that is, to characterize them in a fashion comparable to similar analyses of the proteins.   The initial investigations established that in addition to the phosphate and sugar, the DNA molecule contains the four bases: *adenine, thymine, guanine,* and *cytosine* (p. 32).   Later observations indicated that the phosphate and sugar molecules are joined to form two strands which coil and twist about each other to form a double helix.   We also recall (p. 33) that the combination of a phosphate, a sugar, and a base is a *nucleotide.*   We know now that the adjacent nucleotides of

Figure 21.1. Simple representation of DNA. This spiral of DNA indicates the arrangement of the various components of the molecule in their proper relationship.   Here P = phosphate, S = sugar (deoxyribose), T = thymine, A = adenine, C = cytosine, and G = guanine. Note the bonding between A = T and C = G. (Modified from several sources.)

each strand are coupled by hydrogen bonds to form *nucleotide pairs*. These nucleotide pairs, therefore, serve to tie the coiled sugar-phosphate strands together. The arrangement of the molecules is such that the structure of the DNA molecule often has been described as being similar to that of a rope ladder. The "ropes" would consist of the strands of phosphate and sugar molecules and the "rungs" would be formed by the nucleotide pairs.

The structure of DNA

Using X-ray diffraction techniques, M. H. F. Wilkins determined that the DNA molecule is symmetrical, and Erwin Chagoff made the significant discovery that there is an equality in the amounts of the bases; for example, the amount of adenine is equal to that of thymine and the amount of guanine is equal to that of cytosine. If we now examine the structure of the four bases more carefully, we will note that the *purine bases*, adenine and guanine, are larger than the *pyrimidine bases*, thymine and cytosine. It was with these facts in mind, and at this period in the study of DNA, that J. D. Watson and F. H. C. Crick advanced their revolutionary hypothesis that eventually led to the idea that the model they proposed for the DNA molecule could meet all the known requirements for a gene.

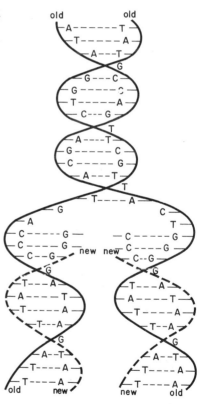

Waston and Crick theorized that the DNA molecules could be symmetrical, as the Wilkins data required, only if one of the larger purine bases was joined to one of the smaller pyrimidine bases. The evidence for the calculated distance between the two strands of the DNA helix is too small for two larger purines and too great for two small pyrimidines. Apparently, however, the distance is adequate for a combination of one large purine and one small pyrimidine. There also exists another extremely important restriction with respect to the pairing of the bases. Cytosine and guanine have three hydrogen bonds but thymine and

Figure 21.2. The replication of DNA, according to Watson and Crick. (Redrawn from Sutton, *Genes, Enzymes, and Inherited Diseases,* Holt, Rinehart, and Winston, New York, 1961. (Modified from Watson and Crick.)

adenine have only two hydrogen bonds. Watson and Crick concluded, therefore, that only two combinations of bases could occur in DNA: (1) *cytosine* (a
small molecule with three hydrogen bonds) could join only with *guanine* (a
large molecule with three hydrogen bonds); and (2) *thymine* (a small molecule
with two hydrogen bonds) could join only with *adenine* (a large molecule with
two hydrogen bonds). A schematic representation of a portion of the DNA
molecule shows it as it is now visualized.

Furthermore, Watson and Crick suggested that the DNA spiral could uncoil,
and that the two threads could separate by a shearing of the hydrogen bonds
between the bases. The major problem remains, however, that *exact duplication of the genetic material must occur.* In order for the Watson-Crick hypothesis to be correct, the new cell must regenerate a new strand for each of the two
original strands of DNA, and the composite old and new strands of DNA must
be exactly like the parent DNA double spiral.

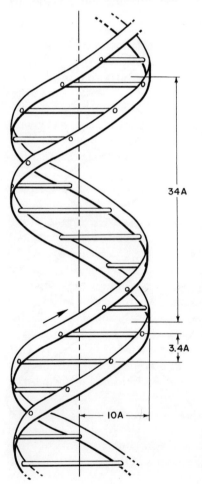

34A

3.4A

IOA

DNA duplication

Let us examine more closely the two un-
raveled strands, A and B, in the diagram.
New DNA strands which are to be synthesized from raw material in the cell, according to Watson and Crick, could use each
single strand of the preexisting DNA as a
model. There are, however, stringent
limitations on the synthesis: adenine can be
joined only with thymine, and guanine only
with cytosine. Molecular size differences
and the number of hydrogen bonds impose
these rigid restrictions. The result would
be that two new double strands, A^1 and B^1,
would be formed, and each would be identical in their base-pair combinations to the
parent double strand of DNA.

A hypothesis as startling and sweeping as
that suggested by Watson and Crick could
not be accepted by biologists regardless of
how impressive it might look on paper unless there was verification with experimental
data. Fortunately, this broad hypothesis

Figure 21.3. The Watson-Crick DNA double
helix. (After Watson and Crick, *Cold Spring
Harbor Symposia on Quantitative Biology,* Vol.
18, 1953. (Modified from Watson and Crick.)

which embraces biochemistry, biophysics, and biology can be tested by modern methods in all three fields. Tremendous numbers of cleverly designed experiments have been directed toward the problem of verifying or disproving the hypothesis that DNA is the genetic material. One experiment of the many which support the Watson-Crick hypothesis will be used as an initial illustration.

Radioactive isotope marker for chromosome duplication

It is possible to analyze many microchemical reactions in cells by using molecules which have been marked by incorporating into them an isotope of a normal element. Isotopes of carbon, hydrogen, phosphorous, and nitrogen are very advantageous in such investigations because these elements are present normally in biological macromolecules. An experiment which served as a first step in the verification of the DNA duplication hypothesis utilized tritium (H^3), the radioactive form of hydrogen, to mark a molecule of thymine (as thymidine). This radioactive molecule provides a source of the base thymine for DNA. The experiment was relatively simple as many significant experiments often are. Rapidly dividing cells were placed in a medium containing the tritiated thymidine, and after a period of exposure some cells were removed, fixed, and covered with a photographic film. Since silver grains in the film will be darkened when a radioactive particle strikes them, a cell will take its own picture, an *autoradiograph*. An image is produced, however, only where the radioactive elements are present.

All of the chromosomes in the fixed cells which had undergone division during exposure to the tritiated thymidine were radioactive, which indicated an incorporation of the radioactive element. The second phase of the experiment was now performed. The cells which remained after the first sample was removed were now placed in a medium without the radioactive isotope and allowed to divide. They in turn were fixed, autoradiographs were made, and it was observed that only one half of the chromosomes were radioactive.

The explanation is that each strand (chromatid) of the chromosome of the cell which divided in the tritiated thymidine acted as a template to organize its complementary strand and used the radioactive thymidine during the process. Each of the new chromosomes, therefore, was radioactive. At the next division, *in a medium free from radioactivity*, the chromatids of the chromosomes again separated, and each "primed" the formation of a new chromatid. One of the newly formed second-generation chromosomes was radioactive but the other was not. The original nonradioactive chromatid had formed a new partner which was also nonradioactive, and a nonradioactive chromosome resulted. The second strand, the "new" one cited above, was radioactive and it also organized a nonradioactive chromatid, but the chromosome formed of these strands was radioactive because one chromatid contained tritiated thymidine molecules. Thus one half of the chromosomes in the second generation were radioactive.

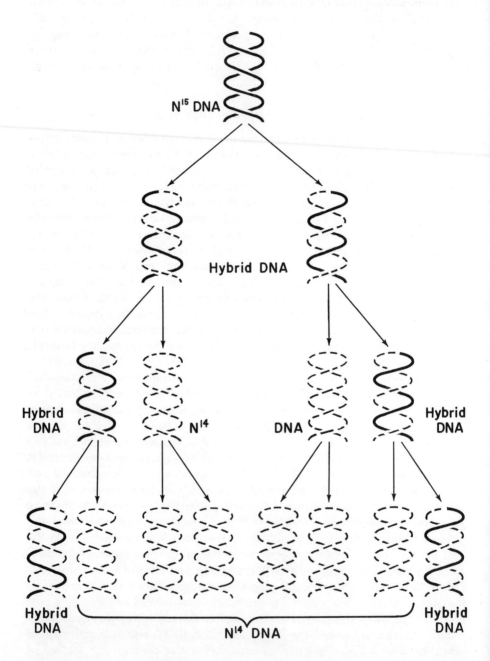

Figure 21.4.   DNA duplication in E. coli.

Heavy isotope marker for DNA duplication

Suggestive as these results are, they actually demonstrate only that the behavior of the chromosomes during division parallels the expected behavior of the DNA molecules they contain. A more critical experiment, however, strongly indicates that the assumption of DNA involvement was correct.

In 1958 M. Meselson and F. Sahl took advantage of the fact that the DNA of the bacterium *E. coli* could be isolated and studied in a test tube. They grew these bacteria in a culture medium which contained the isotope N^{15}, which has greater mass than the more common N^{14}, and after a period of time they extracted the DNA from some of the *E. coli* cells and analyzed it.

The analysis consisted of placing DNA molecules in a centrifuge tube that contained a solution of cesium chloride and subjecting the tubes to high-speed centrifugation (ultracentrifugation). A density gradient is established in the salt solution, the most dense area occurring at the periphery of the centrifugal field. The N^{15}-DNA, which has greater density than does N^{14}-DNA, therefore will occupy a different position in the density gradient than will the less dense N^{14}-DNA, and the two types can thus be separated. The results of the actual experiment were most encouraging.

DNA from cells which were grown for periods of time in a medium which contained N^{15} had DNA molecules with greater than normal density. The DNA, therefore, was concluded to contain N^{15} and was designated as N^{15}-DNA. A second phase of the experiment was then performed. The *E. coli* cells which had only N^{15}-DNA were now grown in a medium which had only N^{14}, and after the first division of the cells some were removed, their DNA extracted, and analyzed in a density gradient. This analysis showed that the DNA was of intermediate density: it had greater density than N^{14}-DNA but lesser density than N^{15}-DNA. It was concluded that this DNA was a hybrid DNA consisting of strands of N^{14}- and N^{15}-DNA.

Some of the *E. coli* cells which were permitted to continue their growth in the N^{14} medium were removed after a second division and the DNA was analyzed. There were equal amounts of both N^{14}-DNA and N^{15}-DNA present, but this time in a ratio of three N^{14}-DNA to one N^{15}-DNA. The diagram which represents the interpretation of the results as given by Meselson and Sahl should further explain the events which occur during DNA duplication. It is evident that the best explanation for the data at present is that each strand of the DNA spiral acts as a pattern for the formation of new DNA, and the results support the basic ideas of Watson and Crick in this respect.

Structure of RNA

We should include a brief account of the nature of the ribonucleic acid molecule at this point. Obviously, the sugar in the RNA molecule is *ribose* instead of deoxyribose. It appears also that RNA consists of a single strand of alternating phosphate and ribose molecules. This single strand, however, can fold back on itself to form a symmetrical helix and the coiling, as in the case of DNA, is influenced by the sizes of the bases and the number of their hydrogen bonds. The presence of ribose and the basic single-strand arrangement of the RNA molecule is accompanied by another highly significant difference between RNA and DNA. The pyrimidine base thymine is not present in RNA, but it is supplanted by another pyrimidine, *uracil*. The uracil molecule being small and with two hydrogen bonds can pair only with *adenine*. The bases of RNA, therefore, are *guanine, cytosine, adenine,* and *uracil*.

The relationship of genes and enzymes

We have considered the first part of the third question concerning the nature of genetic material and must now attempt to answer the second part: How does the genetic material control living processes? Biologists and biochemists have recognized for many years that all chemical processes in the protoplasm are regulated by those organic catalysts, the enzymes, and that enzymes are very specific. Evidence for a direct relationship between the genes and the enzymes, however, was not known until about two decades ago. At that time George W. Beadle and E. L. Tatum, who were studying the bread mould, *Neurospora,* advanced the idea that there exists in organisms a "one gene-one enzyme" relationship. *Neurospora* contains enzymes which enable it to supply its own nutritional needs by synthesizing complex molecules from such simple substances as salts, sugar, water, and ammonia. Important among the nutritional molecules which this mould synthesizes is the amino acid, *tryptophane*. The mould has a special enzyme, *tryptophagenase,* which is necessary for the synthesis of tryptophane, and a single gene mutation will either prevent the formation of the enzyme or cause the development of an inhibitor which blocks the action of the enzyme. Tryptophane can not be formed in either case.

The mutation demonstrates that there is a direct relationship between a gene and an enzyme in *Neurospora,* and the results naturally directed attention to similar studies in other organisms. It has been observed in man that another amino acid, *phenylalanine,* is essential in the human organism for the formation of *melanin,* which is the pigment that determines the color of skin, eyes, and hair. A gene mutation can prevent the formation of an enzyme that is necessary for one of the steps in the transformation of phenylalanine to the pigment melanin. The reaction is stopped before completion and an intermediate substance known as dopa* is accumulated. A person who is homozygous for this mutation will therefore lack the pigment melanin and will be an albino.

There is a second very significant reaction which involves phenylalanine in the human organism. In this reaction phenylalanine is broken down by a series of five enzymes to carbon dioxide and water with the release of energy. We will call the sequence of enzymes V, W, X, Y, and Z. A gene mutation which

*dihydroxyphenylalanine.

leads to a homozygous condition (ww) will prevent the formation of what we have designated as the W enzyme. The chemical reaction will then stop with the formation of an intermediate substance, phenylpyruvic acid. A person who is homozygous recessive will excrete this acid in the urine. It is significant that individuals who have this enzyme deficiency are imbeciles unless they receive medical attention in early infancy. A second gene mutation has also been observed in this enzyme sequence. In this case the homozygous recessive (zz) results in the absence of the Z enzyme, and the chemical reaction stops before completion with the formation of a different intermediate substance, *alcapton*. This chemical darkens when excreted and causes a very black urine, a condition known as *alcaptonuria*. Alcapton can also be deposited in fibrous tissue, bone, and cartilage. In persons having this disorder, darkened cartilage often will show through the thin skin covering the ears. Thus we have

$$\text{Phenylalanine} \rightarrow A \rightarrow B \rightarrow \underset{\text{recessive cc}}{|} \overset{\text{dopa}}{C} \rightarrow D \rightarrow \text{melanin.}$$

$$\text{Phenylalanine} \rightarrow V \rightarrow \underset{\text{recessive ww}}{\overset{\overset{\text{phenylpyruvic}}{\text{acid}}}{|}} W \rightarrow X \rightarrow Y \rightarrow \underset{\text{recessive zz}}{\overset{\text{alcapton}}{|}} Z \overset{\nearrow N}{\underset{\searrow H_2O}{\longrightarrow}} CO_2.$$

The function of RNA

Since the evidence is so overwhelming that the gene is actually associated with DNA and that the gene controls enzyme formation, we can now turn to the solution of our final query: How can DNA control enzyme formation and thus indirectly regulate all living processes? The answer is complex, especially since enzymes are proteins, and many aspects of the problems involved in protein synthesis are not yet clear. It is very apparent, however, that the second of our nucleic acids, RNA, is actively involved as an intermediary. The

Figure 21.5. Lack of skin pigmentation, known as *albinism*, is caused by a gene mutation. In extreme cases such as the brother and sister on the left, the skin, eyes, and hair are all affected and have no pigment. The albino negro on the right demonstrates the further point that this mutation has no influence on the inheritance of other characteristics.

investigations of RNA indicate rather conclusively that actually there are three types of RNA molecules and that they differ in their structure and function.

The first significant results which demonstrated a relationship of RNA to protein (enzyme) synthesis in cells were brought about as a result of ultracentrifugation of ruptured cells. We observed earlier that by using different gravity forces, nuclei can be separated from other cell components. Also, removal of nuclei can be followed by a separation of mitochondria. The application of higher centrifugal forces after the removal of mitochondria results in the isolation of another cell fraction which at first was called a "small particle," or *microsomal* fraction. When certain cells, such as those of the liver, were exposed to radioactive amino acids (the monomers of proteins) and the microsomal fraction was separated and studied, it was discovered that protein synthesis occurred on these small particles. Subsequent investigations revealed two additional facts. First, that the microsomes actually are composed of small fragments of endoplasmic reticulum to which ribosomes are adhering. We should also note that some cells have a very poorly developed endoplasmic reticulum and the ribosomes are in the cytoplasm. Centrifugation of such cells will produce a microsomal fraction af almost pure ribosomes. Second, the ribosomes are composed of protein and RNA and here, therefore, was the initial suggestion that RNA might be associated with enzyme synthesis.

It often happens in all fields of science that an answer, or partial answer, to one problem merely creates additional problems. This was the situation with respect to the RNA associated with the ribosomes. This RNA is now designated as ribosomal RNA (R-RNA). It is a large molecule with a molecular weight of approximately 2 million. The critical question may be asked: If ribosomal RNA is capable of synthesizing proteins which are characteristic of the cells of a given organism, how does the ribosomal RNA get its orders from the hereditary determiner DNA? Once more use of the radioisotope, P^{32}, was helpful in finding an answer because the radioactive phosphorous is readily incorporated into RNA. When cells are placed in a medium containing P^{32}, cell samples can be removed at different time intervals and autoradiographs can then be made. An interesting sequence of events is observed when this is done. Radioactivity associated with RNA appears first in the nucleus, then radioactive RNA moves quickly from the nucleus into the cytoplasm, and finally the radioactivity is found to be associated with the ribosomes.

The RNA which is formed in the nucleus and which migrates to the ribosomes is called *messenger* RNA (M-RNA) and differs from the R-RNA because it is assumed that M-RNA relays a message, or order, from the DNA to the ribosomes. There is evidence that ribosomal RNA is patterned for the synthesis of proteins but not for any specific protein. It is messenger RNA which determines the specificity. Still another problem remains to be solved in the series of events leading to protein synthesis. If we assume that the ribosomal RNA has received "orders" from DNA by way of M-RNA, the question remains how the amino-acid monomers are delivered to the ribosomes and arranged in the proper sequence to form a specific enzyme.   Another significant discovery has provided a clue for solving this problem.

A third type of RNA has been identified.   This RNA is very small and has only about one hundredth the molecular weight of R-RNA.   Furthermore, a terminal portion of the molecule has an unpaired strand with three free bases. When amino acids in the cell are "activated" by ATP, the small RNA molecule will pick them up and transfer them to the ribosomes.   This property of the small RNA molecule has led to its being named transfer RNA (T-RNA).

DNA determination of RNA

The relationship between DNA-RNA and the synthesis of proteins has been based on several assumptions.   It remains to be demonstrated, for example, that DNA can synthesize and "inform" messenger RNA.   Unless this occurs, the primary hypothesis of the regulation of cell activities by DNA will collapse like a house of cards.   It is fortunate that an impressive number of laboratories throughout the world, working independently of each other, have devised experiments which have given results that confirm the suggested role of DNA. Experiments have been performed on a great variety of organisms from bacteria to complex animals, and the observations indicate that DNA truly has universal action.   One of the first experiments involved the infection of bacteria with DNA from a virus.   When the new RNA from the bacteria was removed and analyzed, it was discovered that the arrangement of the bases in the bacterial RNA was like that in the DNA of the virus which was used for infection.   Evidently, the viral DNA served as a model for the RNA which was synthesized by the infected bacteria.

An even more striking study was the one designed to take advantage of the discovery that an enzyme can be extracted from nuclei or from bacteria which can synthesize RNA if DNA is present. The enzyme is appropriately named *RNA polymerase* (an "RNA polymer forming enzyme"), and its role in the synthesis of RNA can be shown in the following simplified reaction in which it is necessary to supply the bases in the form of triphosphates.   The type of RNA

$$
\begin{array}{c}
\text{UPPP} \\
\text{GPPP} \\
\text{APPP} \\
\text{CPPP}
\end{array}
\ \xrightarrow[\text{+ DNA}]{\text{RNA Polymerase}}\ (\text{UP + GP + AP + CP}) + \text{DNA} + 4\,(\text{PP})
$$

(Modified after Weiss and Hurwitz.)

formed in this experiment is a mirror of the DNA which was used as a model in the reaction.

Two additional studies can be cited that will illustrate the remarkable possibilities that exist for the analysis of microchemical events.   The first investigation involved the heating of a solution containing DNA to 40° C. and then the slow cooling of the solution.   Single strands of DNA will couple together into a double-strand helix *if their bases are arranged in proper complimentary sequence*—that is, if A is opposite T, C opposite G, etc.   Utilizing this technique, a second investigation was designed to test an important assumption: if a DNA molecule is the model for the synthesis of a given type of RNA, then upon heating and cooling there could be a coupling of the "parent" DNA with its "daughter" RNA.   It was possible to perform this experiment in an even more precise fashion by labelling the parent DNA with tritium (H^3), as we described earlier, and by marking the daughter RNA with radioactive phosphorous (P^{32}). If a hybrid DNA-RNA molecule double strand should be formed, then it would be marked with both radioactive isotopes.   *Hybrid DNA-RNA double strands were observed*, and these were found to be labelled with both of the radioactive isotopes.   The original assumption that there would be strands of DNA and RNA which were complementary to each other and which would form complexes was thus supported.

The current information on RNA synthesis and the role of the three types of RNA molecules has ben acquired quite recently, much of the data since 1960.   There are many questions that remain to be answered, but the nucleus appears to be the site of RNA synthesis with DNA acting as the model, or template.   Exactly how much of a single strand of DNA is involved is not clear. The evidence is conclusive, however, that the synthesis of new DNA occurs near the time of cell division, whereas RNA synthesis takes place during other periods of the cell cycle.   Later we will make a few statements concerning possible factors that might regulate RNA production.

The genetic code

The story of the DNA→RNA→enzyme relationship has unfolded with amazing rapidity, and for the first time biologists recognize a unifying principle which permeates all biological processes.   However we have failed to discuss the most significant feature of the action of the nucleic acid determiner.   What is the form of the messages transmitted from cell generation to cell generation by DNA or from the nucleus to the cytoplasm by RNA?   Let us return to a simplified representation of two short segments of DNA molecules.   We observe that the letters representing the four bases are arranged linearly, and it also has been discovered by analysis that any sequence of bases is possible on a single strand.   Our illustration shows two possible sequences: strand A has the sequence A, A, A, C, G, T; and strand B has the sequence C, A, T, G, G, G.

$$\frac{A}{A\ A\ A\ C\ G\ T}; \qquad \frac{B}{C\ A\ T\ G\ G\ G}.$$

Crick was one of the first to suggest that the arrangement of bases might constitute letters in a code which could "spell out words" for each of the 20 amino acids used in protein synthesis.

The problem is to decipher the code. Two base "letters" might be used together, for example, AA, AC, or GT in strand A. The difficulty with this code is obvious, inasmuch as only 16 possible two-letter code combinations exist but there are 20 amino acids! Certain code "letters," therefore, would need to be used for more than one amino acid. A number of investigators suggested, however, that a three-letter code, or *triplet,* would provide 64 "codewords" which would be more than enough for the number of amino acids. This code then can be illustrated by the combinations AAA, and CGT in strand A, or by CAT, and GGG in strand B. We can now visualize how messenger RNA molecules could be coded by each of our two strands of DNA during the time of RNA synthesis. The RNA formed by strand A (reading from left to right) would have uracil as complementary for each of the adenine bases, guanine for cytosine, cytosine for guanine, and adenine for thymine. A similar complementary relationship for RNA would occur in strand B.

The coding of RNA. Various investigators, notably M. W. Nirenberg and J. H. Matthaei, and S. Ochoa and collaborators, have made fantastic strides in breaking the triplet code. Nirenberg and Matthaei were able to prepare a synthetic RNA which contained only uracil. When this RNA was used in a special medium which contained the necessary ingredients for synthesizing protein, they observed the formation of a polypeptide chain consisting only of phenylalanine molecules. The RNA "codeword" for the amino acid phenylalanine obviously is the triplet UUU. Other techniques have made it possible to determine additional codewords and even to change one codeword into another. The code for the amino acid leucine is CUU, and if this sequence is changed to UUU by special chemical treatment, it becomes the codeword for phenylalanine. The codewords for many of the amino acids have now been determined. Present evidence indicates that in some instances there may be more than one triplet code for certain of the amino acids. If this is correct it may be a safety device by means of which an organism can assure that certain amino acids will be utilized. A mutation, for example, which might alter the code for a given amino acid and thus prevent its use could be counteracted if other codewords for that particular amino acid also are present.

Additional questions must be answered before we can consider the genetic code to be broken. A few of the answers, however, seem to be reasonably certain. Thus, "activated" phenylalanine will be transferred to the ribosome if the three-base "tail" of transfer RNA contains the UUU sequence. It also appears that AAA is the transfer "word" for "activated" lysine, and AUU for "activated" tyrosine, but the latter base sequence illustrates another problem. When two or three different bases are present in the code, we do not know, at this moment, the exact arrangement of the base "letters." The triplet code for glycine can serve as an example. The "letters" in the codeword for glycine are CGG, and they may "spell" glycine in that order. The possibility exists, however, that the spelling could be GCG or GGC. Another solution which is becoming more certain is that the triplet codes do not overlap. It was suggested that strand B in our schematic illustration had two triplets, CAT and GCG. If our illustration were an actual code instead of only an illustration, the overlapping codewords ATG or TGG would not exist. We also observed earlier that there apparently can be more than one codeword for certain of the amino acids. The code, therefore, is designated as a *"degenerate"* code. Furthermore, not all three letter codes have meanings; some are *"nonsense"* codes. Certain of the triplets seem to serve as commas or even as periods to punctuate the instructions which are being given to the RNA.

The nature of the gene

The early Mendelian interpretations of the gene suggested that it was an indivisible unit, or region, of the chromosome that was capable of mutating. The results which accompanied mutations produced by X-rays indicated that the molecular weight of the gene approximated that of small viruses. This morphological concept of a gene is inadequate today, since it has been demonstrated that DNA is the actual hereditary determiner and is in the form of a continuous double helix. The new designation of a gene is now based on the *functional aspect of the genetic material.* The term *cistron* has been applied to a region of the DNA molecule which regulates a given biochemical process within the cell. There are other requirements for a cistron which are highly technical and are better left for the consideration of a course in Genetics. The cistron, however, does not correspond exactly to a Mendelian gene. The fact that the cistron is subdivisible is one indication of this distinction in definition. The subdivisions withn a cistron are of two types and have been called a *recon* unit and a *muton* unit. The recon is the smallest region which can be *interchanged* between chromatids and which is *not itself divisible.* The muton, on the other hand, is the smallest region in which a change will produce a mutation. Size estimates of the three units which comprise our functional determiner or "modern gene" admittedly are crude. The cistrons apparently can vary greatly in their lengths, from approximately one thousand to several thousand nucleotide pairs. The estimated molecular weight of the cistron would be in the neighborhood of one million. A recon, at the other extreme, might involve only two nucleotide pairs. The size of a muton has been suggested to be about that of five nucleotide pairs. It is perhaps a code word of three bases with accompanying "punctuation." Obviously, if a cistron consists of thousands of nucleotide pairs and a muton of only five pairs, there can be hundreds of mutations within a single cistron.

One of the most striking illustrations of the functional relationship between a muton and a biochemical event concerns the formation of hemoglobin in the human being. Normal hemoglobin is a protein that contains approximately 600 amino acids. Several mutations are known which produce abnormal hemoglobins, and chemical methods have made it possible to determine the changes in the amino acids that have occurred to produce the mutated hemoglobins. A mutant form which has attracted great interest results in a type of anemia in which the red blood cells assume a sickle shape. This is called "sickle-cell anemia" and produces early death in individuals this affected. Chemical fingerprinting demonstrates that the amino acid, *glutamic acid*, of normal hemoglobin is replaced by another amino acid, *valine*, and this appears to be the only difference between the normal and abnormal hemoglobin molecules. The transfer RNA code for glutamic is *UAG* and for valine the code is *UUG*. We can speculate, therefore, that the change of a single base, A to U, could change the amino-acid composition of the hemoglobin and be responsible for the mutation. This perhaps is too simple an explanation, because we recall that we do not know the exact spelling of the codewords, nor do we understand the mechanism for cross-linking the polypeptide strands when hemoglobin is synthesized. Even if we make allowance for inadequate knowledge, it is evident that a muton may be the result of only a minor alteration in the base sequence of the DNA.

Regulation of RNA formation

We indicated earlier that DNA and RNA production in the nucleus occur at different times in the life of the cell. Duplication of DNA is associated with cell division, but we have only sparse information concerning the factors which may regulate RNA synthesis. Recently, P. Karlson and his associates have made significant observations which shed light on this problem. *Ecdysone* (p. 293), the metamorphic hormone of insects, has a marked effect on enzyme production in larvae and pupae. Since enzyme production is associated with M-RNA, T-RNA, and R-RNA, it occurred to Karlson to examine the giant chromosomes of the salivary glands of the midge fly to ascertain if there is any evidence of RNA synthesis. He and his co-workers discovered that when ecdysone is injected into larvae or pupae, there is an enlargement, "puffing," of the chromosomes. This puffing appears at definite regions of the chromosomes, and the location of the puffs varies with the age of the animal. The regions in early larvae differ in location from those in late larvae or pupae. Ulrich Clever also demonstrated that the puffing can move progressively along the chromosome with the result that more and more of the chromosome (and, therefore, the DNA) is involved. Treatment of chromosomes with radioactive uracil (as uridine) indicates that RNA is being produced in the puff regions. It was concluded that ecdysone causes the DNA helix to unwind to produce the puff, and that this loosening makes it possible for RNA to be synthesized. Karlson points out two interesting dosage relationships for the puffing reaction. First, the puffing will appear in chromosomes within 15 to 30 minutes. Second, a dosage of only one-half millionth of a mircogram is sufficient to produce the puffing effect.

The observations of Karlson and his co-workers might be dismissed as a peculiarity of insects were it not for the fact that somewhat comparable results are manifested in mammals following hormone treatments. Thyroxine, for example, stimulates metamorphosis in tadpoles, and there is a simultaneous

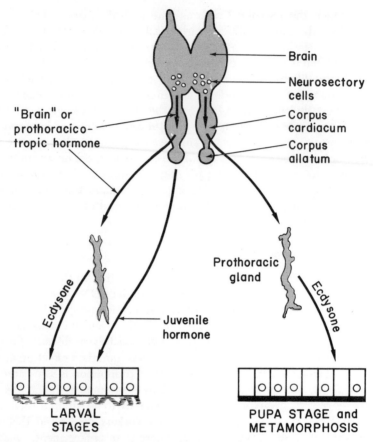

Figure 21.6. Ecdysone and juvenile hormone. This diagram illustrates the relationship between the three major hormones involved in insect metamorphosis. The brain secretes "brain hormone" or more properly, the *Prothoracicotropic hormone*, which in turn stimulates the Prothoracic gland to secrete *Ecdysone*. The corpora cardiaca act as storage sites for the brain hormone. The corpora Allata secrete *Juvenile hormone*. The left-hand side of the diagram indicates that both Ecdysone and Juvenile hormone are exerting effects on larval stages, but it should be noted that the proportions change as the larvae age. Ecdysone, as shown on the right, is the effective hormone at metamorphosis.

increase in RNA production and enzyme formation. The female sex hormone, *estradiol,* and the male sex hormone, *testosterone,* increase both RNA turnover and enzyme formation. The adrenal cortical hormone, *cortisol,* appears to have similar action. Perhaps the most striking illustration of the universality of chromosome changes associated with RNA formation is to be found in "lampbrush" chromosomes. These are chromosomes which have long lateral loops and have the appearance of the old-fashioned brushes used to clean kerosene lamp chimneys. The existence of these chromosomes has been known for nearly 75 years but their significance was not understood. Recently, the brilliant work of Callan and others has demonstrated that the elongated lateral loops are threads of DNA, and that RNA is being synthesized along these DNA threads. Mature amphibian eggs, those which are "prepared" to begin embryonic development, provide one of the best illustrations of the lampbrush chromosome phenomenon.

Extranuclear inheritance

The overwhelming influence of the chromosomal genetic determiners on inheritance tends to submerge the fact that there are instances in which factors outside the nucleus also have hereditary influence. One of the earliest observations of this fact involved the inheritance of the direction of coiling in the shell of the snail, *Limnaea*. The shell of these animals may coil either to the right or to the left. When crosses are made between snails which are heterozygous, the expected ratios of right to left coiling frequently do not appear. Analysis demonstrates that the direction of the coiling of the shell is determined by the organization of the cytoplasm of the egg, and that this cytoplasmic organization is determined in the ovary. Coiling actually is regulated by the maternal genes and not by the genes present in the egg after it has been fertilized. This phenomenon is called a *maternal effect*.

Particulate materials also exist in the cytoplasm of some organisms which reproduce, mutate, and are capable of affecting the inheritance of traits. The nature of the particles is not clear. It is possible that the *sigma* particles which are present in the cytoplasm of *Drosophila* may be viruses, and that the *kappa* particles that have been noticed in the cytoplasm of Paramecia may be bacteria.

A brief discussion of the significance of the kappa particles in Paramecia will serve to illustrate the problem which is involved in this type of inheritance by cytoplasmic factors.

T. M. Sonneborn and his associates observed that certain Paramecia release a substance into the water that will cause the death of other Paramecia. The Paramecia which release

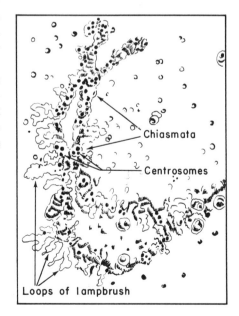

Chiasmata

Centrosomes

Loops of lampbrush

Figure 21.7. Lampbrush chromosome (bivalent). This photograph and sketch are of a lampbrush chromosome of an amphibian. Two chiasmata are obvious as well as numerous loops which give chromosomes of this type their "lampbrush" appearance. (Courtesy H. G. Callan, St. Andrews University.)

the substance are called *killers*, and those which are killed are designated as *sensitives*. A gene referred to by Sonneborn as K is responsible for the transmission of the killer characteristic from parent to offspring. Sonneborn demonstrated that there are particles in the cytoplasm which are responsible for the secretion of the killing substance, and he designated these particles as *kappa particles*. He named the killer chemical substance *paramecin* and established that the secretion of paramecin is dependent on the presence of both the dominant K gene and the presence of kappa particles in the cytoplasm as follows:

$$\text{K gene} + \text{kappa particle} \longrightarrow \text{paramecin.}$$

It is possible, with appropriate experimental techniques, to eliminate kappa from the cytoplasm of killer animals which possess the K gene. Paramecin is not produced under such conditions. It is also possible to introduce kappa into Paramecia which do not possess the K gene. The kappa particles cannot continue to exist in this situation. Special experimental procedures even make it possible to reintroduce kappa particles into animals which possess a K gene but which have previously lost kappa. These animals once again become killers. Kappa, therefore, can only be formed from previously existing kappa, and the K gene is needed for its reproduction. Kappa particles have been shown to be chemically similar to genes; they are self-reproducing, are transmitted from parent to offspring, and are able to mutate. Kappa, therefore, has features in comon with genes but its exact chemical nature is not fully understood. It may be a symbiotic bacterium which has become so closely associated with the Paramecia that it cannot exist in another environment.

The problem of embryonic differentiation

The remarkable series of events which occur during organogenesis in an embryo pose another major biological question. How do the cellular differences which lead to tissue and organ formation arise? This question was asked critically over a century ago by Von Baer (p. 132) and many others. The discovery of chromosomes and the proof they are the carriers of the genetic material suggested that blastomeres might become different because they receive different numbers or kinds of chromosomes. This idea could be tested experimentally. Blastomeres of echinoderm embryos, for example, can be separated from each other by placing the embryos briefly in calcium-free sea water. If this experiment is performed during the first three cleavage divisions, each of the separated blastomeres will develop into a small but normal embryo. The nuclei during early cleavage, are therefore said to be *totipotent*—that is, they have complete embryonic potentialities. The separation of the blastomeres at later stages of development, however, does not lead to the formation of complete embryos. Totipotency is lost.

Separation of blastomeres at even the two- or four-cell stages during cleavage in mollusks, however, results in the formation of abnormal embryos. It is obvious, therefore, that a significant difference exists in the cleavage patterns of echinoderms and mollusks. The eggs of the latter have a concentration of yolk at the vegetal pole, and at the first cleavage a large cell containing most of the yolk forms at the vegetal pole, whereas a smaller cell develops at the animal pole. This physical difference between the two blastomeres suggested that the cytoplasm could be exerting an influence on development. Extensive experimental work with many organisms established that there are two types of embryonic development. In the first type, cells do not differentiate immediately, whereas in the second there is immediate cellular differentiauon. The problem remained at this stage until investigations by Hans Spemann in the twentieth century added greatly to our understanding of embryonic events.

Induction

Spemann examined amphibian eggs and was particularly interested in the grey-crescent area. He did some extremely clever manipulations with hair loops, cautery, and transplantation, and the interpretation of his results has revolutionized our ideas concerning the interrelationship of various regions of the embryo. His experiments and those of others who followed his lead were so extensive that it will be possible to cite only a few definitive ones. Spemann tied a hair loop about the egg shortly after fertilization and constricted it in such a fashion that the zygote nucleus was confined to one half of the egg and no nucleus was present in the other half. The portion of the egg containing the nucleaus cleaved, but the nonnucleated portion did not. If the hair loop was loosened to permit one of the cleavage nuclei to reach the nonnucleated area, the latter also began to cleave and development usually proceeded in a normal fashion. The amphibian nuclei, at least during early cleavage, are totipotent. A second type of experiment, which superficially seemed similar to the first, gave very different results. The egg was constricted but the grey-crescent area was confined to the nonnucleated half of the egg. The nucleated portion cleaved, but its development was abnormal. The grey-crescent half, however, developed normally after a nucleus migrated into that area. The situation was comparable to that found in the mollusk embryo and demonstrated that the cytoplasm does influence development.

Spemann did not terminate his analysis at this point. He proceeded to establish that the blastomeres formed in the grey-crescent area fold under at the dorsal lip of the blastopore, are carried forward below the endoderm, and become involved in notochord development. He was able by means of extremely careful surgery to remove bits of the dorsal lip of the blastopore and to transplant this material to other regions of the embryo, for example, below the epidermis of the ventral surface. He observed that a notochord, a neural tube, and a brain could be induced to form by this procedure. He concluded that the dorsal lip material (from the grey-crescent area) was an *organizer* which by a process of *induction* can regulate development. Recent studies have demonstrated that even dead dorsal lip material can act as an organizer.   Furthermore, when the organizer is separated from cells in a tissue culture by membranes, it is possible for the organizer to be effective.   The use of filter membranes with pores of different sizes has established, however, that the inductor substance must be a rather large molecule.

Amphibian experiments

More recent experiments by Robert Briggs and T. J. King have furthered our knowledge of the role of nuclei in the developmental process.   Briggs and King were able to remove nuclei from unfertilized frog eggs and to replace them with nuclei taken from blastomeres at various stages of embryonic development. They observed that nuclei removed from blastomeres of the blastula stage were totipotent and normal development occurred after their implantation.   The implantation of nuclei taken from various regions of the gastrula stage, however, is usually capable of initiating cleavage and blastulation but, after the blastula

Figure 21.8.   Briggs and King Chart.   This chart was selected from the report of Briggs and King, 1957, which described the results of the transplantation of nuclei of frog embryos.   When nuclei from late gastrula stages were transplanted (second and third lines), cleavage and blastulation regularly occurred.   Nuclei transplanted from blastomeres of later stages of development were less successful in the development of embryos.   (From Robert Briggs and Thomas J. King, *Journal of Morphology* 100, 196, 1957, pp. 269–312).

Donor	Source of nuclei	Total number of blastula	Development of blastula				
	Animal hemisphere	39	2	 0	 0	 4	 33
	Endoderm	26 53	3 I	5 12	2 2	II 27	5 II
	Endoderm	16	2	9	I	3	I
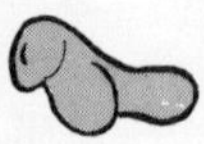	Endoderm	9	I	6	0	2	0

stage is reached, development ceases.   There is a strong suggestion, therefore, that the nuclei have been altered in some fashion with a resultant loss of their totipotency.

No conclusive answers can be given as yet to the physical conditions which are involved in cell differentiation during embryogenesis.   It is clear that the cytoplasm, as well as the nucleus, is exerting an influence.   External conditions of the cellular environment such as oxygen supply, light, temperature, and the position of individual blastomeres in the embryo, can influence the cytoplasm.   What the factor or factors in the cytoplasm may be is speculative.   There are a few clues which may be significant in regard to the nuclear changes.   Certain regions of chromosomes may stain very darkly and are said to be pycnotic.   These pycnotic regions are areas in which the DNA is very condensed.   Certain chromosomes can become entirely pycnotic—for example, one of the two X chromosomes may do so.   It seems reasonable to assume that the pycnotic regions of chromosomes, or an entire pycnotic chromosome, are not producing RNA.   Conversely, we have noted that in insect larvae the puffing of chromosomes is associated with RNA production.   This puffing, we remember, is a result of the action of a hormone, ecdysone, from the cytoplasm.   The embryologists in concert with fellow biologists, therefore, are finding that the DNA-RNA relationship affords a new approach to the century-old problem of embryonic differentiation.

REFERENCES

BARRY, J. M., *Molecular Biology.   Genes and the Chemical Control of Living Cells.* Prentice Hall, Englewood Cliffs, New Jersey, 1964.

BEERMAN, WOFLGANG, and ULRICH CLEVER. "Chromosome Puffs," *Scientific American, 210,* April 1964, pp. 58–65.

BONNER, DAVID M., *Heredity.* Prentice Hall, Englewood Cliffs, New Jersey, 1964.

BRIGGS, ROBERT, and THOMAS J. KING, "Changes in the Nuclei of Differentiating Endoderm Cells as Revealed by Nuclear Transplantation," *Journal of Morphology, 100,* 1957, pp. 269–312.

CHARGAFF, ERWIN, *Essays on Nucleic Acids.* Academic Press, New York, 1960.

CRICK, F. H. C., "The Genetic Code," *Scientific American, 207,* October 1962, pp. 66–77.

DAVIDSON, ERIC H., "Hormones and Genes," *Scientific American, 212,* June 1965, pp. 36–45.

GARDNER, ELDON U., *Principles of Genetics.* John Wiley and Sons, New York, 1964.

GINKS, JOHN L., *Extrachromosomal Inheritance.* Prentice Hall, Englewood Cliffs, New Jersey, 1964.

LEVINE, R. P., *Genetics.* Holt, Rinehart, and Winston, New York, 1962.

LOCKE, MICHAEL (ed.), *Cytodifferentiation and Macromolecular Synthesis.* Academic Press, New York, 1963.

MITTWOCH, URSULA, "Sex Differences in Cells," *Scientific American, 209,* July 1963, pp. 54–69.

MOORE, JOHN A., *Heredity and Development.* Oxford University Press, New York, 1963.

NIRENBERG, N., and P. LEDER, "RNA Code-Words and Protein Synthesis," *Science, 145,* September 1964, pp. 1399–1407.

STRAUSS, BERNARD F., *Chemical Genetics.* W. B. Saunders Co., Philadelphia, 1960.

SUSSMAN, MAURICE, *Growth and Development.* Prentice Hall, Englewood Cliffs, New Jersey, 1964.

WAGNER, ROBERT P., and HERSCHEL K. MITCHELL, *Genetics and Metabolism.* John Wiley and Sons, New York, 1964.

VOGEL, HENRY J., VERNON BRYSON, and J. OLIVER LAMPEN (eds.), *Informational Molecules.* Academic Press, New York, 1963.

22

Changing

Organisms

Organic

Evolution

●

Protoplasm is an amazing substance capable of developing into acellular protozoans, into many-celled men, or into the thousands of different species between these two extremes. It is a fact easily verified that no two individuals are exactly alike; even children are not facsimiles of their parents. Resemblances, on the other hand, make it possible to group large numbers of individuals into a single species, to combine similar species into genera, similar genera into families, and similar families into still larger groups. Likenesses between species, genera, and families indicate relationships and common descent. Organisms intermediate in structure between the various taxonomic groups are rare, however, and seldom do animals (or plants) constitute a continuous series. This has been true for millions of years, as the examination of prehistoric organisms reveals. Biologists, therefore, are faced with a peculiar contradiction: living things simultaneously demonstrate a continuity and a discontinuity. The existence, however, of many common properties in living systems and the evidence of interrelationship suggest that unity among organisms is more fundamental than are the differences.

Attempts to solve this enigma of organic diversity and relationship eventually led to the formulation of the most important generalization in biology: namely, that living things have undergone change, or *evolution*, throughout the ages. There are three basic tenets in this idea of organic evolution: *first*, that present-day animals and plants have descended with change from pre-existing forms; *second*, that the present discontinuities between forms have arisen gradually; and *third*, that the causes and processes of change are operating today. The concept that all animals have evolved from a common ancestral stock by accumulated changes did not spring suddenly into being. Aristotle, approximately 2000 years ago, said, "Nature evolves from one form to another." Democritus and Socrates speculated concerning "ideal" forms, and even during the Dark Ages occasional voices were heard suggesting that species change. It remained, however, for Buffon, Spencer, Erasmus Darwin, Lamarck, and Charles Darwin during the eighteenth and nineteenth centuries to decide whether living organisms were specially created in essentially the form that we see them today, or whether they are products of evolutionary changes.

Linnaeus, the father of taxonomy, believed firmly in the fixity of species, and that new species had not appeared since the time the first organisms were created. The French philosopher-scientist, Georges Buffon, was among the first to make a frontal attack on this idea. Buffon was more impressed by similarities between living things than by minor differences, and he believed that rudimentary structures and fossil forms demonstrated interrelationships. Another Frenchman, Jean Baptiste Lamarck, contended that all species are interrelated. He was certain that the discontinuities which seem to exist between species would disappear, the gaps being filled either by living or by fossil forms as our knowledge became more complete. Lamarck also believed that plants and animals must have been continuous at a remote period, and he invented the term *biology* to apply to the study of the many phenomena that are common to both kingdoms. Facts which would support or disprove the idea of evolution had to be collected and documented, and the mind of man, reluctant to discard accepted principles, had to embrace new facts which were slowly emerging as knowledge expanded. The place of the earth in the universe, the existence of the earth for thousands of millions of years, and the evidence that organisms have lived for a billion or more years required that scientific thinking become

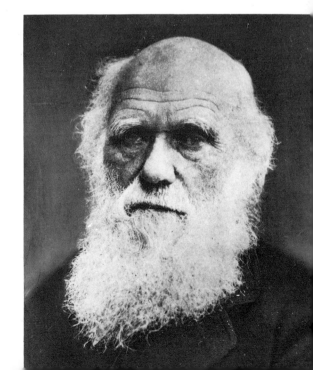

Figure 22.1. It was Charles Darwin who demonstrated that all organisms, including man, must make constant adjustments to environmental changes or cease to exist as living beings. The ability to adjust is the basis for organic change or evolution. (Courtesy Science Service, Inc.)

Figure 22.2. Man is not the only organism to develop a superior nervous system. The great apes, as illustrated by the orangutan and chimpanzee, also have evolved remarkable brains and are second only to man in their mental attainments. (Courtesy American Museum of Natural History.)

imaginative to a degree that was foreign to medieval minds. This transition in scientific thinking can be introduced with the contributions of Darwin; for his great work *On the Origin of Species,* published in 1859, became the major stimulus to the study of evolution.

Charles Darwin had little formal training as a biologist, but while at Cambridge his interest in natural history and his keenness of observation attracted the attention of Professor John Henslow, one of the great botanists of the period. Henslow's influence in turn made it possible for Darwin to be appointed to the position of naturalist on the expedition of *H.M.S. Beagle,* which was to make a geologic and natural-history survey of oceanic islands for the British government. The *Beagle,* a small sailing ship, took nearly five years to circle the globe, and this trip afforded Darwin almost unlimited opportunity for biological training. Unfortunately, Darwin suffered severe attacks of seasickness and was confined to his berth much of the time while the *Beagle* was at sea. The seasickness, however, had two salutary effects: Darwin read avidly while at sea; and at every opportunity he eagerly left the ship to spend as much time as possible on land, observing and collecting. As a sequel to his repeated seasickness Darwin was a semi-invalid for the remainder of his life.

The most formative influence on young Darwin's thinking was the first volume of the *Principles of Geology,* written by the great British geologist, Charles Lyell. The book had been presented to Darwin by Henslow with the advice to read it but not take it too seriously. Lyell suggested that geological changes in the remote past had been small, but that the accumulated effects of these small changes nevertheless produced awesome modifications in the earth's surface. Great mountain ranges, Lyell suggested, had been slowly eroded away as a result of the action of wind and water, and new mountains had been formed by a folding of the earth's crust which progressed with almost imperceptible slowness. Oceans had invaded and spread out over newly formed valleys and low areas but had drained off the rising lands. The result was that many present-day land surfaces were formerly under the sea, whereas some areas of the present ocean bottom were once dry land. The presence of fossils of such marine animals as corals and echinoderms in midwestern United States, the discovery of whale skeletons in bogs in Michigan, thick rock beds rich in fossil sea shells high in the Swiss Alps, and evidences of prehistoric human habitations on the submerged Dogger banks off the Atlantic coast of North America are vivid illustrations of the validity of these ideas.

The seasick young Darwin, who was only 23 at the time, pondered over the possible applications of Lyell's ideas to biology. First of all, if Lyell were correct, then the earth must have been in existence much longer than most scientists of that day believed, and its age must be calculated in millions instead of thousands of years. Secondly, Darwin considered the possibility that biological features, like geological formations, may undergo slight but cumulative modifications. He visualized that in millions of years these modifications could have transformed old species into new ones. Finally, Lyell's theory that the same geological processes then taking place had also occurred in the past stimulated Darwin to look for evidence of biological changes in existing plants and animals which could also be applied to plants and animals of the past.

Darwin found ample evidence to support Lyell's belief in the gradual changes of geological formations. His own observations in the pampas of the Argentine and around the mouths of some of the great rivers of South America convinced him that these land areas had been considerably modified very recently. He observed fossils of marine shells along the riverbanks some distance from the sea, but noted that these shells were similar to those which could be found in the ocean waters immediately offshore. This convinced Darwin that the land had been elevated in recent times. During his travels he heard that fossils were abundant in certain of the areas of the pampas, and these proved to be so numerous that in *The Voyage of the Beagle* he said that "the pampas is one wide sepulchre." Among the more striking fossils which he collected were those of giant prehistoric armored animals which were similar to the smaller present-day armadillos. He also collected evidence which proved that horses had lived in South America in prehistoric times. It was known that horses were not present in historic times in either North or South America until they were introduced by the Spaniards. Darwin, therefore, was intrigued by the discovery that horses had once been numerous in South America but had disappeared.

Darwin did a commendable thing with his collections. He identified materials as best he could and sent samples of his collections to specialists. Fossils were sent for identification to the great comparative anatomist, Sir Richard Owen; packets of earth were sent to Ehrenberg for the identification of the shells of protozoans which were to be found in the samples; and plants were

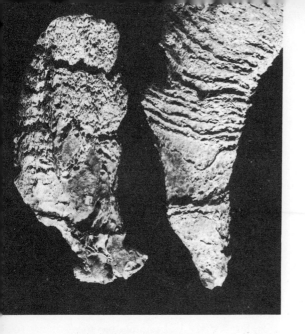

Figure 22.3. These fossil corals were found in Ohio and indicate that a great expanse of ocean water once covered large portions of what we now call the Midwest. (Courtesy American Museum of Natural History.)

sent to the proper specialists for identification. The evidence which Darwin collected on the fossils of plants and animals led him to the conclusion that the varieties and structure of these plants and animals had changed, and that closely related forms had replaced those which had existed previously.

There can be no question that the observations which Darwin made on the Galapagos Islands provided the impetus for his subsequent studies. These islands lie about 500 miles off the coast of South America and are of great biological interest because the animals and plants on the islands, although similar to those on the coast of South America, possess distinctive features not found in the mainland forms. He also found that the features of many of the plants and animals seemed to vary on the different islands. Darwin believed that this demonstrated a common origin for the island and the continental organisms, and he began to think in terms of isolated groups which underwent change and gradually developed into new species because they could not interbreed with those on adjacent islands or on the mainland. It was this idea that the minor changes could arise and be perpetuated in isolated forms of life which eventually led him to formulate his theory of the origin of species. It is important at this point to emphasize that a distinction should be made between the *fact* that changes have occurred and the *theories* which attempt to explain *how* these changes occurred. This obvious distinction between the fact of evolution and the theory of evolution often has been confused.

Darwin made voluminous notes of his observations and conjectures. He speculated concerning the way in which the coral islands of the South Pacific were formed, and his theories concerning the *origin of coral islands* are important today. Darwin's early introduction to the fossils gave him an insight into *paleontology* and *comparative anatomy*, and his discoveries on the Galapagos

Figure 22.4. This sleepy, slow-moving tree sloth is descended from the giant ground sloths which grew to be the size of elephants. The remains of ground sloths suggested to Darwin and others that many animals have managed to compete successfully in the struggle for existence only through their ability to adapt themselves to new conditions. (Courtesy Gendreau; photo by William LaVarre.)

Islands and on the continent of South America plunged him into the problem of *geographical distribution*. He did not limit himself to a study of animals, but made significant discoveries and observations on plants. Thus, upon his return to England after the five-year journey on the *Beagle*, he was a self-trained naturalist and possessed extensive data for subsequent study. The notes which he took were to serve as the basis for his writings over nearly a half century.

It appears that Darwin, during the initial months of the *Beagle* expedition, still believed in the fixity of species. It is equally certain, however, that as the voyage proceeded his ideas altered. His son, in the introduction to *The Foundations of the Origin of Species*, believes it was during the later stages of the expedition that his father's definitive ideas concerning the evolution of living things were crystallized.

It should also be remembered that upon his return to England Darwin was a young man of 28, with little scientific reputation. During the period preceding the publication of the *Origin of Species* he set about to acquire status as a biologist. He wrote papers on barnacles, on the classification of plants and animals, and on the formation of vegetable mould by earthworms, and he published his interesting diary recounting his experiences during the voyage of the *Beagle*. His contacts with great biologists of his time such as Owen, Ehrenberg, Hooker, and Huxley gave him entree into scientific circles, and his scientific stature was soon established. If he had never written the *Origin of Species*, he nevertheless would be considered an important biologist.

The Evidence for Evolution

Darwin's work provided a sound basis for the future studies of evolution, but although voluminous, it was only an introduction to the problem. This is

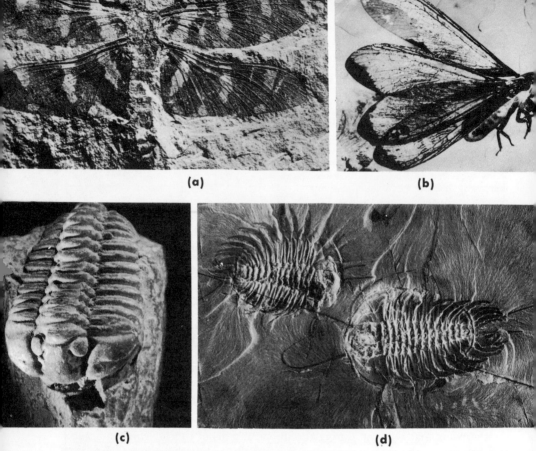

(a)　　　　　　　　　　　　(b)

(c)　　　　　　　　　　　　(d)

Figure 22.5. This fossil dragonfly in (a) left its imprint on the earth more than 200,000,000 years ago. The insect in (b) was trapped in the sticky resin of an ancient tree. The resin turned into amber and a perfect mold of the animal has been preserved. The fossil trilobites: a cast is shown in (c) and an imprint in (d). [(a) Courtesy Ernst Krause; (b) Yale University, Peabody Museum of Natural History; (c) William Eberly; (d) American Nature Association.]

particularly true with respect to evidences that *organic change could be transmitted through successive generations.* Furthermore, it was necessary not only to establish that a new species of the same genus had been formed, but that it had been possible for these species to evolve into the *higher* categories of genera, families, classes, and even phyla. Evidence in support of the fact of evolution has been compiled from many fields: *astronomers* have contributed data relative to the time of origin of the earth; *geologists* have added information concerning the structure of the rocks which make up the earth's surface, and the nature of the fossils entombed in those rocks; *ecologists* have investigated the importance of interactions between organisms and their environment; *comparative anatomists* have made detailed studies of plant and animal structure; and these anatomical observations have been supplemented by comparable studies of the development of organisms made by the *embryologists;* and finally, *geneticists*

Time Scale and Biological Events

Millions of years ago	Period or epoch	Biological events	General features
2000.0	Archeozoic (Precambrian)	Chemical evolution Origin of earth	Heterotrophism Complex molecules
900.0	Proterozoic (Precambrian)	First organism Trilobites appear	Soft-bodied animals Green plants; autotrophism
600.0	Cambrian	Most invertebrates present	Life confined to water Fossils abundant
500.0	Ordovician	First land plants Mollusks, trilobites abundant	Sea scorpions Oceans enlarge
425.0	Silurian	Primitive vertebrates, fishes	Coral reefs, land rose
405.0	Devonian	First land animals Fishes, arthropods abundant	Diversity of climate Mountain building
345.0	Mississippian	Insects, amphibians increase	Damp, hot, swamp lands
310.0	Pennsylvanian	Reptiles appear Insects, amphibians abundant	Coal deposits
280.0	Permian	Evergreens appear Insects, amphibians abundant	Appalachians formed Modern insects Reptiles increase
230.0	Triassic	Reptiles abundant and varied	Mammal-like reptiles
181.0	Jurassic	Giant reptiles	Reptile-like birds The Great Age of Reptiles
135.0	Cretaceous	Flowering plants appear First mammals (pouched)	Rocky Mountains formed Modern fishes, birds
70.0	Paleocene	Modern plants Placental mammals appear	Dinosaurs gone Himalayas and Alps formed
58.0	Eocene	Marine mammals appear Birds abundant Horse appears	Mountains erode Modern mammals
36.0	Oligocene	Titanic mammals appear Mammals abundant	Ancestors of carnivores Warm climate
25.0	Miocene	Mastodon appears Mammals at peak	Climate progressively cooler Saber-toothed tiger
13.0	Pliocene	Mammoths and mastodons Manlike apes	Hoofed mammals prosper Sierras rise
1.0	Pleistocene	Primitive man	Giant mammals gone Polar icecaps and glaciers
0.025	Recent	Modern man	Age of man

Figure 22.6. The fossil bones of this marine reptile are over 150,000,000 years old. The original bones have been replaced by minerals, leaving an exact duplication of the animal. The flesh of the reptile has been reduced to a thin film of carbon, outlining the animal's body perfectly. (Courtesy American Museum of Natural History.)

have helped to interpret the mechanisms which have made possible the development of new forms. No single line of investigation has been complete in itself, and indeed, the circumstantial evidence compiled from the various scientific disciplines still leaves certain gaps in our record. The collective information, however, makes an imposing story of the evolution of living things.

Paleontology

The study of the remains of prehistoric animals and plants is called *paleontology,* and it has been one of the major sources of information concerning evolution. Organisms that lived thousands or millions of years ago occasionally were preserved as *fossils,* of which there are several different types. Some fossils are almost perfect replicas of entire living organisms, whereas only fragments of others were preserved. Animals with armored shells or hard coverings, such as chitin, made excellent fossils, and the skeletons of vertebrates were often remarkably well preserved. Four major types of fossils can be recognized, and these vary in their value for the study of paleontology. First of all, many organisms at their death were trapped in mud, or fell in sand, in such a fashion that they left an *imprint.* Some of the more delicate parts of soft-bodied animals have left traces in this fashion, and the minute detail of wings of insects occasionally can be analyzed from such fossil imprints. The dinosaurs as they walked across the mud frequently left their tracks, and these imprints were preserved.

The imprint is directly related to a second type of fossil, called a *cast,* which is formed *within* the imprint. A cast is formed when an imprint is filled with inorganic matter which hardens to form a replica of the original material that made the imprint. The imprint serves as a mold in which the cast is made. Remarkable *molds* of animals have been formed in amber, which is the hardened

Figure 22.7. Thousands of animals were trapped in tar pits like the one shown in this painting by Charles Knight. Often the animals have been well-preserved in the hardened tar and may be recovered for study. Notice the giant ground sloths and the saber-toothed tiger.

resin originally secreted by trees. Insects and spiders were trapped and embedded in the gummy resin while it was still sticky and semifluid, and when the resin subsequently hardened into amber, the details of the animals often were preserved so perfectly that even microscopic structures can be studied. These are not mummies within the amber, however, because the tissues and organs have completely disappeared, leaving only an opaque mold in the amber. Insects in Baltic amber have been dated as far back as the Oligocene period, approximately 30,000,000 years ago. Ancient life so perfectly preserved in the form of imprints, molds, and casts unfortunately is among the rarest of geological phenomena, because unusually favorable circumstances were required for such unique replicas.

Petrified fossils, in which the body substance has been replaced by mineral salts, are invaluable. A few such fossils have been discovered in which the replacement of the blood vessels and nerves was so perfect that it is possible to work out their finest branches. Some fossils of the most primitive fishes, discovered in Greenland, were so thoroughly mineralized that a complete reconstruction of the cephalic blood vessels, brain, cranial nerves, and spinal nerves has been possible. This information has been applicable in the study of the relationship of the ammocoete larva to the primitive vertebrates. Sometimes the mineralized parts of the body were surrounded by a carbon film which gave a detailed outline of the soft body surface. These are nature's "carbon copies."

The fourth fossil type perhaps should not be spoken of as a fossil, because in this instance the *intact body* of the organism is preserved. The momentous discoveries of the elephantlike mammals in the arctic regions, especially in Siberia, are excellent examples of this type of preservation. When the animals died they were "fast-frozen" in ice for thousands of years and so well refrigerated that the food they were eating at the time of their death occasionally is found perfectly preserved in their mouths and stomachs—and there are reports that these prehistoric monsters have been used as food for sled dogs. Much attention has been directed in recent years to the La Brea tar pits in California, because centuries ago these asphalt pools, like sticky flypaper, caught countless numbers of animals. The remains of saber-toothed tigers and sloths are especially notable among the many forms which have been recovered from the La Brea pits. Fossils preserved in ice or asphalt have been particularly advantageous, because they furnish detailed information concerning the kinds of animals that were in existence during the period when man was beginning to appear on this planet.

Unfortunately the fossil record will always be fragmentary. Part of the difficulty lies in the fact that the oldest rocks—rocks of igneous and metamorphic, not of sedimentary, character—have been warped and twisted by the great heat and pressure below the earth's surface, where the rocks were buried. As a result of the shifting of masses of the earth's crust, any fossils of animals from the dawn of life were smashed and melted and have been lost. Almost the only evidence we have of the Precambrian existence of life (in excess of 500,000,000 years ago) is the relatively high carbon content of some of the ancient rocks. The fossil story in sedimentary rocks which were formed by slow deposition over long periods of time is also incomplete, but fossils formed in sedimentary rocks often were excellently preserved. It was pointed out that animals with armor or shells preserved well; and conversely, soft-bodied animals were rarely preserved. Since coelenterates, worms, and many other of the earliest animals were soft-bodied, we can never hope to find much record of their existence. Authentic fossils date back only 500,000,000 years and, therefore, three fourths of geologic time is inaccessible for the study of organic evolution.

The paleontological record, in spite of its inadequacies, has been highly significant in the reconstructing of events in evolution, and this is due in no small measure to the fossils that have been preserved in the sedimentary rocks. The sedimentary rocks are in layers, and in some instances the deposition of sediment reproduced the conditions under which the materials were deposited with such amazing exactness that even seasons of the year can be detected within the individual layers. Thin layers of such rocks are called *varves*, and particularly significant are the Oeningen varves of Europe, in which the annual layers can be subdivided into spring, summer, and fall depositions. The blossoms of plants, the full growth of the leaves, and finally, the seeds of plants can be distinguished within the subdivisions of an annual varve.

The passage of time can be detected in the sedimentary rocks because, in general, the older layers are the deeper ones, and the most recent layers are near the surface of the formation. It is obvious that the dating of such layers is very important, because it is essential to know when an organism first appeared, how long it existed, and when it finally disappeared. The trained paleontologist, therefore, has an opportunity to read the past history of the earth as a story inscribed in stone.

Figure 22.8. Varves are thin layers of ancient sediment, laid down seasonally and containing trapped organisms. These layers can be used to date rock in the same way that rings can be used to date trees. (Courtesy Richard Foster Flint, Yale University.)

The recent discovery of a remarkable "radioactive clock" has made it possible to ascertain the time of origin of many rock formations. *Radioactive* elements, such as uranium-238, uranium-235, and thorium, are slowly converted to lead, and the type of lead which results is slightly different with each element. The rates at which the uranium and the thorium change to lead have been determined, for example, as:

$$\text{Time} = \frac{\text{amount of lead}}{\text{amount of uranium}} \times 7,600,000,000 \text{ years.}$$

Accordingly, an analysis of the ratio between the lead and the uranium or thorium in any given sample of rock will give an estimate of the age of the rock. It can be demonstrated that many rocks were formed 2,000,000,000 years ago; the oldest rocks, as determined by the radioactive clock, are 2,300,-000,000 years old. The age of much younger rock formations also can be determined with accuracy, and it is possible, therefore, not only to study the fossils which are found in different layers but also to ascertain the time at which those fossils were produced.

The significant fact that many rock formations have their own characteristic fossil animals was discovered more than 150 years ago by the English geologist, William Smith. Furthermore, the oldest fossil-bearing rocks have been found to possess fossils which are most unlike present-day organisms, and the most recently deposited layers of rock to contain fossils which are most similar to present-day forms. Darwin and his followers had hoped that as more intensive paleontological studies were made, intermediate fossil forms would be found which would serve as connecting links between the major groups of the animal kingdom. Few of these so-called missing links have been discovered, hence many of the gaps cannot be filled. The fossil record, however, demonstrates clearly that most of the major phyla and classes can be traced backward for millions of years in the paleontological record.

Among the few discovered "missing links" are some fossils which do demonstrate relationships between present-day and pre-existing animals. The fossil "bird" *Archaeopteryx* is a case in point, because it had characteristics of both

Figure 22.9. Literally neither fish nor fowl, this creature combines the wings of a bird with the claws, teeth, and jointed tail of a reptile. (Courtesy Clarence Flaten.)

birds and reptiles. *Archaeopteryx* had a long jointed tail, teeth, claws, and many other structures typical of the reptiles; but this animal had wings which were feathered, and the pointed tail also was feathered. There were, in addition, other avian features. The animal definitely was a link between the reptiles and the birds. Evidence from a study of comparative anatomy and embryology supports the fact of this relationship. The development of the horse's hoof has been cited frequently as a classic example of the way in which an organism has evolved. Fortunately, an almost complete record exists of the transition of the horse from a stage in which it was an animal whose appendages had four toes to that of the present-day animal with only a single, well-developed toe, or hoof. The horse literally walks on its middle toe, or finger, and the hoof corresponds to the human fingernail. There are two "splint bones" in the leg of the modern horse, and these bones are the rudiments of the original second and fourth digits of the limbs. The record is incomplete beyond the four-toed stage. The development of the elephant also has been worked out carefully, and gradual transitions can be traced in the evolution of the trunk and tusks, and the increase in body size. The relationship of the reptiles can be traced not only to birds, but also to the mammals. Fossils of some of the primitive reptiles possessed mammalian characteristics, and some of the earliest mammalian fossils had reptilian structures.

Another apect of paleontology which is of interest to the biologist is the evidence that the climate of the earth has varied in the past. Fossils prove that the icebound regions of the Antarctic once had a tropical climate, and that the earth has undergone long periods of prolonged rainfall, interspersed with thousands of years of drought. These fluctuations in climatic conditions, of course, had a profound influence in regulating the organisms which could have lived in a given area. The movement of the great ice sheets can be traced from the paleontological as well as from the geological record, and the influence of the ice on the distribution of life on the earth also can be evaluated. It is in connection with these studies of more recent geological periods that other methods of determining time have become important. Radioactive carbon-14 (C^{14}), which loses half its radioactivity in slightly more than 5500 years, is particularly significant in these studies. For example, during bone formation small amounts of C^{14} are deposited, and after the death of the animal this element slowly loses its radioactivity. The determination of carbon radioactivity in the bones, therefore, makes it possible to ascertain approximately when the animal died. The date of the last great ice sheet which covered portions of North America can be estimated by determining the geological age of the trees which were killed by the advancing glacier. The time of the retreat of this glaciation was approximately 11,000 years ago.

The C^{14} technique leads to the determination of the time when prehistoric man lived in caves or villages. A study of carbon from bark sandals and from the charcoal of his fires shows that man entered North America shortly after the retreat of the last great glaciation, and that in only 2000 years he had migrated the length of the continent. It is interesting that the great explosion

Figure 22.10. The horse was originally a small, doglike animal. His development into the handsome creature of today is one of the best-understood stories in evolution. Several aspects of this development are shown below. (Courtesy Chicago Museum of Natural History.)

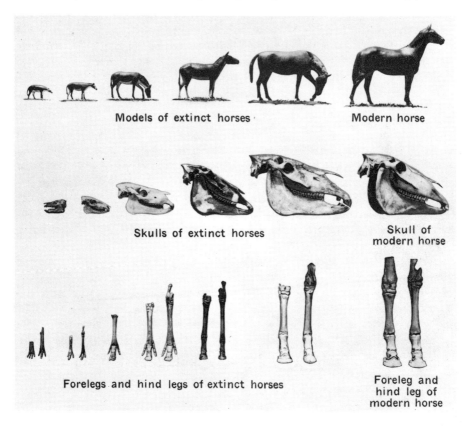

Models of extinct horses ·   Modern horse

Skulls of extinct horses   Skull of modern horse

Forelegs and hind legs of extinct horses   Foreleg and hind leg of modern horse

which formed Crater Lake in Oregon has been dated by analysis of the wood in the trees which were destroyed by this explosion.. The time of the formation of Crater Lake was approximately 4500 years ago.

Recent investigations of heavy oxygen, oxygen-18, have been as remarkable as the studies of radioactive carbon. Since the ratio between the amounts of oxygen-18 and oxygen-16 varies with temperature, these isotopes will be deposited in animal shells in different proportions, according to temperature. A study of oxides in fossil shells should, theoretically, provide an index of the temperatures of prehistoric seas. It has been possible to demonstrate that the rate of deposition of the oxides in the shell actually changed at different times of the year, and it is apparent that the temperatures of the ancient seas fluctuated during the seasons. This is remarkable, because the method affords an analysis of the temperature of seas that existed 100,000,000 years ago!

Fossils are not only a record of the structure of individual animals, but also, surprisingly enough, a valuable source of information on the rate of evolution. The fact that the ancestral history of a certain kind of animal can be reconstructed by studying the successive strata of rocks makes it possible to determine how long a period of time was required to evolve a new structure or a new species. The rate of change is not the same for all animals; for example, the *trilobites* changed very little over millions of years, and Simpson has estimated that the increase in the length of the molar tooth of the horse proceeded at a rate of 0.1 to 0.2 millimeter per million years. The elephantlike mammals, on the other hand, evolved their tusks and trunk in a comparatively short period of time. It is such evidence from paleontology which enables man to transcend the limited observational period imposed by his own short life span.

Comparative adult anatomy

The science of comparative adult anatomy interrelates in detail the structural elements of a group of animals. The comparative study of animal struc-

Figure 22.11. Homologous structures. This striking photograph demonstrates the similar patterns of body structure in a man and a horse and shows how similar structures (homologues) may be modified to perform special functions. (Courtesy American Museum of Natural History.

(a)   (b)

(c)   (d)

Figure 22.12. Although the wings of the insect, the "wings" of the flying fish, and the wings of the bat look alike, they do not have any common structural or embryonic origin and are not homologous. The wings of the bird and the bat, however, are homologous. [(a) Courtesy Sperry Gyosope Company; (b), (d) Harold E. Edgerton; (c) National Audubon Society; photo by Paul J. Fair.]

ture, especially of skeletal elements, was the most productive phase of the investigation of evolution in the half century which followed the publication of Darwin's *Origin of Species*. Buffon had suggested on theoretical grounds that a study of anatomy with special emphasis on rudimentary features could demonstrate relationships between animals that otherwise are obscure. Buffon, however, was not an anatomist; and it was Cuvier, the "father of comparative anatomy," who elevated comparative anatomy to its eminent position in biological science. Cuvier gave precise descriptions of the anatomy of fossils as well as of living vertebrates and laid stress on the interrelationship between structure and function. This interrelationship became an important guiding principle in comparative anatomy, although Cuvier carried the idea to an extreme which is not considered justifiable today.

The concept of *homology* is the central theme on which comparative anatomy revolves. *Homologous structures*, or *homologs*, develop from similar embryonic structures and may or may not have the same function in different adult animals. The advantage of the study of homologes lies in the fact that they demonstrate basic patterns of body architecture and prove that structures of similar origin may be modified radically to perform special functions. We commented on the alterations in the biramous appendages of the crayfish earlier, and these are excellent examples of the extent to which structures can be adapted. We recall that some crayfish appendages were specialized for sensory functions (antennae); others as mouth parts (mandibles, maxillae), as walking legs, and as swimmerets. This is a special type of homology, *serial homology*, and the appendages may be compared individually with those of other arthropods. The adaptability of the forelimb of the various vertebrates is so striking that the varying features of this appendage are used repeatedly to illustrate homology. The flipper of the whale, the wing of the bird and the bat, the foreleg of the horse, and the forearm of man appear superficially to have little similarity; but a careful analysis of the parts demonstrates a common construction with comparable skeletal elements. Variations in basic patterns can be observed also in the blood vessels, nerves, muscles, and alimentary canals of the different vertebrates.

The study of homologous structures illustrates a second type of situation in which structures or parts of structures are greatly reduced. Such reduced features are said to be *vestigial;* the "splint bones" of the leg of the horse have been noted as an example. There are almost 200 vestigial structures in man, many of which are well known to nearly everyone. The muscles which move the scalp or the ears, the reduced third eyelid, the remnant of a tail, the appendix, and even the heavy coat of hair which covers the fetus are illustrations of vestigial structures in human beings. The small cluster of bones representing the remains of the pelvic girdle in whales and the presence of traces of hind limbs in some snakes are other well-known examples of this type.

A third category of modified elements important in such a study of comparative anatomy is represented by organs that have been very significantly

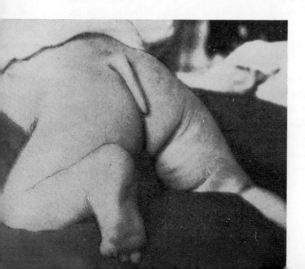

Figure 22.13. Although rare, a vestigial tail is sometimes observed in human beings, as in the case of the child at the left. This is only one of many such characters which emphasize man's structural relationship to other organisms. (Courtesy Dr. A. M. Winchester, Stetson University.)

altered to perform functions markedly different from those commonly expressed. This type of structural alteration is illustrated by the modification of salivary glands into poison glands in some reptiles, the reorganization and migration of certain bone elements of the jaw region to form the ear bones, the transformation of certain sweat glands into milk glands in the mammals, and the complex reallotment of functions to the blood vessels, which occurred when vertebrates changed from respiration by gills to respiration by lungs.

The only reasonable assumption that can explain the intricacies of homologous relationships is that animals inherit certain basic plans of body architecture, and it must be concluded that the structural units have an adaptability which has enabled many different forms to evolve by change from a few basic type forms. This is the concept of evolution as supported by the evidence from comparative anatomy.

Comparative embryological anatomy

This study is actually a handmaiden of comparative adult anatomy and supplements such adult studies. The most significant contribution of embryology is the emphasis on the similarity of development. The formation of the body of all vertebrates during the embryonic stages, for example, is amazingly similar, irrespective of the adult end product. It is routine practice in embryology classes to study chick and pig embryos and to correlate the observations on these animals with the developmental stages of man. Credit for directing attention to embryonic development for evidences of evolution undoubtedly must be given to von Baer, although Haeckel popularized the study. We discussed the differences in the interpretation advanced by these men in an earlier chapter, and we noted that von Baer's ideas are considered to be more valid. He suggested that the *embryonic stages* of the "higher" animals resembled the *embryonic stages* of the "lower" animals more than the adults resembled each other. Haeckel modified von Baer's statement in a very significant way. Haeckel stated that the *embryo* of higher forms resembles the *adult* of lower forms. This idea was so attractive to biologists for so many years that it was expanded into the *law of recapitulation:* namely, that during its embryonic stages an animal repeats (recapitulates) the adult stages of its ancestors. This law has been so seriously questioned and is so obviously inapplicable in many instances that as a law it now is of historical interest only.

Certain relationships in the animal kingdom are difficult to decipher without the aid of the developmental story. The classification of barnacles as crustaceans is facilitated because the larval stage is typically crustacean, whereas the adult is so modified that its relationship is obscure. The probable relationship of echinoderms and chordates to a common ancestral type taxes credulity, since the adult starfishes (echinoderms) and their relatives are radially symmetrical, in contrast to the bilateral symmetry of the acorn worm or of Amphioxus. The echinoderm larva, however, is bilaterally symmetrical and very similar to some marine chordate larvae. The change to radial symmetry occurs during embryonic development by the suppression of one side and the overgrowth of the other and is easily traced.

One may wonder why *gill pouches* appear in mammalian embryos, because these do not function in respiration in either the embryonic or the adult stages of mammals. The role of the pouches is clarified by reference to the part they play in development. Gill pouches give rise to the thymus and parathyroid glands and to the ultimobranchial bodies. The *gill arches,* which support the pouches, are transformed into parts of the skeleton of the jaw region and into the bones of the ear. Embryology, therefore, may be said to define a pattern of development, just as comparative anatomy defines a pattern of structure.

Taxonomy, or classification

The separation of plants or animals into taxonomic divisions is based upon likenesses and differences, and the clear-cut *differences* between organisms would often appear to offer evidence contrary to evolution. A careful examination of any valid scheme of classification proves definitely that the allotment of a number of organisms to a common category is determined more by their *similarity to each other* than it is by their dissimilarity to other organisms. We are often overly impressed, however, by the distinctions, or dissimilarities, between such groups as fishes, amphibians, reptiles, birds, and mammals; and we may overlook many of the important features which these groups share in common: the notochord, the dorsal tubular nervous system, the gill slits, the brain structure, the distribution of the blood vessels, the embryological devel-

Figure 22.14. The flying mammal, the bat, demonstrates the modifications which can occur in common structures when adapted to specific functions. The wing of the bat is radically different from that of the bird (Figure 18.9). The fingers (phalanges) are the supporting structures for the membranous folds which are the wings. (Courtesy Clarence Flaten.)

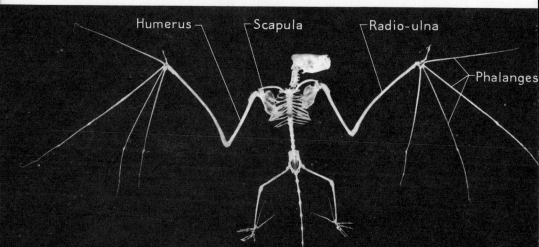

opment, and other criteria which proclaim close relationship. Modern classification is based upon the belief that the degree of *structural* and *functional* similarity between organisms is an accurate delineation of the degree of *genetic* similarity that exists. Similar species are grouped into one genus, similar genera are united into one family, similar families are combined into one order, until the major units of phylum and kingdom are reached.

It was observed several times during the study of the phyla that it is sometimes impossible to place an animal, or group of animals, in a taxonomic category with any exactness. *Peripatus* has features in common with annelids and arthropods; proboscis worms suggest the ancestry of the coelomate animals; the fossil *Archaeopteryx* had both reptilian and avian characteristics; *Volvox* and *Proterospongia* are many celled and are intermediate between the acellular and multicellular organisms. It is annoying to be faced with such enigmas when attempting to classify organisms, but the presence of such forms is to be expected if evolution is a fact. The specialist who repeatedly finds exceptions that do not fit readily into classification patterns thus finds in taxonomy evidences for evolution just as conclusive, even though not so dramatic, as in paleontology, comparative anatomy, or embryology.

Biochemical evidence

It has been suggested on several occasions that the annelids, mollusks, and arthropods are rather closely related, and that their relationship is distinguishable from that of the echinoderms and chordates. Certain biochemical lines of evidence support this distinction. It is known, for example, that the *muscle phosphagens* (creatinine compounds concerned with muscle contraction) and the *respiratory pigments* are different. The following table, modified from Scheer, illustrates this point.

Biochemical Evidence of Relationship					
	Mollusks	Annelids	Arthropods	Echinoderms	Chordates
Muscle phosphagen Arginine phosphate Creatine phosphate	+++ —	+++ —	+++ —	+ +	+ ++
Respiratory pigment Hemocyanin	++	—	++	—	—

Similar studies of the *size of protein molecules* indicate a correlation between the molecular size and the closeness of relationship. Even more striking are the investigations involving the *rate at which red blood cells will swell in different solutions.* This is a measure, of course, of the selective nature of the plasma membrane of the cells (p. 55). The more closely related the animals are, the more nearly alike will be the rates of swelling.

Serology, the analysis for differences in the chemical substances of the blood fluids, furnishes the most sensitive biochemical test for determining relationship. The technique is relatively simple and may be illustrated by a procedure which is followed in numerous laboratories. The fluid part of the blood, the *serum,* is separated from the rest of the blood and injected at intervals into a suitable test animal, usually a rabbit. The test animal, after a short time, develops substances, called *antibodies,* which are antagonistic to materials in the injected serum. Specific antibodies may be developed, for example, to human serum, chimpanzee serum, monkey serum, or any other type of blood serum. If serum from a rabbit which has developed antibodies to human serum is mixed in a test tube with human serum, a heavy precipitate develops, and this can be measured quantitatively by several methods. If blood serum from one of the great apes, a gorilla or a chimpanzee, is mixed with a new sample of anti-human rabbit serum, a precipitate will again be present, but it will not be as heavy as in the previous test. Monkey serum reacts still less than does serum from the apes. Repeated analysis demonstrates conclusively that the more closely related two different groups are, the greater will be the precipitation reaction. The use of serology has extended to studies of reptiles and birds, sheep and goats, echinoderms and chordates, and other combinations too numerous to list.

The gratifying feature of serological tests is that the results, with very few exceptions, verify the relationships previously determined by paleontology, comparative anatomy, embryology, and taxonomy. Serological analysis, in some instances, has helped to clarify relationships which were inexplicable by other analyses.

Domestic plants and animals

Reference to changes which occurred millions of years ago, or to changes which required millions of years to develop, requires a degree of abstraction which is difficult for the human mind to achieve. Darwin was aware of this difficulty and began a study of domestic plants and animals in the hope that these would furnish evidences for evolution which might be evaluated within historical times. Man, by *artificial selection,* has been able to modify domestic forms to a remarkable degree. Everyone is acquainted, at least slightly, with the great range of variation in dogs, in which breeding and selection for size, for hunting, for retrieving, and for many other special qualities have been practiced for centuries. Chihuahuas weighing only a few ounces, for example, can be contrasted with great Danes and Saint Bernards weighing more than 100 pounds. The slow-moving bloodhound has the swift-coursing greyhound as its opposite. The variation in pigeons, in which homing, pouting, and fantail pigeons are a few of the types commonly known, presents a situation comparable with that of dogs. The horticulturist who develops new types of flowers,

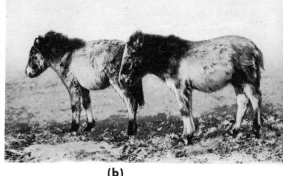

(a)   **(b)**

Figure 22.15. Man has speeded up the process or organic change. The wild, dwarf Prejval-sky's horses in (b) still roam the plains of Siberia. Yet man has developed magnificent work-horses and beautiful saddlehorses like the aristocrat in (a). [(a) Courtesy L. S. Sutcliffe; (b) New York Zoological Gardens.]

or the plant breeder who selects for increased yield, earlier maturity, or disease resistance, deals with plant variation.

It is recognized that mutations frequently play an important role in the development of new domestic types. Hornless cattle, short-legged sheep, or ewes which consistently give birth to twin lambs are a few examples of hereditary variations which have been analyzed. The occurrence of plants with extra sets of chromosomes is well known to horticulturists, who take advantage of this genetic modification to produce new types. The significance of mutations in evolution will be discussed later, when the theories of evolution are evaluated;

Figure 22.16. If genes from a friendly mongrel are introduced into a purebred line, the results may be difficult to classify. The pedigreed dachshund in this cartoon could not have endeared herself to her owner. (Drawing by Alajalov, reproduced by permission. Copyright 1938. The New Yorker Magazine, Inc.)

but even this brief introduction indicates that evolution, or organic change, is continuing today, and is not confined to the remote past.

The new animals or plants produced under domestication usually are spoken of as *races, breeds,* or *varieties.* This characterization, however, reflects a considerable amount of conservatism on the part of the biologists. Certainly many of the new varieties can breed with original types with only great difficulty, if at all, and if some were isolated (and could exist) in the wild, they would probably be elevated to the rank of new species.

Geographical distribution

One of the earliest sources of evidence for evolution was that of geographical, or spatial, distribution of plants and animals. It will be recalled that Darwin was impressed by the differences he observed among the species of plants and animals on the various islands of the Galapagos, and also by the variations between island and continental forms. The distribution of organisms shows many peculiarities for which the only reasonable explanation is evolution. Organisms inhabit specific environments, but there are many instances in which an animal or plant does not occupy all the areas of the world which are environmentally suited to it. The distribution of fossils also demonstrates that many plants and animals were once much more world wide in their distribution than at present. The horse in prehistoric times was found in great numbers in North and South America, as were also the ancestors of the camel and the tapir, but these animals had disappeared from the Americas by historic times. Fossils of dinosaurs that lived in moist, tropical climates are to be found now in the semi-desert areas of Wyoming. A clear explanation for some of these facts of distribution is known, and modern students of taxonomy and distribution, such as Mayr and Kinsey, have depended to a considerable extent on such knowledge in tracing the ancestry of present-day species.

There is an over-all tendency for the range area of organisms to change. The elephants, mastodons, and tapirs were once widely dispersed but are now found in only a few limited areas of the world. Changes in climate, expressed in temperature and rainfall fluctuations, are known to have occurred. The frigid arctic and antarctic regions were once tropical, and as they cooled, animals and plants that could live only in warm climates were driven out or died. Land bridges from Europe to North America by way of Greenland, and from Asia to North America by way of the Aleutian Islands and Alaska, allowed animals (including man) to migrate. The disruption of these bridges prevented further migration in recent times, with the result that many forms of life are now split into isolated populations. The example frequently cited is that of the isolation of the pouched (marsupial) mammals on the island continent of Australia. At the time of their isolation millions of years ago the pouched mammals were world wide in distribution and were the dominant mammalian group. Subsequent to this time the placental mammals evolved; the pouched mammals could not compete successfully with them, and so were greatly reduced, both in total numbers and in number of species. The opossum, for example, is the only

Figure 22.17. Jean Baptiste Lamarck. (Courtesy Brown Brothers.)

successful marsupial mammal that is present in North America. The Australian marsupials, however, did not encounter this competition because of their isolation and evolved into bearlike, rodentlike, doglike, or molelike animals. Placental animals such as dogs and rabbits introduced into Australia by man have thrived there to the disadvantage of the marsupials, a situation which answers two questions: the ability of organisms to evolve in isolation, and the ability of introduced animals to thrive in environments in which they were not present previously. Sparrows, starlings, and corn borers are examples of animals with expanding ranges in North America.

The activity of man has been an important factor in the expansion of ranges in many instances. Rats, mice, roaches, flies, many cereal grasses, and some weeds have been transferred to new localities by human means. It will be of interest in the future to watch for possible changes in these forms, because it is known that organisms at the edge of an extensive range gradually develop differences from those in the center of the range. This is because distance is an important factor in preventing breeding between all individuals in a population, with the result that genetic differences gradually develop between organisms in the center and at the periphery.

Geographical distribution, when associated with facts derived from paleontology and geology, provides ample evidence that organisms change to produce new types. The evidence has been especially important in directing attention to the importance of isolation in the mechanism of evolution.

Theories of Evolution

The fact of organic evolution has been established to the satisfaction of biologists, but the mechanism by which evolution occurred is not explained adequately. Two major theories of evolution have been the center of attention for over a century. The first of these was formulated by Lamarck about 1809. Commonly known as the *inheritance of acquired characters*, it had considerable

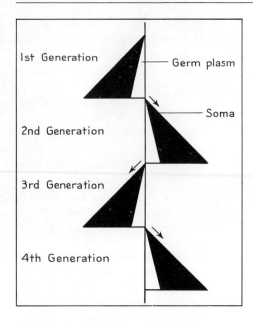

1st Generation

Germ plasm

Soma

2nd Generation

3rd Generation

Figure 22.18. Germ plasm (reproductive cells) and soma (body cells). (Courtesy Buffalo Museum of Science.)

4th Generation

popular appeal, but its major tenets have been discarded. Lamarck was impressed, as any careful observer always is, by the adaptations which fit an organism for the special environment in which it lives. He advanced the hypothesis that the environment directs the adaptations during the lifetime of a plant or animal, and that these "acquired" adaptations are inherited. As an extension of this hypothesis, he postulated that any structure that was *used* would develop, but that any structure in *disuse* would degenerate. The idea of *use* or *disuse* and the *inheritance of acquired characters* became the fundamentals of the Lamarckian theory of evolution.

The attractiveness of this theory is apparent. If true, any improvement in one generation could be transmitted to succeeding generations, and structures that are not used would be eliminated as excess baggage through disuse. The difficulty with such an appealing theory lies in the lack of proof that acquired characters can be inherited. An organism can make almost fantastic structural and functional adjustments to environmental situations, but the reproductive cells of the organism are not modified. The fact that the reproductive cells are not altered is fatal to the theory, because an adaptation can be effective in evolution only if it can be perpetuated by transmission through the reproductive cells to succeeding generations.

Many attempts have been made to prove experimentally that the Lamarckian theory is valid, but these have been fruitless. August Weismann is generally accorded the role of executioner in the demise of the theory. Weismann pointed out that any organism is composed of body cells, or *soma,* and reproductive cells, or *germ plasm.* The soma is susceptible of modification but is mortal and dies. The germ plasm, which carries the hereditary units, is said to be immortal and is the bridge between generations. It was Weismann's contention that the germ plasm is not modified by environmental factors that alter the soma and, with respect to the environmental factors as conceived by Lamarck, this has been verified repeatedly. There are limits, however, to the extension of Weismann's concept, because X-rays, ultraviolet light, mustard gas, atomic radiation, and other comparable stimuli can produce hereditary changes in germ cells. These can be discounted as to their importance relative to Lamarck's theory, because they do not constitute environmental factors. Unfortunately, man's exposure to atomic radiation and X-rays constitutes a threat to his future evolution. The closest that the modern biologist has been able to come in support of the Lamarckian theory is the discovery of hereditary factors in the cytoplasm of plants and animals, and the evidence that some of these actually can be changed by alteration of environmental conditions. Such changes, however, are random and apparently are not associated in a use-or-disuse relationship with the stimuli that produce them.

The second major theory of evolution is that advanced by Darwin and is usually referred to as the *theory of natural selection.* It was noted that Lyell's *Principles of Geology* had stimulated Darwin to look for *evidences* of evolution. A second book, *An Essay on the Principle of Population,* by Thomas Malthus, suggested to Darwin a *mechanism* which might explain the process of evolution. Malthus theorized that human populations were increasing more rapidly than was man's ability to increase food production, and that a "struggle for existence" was confronting mankind. Darwin thought Malthus's idea could be applied to all organisms, and the Darwinian theory, stated simply, is as follows:

1. Organisms tend to *overproduce,* which results in
2. A *struggle for existence,* and this is coupled with
3. *Advantageous variations,* which adapt an organism to its environment, and result in
4. A *survival of the fittest.*

The two phrases, *struggle for existence* and *survival of the fittest* captured popular fancy, and Darwin's theory too often is distorted by undue reference to the

Figure 22.19. When irradiation was applied to the head of this rat, the tooth-germ area was stimulated to grow an additional set of incisor teeth. Had this happened in nature, and been transmitted to later generations, a new "variety" of rat could have been "evolved." (Courtesy Capt. James A. English, Naval Research Institute.)

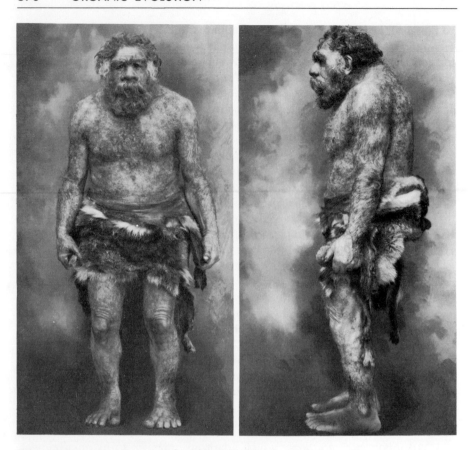

Figure 22.20. Man, too, has evolved the prehistoric man above was enough like modern man to be placed in the same genus, *Homo*, but was sufficiently different to be classed as a separate species, namely *neanderthalansis* or neanderthal man.

latter phrase. The merits of his theory can be evaluated only on the basis of all the elements which compose it, and these may be analyzed in turn.

It is evident that organisms overproduce. The "plagues" of locusts, the migrations of the lemmings, and the almost astronomical numbers of young produced by many marine animals are but a few of the examples which can be given to illustrate this fact. It is also obvious that only a small proportion of the individual organisms that begin life are biologically successful—that is, reach maturity and reproduce. Frequently the advantage in the struggle for existence goes to those animals which mature most rapidly, exist in more protected places, are situated more favorably with respect to food supply, or are able to escape from predators most successfully. The first two points of Darwin's theory, therefore, appear to have considerable merit, with much indirect evidence in their support.

Two problems, however, are confronted: the relationship of variations to adaptation, and the survival value of the variations. Both are open to considerable question. Some aspects of these two problems have been analyzed experimentally, and such analyses have led to modifications of the original hypothesis. One of the earliest experiments designed to test the importance of variations in evolution was made by the botanist Johannsen, who studied the inheritance of weight in bean seeds. Johannsen self-fertilized bean plants which had been selected as being genetically pure and observed that seed weight varied from about 350 to 650 milligrams. He planted the lightest and the heaviest seeds produced by a single plant and determined the seed weight in the offspring. The *average* weight of the seeds in each group was practically the same, even though the experiment was repeated for several generations. The individual seeds, of course, did not all weigh the same, but any weight variation within the genetically pure line was clearly a result of environmental conditions and was not inherited. Comparable results have been observed repeatedly in both plants and animals. Opponents of Darwin's theory seized upon these experiments as evidence that selection is of no value in evolution, but modern genetic studies have contributed new information in support of the theory by the study of variations that result from *mutations*.

Mutations, either as *gene changes* or as *chromosomal rearrangements,* occur in pure lines as well as in heterozygous organisms and do produce hereditary changes. If, therefore, selection is practiced after a mutation occurs, new characters or greatly modified characters can be developed. Darwin had recognized that not all variations were alike and was aware that extreme variations could arise suddenly. The latter were known in Darwin's time as *saltations,* or "jumps," but little importance in evolution was ascribed to them. We noted the hereditary significance of mutations previously (p. 525) in the discussion of genetics, and modern students of evolution believe that if the "variations" in Darwin's theory are limited to those that are a result of mutations, the theory will explain the mechanism of evolution. Hereditary variations in evolution, therefore, arise in single steps and behave according to Mendelian laws. Thus,

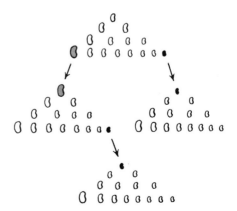

Figure 22.21. When seeds were selected from a pure line, the successive generations showed the same variability as the original seed type. Thus, the small seeds gave rise to seeds of the same size variations as the large seeds.

"survival of the fittest" would serve as a sieve to separate advantageous from harmful or neutral mutations and make possible the perpetuation of new characters arising from such mutations. These conclusions lead to what is usually called the *new-Darwinian,* or *neo-Darwinian, theory.*

Theoretically, survival of the fittest should operate in the selection of variations that adapt organisms to their environment and would result in the creation of new species. Direct evidence in support of the theory, however, is singularly absent. This disturbing fact is a result largely of the intrinsic difficulty of testing a situation which can be effective only when large numbers of organisms are subjected to natural selection for many generations. Some attempts have been made to study the problem under laboratory conditions, and in addition, data are available on the ability of parasites or disease organisms to develop resistance to the effects of poisons and antibodies. Wild-type and mutant *Drosophila* have been mixed in known proportions in test boxes in which they competed for food and space. The relative numbers of the different types were determined at intervals, and usually the wild type became dominant. But there were exceptions, as in the experiment in which long-winged and vestigial-winged flies were mixed and the test boxes placed so that they were open to the wind. In this experiment the vestigial-winged flies became dominant, possibly because they were less disturbed by the wind.

Insects which attack fruit trees cannot be eradicated completely by fumigation with poison gases, because some of the insects will develop resistance to the treatment. Similarly, certain blood parasites of man can survive drug treatment and give rise to resistant strains. There can be little doubt that in some cases the resistance was a product of mutated genes and was inherited. The rust which parasitizes wheat has been studied extensively by Stakman and his co-workers, who have observed that the different strains of rust vary greatly in frequency in different years in the several regions of North America. The wheat farmer is undoubtedly responsible in part for the fluctuations in the rust population, because he constantly attempts to develop new varieties of wheat which are rust resistant. The rust is forced either to adapt to the new type of wheat or die out. As the grower practices artificial selection on the wheat, natural selection operates on the rust and mutated strains appear.

The persistence of characters without survival value, and even of characters which are disadvantageous, has been cited by opponents of Darwinism as evidence that survival of the fittest is not operating as an evolutionary process. Genetics, however, has been able to account for such inconsistencies in a satisfactory manner. It is known that a gene has many effects in an organism, and that a gene must always function in cooperation with many other genes in the protoplasm. A single gene mutation, for example, may produce an observable change in an external structure without seriously disrupting the normal physiology of the organism, or with only slightly deleterious effects. As the number of mutations increases, however, a point will be reached at which physiological processes are disrupted, and the plant or animal must make physical or functional adjustments. It is at this time that selection operates.

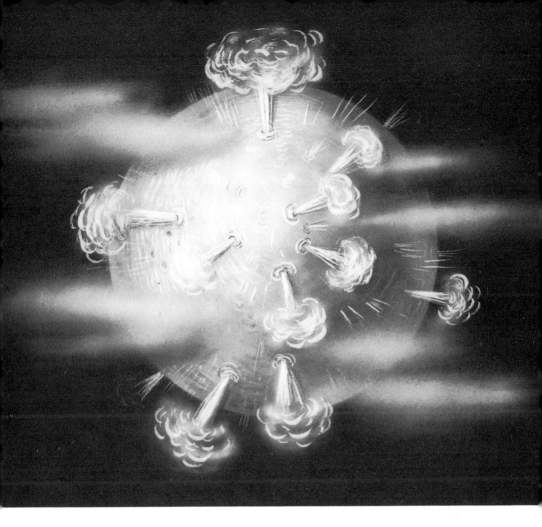

Figure 22.22. The earth was once a smaller, hotter sphere than now. It was not until millions of years had passed that the earth became cool enough to support life.

Genetics has focused attention on another fact which has bothered students of evolution. This is the loss of structures, or the retention of structures in a vestigial condition. Many mutations result in the loss or reduction of a character, and if the mutated gene becomes established in a species, the corresponding modification will be retained. It is unnecessary, therefore, to assume disuse in order to account for rudimentary structures or organs. Goldschmidt has suggested that if the mutations caused the loss of structures normally present in an embryo, the pattern of development would be greatly modified. Should such a "monster" survive, it might be so different from its relatives that it could be placed in a different family or class, and thus evolution in one gigantic step

581

would transcend countless small advances. This stimulating hypothesis of *macroevolution* has not been generally accepted by biologists, but it indicates an area where new information is needed.

Modern genetic study has re-emphasized another factor that must be considered if evolution is to take place. This is the factor of *isolation*. Each species may be thought of as a group of organisms which possesses a common store of genes, and a promiscuous interbreeding between species would result in a thorough mixing of genes, with a disappearance of the characteristic differences between species. Since crosses between species are impossible when the species are isolated, many worthless new characters and new gene combinations are prevented. Isolation, on the other hand, makes it possible for new mutations to establish themselves in a species with the minimum of competition from genes of other species. It should be recognized that the factors which isolate organisms are extremely diverse. Two related species may occupy different types of environment and hence do not meet; one species may reproduce at one season of the year, whereas the second species reproduces at a different season; there may be physical differences which make copulation impossible; sexual behavior might differ, and the species might not be attracted to each other; fertilization could be impossible, or the offspring might not live or be able to reproduce; and finally, distance may prevent the two species from coming together, even though all other conditions would permit mating.

It can be seen in retrospect that evolution is a concept which unifies biology. Without the generalizations of evolution, the diversities of organic form and function and the adaptations to a multitude of environmental situations are meaningless. The *fact* of evolution is well established by many lines of evidence from paleontology, taxonomy, comparative anatomy, embryology, serology, animal and plant breeding, and genetics. Our understanding of the mechanism of evolution is less satisfactory, and at present the most widely accepted theory is based upon modifications of Darwin's original hypothesis. Genetics must occupy a prominent place in any interpretation of the evolutionary mechanism. Mutations are the raw materials for adaptive variations, and natural selection coupled with isolation affords the most satisfactory explanation for the development and preservation of the differences which distinguish species. One of the major contributions of modern studies to the problem of evolution has been a demonstration that evolution may be degenerative as well as progressive. The random nature of mutations correlates perfectly with this observation.

Origin of Life

There can be no doubt, in the light of the vast array of facts assembled by astronomers and physicists, that the earth in the stages following its origin was an incandescent ball of gas, with temperatures measured in thousands of degrees. Clearly, life could not have existed on such a flaming sphere but must have appeared sometime during the "cooling off" period, which took a billion or so years. There is, of course, no direct evidence as to the time or method of the origin of life. Only speculations are possible. Three alternative hypotheses have been advanced: (1) that life is a result of special creation; (2) that organisms came to the earth from another planet in the solar system; and (3) that protoplasm was formed on earth from nonliving matter. These hypotheses may be considered in order.

Unfortunately, *special creation* cannot be analyzed by scientific methods, and biologists are reluctant to accept this explanation if other logical possibilities can be advanced. This does not mean that biologists are atheists, but only that they believe natural processes are adequate to account for the phenomenon of life.

Biologists are also hesitant to adopt the idea that protoplasm migrated from *another planet*. Assuming that life exists elsewhere, which has been neither proved nor disproved, the problem of transportation to the earth presents an imposing difficulty. Living matter might conceivably journey to the earth embedded in a meteor; or ultramicroscopic organisms possibly could reach the earth, propelled by the pressure of light waves. Serious objections, however, seem to refute either possibility.

Meteors traveling at terrific speeds become white hot when they enter the atmosphere of the earth; and while it could be argued that the earth did not have an atmosphere in its early stages, this in itself would eliminate the possibility of meteor-borne life, since life cannot exist except in special atmospheric conditions. The interior temperatures of meteors would appear to be too high for the existence of even the simplest type of protoplasm. A few bacteria have been reported from the centers of meteors, but the probability is that they have reached this location after the meteor arrived on earth. The migration of ultramicroscopic living particles is remotely possible, but again such matter would have to overcome tremendous difficulties. If the pressure of light waves was the propulsive force for travel, the journey would have required thousands or millions of years. Time is not a serious objection in itself, because such millions of years were available, but the lack of oxygen and exposure to the intense cold of interstellar space would be deleterious if not fatal. More serious than these adverse conditions are other harmful agents to be found in space. Any organisms making a slow journey to earth would be exposed to ultraviolet and cosmic rays. The intensities of these radiations in the interstellar spaces is so great that it is inconceivable that protoplasm could survive exposure to them for the length of time which would be involved.

Should the unlikely event of the inoculation of the earth by life from space have occurred, the curiosity of biologists still would not be satisfied. They would find it necessary in such a case to explain how life originated elsewhere, a more difficult problem than to account for the birth of life on earth.

The third alternative, that living matter was formed from *nonliving substances,* has been considered repeatedly and was viewed as a definite possibility by Darwin. Many earlier objections to this hypothesis have been removed by an increased understanding of the fact that viruses are transitional in structure and activity between living and nonliving systems. The minuteness of the viruses and the chemical simplicity of certain of them hint that original living matter may have been comparable. A nutritional difficulty arises, however, since viruses can live only by feeding on other organisms, whereas the first living things must have depended on simple organic compounds for sustenance.

Autotrophic and heterotrophic nutrition both have been considered as the first nutritive condition, and modern ideas on this problem have been well expressed by A. E. Oparin and by N. H. Horowitz. The more appealing of the two possibilities would be to assume that the first organisms were autotrophic and, like the green plants of today, manufactured their own food from carbon dioxide, water, and simple nitrogen compounds. We recall, however, that the first step—the manufacture of glucose—is not a simple one, and that the subsequent formation of fats and proteins is still more complex. These syntheses require the participation of many enzymes, and we know that there is a close correspondence between the number of enzymes and the number of genes. If, therefore, autotrophic organisms were the first to appear, it would have been necessary for them to have possessed a large number of both enzymes and genes. It is inconceivable that such a complicated protoplasmic organization could have been the first.

Heterotrophic organisms do not need such complicated enzyme systems, but the acceptance of the hypothesis that the first organisms were heterotrophic immediately encounters what appears to be an unanswerable question: Upon what would the heterotrophs feed? Modern heterotrophic forms can exist only on other organisms and are ultimately dependent, as we have seen, on plants. The "first heterotroph" would have had no other protoplasm upon which it could prey. It is relative to this dilemma that modern chemistry and genetics have made significant contributions. We now know that a great variety of organic (carbon) compounds can be formed in the laboratory independently of organisms, and that enzyme systems can be altered by gene mutations. The significance of these two facts may be adjudged in turn.

It is certain that the cooling of the earth was accompanied by the formation of molecules and simple compounds. Oxygen was combined with carbon, hydrogen, and other elements to form carbon dioxide, water, and the countless oxides we know so well today. The surface of the earth at one time must have resembled a vast ash pit composed of oxides and carbon compounds. The water when first formed was, of course, superheated steam; but as the cooling process continued, clouds formed, rains fell, and the chemical mixture was converted into a seething mass of reacting substances. The earth without any protecting shade was bathed with stupendous amounts of energy-rich radiations, especially ultraviolet radiation, which would supply energy for photochemical reactions. It is possible, on a very limited scale, to duplicate this condition in the laboratory today. The results are highly significant: mixtures of ammonia, carbon dioxide, and water—when strongly irradiated with ultraviolet light—are converted into an imposing array of organic (carbon) compounds.

When we think of the much more elaborate chemical reactions performed by nature on the cooling surface of the primordial earth, it taxes our imagination to conceive of the many substances that must have been formed.

Somewhere, large molecules were created, and complex colloidal systems would have appeared. Certain of these must have been comparable to the simplest viruses and must have been in the nature of the *nucleoproteins*. They existed in a warm, rich organic soup and were able to utilize the simpler organic materials in which they "lived" for energy and growth. These, by definition, would have been heterotrophs, having acquired the ability to synthesize other molecules like themselves. These *preorganisms*, however, soon began to exhaust the supply of organic compounds which constituted their menu, and as Horowitz has suggested, a struggle for existence must have developed at the molecular level!

Horowitz has advanced the hypothesis that these preorganisms mutated exactly as we know today that viruses mutate, and that these mutations made survival possible. If, for example, the viruslike molecule depended upon an organic complex, which we might call A, for its energy, growth, and reproduction, and compound A was exhausted, the molecule no longer could maintain itself. Should a mutation have occurred, creating a new gene-enzyme complex which would have enabled the molecule to *synthesize* A from molecules X and Y, then the preorganism could have survived. A subsequent depletion of X or Y would result in the "death" of the molecule unless additional mutations occurred which made it possible for X to be resynthesized from R and S, or Y from P and Q. This chain of events would lead eventually to the production of complex gene-enzyme systems, and, of course, finally to an *autotrophic organism.*

This idea that complicated gene-enzyme systems could be produced by ultramicroscopic protein molecules would have been deemed fantastic little more than a decade ago. S. E. Luria and others, however, have demonstrated clearly that the "phage" viruses are made up of many genelike subunits, and that these frequently mutate. The discussion of gene-enzyme relationships (pp. 538–539) illustrates that there is ample evidence to support the idea that mutations are related to biosynthesis. We must conclude, on the basis of our knowledge of genetics and biochemistry, that it is no more difficult to account for the origin of multigenic enzyme systems (living matter) than it is to explain the origin of the many-celled organisms from the acellular organisms. The hypothesis is not simple in either case, but each explanation is logical, with strong evidence to support it.

The question may be asked whether new protoplasm is being created today from nonliving matter. The results of experiments of Pasteur and the eighteenth-century Italian scientist, Spallanzani, are contrary to this idea. Darwin also pointed out that any complex organic molecules formed in nature today would be eaten or disintegrated quickly by existing organisms. It is, therefore, inconceivable to biologists that life could have been created spontaneously several times, because the conditions favorable to spontaneous creation could have existed only during the earliest period of the earth's history.

REFERENCES

BLUM, H. F., *Time's Arrow and Evolution*, pp. 34–43, 156–178. Princeton University Press, 1951.

DARWIN, C. R., *Origin of Species* (6th ed.). P. F. Collier and Son, New York, 1905.

DARWIN, C. R., *The Foundations of the Origin of Species*. Cambridge University Press, London, 1909.

DARWIN, C. R., *Journal of Researches into the Geology and Natural History of the Various Countries Visited by H.M.S. Beagle* (1839). Hefner Publishing Company, New York, 1952.

DARWIN, C. R., *The Voyage of the Beagle*. Everyman's Library, No. 104. E. P. Dutton, Inc., New York, 1955.

DE BEER, SIR GAVIN R., *Charles Darwin: Evolution by Natural Selection*. Doubleday, Garden City, New York, 1964.

DOUBZHANSKY, T., "Evolution at Work," *Science, 127,* 1958, pp. 1091–1098.

DUNBAR, C. O., *Historical Geology*. John Wiley and Sons, New York, 1949.

HOROWITZ, N. H., *On the Evolution of Biochemical Syntheses,* Proceedings of the National Academy of Sciences, *31,* 1945.

JEPSON, G. L., E. MAYR, and G. G. SIMPSON, *Genetics, Paleontology, and Evolution*. Princeton University Press, Princeton, 1949.

LASKER, GABRIEL WARD, *Human Evolution; Physical Anthropology and the Origin of Man*. Holt, Rinehart, and Winston, New York, 1963.

LURIA, S. E., *Reactivation of Irradiated Bacteriophage by Transfer of Self-Reproducing Units*. Proceedings of the National Academy of Sciences, Vol. 33, 1947.

OPARIN, A. E., *The Origin of Life*. Macmillan and Company, 1938.

RAYMOND, P. E., *Prehistoric Life*. Harvard University Press, Cambridge, Mass., 1947.

SAVAGE, JAY M., *Evolution* (Modern Biology Series). Hope, Rinehart, and Winston, New York, 1963.

SINGER, C., *A History of Biology*, pp. 430–457. Henry Schuman, New York, 1950.

23

Present

Indicative

●

Some

Biological

Concepts

and Problems

Thus, biologists have arrived at the conclusion that a fundamental uniformity of structure pervades the animal and vegetable worlds, and that plants and animals differ from one another simply as modifications of the same general plan.—T. H. Huxley, On the Study of Biology, 1876

Man is the only organism able to evaluate his own past and that of other species. It is also within his power to direct his future evolution by the application of the lessons that may be learned from these evaluations, and no other species possesses such an advantage in nature. It remains to be demonstrated, however, whether this power of self-determination will be exercised in a manner which will result in human progress, or whether *Homo sapiens* will follow the pathway of the dinosaur and the dodo. Any sound conclusions relative to the problem of man's future must rest on the validity of the facts which he has gathered and the deductions which science has made on the basis of these facts. It is well, therefore, before considering the future of mankind, to examine both the accumulated facts and the methodology used to acquire them.

The accumulation of facts is essential for the advancement of knowledge, but it is characteristic of scientific investigation that factual information is valuable only as it contributes to the formulation of concepts which will direct attention to new problems. This has been well stated by Dr. James Bryant Conant, who has defined science as "... an interconnected series of concepts and conceptual schemes that have developed as a result of experimentation and observation and are fruitful of further experimentation and observation." It is important, therefore, to summarize the major biological concepts which have been developed, and to state a few of the biological problems that affect man's future.

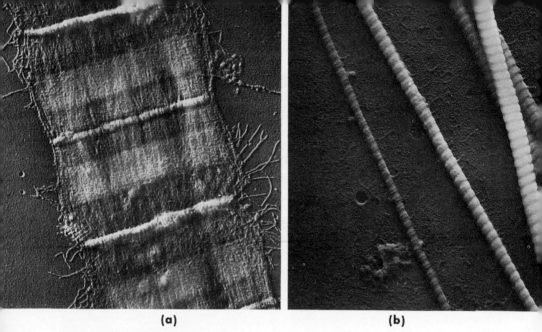

(a)   (b)

Figure 23.1. The photograph in (a) shows striated muscle at a magnification of 28,000X; in (b) the photograph shows the collagen fibers of the skin at a magnification of 47,000X. These pictures illustrate the opportunities afforded by electron-microscope studies. (Courtesy C. E. Hall, Massachusetts Institute of Technology.)

Concepts

Protoplasm

First, all life is protoplasm, a colloidal substance of inconstant but intricate chemical composition, which possesses the unique ability of appropriating to itself common chemicals and creating from them its own peculiar type of matter. All organisms are protoplasm, but some may be subdivided into cells, whereas others are acellular.

Activities and functions

A second concept is that the activities and functions of all living things are comparable. Protoplasm, however, has exercised a wide latitude in devising structures to perform these activities and functions. Structural diversities are present in the acellular as well as in the many-celled animals, but the first major step in evolutionary progress was the development of the many-celled condition, with its structural advantages.

Adaptability

The third concept is related intimately to the second: namely, that over great expanses of time, organisms have adapted their activities, functions, and structures to constantly changing environmental conditions. The basis for adaptations is to be found in the changing genetic composition of the organism, and it is increasingly apparent that to understand life the organism must be considered as a whole, because every organism is *more* than the mere sum of its parts.

Organic change

Fourth, the concept which unifies biological knowledge is the recognition that organisms are related, but that they have changed, are changing, and will continue to change. The initial variations are independent of the environment, but the adaptations which result are a product of the interrelationship of change and environment. An otherwise chaotic biological world, therefore, is given order and significance by this principle of evolution.

Before considering the impact of these concepts on man as one representative organism, it may be well to review briefly a few features of scientific investigation which led to the formulation of these concepts. Several examples of the scientific method have been cited during the course of the presentation of various phases of biology. These were chosen deliberately to illustrate various techniques which have been employed and to demonstrate some of the pitfalls that can beset the path of an investigator.

Basic observations

Great admiration must be extended to Leeuwenhoek because of his insatiable curiosity and his magnificent observations with equipment so poor that biology students of our day would be insulted if asked to use such inferior tools. It will be recalled that he pioneered in the study of protozoans, bacteria, blood cells, capillary circulation, and human male reproductive cells, and was particularly interested in those "little animals" which live in mutual associations. Leeuwenhoek, however, formulated no great generalizations or concepts in biology. It was not until the 1830's and 1840's, when Ehrenberg and Dujardin emphasized that the Protozoa were complete organisms, and Schleiden and Schwann gathered together their own observations with those of many others to formalize the cell theory, that the concept of the fundamental unity of structure of all life was developed. The impetus to biological investigations provided by these observations of uniformity has continued to the present day, and although it has been necessary to modify the cell theory, no one at present challenges the idea that the activities and functions of all living things are comparable. It also should be noted that errors in observations may lead to false conclusions and generalizations. Ehrenberg's idea that protozoans possessed organ systems was erroneous, but he and his followers adhered to this false notion until voluminous data to the contrary became irrefutable.

Experimental method

The observations made by Harvey were the stimulus to the development of the experimental method. This method is so much a part of procedure in all

Figure 23.2. In front of the man's hands you will see a piece of paper—this is a photograph of actual molecules and represents a magnification of 1,000,000X! Between the man's hands is a model of one of these molecules. Each ball represents an atom. (Courtesy of *Life;* copyright *Time,* Inc.)

fields of modern biology that it is difficult to conceive how biological science could progress without its aid. Although nearly two and one half centuries elapsed between Harvey's report of his observations and the experiments and findings of Mendel, there are some striking similarities in the methodology employed by the two men.

The investigations of both were designed to assess variable factors by simple, direct experiments which could be repeated easily. The data from these experiments were used to develop concepts which were readily verified. The conclusions arrived at by both men were based on incomplete data which, however, directed the attention of subsequent investigators to the points that needed further clarification. Harvey, for example, did not have information relative to capillary circulation, nor did Mendel know about reduction division in reproductive cells. Finally, each man made errors. Harvey miscalculated the volume of blood flow, and Mendel either did not discover linkage or ignored it. It should be emphasized, however, that so well documented were the results and so well conceived were their investigations that later studies had the effect of correcting and extending their observations without altering appreciably their basic conclusions. It is the hope of every scientist that his own observations and conclusions will be sound enough to warrant such treatment.

Common information in science

Darwin's contribution to science was discussed in some detail in the historical approach to the problem of evolution. Not only did his work establish the foundation for the concept of the interrelationship of organisms, but his studies directed attention to the need for correlating data from diverse fields of knowledge. It was noted that the sciences of astronomy, chemistry, physics, geology, paleontology, botany, zoology, and genetics each made major contributions to the data necessary for the understanding of organic change. Modern biology has continued to expand along these lines, as is evidenced by the existence of such fields of study as biochemistry, biophysics, and even biometrics.

Some Biological Problems

Ecology

Man is a unique organism, endowed with faculties for reasoning which are not found elsewhere in the animal kingdom. He has acquired, as a result of this exceptional quality, a degree of independence unknown to other organisms. It is often disconcerting, because of man's apparent self-sufficiency, to discover that he is subject to the same rules and regulations as are other organisms. The vicissitudes of life always confront human beings to a limited extent, but occasionally the rigors of existence are brought forcibly to man's attention. We have noted a few of the biological problems affecting mankind briefly in earlier discussions, but now we may analyze their relevance in more detail.

An important field of science which deals with the problems of the interrelationship between organisms and their environment is *ecology*. The major aspects of the ecology of man, as well as that of other organisms, are concerned with *physical factors*—such as temperature, sunlight, rainfall, and natural resources—and with *biological factors*—such as living room (the *lebensraum* of Hitler), soil fertility, food supply, and parasitism. Even before Darwin's time biologists demonstrated that overpopulation within a species led to migrations (for example, those of locusts, lemmings), to an expansion of the normal range, and almost invariably to interspecific conflicts and the death of multitudes. Man, with his intelligence, if he realizes the significance of what is happening to him, should be able to check and control the development of adverse conditions of this type.

The population of the world has been increasing by leaps and bounds in the last 150 years. It is true that the number of people has already exceeded the limit of human population which the earth could support, as visualized by Malthus, but this is because he did not comprehend the advances of an industrial civilization nor the possibilities of improved food production. Still, our advances in technology and science have merely extended the problem of human overpopulation, not solved it. The saturation point in population has

Figure 23.3. The waving, geometric patterns seen in much farming country today are produced by strip farming and terracing. These practices prevent erosion, and by their use many farmers have turned marginal farm areas into productive land. (Courtesy United States Department of Agriculture, Soil Conservation Bureau.)

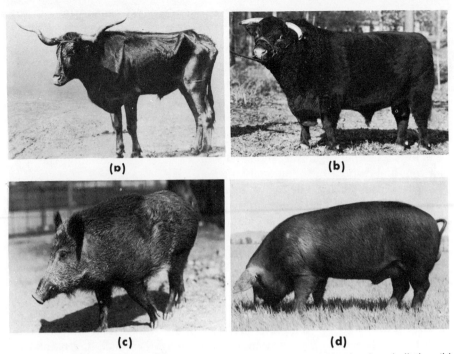

(a)   (b)

(c)   (d)

Figure 23.4. The study in contrasts above, the longhorn steer versus the shorthorn bull, the wild boar versus the black Hampshire race hybrid, shows the work of improved breeding techniques. By applying his knowledge of genetics, man has been able, from his own point of view, to improve many of the domestic animals on which he depends for so many of his needs. [(a), (b), (d) Courtesy United States Department of Agriculture, Bureau of Animal Husbandry; (c) courtesy New York Zoological Society.]

been reached in some areas of the world—for example, in India—and is being approached rapidly in the Western world. This increase in the number of human beings is a product of several factors. The greatly improved control of diseases, especially those of epidemic nature, has been accompanied by a decrease in the rate of infant mortality; more people are living longer. Improved agriculture, with better distribution and storage of food, has decreased the number of deaths from starvation. Thus, with lower death rates in the early ages, more people are reaching reproductive age, and more children are being born. World population, therefore, is on an increasing spiral. It is significant that the situation is identical with that which has faced many species of animals again and again in the past, and it is possible on this basis to analyze the problem which faces mankind.

Improvement can be made in food production by utilizing genetic methods to increase yield, as in hybrid corn; to develop varieties of plants and animals that can live in arctic or subarctic areas or in semidesert regions, as in varieties of wheat; and to improve domestic animals for faster growth and earlier maturity. The sea has vast potentialities for food production. An acre of water is many times more productive than an acre of land in terms of tons of

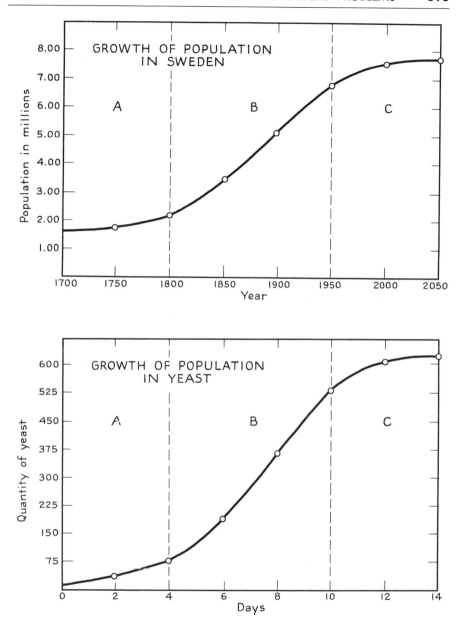

Figure 23.5.   These two curves, population growth of people in Sweden and population growth of yeast cells in culture, are remarkably alike.   Each can be subdivided into three phases: (a), a phase of slow growth; (b), a phase of tremendous growth; and (c), a phase at which growth is relatively steady.   The similarity of these curves is more than coincidence, for population increases usually conform to this same pattern.

protoplasm which can be grown.   This fact has been known for years, but it has not been exploited.

Since man has demonstrated an ability to devise methods of controlling his environment by central heating and by air-conditioning, it should be possible for him to live in greater numbers in the arctic regions, especially since he is learning rapidly how to control the diseases which beset him in the remote areas of the world.   It is possible also that desert regions may be irrigated to provide enlarged living space.

A specific problem will serve to illustrate the above generalizations.   It has been estimated that by 1975 the population of the United States will reach 190,000,000.   The present rate of food production is insufficient to maintain this population and must be increased; otherwise the planting of at least an additional 100,000,000 acres of cropland will be required if the present rate is maintained.   More acres can be added by irrigation and flood control, but more effective measures for the improvement of the food supply must rest on biological controls.   We observed earlier that 10 per cent of the crops are destroyed annually by insect pests.   In addition, 10 per cent of farm animals die from disease and parasites, and as much as 30 per cent of stored crops are damaged or destroyed.   Improved control methods can prevent this waste and would effect a production increase without planting additional land.

The augmented production of food and the possibility of greater living room, however, do not solve the basic problem of overpopulation.   These merely alleviate the conditions; and sooner or later, populations will again become too large.   The fundamental cure is to be found only in a lower birth rate, and although the biological aspects of this solution are complex, the social and religious factors involved are far more weighty.   We do not propose to solve such problems here; but the human race must realize that the ecology of man requires constructive consideration.

Biology and medicine

The foregoing brief account illustrates only one of the many ways in which a knowledge of biological principles is important to mankind.   We have observed how effective the control of parasites has been for the improvement of human health, and that the eradication of insect disease carriers also has been efficacious.   Less well-known applications of biology to medicine, however, are even more significant, as is well illustrated by the use of isotopes.   Some isotopes are radioactive, emitting energy and behaving within the cells or tissues like X-radiation.   Others are the heavy isotopes, such as heavy hydrogen (H^2) and deuterium (H^3).   The radioactive isotopes, phosphorus (P^{32}) and iodine (I^{131}), are well known to everyone who reads newspapers, because of their use in the treatment of malignant growths.   Sodium (Na^{24}) shows promise as an important tool for the treatment of certain blood diseases, because of its localization in the extracellular spaces.   Cobalt (Co^{60}), in addition, gives promise as a substitute for radium.

The therapeutic use of isotopes, however, is only a minor facet of their

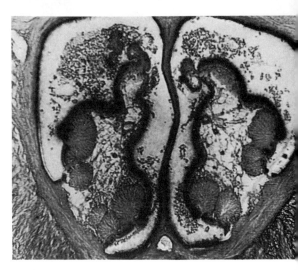

Figure 23.6. Biological tracers. Many substances can be used to trace chemical molecules in the body. This cross section of an ammocoete larva shows how the body concentrated an injection of I^{131} (blackened areas). When the animal was cross-sectioned and placed under a photographic emulsion, the radioactive I^{131} took its own photograph. (Courtesy Dr. R. H. Shellhammer.)

utility; their greatest importance lies in their application to diagnostic procedures, especially in analyzing biochemical reactions. Carbon (C^{14}) and the hydrogen isotopes, deuterium (H^2) and tritium (H^3), already have proved to be of incalculable value. It is essential to know, for example, what happens to substances such as glucose, cholesterol, and lipids in normal and malignant tissues; by "marking" these or similar compounds with C^{14}, H^2, or H^3, it is possible to trace them through the body. It is possible also to mark proteins and to trace these complex molecules in antibody reactions. The use of P^{32} has shown that the bone salts are not permanently fixed, as was thought previously, but may be mobilized in 24 hours; and the marking of glucose has permitted an analysis of sugar utilization in diabetic patients. Iodine (I^{131}) has been used to determine the rate at which normal and abnormal thyroid glands concentrate iodides, and this has led to improvement in the treatment of thyroid disorders.

The most fundamental problem in biology—the formation of carbohydrates during photosynthesis—has been investigated by "feeding" plants carbon dioxide containing radioactive carbon (written $C^{\circ}O_2$). The balance of sodium and potassium in osmosis and mineral metabolism, and the absorption and excretion of metabolites may be studied with isotopes. The preparation of fertilizers containing isotopes has made it possible to determine the nutritive needs of plants and the relative speed at which different elements are utilized.

The use of isotopes in biology is only in its initial phase, and the possibilities are almost unlimited. It should be emphasized that the application for human good of the discoveries based on isotope studies is a final step in a long process of research. The isotopes have been exhaustively tested, in most instances on rats, rabbits, tadpoles, ammocoete larvae, and even invertebrates. This is a dramatic demonstration of the validity of our concepts of the uniformity of living matter and of the basic similarity of activities and functions. Many of the most beneficial treatments in modern medicine would have been delayed indefinitely if it had not been possible to make preliminary investigations on animals.

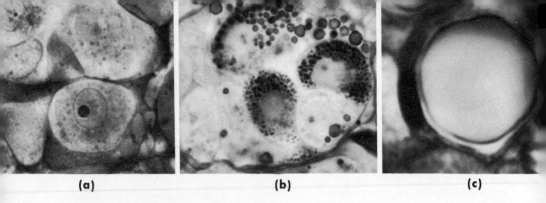

| (a) | (b) | (c) |

Figure 23.7. These pictures of fowl pituitary glands show changes which can develop with age. (a) Section of the anterior pituitary gland of a young fowl shows normal cells; (b) in the pituitary of an older fowl, a number of spherical bodies have accumulated within the cells; (c) in the pituitary of an aged fowl, the smaller spheres have fused into a large mass, which has pushed the nucleus to one side and will eventually rupture the cell. (Courtesy Dr. F. Payne.)

Aging

There has been a notable increase, both relatively and absolutely, in the number of people over 65 years of age. There were only 3,000,000 such persons in the United States in 1900, but in 1950 this number exceeded 13,000,000 and is growing rapidly. It is now customary to ask people of age 65 or 70 to retire, but we know that many people of this age are healthy and alert and have many productive years ahead of them. This fact has aroused an increased interest in the study of aging, *gerontology;* and the biological factors are as noteworthy as the sociological in this regard. We observed that significant discoveries have been and are being made relative to the physiological processes of aging in protozoans, rotifers, and planarians. It may be expected, on the basis of our experience in other fields of biology, that these studies will eventually contribute to a better understanding of the physiology of the older members of the human species, with a corresponding improvement in health and well-being. Biology in the final analysis may be of as much practical benefit as social security.

Human improvement and the perpetuation of "good heredity"

Man as well as other organisms is a product of the interaction of environment and heredity, but it should be emphasized that neither environment nor heredity operates to the exclusion of the other. Variability in the human race, therefore, is a product of both factors, and it is to be expected that man's status eventually will be determined by the adaptations which will be made. It is in this regard that certain practical applications of genetic laws become important to human welfare. These applications are to be found in the analysis of susceptibility to disease, in the prevention of the transmission of fatal abnormalities from generation to generation, and in the long-range improvement of the genetic composition of the human race. All these problems are complex, because they involve nonbiological factors of individual psychological adjustments, sociological regulations, and religious beliefs. It will be best to illustrate a few of the complications by specific examples.

Our increasing knowledge of human heredity has shown that susceptibility to certain diseases is at least partially controlled by genetic factors. Susceptibility to diphtheria and the development of diabetes are two well-known examples. It also has been suggested that diabetes may be inherited in a rather simple Mendelian pattern, with the heterozygous person serving as a "carrier." A child of diabetic parents will almost invariably develop diabetes. Since diabetes often does not develop until middle age, the genetic determination is somewhat difficult. A physician who is aware of the family history may be alert to the danger of such conditions and may begin treatments at a much earlier time than would otherwise be indicated. Still other important applications of genetic knowledge can be used in a preventive way.

Some very tragic consequences of genic mutation are the fatal abnormalities of hemophilia, muscular dystrophy, leukemia, infantile and juvenile amaurotic idiocy, and sensitization to the Rh blood factor. Prospective husband and wife should be warned of the danger that these conditions may develop in their children or grandchildren when there is a past family history of such abnormalities. We commented earlier on the unfortunate results of the cousin marriages in the royal houses of Europe with respect to the occurrence of hemophilia. This type of transmission of harmful genes from generation to generation with their perpetuation should be discouraged, or better, should be prevented. It does not matter whether the genes are dominant or recessive, because in the final result it is their gradual increase in the human population which will bring about increasing genetic degeneration.

We commented upon the reaction of blood to proteins in the discussion of serology as a means of evaluating evolution. The inheritance of at least 13 factors, the *antigens*, which control antibody formation, is known in the human being. These antigens, which can be grouped into classes (see table, p. 598, make it possible to determine with accuracy the parentage (or nonparentage) of infants, to ascertain the blood type of blood stains in homicide cases, and

Figure 23.8. The transmission of diabetes from generation to generation is not clearly understood. The simplest explanation, diagrammed in this chart, assumes that diabetes behaves like a Mendelian recessive.

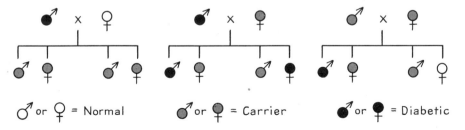

Human Blood Groups*		
Systems	Groups and classes		Antigens
A-B-O system	O, A^1, A^2, A^3, B, A^1B, A^2B, A^3B	8 classes	A^1, A^2, A^3, B
MN system	M, N^1, N^2, MN^1, MN^2	5 classes	M, N^1, N^2
P system	P^1, P^2, P^1P^2, P^-	4 classes	P^1, P^2
S system	S^+, S^-	2 classes	S^+
Rh system	Rh^0, $Rh^{0'}$, $Rh^{0''}$, $Rh^{0'}Rh^{0''}$, Rh', Rh'', $Rh'Rh''$, Rh^-	8 classes	Rh^0, Rh', Rh''

*Adapted from Snyder, *Genetics, Medicine, and Man.*

to make certain that blood transfusions are not fatal. The possible combinations are $8 \times 5 \times 4 \times 2 \times 8$, or 2560 groups; thus, if all blood types were tested, relationship could be determined with accuracy.

The practical applications of genetic and serological knowledge in everyday life may be illustrated by reference to a medical procedure of blood tests which has become routine in the last decade. A person who is Rh-negative will be sensitized when given a transfusion of Rh-positive blood and will form Rh antibodies. A second transfusion with Rh-positive blood will cause the donor blood cells to clump, and the person receiving the transfusion will die. Blood is routinely typed, therefore, for the Rh as well as for the A and B antigens.

A further complication occurs during childbirth. An Rh-negative woman who is married to an Rh-positive man may have children who inherit the Rh-positive antigen. The mother in such a case may become sensitized, and although the first child is not harmed, subsequent children who are Rh-positive will be affected by the antibodies which are generated within the mother. Destruction of red blood cells occurs in these children during late pregnancy, and frequently this is fatal. When a case history of this type is known to the attending physician, he may deliver the baby at eight months and the child's life may be saved. Transfusions may be given the infant, if necessary.

A more difficult problem to attack is that which deals with the general level of intelligence. It is clear that environment has an important effect on the expression of mental ability. The amount of thyroid hormone produced normally is only about 0.3 milligram per day, but this amount may mean the difference between a normal member of society and one who is apparently of low-grade intelligence. The daily oral dosage of only a fraction of a milligram of thyroid hormone to a patient suffering from inadequate amounts of the hormone may change the appearance, attitude, and mental reactions of that person in a seemingly miraculous fashion. The individual so treated is given an opportunity to develop in a normal manner and to utilize *that which was granted to him by his heredity*. A similar metamorphosis is often noted during the eradication of hookworm from a person parasitized by that nematode. It should be emphasized, however, that idiots and morons cannot be transformed by administration of thyroid hormone, by better nutrition, better living conditions, or by the elimination of parasites, because such individuals possess an hereditary inadequacy of the nervous system. It is at this point that society performs both a service and a disservice to mankind. The individual of low-grade intelligence should be trained to be a useful member of society, and in many instances can be self-supporting. It is, however, a very different matter to allow such persons unlimited reproduction. Until recently the average number of children in families with low intelligence was several times greater than the number of children in the families of high intelligence quotients, and unfortunately, the average mental level of the children of the first group is low. The end result of such a reproductive trend will be a gradual lowering of the average intelligence of mankind in the centuries to come, unless the reproductive rates of the idiots and morons are lowered and the reproductive rate of superior persons is increased. Although the problem is clearly delineated, the solution is not simple, and it is beyond the scope of this discussion to do any more than indicate certain feasible procedures.

Figure 23.9. This diagram shows the hereditary pattern of the Rh blood factor.

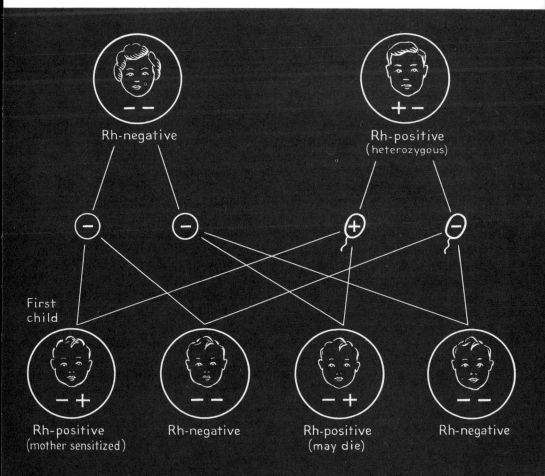

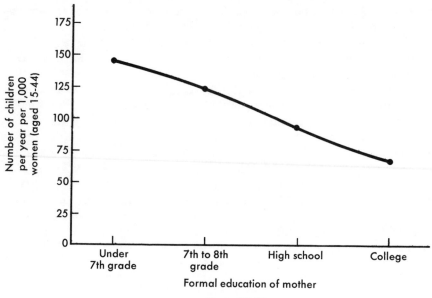

Figure 23.10

There should be developed within our social framework some means to encourage superior individuals to marry earlier and to have larger families. The college graduate, especially one who enters a profession, devotes a large portion of his life to training, at which time he cannot afford to marry and have a family. A study in Indianapolis in 1941 showed, for example, that wives with 4 years of college had an average of only 0.88 children, and it is obvious that a valuable biological potential is being lost to the human race. The Indianapolis study also indicated that wives with less than 7 years of schooling had 2.81 children. The contrast between the two groups is apparent, and it would appear that unless the persons of poorer genetic make-up are discouraged from unlimited reproductive activity, there will be a wider distribution of their inferior genes in the population.

Certain factors, however, must be weighed heavily before such simple solutions are accepted. Our social system must provide opportunities for education to persons with ability; but it is difficult to establish criteria of ability. Progress in school may serve to indicate mental aptitude, but there are many examples of superior individuals who received little formal education. Mendel twice failed examinations for advanced degrees, Darwin was a poor student in both theology and medicine, and Whistler was dropped from West Point for poor scholastic work; yet each made great contributions to mankind. Conversely, it is equally true that a college education does not always mean superior mental ability. Perseverance and hard work also are factors of importance, and the possessors of these qualities are often rewarded by college degrees even though their ability is rather mediocre. The evaluation of ability, therefore, is

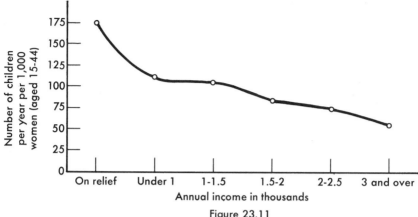

Figure 23.11

most difficult to assess. It is the hope of the students of *eugenics*, who wish to design methods for the perpetuation of "good heredity," that biological, social, and political procedures may be devised to make the goal of human improvement a reality.

Homo sapiens has been an inhabitant of this planet for only approximately 100,000 years, and during the course of his brief existence his achievements have been magnificent and his blunders colossal. Except for a major stellar catastrophe, the earth will serve as a haven for life for several billion years; but, as was pointed out in the introduction to this chapter, whether man himself continues to exist is largely in his own power to determine. He has the ability successfully to control diseases, increase food supply, and provide protection from the elements; but he has yet to demonstrate that he can control himself. *Homo sapiens* is the only organism which wages war in the species, and with the advent of the atomic age he is providing himself with the force which can either lead to his extinction or place the solar system within his reach. The brain which has been man's inheritance as a product of millions of years of evolution may dislodge him from a place in the future course of evolution, or it may give him biological immortality as a species.

REFERENCES

GRUNEBERG, H., *Animal Genetics and Medicine.* Hamish Hemilton Medical Books, London, 1947.

HARDIN, GARRETT (ed.), *Population, Evolution, and Birth Control.* W. H. Freeman Company, San Francisco, 1964.

LARIMER, F., and F. OSBORN, *Dynamics of Population.* The Macmillan Company, New York, 1934.

MONTAGU, ASHLEY (ed.), *Genetic Mechanisms in Human Disease; Chromosomal Aberrations.* Thomas, Springfield, Illinois, 1961.

MULLER, H. J., C. C. LITTLE, and L. H. SNYDER, *Genetics, Medicine, and Man*, pp. 67–154. Cornell University Press, Ithaca, New York, 1947.

WILLIAMS, R. H. (ed.), *Textbook of Endocrinology*, pp. 455–462. W. B. Saunders Company, Philadelphia, 1950.

Appendix | *Some Elementary Chemistry*

The following pages provide a very brief introduction to simple chemistry and chemical terminology. We realized that some students may have had either very little chemistry or none recently. The material in the Appendix is therefore designed as a simple introduction to chemistry, or a relatively pain-less review, to enable the reader to understand the biochemistry in the text.

Atomic structure

There are 92 basic chemical substances in the universe, and additional ones which can be formed in atomic piles. These are the *elements,* and each element is composed of similar unit particles, the *atoms.* Elemental oxygen, for example, is written O_2 because it is composed of two oxygen atoms. The atom is mostly space, with a central positively charged *nucleus,* about which revolve negatively charged particles, the *electrons.* The nucleus comprises most of the *mass* (weight) of the atom and contains two types of particles, the positively charged *protons,* and the *neutrons,* which carry no charge. The protons and neutrons are of equal mass, and each is 1800 times the mass of the electron. The electrons revolve about the nucleus and are grouped into *shells* at varying distances from the central nucleus. Each shell is actually only the *pathway* of an electron or electrons, which whirl at terrific speed in a plane-tary fashion about the nucleus. The helium atom is illustrative of simple atomic structure, with a nucleus containing two protons, two neutrons, and a single shell of two electrons.

The electrons (negative) are held in their orbits by the protons (positive) of the nucleus. In hydrogen, with one proton, there is one electron; carbon, with six protons, has six electrons; and in oxygen, with eight protons, there are eight electrons. There is an important difference between hydrogen, oxy-gen, and carbon in the number of shells about the nucleus. The innermost shell is capable of holding only two electrons, so that if more than two electrons are present, as in carbon, the additional ones must start to fill a second shell, which can have a maximum of eight electrons. The outermost shell also can have a

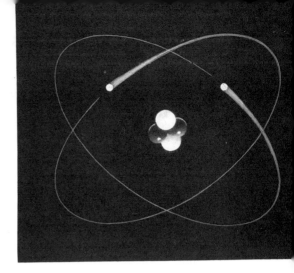

Figure A1. The structure of an atom is illustrated very well by helium, in which electrons revolve about a central nucleus composed of protons and neutrons. The single shell of this atom has its full complement of two electrons.

maximum of only eight electrons. A total of seven shells is possible about a nucleus, and these may hold a maximum number of 92 electrons. It should be realized that this is an oversimplification of the atomic theory and is applicable only to the 92 natural elements.

Molecules

Atoms do exist alone, but the biologist is much more interested in the fact that atoms can combine with other atoms. This is a result of the fact that atoms have a tendency to "capture" or to "lose" electrons. Those atoms with *more* than half the maximum number of electrons in the outer shell tend to *gain electrons*, whereas those with *less* than half the maximum number of electrons in the outer shell tend to *lose electrons*. Atoms with exactly one half the maximum number neither gain nor lose electrons but *share electrons* with other atoms. *Hydrogen*, however, which has only one of two possible electrons in its single shell, tends to lose that one. *Oxygen*, which has six electrons of a possible eight, tends to seize electrons; and *carbon*, with exactly one half, or four electrons of a possible outer eight, shares electrons. For example, two hydrogen atoms, each having one electron to lose, will enter the outer shell of oxygen, completing that shell; and the two protons of hydrogen atoms are then attracted to the outer shell of the oxygen. Since oxygen can attract two atoms of hydrogen, oxygen is said to have a *valence* of two.

An atom which has gained or lost an electron will no longer have its electrical charges in balance: if an electron is lost, the atom will carry a *positive charge;* or a *negative charge* if an electron is gained. Such charged particles are called *ions*. Sodium (Na), which has one electron in the outer shell, will lose this to become a Na^+ *ion*. Chlorine (Cl), with seven electrons in the outer shell, will gain an electron to become a Cl^- *ion* and thus the chlorine will act like a magnet to hold the sodium and will form a *molecule* of sodium chloride. Each atom of sodium or chlorine can have only one electron involved in the exchange; therefore each has a valence of one.

Carbon behaves very differently from sodium or chlorine, because the carbon atom shares its four outer-shell electrons with other atoms, *including other carbon atoms*. The single electron of each of four hydrogen atoms may be incorporated into the outer shell of the carbon, and the carbon simultaneously contributes one of its own electrons to the shell of each hydrogen atom. This is called *covalence*, because the valences are common to two atoms. We have noted that carbon can combine with other carbon atoms and, as a result of this sharing, can create long *carbon chains*. These carbon chains constitute the ultramicroscopic framework of protoplasm.

Compounds

Groups of atoms may combine to form larger particles, the molecules, which behave as units. Furthermore, when a substance is formed by a combination of

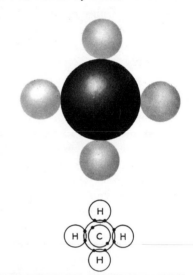

Figure A2.   Atoms may join to form molecules by sharing electrons. In the methane molecule, CH$_4$, at the right, the carbon atom shares electrons with each of four hydrogen atoms.

Figure A3.   Molecules may be composed of different types of atoms. In methyl alcohol, below, one hydrogen atom has been displaced by an oxygen atom, and the oxygen atom, in turn, shares electrons with a hydrogen atom to form the molecule CH$_3$OH.

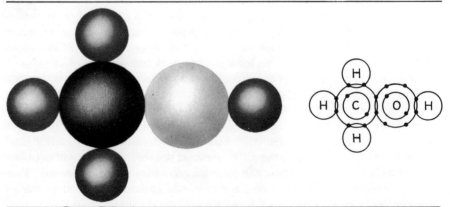

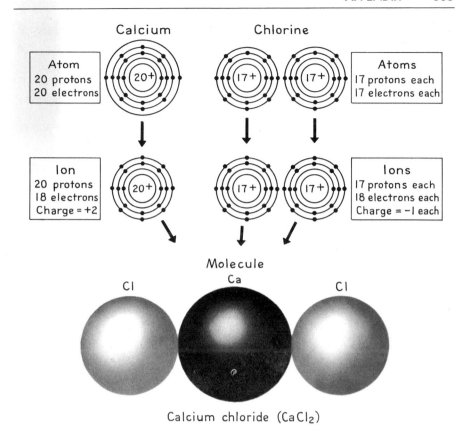

Calcium chloride (CaCl₂)

Figure A4. Some atoms can "capture" electrons readily from other atoms which "lose" electrons readily. Each of two chlorine atoms can capture an electron from a calcium atom. Each chlorine atom will attain a negative charge, the calcium a positive charge. Such charged particles are ions and, since particles with unlike electric charges will be attracted to each other, molecules such as calcium chloride will be formed as a result of this electron transfer.

two or more different atoms in a definite ratio, such a substance is a *compound*. Carbon, for example, combines with hydrogen and oxygen in the proportion of two hydrogen to one oxygen to form *carbohydrate molecules* (for example, $C_6H_{12}O_6$); with hydrogen and oxygen in different proportions to form the *fat*, or *lipin*, *molecules*; and with hydrogen, oxygen, nitrogen, and often phosphorus and sulfur, to make immense molecules—the *proteins*. Although carbohydrates and some lipins can be prepared in the laboratory, the proteins thus far are exclusively a product of protoplasmic synthesis. Large molecules, however, have been synthesized in the laboratory and approximate in size, and to a limited extent in chemical composition, small natural protein molecules.

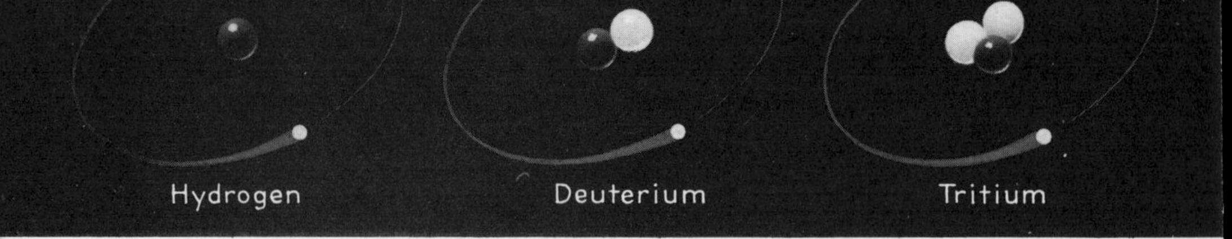

Hydrogen   Deuterium   Tritium

Figure A5. Hydrogen isotopes. Atoms that may possess the same number of electrons but have different masses (nuclei) are isotopes.

Isotopes

We may conclude this elementary discussion of chemistry with a brief statement about isotopes. Some atoms contain extra neutron particles within the nucleus; such atoms are *isotopes*. Certain of these atoms are unstable, or radioactive, and decompose, thus emitting energy (such as gamma rays). Others are called the *heavy isotopes*, for example, heavy hydrogen (H^2), or deuterium, and tritium. The use of isotopes of various kinds has many applications in the study of biology and medicine.

Glossary

Ab·do'men The portion of the body that is posterior to the thorax; contains the viscera.

Ab·o'ral Side opposite the mouth.

A·coe'lo·mate Without a coelom.

Ac'ro·meg'a·ly A disease characterized by an overgrowth of the bones of the hands, face, and feet. A result of an excessive secretion of the growth hormone from the anterior lobe of the pituitary.

Ad·re'nal gland An endocrine gland composed of cortex and medulla, on or near the kidney.

Ad·re'nalin The hormone secreted by the adrenal medulla.

Af'fer·ent Bringing or carrying to or toward a certain region.

Al·ve'o·lus An air sac of the lungs.

A·mi'no ac'id Any one of thirty or more compounds possessing an amino group (NH_2) and a carboxyl group (COOH). They form the essential parts of the protein molecule.

Am'i·to'sis Direct cell division, without the formation of threads or mitotic figures.

Am'ni·on The inner membrane that surrounds the embryo of reptiles, birds, and mammals.

Am'ni·ote A vertebrate that posseses an amnion during embryonic development.

A·moe'boid Resembling movements of an amoeba.

Am·phib'i·a A class of vertebrates, most of the members of which are capable of living in both air and water; for example, frog salamander.

Am·pul'la A small, bladderlike enlargement.

An·ab'o·lism The constructive phase of metabolism.

A·nal'o·gous Having analogs, structures similar in function but not necessarily alike in origin.

An·am'ni·ote A vertebrate that does not possess an amnion during embryonic development.

An'a·phase The stage in cell division when the chromosomes move away from the equatorial plate toward the poles of the cell, just before the new cell wall forms.

A·nat'o·my The study of the structure of the body and the relation of its parts.

An·nel'i·da The phylum to which the segmented worms, such as the earthworm, belong.

An·ox'y·bi·ot'ic Living in the absence of oxygen.

An·ten'na Whiplike, jointed sensory appendage of arthropods.

An·te'ri·or Situated toward the forward, or head, end of the body.

An'ti·bod'y A particular substance in the blood that is antagonistic to a foreign substance.

An'ti·gen' A substance produced by the organism when reacting to a foreign substance.

An'ti·tox'in A substance produced by white blood corpuscles, that neutralizes a toxin.

A'nus The posterior opening of the digestive system.

A·or'ta The main artery leaving the heart.

Ap·pend'age A projecting portion of the body which has a free end, as a leg or arm.

Ar·chen'ter·on The digestive cavity of an embryo; lined with entoderm and opening by the blastopore.

Ar'ter·y A vessel which carries blood from the heart.

Ar·throp'o·da A phylum which includes those animals with externally jointed appendages; for example, crayfish, grasshopper.

A·sex'u·al re·pro·duc'tion Reproduction without the formation of either eggs or sperm. *See* Sexual reproduction.

As'ter A portion of the mitotic figure composed of the centrosome and the "fibers" which radiate from the centrosome.

A·sym'me·try A condition in which the opposite sides of an organism are unlike.

At'om One of the ultimate particles of a molecule or of any matter. Composed of a positively charged nucleus about which negatively charged electrons (or an electron) revolve.

A'tri·um An outer cavity, such as the space about the pharynx in the tunicates or in the ammocoete.

At'ro·phy A degeneration of the body or parts of the body of an organism.

Au'ri·cle One of the receiving chambers of the heart, in contrast to the ventricle or pumping chamber.

Au·to·nom'ic ner'vous sys'tem A motor system subdivided into sympathetic and parasympathetic divisions.

Au'to·some Any chromosome other than the sex chromosome. *See* Chromosome; Sex chromosomes.

Au·tot'o·my The automatic or voluntary breaking off of a part of an organism.

Au'to·troph' A "self feeding" organism; one which manufactures its own food.

Ax·i'al gra'di·ent Variation of the metabolic rate along the main axis of the body.

Ax'i·al skel'e·ton The skull, vertebrae, ribs, and sternum of the vertebrate.

Ax'on The process of a nerve cell along which impulses are conducted away from the nerve cell body.

Bac·te·ri·ol'o·gy The division of biology which deals with bacteria.

Bi·lat'er·al sym'me·try The types of symmetry in which the right and left sides of the body are mirror images of each other.

Bi·no'mi·al no'men·cla'ture In taxonomy, the giving of a generic and specific name to an organism.

Bi·o·chem'is·try The study of the chemistry of vital processes.

Bi·ol'o·gy The study of organisms, both plants and animals, and their relationships.

Bi·ra'mous ap·pend'age An appendage with two branches joined to a basal portion; for example, swimmeret of crayfish.

Bi·sex'u·al The presence of the reproductive organs of both sexes in one individual. *See also* Hermaphrodite.

Blas'to·coel The segmentation cavity within the blastula.

Blas'to·mere One of the cells formed during the cleavage of an egg cell.

Blas'to·pore The mouthlike opening of a gastrula.

Blas'tu·la The embryonic stage in which the embryo usually is a hollow ball of cells.

Bow'man's cap'sule A two-layered, cuplike enlargement of the kidney tubule which surrounds a glomerous in a kidney.

Bra'chi·al Associated with the forelimb or arm.

Cal·ca're·ous Containing calcium carbonate ($CaCO_3$); chalklike.

Cal·cif'er·ous glands Lime-secreting glands associated with digestion in the earthworm.

Cap'il·la·ry A minute tube, especially one of the very small branches of the blood vessels.

Car'bo·hy'drate CHO compounds, such as sugars and starches. The proportion of hydrogen to oxygen is 2:1.

Car·bon'ic ac'id A weak acid, H_2CO_3, which exists only in solution and breaks down into CO_2 and H_2O.

Car'di·ac Associated with the heart.

Car'ni·vore A meat-eating organism.

Ca·tab'o·lism The destructive phase of metabolism.

Ca·tal'y·sis The controlling of a chemical reaction by an enzyme which is not altered by its participation in the reaction.

Cau'dal Associated with the tail region of an animal; in contrast with cephalic.

Cell A bit of protoplasm containing a nucleus and limited by a plasma membrane.

Cen'tro·some A limited region of the cytoplasm containing the centriole. Present during mitosis.

Ce·phal'ic Associated with the head region; in contrast to caudal.

Ceph'a·lo·tho'rax A fusion of the head and thoracic regions of the body into an important functional unit, as in crayfish and spider.

Cer·ca'ri·a A larval stage of the fluke.

Cer'e·bel'lum The fourth major division of the brain in the vertebrates. Center for muscular coordination.

Cer'e·brum The large bilobed anterior part of the brain of the vertebrates; center for intelligence.

Cer'vi·cal Associated with the neck region.

Chi'tin The tough, horny exoskeletal material of arthropods and some other animals.

Chlo'ra·go'gen cells Modified peritoneal cells that surround the intestine of the earthworm and other annelids.

Chlo'ro·phyll The green coloring matter in plants, which is a catalyst in photosynthesis.

Cho'a·no·cyte' One of the collar cells (flagellated) found in sponges and colonial protozoans.

Chor′dates Animals which possess a notochord as a skeletal axis at some stage.

Chro′ma·tin The stainable substances within the nucleus which give rise to the chromosomes during mitotic and meiotic divisions.

Chro′mo·some A gene-bearing, darkly staining body derived from the chromatin. Especially prominent during the phases of mitosis.

Cil′i·a Microscopic motile processes of the protoplasm which project from the surface of certain cells and organisms.

Cir′ri Microscopic stiff bristles composed of fused cilia; may be used like legs for locomotion by acellular organisms.

Cleav′age The mitotic subdivisions which cut (cleave) the ovum into blastomeres.

Cli·tel′lum The thickened glandular portion of the body wall of the earthworm, which secretes the cocoon.

Clo·a′ca The portion of the body into which the undigested food material, the excretory products, and often the reproductive cells, are emptied.

Clone The aggregate of individuals produced by asexual reproduction from a single organism.

Cni′do·blast A cell in the coelenterates within which the nematocyst is formed.

Coe′lom A body cavity formed within the mesothelium and lined by the peritoneum.

Coe′lom·o·duct A type of excretory duct derived from the coelom.

Coe′no·sarc The protoplasmic tube in hydroids, composed of epidermis and gastrodermis.

Col′loid A state of matter in which very large molecules or aggregations of molecules are dispersed through a medium which may be a gas, a liquid, or a solid.

Com·men′sal·ism Individuals of two species living together to the benefit of one but to neither the benefit nor the harm of the other.

Com′pound eye A type of eye composed of numerous units, ommatidia; found in insects.

Con′ju·ga′tion A temporary sexual union of two individuals during which nuclear material is exchanged.

Cop′u·la′tion Sexual union during which sperm are introduced into the reproductive tract of the female.

Cor′tex The "rind," or outer layer, of an organ or gland.

Cra′ni·um The braincase, or the portion of the skull which encloses the brain.

Crop An enlargement of the anterior portion of the digestive tract, adapted for storage.

Cross-fer′ti·li·za′tion A type of reproduction which begins when the egg from one individual is fertilized by sperm from a second individual. The opposite of self-fertilization, which may occur in hermaphrodites.

Cross′ing o′ver The exchange of genes between chromosomes.

Cu′ti·cle The thin, tough, noncellular covering of an organism; often an exoskeleton.

Cyst An organism surrounded by a protective covering, or a thin-walled sac. Also, a small sac or capsule.

Cy·tol′o·gy The study of cell structure or cell function.

Cy′to·plasm The region of the protoplasm outside the nucleus.

Den′drite One of the processes of a nerve cell, along which impulses are conducted toward the nerve-cell body.

Der′mal Pertaining to or associated with the skin.

Der′mis The underlying or inner layer of the skin (beneath the epidermis) in a vertebrate.

Di′en·ceph′a·lon The region of the brain between the cerebrum and the mid-brain; the "tween-brain."

Dif′fer·en′ti·a′tion The process by which cells or parts of an organism become specialized for particular functions.

Dif·fu′sion The movement of molecules from greater to lesser concentration as a result of their kinetic energy.

Di·ges′tion The transformation of complex food materials into smaller, soluble molecules which can be absorbed.

Di·mor′phism Having two body forms of individuals of the same species; for example, the feeding and reproductive polyps of an *Obelia* colony.

Dip′lo·blas′tic Derived from two primary tissue layers, the ectoderm and the entoderm.

Dip′loid Having the double number of chromosomes; typical of body cells in which the chromosome number is twice that found in the reproductive cells.

Di′ver·tic′u·lum A saclike projection of a hollow organ; for example, the human appendix.

Dom′i·nant gene Refers to one of a pair of genes which dominates the effect of the other.

Dor′sal Pertaining to the upper, or back, surface.

Drone A male bee.

Duct A tube which leads from one part of an organism to another part.

Du′o·de′num   The first region of the small intestine, adjacent to the stomach.

E·col′o·gy   The study of the interrelationship between organisms and their environments.

Ec′to·derm   The outer layer of cells in the gastrula.

Ec′to·par′a·site   A parasite which exists on the surface of the host's body.

Ec′to·plasm   The outer layer of the cytoplasm.

Ef·fect′or   Any part of an organism which responds to a motor impulse; for example, a gland or muscle.

E·lec′tron   A negatively charged particle of very little mass which revolves about the nucleus of an atom.

El′e·ment   A substance consisting of only one type of atom.

Em′bry·o   An immature organism passing through its early developmental stages.

Em·bry·og′e·ny   The formation of organisms.

Em·bry·ol′o·gy   The study of the development of the new individual.

E·mul′sion   A system in which droplets of one liquid are suspended or dispersed in another liquid.

En′do·crine   Pertaining to secretions released directly into the blood stream or body fluids without being transported by ducts.

En′do·derm   *See* Entoderm.

En′do·par′a·site   A parasite which lives within the host.

En′do·plasm   The portion of the cytoplasm surrounded by the ectoplasm.

En′do·skel′e·ton   In internal skeleton, as in vertebrates.

En′do·style   The ciliated rod and groove in the ventral pharyngeal region of some chordates.

En′do·the′li·um   The sheet of cells lining the heart and vascular system.

En′ter·on   The alimentary canal, or gut.

En′to·derm   The innermost layer of a triploblastic animal; the layer which lines the enteron.

En′to·mol′o·gy   The study of insects.

En′to·plasm   *See* Endoplasm.

En′zyme   An organic catalyst which controls the rate of a chemical reaction.

Ep′i·der′mis   The outer layer of the skin.

Ep′i·neph′rine   *See* Adrenalin.

Ep′i·the′li·um   The sheet of cells which covers the internal and external surfaces of an organism.

E·qua′tion di·vi′sion   A stage in meiosis in which the chromosome number may be reduced. *See* Reduction division.

E·ryth′ro·cyte   A red blood cell, or corpuscle; characteristic of vertebrates.

E·soph′a·gus   The tube joining the mouth and the stomach; the gullet.

Es′tra·di′ol   A female sex hormone.

Ev′o·lu′tion   The process by which organisms have changed and are changing.

Ex·cre′tion   The process of the elimination of the waste products of metabolism.

Ex·cur′rent   Providing an exit; leading outward.

Ex′o·skel′e·ton   The nonliving external covering of an animal; for example, the chitinous covering of an arthropod.

Fal·lo′pi·an tube   The oviduct in mammals.

Fam′i·ly   The major subdivision of an order.

Fau′na   The collective term applied to animals of a region or period.

Fe′tus   The unborn embryo of any viviparous animal.

Fis′sion   Asexual reproduction by subdivision into two or more individuals.

Fla·gel′lum   A motile, whiplike projection of a cell or of an acellular organism.

Flame bulb   Ciliated excretory structure, found chiefly in flatworms.

Fol′li·cle   A sac or covering, often glandular.

Fos′sil   The remains of a prehistoric organism, often mineralized.

Func′tion   The action performed by an organism or part of an organism.

Gam′ete   Any sexual reproductive cell; sperm or egg.

Gang′li·on   A group of nerve-cell bodies.

Gas′tric   Pertaining to the stomach.

Gas′tro·der′mis   The lining of the gastrovascular cavity or alimentary canal; derived from the entoderm.

Gas′tro·vas′cu·lar cav′i·ty   A sac serving for both digestion and circulation.

Gas′tru·la   A stage in embryonic development; a two-layered cup with an outer ectoderm and an inner entoderm.

Gel   The jellylike state of the protoplasm.

Gemm′ule   A mass of amoebocytes in a sponge, surrounded by a protective covering; can survive adverse conditions and form a new sponge.

Gene   The hereditary unit located on a chromosome, which controls the development of an inherited character.

Ge·net′ics   The study of inheritance.

Gen′i·tal Pertaining to the reproductive system of either sex.

Gen′o·type The genetic, hereditary constitution possessed by an individual, as opposed to *phenotype*.

Ge′nus The major subdivision of a family.

Germ plasm The term applied to cells restricted to reproduction.

Gill A respiratory organ of an aquatic animal.

Gill slits Paired openings through the pharynx and body of chordates.

Giz′zard An anterior musclar division of the alimentary canal.

Gland Any structure specialized for secretion; may be unicellular or many-celled.

Glo·mer′u·lus A tuft of capillaries within Bowman's capsule of the vertebrate kidney.

Glot′tis The opening from the pharynx into the larynx.

Glu′cose A simple sugar, $C_6H_{12}O_6$.

Glu′ca·gon One of the hormones secreted by the islet cells of the pancreas.

Gly′co·gen A carbohydrate (polysaccharide) stored as reserve food in the liver and muscles; "animal starch."

Goit′er An enlargement of the thyroid gland.

Go′nad A reproductive organ, either ovary or testis.

Gon′o·the′ca The covering of the reproductive polyp of a hydroid.

Graaf′i·an fol′li·cle The developing ovum and its surrounding cells in a mammalian ovary.

Hap′loid The single set or halved set of chromosomes found in mature reproductive cells.

Heart The organ which contracts or pulsates rhythmically to pump the blood through the vessels of the body of an animal.

He′mo·coel An irregular body cavity in which the blood circulates; especially prominent in arthropods..

He′mo·cy′an·in A copper-protein compound serving as a respiratory pigment.

He′mo·glo′bin An iron-protein compound serving as a respiratory pigment.

He′mo·phil′i·a The disease in which the blood fails to clot properly; inherited as a sex-linked characteristic.

Her′bi·vore A plant-eating animal; a vegetarian.

He·red′i·ty The transmission of parental characteristics to offspring.

Her·maph′ro·dite An organism possessing both male and female reproductive organs.

His·tol′o·gy A study of the tissues of an organism; microscopic anatomy.

Het′er·o·zy′gous Possessing unlike genes for a given character.

Hol′o·phyt′ic Completely plantlike nutrition by photosynthesis.

Hol′o·zo′ic Completely animal-like nutrition by eating other organisms.

Ho·mol′o·gy Correspondence of structures which have a common origin; the functions of such structures may or may not be the same.

Ho′mo·zy′gous Possessing like genes for a given character.

Hor′mone A chemical substance released directly into the blood or body fluids; a secretion of an endocrine gland.

Hy′brid An individual produced by the union of gametes which differ in one or more genes; heterozygote.

Hy′droid The polyp form of a hydrozoan (coelenterate).

Hy′po·thal′a·mus A region of the brain below the thalamus and connected to the pituitary gland.

Il′e·um Posterior part of the small intestine.

Il′i·um The dorsal bone of the pelvic girdle.

In·gest′ To take food into the body.

In·gres′sion (polar). A method of entoderm formation by the moving inward of cells.

In·or·gan′ic Not of organic origin; not containing carbon.

In′su·lin One of the hormones secreted by the islet cells of the pancreas.

In·teg′u·ment The sheath or outer covering of the body.

In′ter·phase′ State of a cell between mitotic or meiotic divisions.

In·tes′tine The part of the alimentary canal between the stomach and the anus.

In′tra·cel′lu·lar Pertaining to materials within cells.

In·vag′i·nate To infold a layer of cells into a cavity.

In·ver′te·brate An animal which does not possess a backbone or vertebral column.

Ir′ri·ta·bil′i·ty The ability of protoplasm to be aware and to respond.

I′so·tope A chemical element which has the same chemical properties as another element, but which differs in atomic weight or in the structure of the nucleus.

Joint Place of union between separate bones or other hardened structures.

Jug′u·lar Associated with the throat; for example, the jugular vein.

Kid′ney An organ which excretes liquid wastes containing nitrogenous waste materials.

Kin·et′ic en′er·gy The energy of motion or action, in contrast to potential energy.

La′bi·um The lower lip of arthropods.

La′brum The upper lip of arthropods.

La·cu′na A small cavity or space; for example, the space in which bone cells are found.

Lar′va A free-living embryonic stage which develops into an adult by metamorphosis.

Lar′ynx That part of the trachea in which the vocal apparatus is located.

Lat′er·al At the side of the body.

Leu·co′cyte A white, or nonpigmented, blood cell.

Le′thal gene A gene, the presence of which can produce the death of an organism.

Lig′a·ment A band of white fibrous connective tissue that joins bones.

Link′age The tendency of different characters to be transmitted together in heredity because the genes controlling the characters are located on the same chromosome.

Lip′oid Of a fatty nature.

Li′pase An enzyme which has fat-splitting action.

Lo′cus A place or a location, as the position of a gene.

Lum′bar Pertaining to the region in the small of the back.

Lu′men An internal cavity.

Lymph Blood plasma which has filtered through the capillaries to bathe the tissues; contains white blood cells.

Mac′ro·nu′cle·us The large nucleus found in many ciliates.

Mal·pigh′ian tu′bules The threadlike excretory tubules of many arthropods.

Man′di·ble A jawlike mouth part; also the lower jaw of a vertebrate.

Man′tle The sheet of tissue, or fold, of the body, which covers (mantles) the body proper.

Ma·nu′bri·um The projection on the subumbrellar surface of a jellyfish.

Mar·su′pi·al A pouched mammal; for example, a kangaroo.

Ma′trix The noncellular substance between cells; for example, in cartilage or bone.

Mat′u·ra′tion The final stages in the development of reproductive cells when the chromosome number is reduced.

Max·il′la A mouth part in arthropods; the upper face of vertebrates.

Max·il′li·ped One of the thoracic leg jaws of some arthropods.

Me′di·an In the middle or mid-line of the body.

Me·dul′la ob·lon·ga′ta The posterior division of the vertebrate brain.

Me·du′sa A jellyfish. A reproductive polyp.

Mei·o′sis The sequence of cell divisions in a reproductive cell, in which the chromosome number in the reproductive cell is reduced.

Mem′brane A thin sheet of covering tissue.

Mes′en·chyme A loose, embryonic connective tissue derived primarily from mesoderm.

Mes′en·ter′y A thin sheet of tissue which supports an organ or serves as a partition.

Mes′o·derm The middle, or third, embryonic layer.

Mes′o·gle′a The jellylike substance between the epidermis and gastrodermis, often noncellular.

Mes′o·neph′ros The second stage in the development of the vertebrate kidney.

Mes′o·the′li·um The derivative in the adult of the mesoderm.

Me·tab′o·lism The sum of the chemical activities of protoplasm; consists of constructive and destructive phases.

Met′a·gen′e·sis Alternation of generations.

Me·tam′er·ism Segmentation, where the body is composed of a succession of homologous parts.

Met′a·mor′pho·sis Transformation in form or function in an organism, usually accompanied by pronounced external changes. These occur after hatching and before maturity.

Met′a·neph′ros The third stage of the vertebrate kidney.

Met′a·phase The stage in mitosis at which the chromosomes are lined up in the equatorial plate.

Met′a·zo′a The phylum to which the many-celled animals belong.

Mi′cron One one-thousandth of a millimeter.

Mi′cro·nuc′le·us The smaller reproductive nucleus of many ciliates.

Mi′ra·cid′i·um A larval stage of the fluke.

Mi′to·chon′dri·a Cytoplasmic particles of varying size and shape; probably associated with enzymes and the metabolic activity of the cell.

Mi·to'sis Indirect cell division, during which the chromosomes are duplicated; and usually equally distributed to daughter cells.

Mol'e·cule A chemical unit composed of two or more atoms.

Molt The shedding of the exoskeleton; or of external structures, such as hair or feathers.

Mor·phol'o·gy The study of structure.

Mu'cus A slimy secretion containing the glucoprotein, mucin.

Mu'tant An organism containing one or more altered genes.

Mu·ta'tion A sudden hereditary gene change; in a broader sense, any hereditary change which results from an alteration in chromosome composition.

Mut'u·al·ism The living together of two species for mutual benefit.

Na'res The openings into the nasal passages; the nostrils.

Na'sal Pertaining to the nose.

Nem'a·to·cyst' The stinging thread and capsule in the coelentrates.

Nem'a·thel·min'thes The phylum which includes the rotifiers, nematodes, and gordiacea.

Ne·phrid'i·um The tubular excretory system of several invertebrates; especially prominent in annelids.

Neph'ron The functional and structural unit of a vertebrate kidney.

Neph'ro·stome The ciliated funnel-like opening into an excretory tubule.

Nerve A cordlike bundle of processes from nerve cells for the transmission of impulses from one part of the body to another; for example, spinal nerve, cranial nerve.

Neu'ral Associated with the nervous system.

Neu'ron A nerve cell, including all its processes.

Neu'tron A neutral (uncharged) unit of structure as part of the nucleus of an atom.

No'to·chord The supporting rod or chord which serves as the skeletal axis in a chordate.

Nu·cle'ol·us A well-defined, usually spherical, body within the nucleus of most cells.

Nu'cle·us A specialized structure containing chromatin, found within the cell; also, the central mass of an atom.

Nu·tri'tion The sum total of the processes concerned with growth, repair, and maintenance of an organism or its parts.

O·cel'lus A simple eye of an invertebrate.

Oc'u·lo·mo'tor A muscle or nerve associated with eye movement.

Ol·fac'to·ry Pertaining to the sense of smell.

Om'ma·tid'i·um A single rodlike unit of a compound eye of an arthropod.

Om'ni·vore An animal which eats both plants and animals.

O'o·cyte An immature egg cell.

O·per'cu·lum The gill covering of many fishes and of tadpoles.

Oph·thal'mic Pertaining to the eye.

Op'tic chi·as'ma The X-like crossing of the optic tracts on the ventral surface of the brain.

Op'tic tract Neural connection between the brain and the eye of vertebrates.

O'ral groove A ciliated groove leading to the mouth and gullet of ciliates.

Or'gan A group of tissues which work together to perform a definite function, or functions.

Or'gan·elle' A specialized region within an acellar organism; has a function comparable to that of an organ in metazoans.

Or·gan'ic Pertaining to any carbon compound.

Or'gan of Cor'ti Structure in the inner ear of many vertebrates.

Os'cu·lum The large external opening of the spongocoel of sponges.

Os·mo'sis Diffusion of materials from greater to lesser concentration through a selectively permeable membrane.

O'to·lith Small calcareous mass associated with balancing organ.

O'va·ry The female reproductive organ which produces eggs.

O'vi·duct The tube which carries the eggs from the ovary to the exterior.

O·vip'a·rous Reproducing by laying eggs.

O'vo·vi·vip'a·rous Reproducing by eggs which hatch in the mother before laying.

O'vum An egg, or female gamete.

Ox'i·da'tion A combining with oxygen; or a chemical change involving the loss of one or more electrons.

Ox'y·bi·o'tic The use of oxygen in metabolism.

Pa'le·on·tol'o·gy The science of ancient life as revealed by the study of various types of fossils.

Palps Short tactile appendages; feelers.

Pan'cre·as A gland of dual function which secretes digestive enzymes and the hormones, insulin and glucagon.

Par'a·po'di·um A flattened, movable, paired appendage on the body of some annelids.

Par'a·site An organism which lives upon or within another organism, at whose expense it secures its food.

Par'a·si·tol'o·gy That branch of biology which deals with the study of parasites.

Par'a·sym'pa·thet'ic The cranial and sacral regions of the autonomic nervous system.

Par'a·thy'roid Endocrine glands located beside or embedded in the thyroid gland.

Pa·ren'chy·ma A connective tissue of a loose, spongy nature.

Par'the·no·gen'e·sis The development of an egg without fertilization.

Pec'to·ral gir'dle The bones and cartilages in the region of the forelimbs.

Ped'i·cel·la'ri·a One of the small pincers on the surface of some echinoderms.

Ped'i·palp' An appendage of arachnids which has sensory function and may be used to capture prey.

Pel'li·cle The thin, nonliving covering secreted by some cells or by some cellular organisms.

Pel'vic gir'dle The bones in the region of the hind limbs.

Pe'nis The male copulatory organ.

Pep'sin A protein-digesting enzyme; acts in an acid medium.

Per'i·car'di·um A membrane surrounding the heart.

Pe·riph'er·al Situated at or near the surface.

Per'i·sarc The protective tube, sometimes chitinous, secreted by the epidermis of some hydroids, as in *Obelia*.

Per'i·stal'sis A progressive wave of contraction and relaxation along a tube; as the peristaltic waves in the alimentary canal.

Per'i·to·ne'um The thin, cellular membrane which lines the coelom.

Phag'o·cyte' A cell which engulfs foreign material (for example, a white blood cell); an "eating cell."

Phar'ynx The region of the digestive tract between the mouth and the esophagus.

Phe'no·type The external appearance of an individual, in contrast with its genetic constitution, or *genotype*.

Pho'to·syn'the·sis The manufacture of glucose from carbon dioxide and water, using chlorophyll as a catalyst and light as an energy source.

Phy·log'e·ny The ancestral or evolutionary history of a group.

Phy'lum A primary taxonomic division of the plant or animal kingdoms.

Phys'i·ol'o·gy The study of the functions of organisms.

Pi·tu'i·tar'y gland An endocrine gland located ventral to the brain and composed of an anterior, posterior, and sometimes, an intermediate lobe.

Pla·cen'ta The highly vascular connection between the mammalian fetus, or embryo, and the uterus of the mother; for nutrition, respiration, and excretion.

Plan'u·la The ciliated larval form of some invertebrates; chiefly the coelenterates.

Plas'ma The fluid part of the blood or lymph.

Plas'ma mem'brane The surface layer of the protoplasm; of ultramicroscopic thickness, and selectively permeable.

Plas'tid A pigmented body found in the cytoplasm of many plant cells.

Plat'y·hel·min'thes The phylum which includes the flatworms, planarians, flukes, and tapeworms.

Pleur'al cav'i·ty The cavity in which the lungs are to be found; part of the coelom.

Pol'y·mor'phism The condition of having more than two body types in a single species; as for example, in the Portuguese man-of-war.

Pol'yp The coelenterate body form which is elongated and is usually attached by the aboral surface.

Pol'y·ploid Containing more than the normal (double) set of chromosomes.

Por'tal sys'tem A blood system which begins and ends in capillaries; for example, the hepatic portal system.

Pos·te'ri·or Situated toward the rear, or tail, end of an animal.

Po·ten'tial en'er·gy Energy existing and ready for action, but not yet active.

Prin'ci·ple A scientific law with broad application; also, a chemical component.

Pro·bos'cis An elongated tubular extension of the mouth or pharyngeal region.

Pro·ges'ter·one The hormone from the corpus luteum of the ovary; and, in pregnancy, from the placenta.

Pro·glot'tid A segment of a tapeworm.

Pro·neph'ros The first stage in the development of the vertebrate kidney.

Pro'phase The first phase of cell division, at which time the chromosomes become visible.

Pro·sto'mi·um An anterior projection of the first segment; extends in front of the mouth.

Pro'te·in An organic compound composed of amino acids, and therefore containing carbon, hydrogen, oxygen, and nitrogen; essential to the existence of protoplasm.

Pro'ton An elementary positively charged particle in the nucleus of an atom.

Pro'to·plasm The viscous, granular, complex colloid of which all organisms are composed.

Pro'to·zo'a The phylum to which the acellular organisms belong.

Pseu'do·coel A body cavity, as in the nematodes, neither completely within the mesothelium nor lined with a peritoneum.

Pseu'do·po'di·um The protoplasmic process used as a locomotor organelle by *Amoeba* and by certain special cells in the metazoans.

Pul'mo·nar·y Pertaining to the lungs.

Queen The reproductive female of ants, bees, and termites.

Ra'di·al sym'me·try The condition in which similar parts of an organism are arranged about a common center.

Rad'u·la A bandlike rasping structure found in mollusks.

Ra'mus A branch or an outgrowth of a structure.

Re·cept'or A sensory end organ, a group of sensory cells, or even a single sensory cell.

Re·ces'sive gene A gene which does not express itself in the presence of a dominant gene for the character.

Rec'tum The posterior portion of the intestine.

Red blood cell *See* Erythrocyte.

Re'di·a A larval stage of the fluke.

Re·duc'tion di·vi'sion A stage in meiosis, in which the chromosome number usually is reduced by the separation of the members of homologous pairs of chromosomes. *See* Equation division.

Re'flex An automatic response to a stimulus which is independent of the higher nerve centers such as the brain.

Re·gen'er·a'tion The replacing of parts or structures lost or destroyed.

Re'nal Pertaining to the kidney.

Re'pro·duc'tion The process of creating new individuals, by which a species is maintained from generation to generation.

Res'pi·ra'tion The gaseous metabolism of a cell or organism; the absorption of oxygen and the elimination of carbon dioxide.

Re·sponse' The internal or external reaction to a stimulus.

Ret'i·na The inner light-sensitive area of an eye.

Rh fac'tor A type of antigen found in some red blood cells.

Ru'di·men'ta·ry A partially developed structure having little or no function.

Ru'men The large storage "stomach" of cud-chewing animals.

Sa'crum The posterior part of the vertebral column, attached to the pelvic girdle.

Sap'ro·zo'ic Living on decaying organic matter in suspension or solution.

Sed'en·tar'y *See* Sessile.

Sem'i·nal Pertaining to or associated with sperm.

Sen'so·ry cell A cell which is sensitive to stimuli.

Sep'tum A partition or dividing wall.

Ser'i·al ho·mol'o·gy The repetition of homologous structures on different segments of an animal.

Ser·ol'o·gy The study of blood serum, particularly in the immunity reactions of mammals.

Ser'um The plasma of blood that separates from a clot and which contains no cells or fibrin.

Ses'sile Attached; without locomotion.

Se'tae Bristles.

Sex chro'mo·somes The chromosomes which differ in number and distribution in the male and the female of a species. The X and the Y chromosomes.

Sex'u·al re·pro·duc'tion The production of new individuals through the fertilization of eggs by sperm.

Si'nus A large, often irregular, thin-walled space.

Soma The body of an organism, exclusive of the reproductive cells.

So'mite One of the segments of a segmented animal.

Spe'cies A taxonomic division consisting of individuals having a common fund of genes.

Sperm The male sex cell.

Sper'mat·o·gen'e·sis The maturation of the male reproductive cells.

Spin'dle The gelatinous, spindle-shaped region of the cell which, with its associated "fibers," is the central figure in mitosis.

Spi'ra·cle The external opening into the respiratory system.

Spong'o·coel The large central cavity in sponges which opens externally through the osculum.

Squa'mous Flat, scalelike.

Stat'o·cyst An organ of equilibrium found in many invertebrates.

Stat'o·lith The small calcareous structure within the statocyst.

Stim′u·lus An alteration in the environment, either external or internal, which may influence some activity in an organism or its parts.

Swim′mer·et One of the biramous appendages on the abdomen of a crustacean.

Sym′bi·o′sis *See* Mutualism.

Sym′me·try The repetition of parts of an organism around an axis or on opposite sides of a plane.

Sym′pa·thet′ic The thoracic and lumbar regions of the autonomic nervous system in vertebrates.

Syn·apse′ The point of contact where the impulse passes from the axon of one nerve cell to the dendrite of another nerve cell.

Syn·cy′ti·um A multinucleated mass of protoplasm.

Tac′tile Associated with touch.

Tax·on′o·my The science of classification; not only the naming, but also the relationship, of organisms.

Tel′o·phase The final stage in cell division.

Tel′son An extension from the last segment of a segmented animal; for example, the extension of the sixth abdominal segment of the crayfish.

Tes′tis The male reproductive organ in which sperm are formed.

Tes·tos′ter·one′ The male sex hormone.

Tho′rax That portion of the body (trunk) which usually encloses the heart and respiratory organs.

Thy′roid A vertebrate endocrine gland located in the throat region.

Tis′sue A group of cells which, with their intercellular substances, perform a special (or similar) function.

Tra′che·a A duct which conveys air from the exterior to the respiratory organs.

Trich′o·cyst A body in the ectoplasm of *Paramecium*, which produces threadlike processes used for defense or to anchor the animal during feeding.

Tym·pan′ic mem′brane The eardrum, or the vibrating membrane involved in hearing.

Typh′lo·sole An infolding of the wall of the intestine of the earthworm which increases the surface area of the intestine.

U·re′a The chief nitrogenous excretory compound in many vertebrates; also found in small amounts in other animals.

U·re′ter Duct through which urine passes from the kidney.

U·re′thra Duct through which urine passes from the bladder to the exterior. Also carries sperm in male mammals.

U′rine The secretion of the excretory organs, especially the kidneys of vertebrates.

U′ro·gen′i·tal Pertaining to both the excretory and reproductive systems.

U′ro·pod The flat, paddlelike swimmeret on the sixth abdominal segment of the crayfish.

U′ro·style The long, terminal, rodlike bone of the frog vertebral column.

U′ter·us The enlarged posterior portion of the oviduct in which the embryo may develop.

Vac′u·ole Any small cavity in the protoplasm which may be filled with fluid, fat, or other substances.

Va·gi′na That portion of the female reproductive system which receives the male copulatory organ.

Va′gus The tenth cranial nerve in the vertebrate.

Valve The structures in animals which limit or close an opening.

Vas′cu·lar Pertaining to vessels or ducts.

Vein A blood vessel transporting blood to the heart.

Ven′tral The lower, or belly, side; opposite of dorsal.

Ven′tri·cle The pumping chamber of the heart, or a cavity of the brain.

Ver′te·brate An animal having a vertebral column, or backbone.

Ves′sel A tube or canal by which body fluids are conducted.

Ves·tig′i·al A small or degenerate structure which was better developed in the embryo or in some previous species.

Vis′cer·a The organs within the body cavity.

Vi·vip′a·rous Producing living young which were previously nourished within the mother by her blood.

White blood cell *See* Leukocyte and Phagocyte.

Zo·ol′o·gy The study of animals.

Zy′gote A fertilized egg cell—i.e., a cell formed by the union of male and female gametes.

Index